$\sin A = \frac{h}{r}$

$r \sin A = h$

$r = \frac{h}{\sin A}$

$\log r = \log h + \text{colog} \sin A$

$\tan A = \frac{h}{c/2} = \frac{2h}{c}$

$c \tan A = 2h$

$c = \frac{2h}{\tan A}$

Sin	30	45	60
	$\frac{1}{2}\sqrt{1}$	$\frac{1}{2}\sqrt{2}$	$\frac{1}{2}\sqrt{3}$
			$\frac{1}{2}\sqrt{1}$
			$\sqrt{3}$
			$\frac{1}{3}\sqrt{3}$
Memorize	$\frac{2}{3}\sqrt{3}$		2
	2	$\sqrt{2}$	$\frac{2}{3}\sqrt{3}$

L-20

$\log c = \log 2h + \text{colog} \tan A$

$(a^2+2ab+b^2)\sin 90^\circ + (a^2-2ab+b^2)\cos 180^\circ$

$(a^2+2ab+b^2)1 + (a^2-2ab+b^2)(-1) - 4ab$

$a^2 + 2ab + b^2 - a^2 - 2ab - b^2 - 4ab$

$2a^2 - 4ab + 2b^2 = x$

$\sin 145^\circ = \sin 25$

15

A, B, C, 4", 45°

$\tan^2 x = 1$.

$\sin 3x = \sin(2x + x) = \sin 2x \cos x + \cos 2x \sin x$

$\cos x(2 \sin x \cos x) + \sin x(\cos^2 x - \sin^2 x)$

$2 \sin x \cos^2 x + \sin x \cos^2 x - \sin^3 x$

$2 \sin x(1 - \sin^2 x) + \sin x(1 - \sin^2 x) - \sin^3 x$

$2 \sin x - 2 \sin^3 x + \sin x - \sin^3 x - \sin^3 x$

$3 \sin x - 4 \sin^3 x$

c = 69897
9.99651 - 10
~~10.69548 - 10~~

2

4.960
6
29.76 sq in

m

73

4

c = 86629
9.82927 - 10
10.69556 - 10

4.961
7.35
36.46335 sq in

WENTWORTH-SMITH MATHEMATICAL SERIES

PLANE TRIGONOMETRY AND TABLES

BY

GEORGE WENTWORTH

AND

DAVID EUGENE SMITH

GINN AND COMPANY

BOSTON · NEW YORK · CHICAGO · LONDON
ATLANTA · DALLAS · COLUMBUS · SAN FRANCISCO

225.5

The Athenæum Press
GINN AND COMPANY · PROPRIETORS · BOSTON · U.S.A.

PREFACE

In preparing a work to replace the Wentworth Trigonometry, which has dominated the teaching of the subject in America for a whole generation, some words of explanation are necessary as to the desirability of the changes that have been made. Although the great truths of mathematics are permanent, educational policy changes from generation to generation, and the time has now arrived when some rearrangement of matter is necessary to meet the legitimate demands of the schools.

The principal changes from the general plan of the standard texts in use in America relate to the sequence of material and to the number and nature of the practical applications. With respect to sequence the rule has been followed that the practical use of every new feature should be clearly set forth before the abstract theory is developed. For example, it will be noticed that the definite uses of each of the natural functions are given as soon as possible, that the need for logarithmic computation follows, that thereafter the secant and cosecant assume a minor place, and that a wide range of practical applications of the right triangle awakens an early interest in the subject. The study of the functions of larger angles, and of the sum and difference of two angles, now becomes necessary to further progress in trigonometry, after which the oblique triangle is considered, together with a large number of practical, nontechnical applications.

The decimal division of the degree is explained and is used enough to show its value, but it is recognized that this topic has, as yet, only a subordinate place. It seems probable that the decimal fraction will in due time supplant the sexagesimal here as it has in other fields of science, and hence the student should be familiar with its advantages.

Such topics as the radian, graphs of the various functions, the applications of trigonometry to higher algebra, and the theory of trigonometric equations properly find place at the end of the course in plane trigonometry. They are important, but their value is best appreciated after a good course in the practical uses of the subject.

They may be considered briefly or at length as the circumstances may warrant.

The authors have sought to give teachers and students all the material needed for a thorough study of plane trigonometry, with more problems than any one class will use, thus offering opportunity for a new selection of examples from year to year, and allowing for the omission of the more theoretical portions of Chapters IX–XII if desired.

The tables have been arranged with great care, every practical device having been adopted to save eye strain, all tabular material being furnished that the student will need, and an opportunity being afforded to use angles divided either sexagesimally or decimally, as the occasion demands.

It is hoped that the care that has been taken to arrange all matter in the order of difficulty and of actual need, to place the practical before the theoretical, to eliminate all that is not necessary to a clear understanding of the subject, and to present a page that is at the same time pleasing to the eye and inviting to the mind will commend itself to and will meet with the approval of the many friends of the series of which this work is a part.

GEORGE WENTWORTH
DAVID EUGENE SMITH

CONTENTS

PLANE TRIGONOMETRY

PLANE TRIGONOMETRY

CHAPTER I

TRIGONOMETRIC FUNCTIONS OF ACUTE ANGLES

1. The Nature of Arithmetic. In arithmetic we study computation, the working with numbers. We may have a formula expressed in algebraic symbols, such as $a = bh$, but the actual computation involved in applying such a formula to a particular case is part of arithmetic.

Arithmetic enters into all subsequent branches of mathematics. It plays such an important part in trigonometry that it becomes necessary to introduce another method of computation, the method which makes use of logarithms.

2. The Nature of Algebra. In algebra we generalize arithmetic. Thus, instead of saying that the area of a rectangle with base 4 in. and height 2 in. is 4×2 sq. in., we express a general law by saying that $a = bh$. Algebra, therefore, is a generalized arithmetic, and the equation is the chief object of attention.

Algebra also enters into all subsequent branches of mathematics, and its relation to trigonometry will be found to be very close.

3. The Nature of Geometry. In geometry we study the forms and relations of figures, proving many properties and effecting numerous constructions concerning them.

Geometry, like algebra and arithmetic, enters into the work in trigonometry. Indeed, trigonometry may almost be said to unite arithmetic, algebra, and geometry in one subject.

4. The Nature of Trigonometry. We are now about to begin another branch of mathematics, one not chiefly relating to numbers although it uses numbers, not primarily devoted to equations although using equations, and not concerned principally with the study of geometric forms although freely drawing upon the facts of geometry.

Trigonometry is concerned chiefly with the relation of certain lines in a triangle (*trigon*, "a triangle," + *metrein*, "to measure") and forms the basis of the mensuration used in surveying, engineering, mechanics, geodesy, and astronomy.

5. How Angles are Measured. For ordinary purposes angles can be measured with a protractor to a degree of accuracy of about 30′.

The student will find it advantageous to use the convenient protractor furnished with this book and shown in the illustration below.

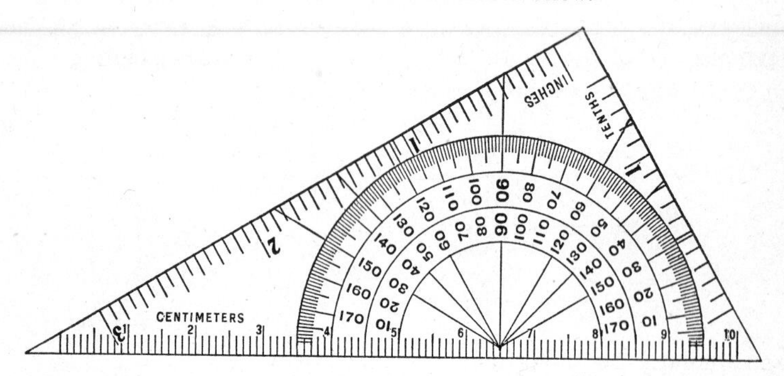

For work out of doors it is customary to use a transit, an instrument by means of which angles can be measured to minutes. By turning the top of the transit to the right or left, horizontal angles can be measured on the horizontal plate. By turning the telescope up or down, vertical angles can be measured on the vertical circle seen in the illustration.

For astronomical purposes, where great care is necessary in measuring angles, large circles are used.

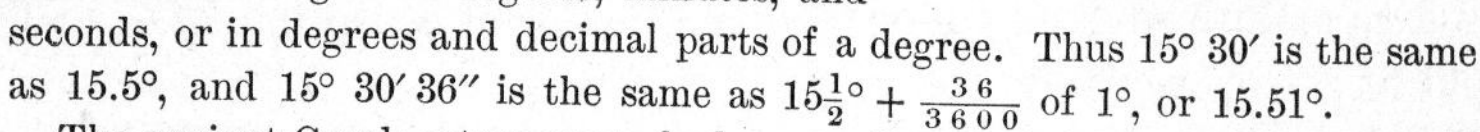

The degree of accuracy required in measuring an angle depends upon the nature of the problem. We shall now assume that we can measure angles in degrees, minutes, and seconds, or in degrees and decimal parts of a degree. Thus 15° 30′ is the same as 15.5°, and 15° 30′ 36″ is the same as $15\frac{1}{2}° + \frac{36}{3600}$ of 1°, or 15.51°.

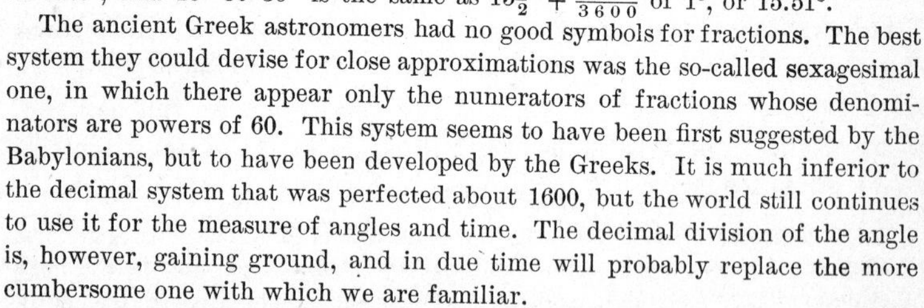

The ancient Greek astronomers had no good symbols for fractions. The best system they could devise for close approximations was the so-called sexagesimal one, in which there appear only the numerators of fractions whose denominators are powers of 60. This system seems to have been first suggested by the Babylonians, but to have been developed by the Greeks. It is much inferior to the decimal system that was perfected about 1600, but the world still continues to use it for the measure of angles and time. The decimal division of the angle is, however, gaining ground, and in due time will probably replace the more cumbersome one with which we are familiar.

In this book we shall use both the ancient and modern systems, but with the chief attention to the former, since this is still the more common.

6. Functions of an Angle. In the annexed figure, if the line AR moves about the point A in the sense indicated by the arrow, from the position AX as an initial position, it generates the angle A.

If from the points $B, B', B'', \ldots$, on AR, we let fall the perpendiculars $BC, B'C', B''C'', \ldots$, on AX, we form a series of similar triangles $ACB, AC'B', AC''B''$, and so on. The corresponding sides of these triangles are proportional. That is,

$$\frac{BC}{AB} = \frac{B'C'}{AB'} = \frac{B''C''}{AB''} = \cdots;$$

$$\frac{BC}{AC} = \frac{B'C'}{AC'} = \frac{B''C''}{AC''} = \cdots;$$

$$\frac{AB}{AC} = \frac{AB'}{AC'} = \frac{AB''}{AC''} = \cdots;$$

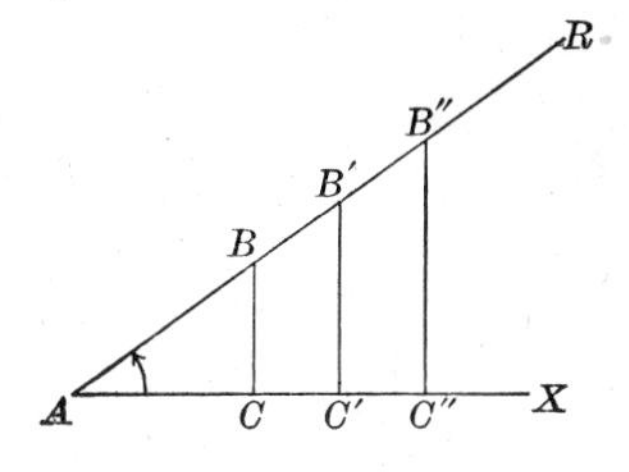

and similarly for the ratios

$$\frac{AB}{BC}, \quad \frac{AC}{BC}, \quad \frac{AC}{AB},$$

each of which has a series of other ratios equal to it.

For example, $$\frac{AB}{BC} = \frac{AB'}{B'C'} = \frac{AB''}{B''C''}.$$

That is, *these ratios remain unchanged so long as the angle remains unchanged, but they change as the angle changes.*

Each of the above ratios is therefore a *function* of the angle A.

As already learned in algebra and geometry, a magnitude which depends upon another magnitude for its value is called a *function* of the latter magnitude. Thus a circle is a function of the radius, the area of a square is a function of the side, the surface of a sphere is a function of the diameter, and the volume of a pyramid is a function of the base and altitude.

We indicate a function of x by such symbols as $f(x)$, $F(x)$, $f'(x)$, and $\phi(x)$, and we read these "f of x, f-major of x, f-prime of x, and phi of x" respectively.

For example, if we are repeatedly using some long expression like $x^4 + 3x^3 - 2x^2 + 7x - 4$, we may speak of it briefly as $f(x)$. If we are using some function of angle A, we may designate this as $f(A)$. If we wish to speak of some other function of A, we may write it $f'(A)$, $F(A)$, or $\phi(A)$.

In trigonometry we shall make much use of various functions of an angle, but we shall give to them special names and symbols. On this account the ordinary function symbols of algebra, mentioned above, will not be used frequently in trigonometry, but they will be used often enough to make it necessary that the student should understand their significance.

7. The Six Functions. Since with a given angle A we may take any one of the triangles described in § 6, we shall consider the triangle ACB, lettered as here shown.

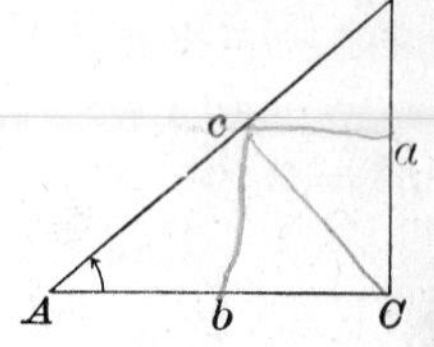

It has long been the custom to letter in this way the hypotenuse, sides, and angles of the first triangle considered in trigonometry, C being the right angle, and the hypotenuse and sides bearing the small letters corresponding to the opposite capitals. By the *sides* of the triangle is meant the sides a and b, c being called the hypotenuse. The sides a and b are also called the *legs* of the triangle, particularly by early writers, since it was formerly the custom to represent the triangle as standing on the hypotenuse.

The ratios $\frac{a}{c}, \frac{b}{c}, \frac{a}{b}, \frac{b}{a}, \frac{c}{b}$, and $\frac{c}{a}$ have the following names:

$\frac{a}{c}$ is called the *sine* of A, written $\sin A$;

$\frac{b}{c}$ is called the *cosine* of A, written $\cos A$;

$\frac{a}{b}$ is called the *tangent* of A, written $\tan A$;

$\frac{b}{a}$ is called the *cotangent* of A, written $\cot A$;

$\frac{c}{b}$ is called the *secant* of A, written $\sec A$;

$\frac{c}{a}$ is called the *cosecant* of A, written $\csc A$.

That is,

$$\sin A = \frac{a}{c} = \frac{\text{opposite side}}{\text{hypotenuse}}, \qquad \cos A = \frac{b}{c} = \frac{\text{adjacent side}}{\text{hypotenuse}},$$

$$\tan A = \frac{a}{b} = \frac{\text{opposite side}}{\text{adjacent side}}, \qquad \cot A = \frac{b}{a} = \frac{\text{adjacent side}}{\text{opposite side}},$$

$$\sec A = \frac{c}{b} = \frac{\text{hypotenuse}}{\text{adjacent side}}, \qquad \csc A = \frac{c}{a} = \frac{\text{hypotenuse}}{\text{opposite side}}.$$

These definitions must be thoroughly learned, since they are the foundation upon which the whole science is built. The student should practice upon them, with the figure before him, until he can tell instantly what ratio is meant by $\sec A$, $\cot A$, $\sin A$, and so on, in whatever order these functions are given.

There are also two other functions, rarely used at present. These are the versed sine $A = 1 - \cos A$, and the coversed sine $A = 1 - \sin A$. These definitions need not be learned at this time, since they will be given again when the functions are met later in the work.

Exercise 1. The Six Functions

1. In the figure of § 7, $\sin B = \frac{b}{c}\cdot$ Write the other five functions of the angle B.

2. Show that in the right triangle ACB (§ 7) the following relations exist:

$$\sin A = \cos B, \quad \cos A = \sin B, \quad \tan A = \cot B,$$
$$\cot A = \tan B, \quad \sec A = \csc B, \quad \csc A = \sec B.$$

State which of the following is the greater:

3. $\sin A$ or $\tan A$.
4. $\cos A$ or $\cot A$.
5. $\sec A$ or $\tan A$.
6. $\csc A$ or $\cot A$.

Find the values of the six functions of A, if a, b, c respectively have the following values:

7. 3, 4, 5.
8. 5, 12, 13.
9. 8, 15, 17.
10. 9, 40, 41.
11. 3.9, 8, 8.9.
12. 1.19, 1.20, 1.69.

13. What condition must be fulfilled by the lengths of the three lines a, b, c (§ 7) to make them the sides of a right triangle? Show that this condition is fulfilled in Exs. 7–12.

Find the values of the six functions of A, if a, b, c respectively have the following values:

14. $2n,\ n^2 - 1,\ n^2 + 1.$
15. $n,\ \frac{n^2 - 1}{2},\ \frac{n^2 + 1}{2}.$
16. $2mn,\ m^2 - n^2,\ m^2 + n^2.$
17. $\frac{2mn}{m - n},\ m + n,\ \frac{m^2 + n^2}{m - n}.$

18. As in Ex. 13, show that the condition for a right triangle is fulfilled in Exs. 14–17.

Given $a^2 + b^2 = c^2$, find the six functions of A when:

19. $a = b.$
20. $a = 2b.$
21. $a = \frac{2}{3}c.$

Given $a^2 + b^2 = c^2$, find the six functions of B when:

22. $a = 24,\ b = 143.$
23. $b = 9.5,\ c = 19.3.$
24. $a = 0.264,\ c = 0.265.$
25. $b = 2\sqrt{pq},\ c = p + q.$

Given $a^2 + b^2 = c^2$, find the six functions of A and also the six functions of B when:

26. $a = \sqrt{p^2 + q^2},\ b = \sqrt{2pq}.$
27. $a = \sqrt{p^2 + p},\ c = p + 1.$

In the right triangle ACB, as shown in § 7:

28. Find the length of side a if $\sin A = \frac{3}{5}$, and $c = 20.5$.

29. Find the length of side b if $\cos A = 0.44$, and $c = 3.5$.

30. Find the length of side a if $\tan A = 3\frac{2}{3}$, and $b = 2\frac{5}{11}$.

31. Find the length of side b if $\cot A = 4$, and $a = 1700$.

32. Find the length of the hypotenuse if $\sec A = 2$, and $b = 2000$.

33. Find the length of the hypotenuse if $\csc A = 6.4$, and $a = 35.6$.

Find the hypotenuse and other side of a right triangle, given:

34. $b = 6$, $\tan A = \frac{3}{2}$.

35. $a = 3.5$, $\cos A = 0.5$.

36. $b = 4$, $\csc A = 1\frac{2}{3}$.

37. $b = 2$, $\sin A = 0.6$.

38. The hypotenuse of a right triangle is 2.5 mi., $\sin A = 0.6$, and $\cos A = 0.8$. Compute the sides of the triangle.

39. Construct with a protractor the angles 20°, 40°, and 70°; determine their functions by measuring the necessary lines and compare the values obtained in this way with the more nearly correct values given in the following table:

	sin	cos	tan	cot	sec	csc
20°	0.342	0.940	0.364	2.747	1.064	2.924
40°	0.643	0.766	0.839	1.192	1.305	1.556
70°	0.940	0.342	2.747	0.364	2.924	1.064

Find, by means of the above table, the sides and hypotenuse of a right triangle, given:

40. $A = 20°$, $c = 1$.

41. $A = 20°$, $c = 4$.

42. $A = 20°$, $c = 3.5$.

43. $A = 20°$, $c = 4.8$.

44. $A = 20°$, $c = 7\frac{1}{2}$.

45. $A = 40°$, $c = 1$.

46. $A = 40°$, $c = 3$.

47. $A = 40°$, $c = 7$.

48. $A = 40°$, $c = 10.7$.

49. $A = 40°$, $c = 250$.

50. $A = 70°$, $c = 2$.

51. $A = 70°$, $a = 2$.

52. $A = 70°$, $b = 2$.

53. $A = 70°$, $a = 25$.

54. $A = 70°$, $b = 150$.

55. By dividing the length of a vertical rod by the length of its horizontal shadow, the tangent of the angle of elevation of the sun at that time was found to be 0.82. How high is a tower, if the length of its horizontal shadow at the same time is 174.3 yd.?

56. A pin is stuck upright on a table top and extends upward 1 in. above the surface. When its shadow is $\frac{7}{8}$ in. long, what is the tangent of the angle of elevation of the sun? How high is a telegraph pole whose horizontal shadow at that instant is 21 ft.?

8. Functions of Complementary Angles. In the annexed figure we see that B is the complement of A; that is, $B = 90° - A$. Hence,

$$\sin A = \frac{a}{c} = \cos B = \cos(90° - A),$$

$$\cos A = \frac{b}{c} = \sin B = \sin(90° - A),$$

$$\tan A = \frac{a}{b} = \cot B = \cot(90° - A),$$

$$\cot A = \frac{b}{a} = \tan B = \tan(90° - A),$$

$$\sec A = \frac{c}{b} = \csc B = \csc(90° - A),$$

$$\csc A = \frac{c}{a} = \sec B = \sec(90° - A).$$

That is, *each function of an acute angle is equal to the co-named function of the complementary angle.*

Co-sine means *complement's sine*, and similarly for the other *co*-functions.

It is therefore seen that $\sin 75° = \cos(90° - 75°) = \cos 15°$, $\sec 82° 30' = \csc(90° - 82° 30') = \csc 7° 30'$, and so on.

Therefore, *any function of an angle between 45° and 90° may be found by taking the co-named function of the complementary angle, which is between 0° and 45°.*

Hence, we need never have a direct table of functions beyond 45°. We shall presently see (§ 12) that this is of great advantage.

Exercise 2. Functions of Complementary Angles

Express as functions of the complementary angle:

1. $\sin 30°$.
2. $\cos 20°$.
3. $\tan 40°$.
4. $\sec 25°$.
5. $\sin 50°$.
6. $\tan 60°$.
7. $\sec 75°$.
8. $\csc 85°$.
9. $\sin 60°$.
10. $\cos 60°$.
11. $\tan 45°$.
12. $\sec 45°$.
13. $\sin 75° 30'$.
14. $\tan 82° 45'$.
15. $\sec 68° 15'$.
16. $\cos 88° 10'$.

Express as functions of an angle less than 45°:

17. $\sin 65°$.
18. $\tan 80°$.
19. $\sec 77°$.
20. $\cos 52°$.
21. $\cot 61°$.
22. $\csc 78°$.
23. $\sin 89°$.
24. $\cos 86°$.
25. $\sec 88°$.
26. $\sin 77\frac{1}{2}°$.
27. $\cos 82\frac{1}{2}°$.
28. $\tan 88.6°$.

Find A, given the following relations:

29. $90° - A = A$.
30. $\cos A = \sin A$.
31. $90° - A = 2A$.
32. $\cos A = \sin 2A$.

9. Functions of 45°. The functions of certain angles, among them 45°, are easily found. In the isosceles right triangle ACB we have $A=B=45°$, and $a=b$. Furthermore, since $a^2+b^2=c^2$, we have $2a^2=c^2$, $a\sqrt{2}=c$, and $a=\frac{1}{2}c\sqrt{2}$. Hence,

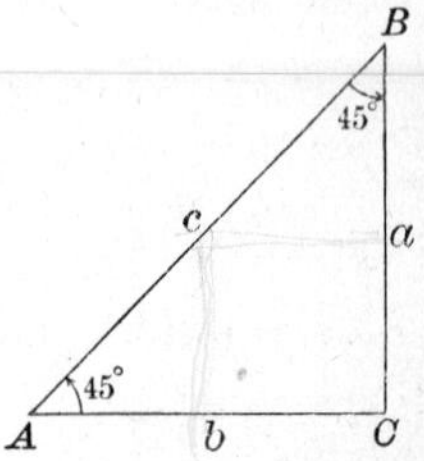

$$\sin 45° = \cos 45° = \frac{\frac{1}{2}c\sqrt{2}}{c} = \frac{1}{2}\sqrt{2};$$

$$\tan 45° = \cot 45° = \frac{a}{b} = 1;$$

$$\sec 45° = \csc 45° = \frac{a\sqrt{2}}{a} = \sqrt{2}.$$

We have therefore found all six functions of 45°. For purposes of computation these are commonly expressed as decimal fractions. Since $\sqrt{2} = 1.4142+$, we have the following values:

$\sin 45° = 0.7071$,	$\cos 45° = 0.7071$,
$\tan 45° = 1$,	$\cot 45° = 1$,
$\sec 45° = 1.4142$,	$\csc 45° = 1.4142$.

10. Functions of 30° and 60°. In the equilateral triangle $AA'B$ here shown, BC is the perpendicular bisector of the base. Also, $b=\frac{1}{2}c$, and $a=\sqrt{c^2-b^2}=\sqrt{c^2-\frac{1}{4}c^2}=\frac{1}{2}c\sqrt{3}$. Hence,

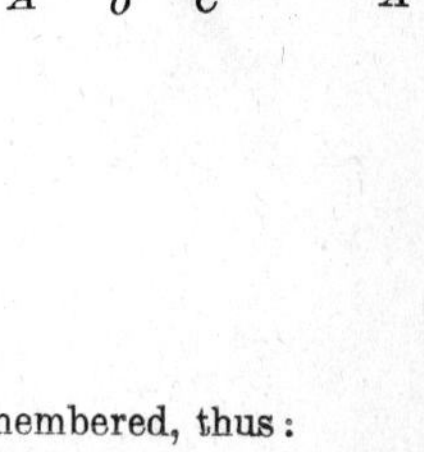

$$\sin 30° = \cos 60° = \frac{b}{c} = \frac{1}{2};$$

$$\cos 30° = \sin 60° = \frac{a}{c} = \frac{1}{2}\sqrt{3};$$

$$\tan 30° = \cot 60° = \frac{b}{a} = \frac{1}{\sqrt{3}} = \frac{1}{3}\sqrt{3};$$

$$\cot 30° = \tan 60° = \frac{a}{b} = \sqrt{3};$$

$$\sec 30° = \csc 60° = \frac{c}{a} = \frac{c}{\frac{1}{2}c\sqrt{3}} = \frac{2}{3}\sqrt{3};$$

$$\csc 30° = \sec 60° = \frac{c}{b} = 2.$$

The sine and cosine of 30°, 45°, and 60° are easily remembered, thus:

$\sin 30° = \frac{1}{2}\sqrt{1}$,	$\sin 45° = \frac{1}{2}\sqrt{2}$,	$\sin 60° = \frac{1}{2}\sqrt{3}$;
$\cos 30° = \frac{1}{2}\sqrt{3}$,	$\cos 45° = \frac{1}{2}\sqrt{2}$,	$\cos 60° = \frac{1}{2}\sqrt{1}$.

The functions of other angles are not so easily computed. The computation requires a study of series and is explained in more advanced works on mathematics. For the present we assume that the functions of all angles have been computed and are available, as is really the case.

Exercise 3. Functions of 30°, 45°, and 60°

Given $\sqrt{3} = 1.7320$, express as decimal fractions the following:

1. $\sin 30°$.
2. $\cos 30°$.
3. $\tan 30°$.
4. $\cot 30°$.
5. $\sec 30°$.
6. $\csc 30°$.
7. $\sin 60°$.
8. $\cos 60°$.
9. $\tan 60°$.
10. $\cot 60°$.
11. $\sec 60°$.
12. $\csc 60°$.

Write the ratios of the following, simplifying the results:

13. $\sin 45°$ to $\sin 30°$.
14. $\cos 45°$ to $\cos 30°$.
15. $\tan 45°$ to $\tan 30°$.
16. $\cot 45°$ to $\cot 30°$.
17. $\sec 45°$ to $\sec 30°$.
18. $\csc 45°$ to $\csc 30°$.
19. $\sin 30°$ to $\sin 60°$.
20. $\cos 30°$ to $\cos 60°$.
21. $\tan 30°$ to $\tan 60°$.
22. $\cot 30°$ to $\cot 60°$.
23. $\sec 30°$ to $\sec 60°$.
24. $\csc 30°$ to $\csc 60°$.

Express as functions of angles less than 45°:

25. $\sin 62° 17' 40''$.
26. $\tan 75° 28' 35''$.
27. $\sec 87° 32' 51''$.
28. $\cos 88° 0' 27''$.
29. $\sin 75.8°$.
30. $\cos 82.75°$.
31. $\tan 68.82°$.
32. $\sec 85.95°$.

Find A, given the following relations:

33. $90° - A = 45° - \frac{1}{2}A$.
34. $90° - \frac{1}{2}A = A$.
35. $45° + A = 90° - A$.
36. $90° - 4A = A$.
37. $90° - A = nA$.
38. $\cos A = \sin(45° - \frac{1}{2}A)$
39. $\cot \frac{1}{2}A = \tan A$.
40. $\tan(45° + A) = \cot A$.
41. $\cos 4A = \sin A$.
42. $\cot A = \tan nA$.
43. By what must $\sin 45°$ be multiplied to equal $\tan 30°$?
44. By what must $\sec 45°$ be multiplied to equal $\csc 30°$?
45. By what must $\cos 45°$ be multiplied to equal $\tan 60°$?
46. By what must $\csc 60°$ be divided to equal $\tan 45°$?
47. By what must $\csc 30°$ be divided to equal $\tan 30°$?
48. What is the ratio of $\sin 45° \sec 45°$ to $\cos 60°$?
49. What is the ratio of $\cos 45° \csc 45°$ to $\cos 30° \csc 30°$?
50. What is the ratio of $\sin 45° \sin 30°$ to $\cos 45° \cos 30°$?
51. What is the ratio of $\tan 30° \cot 30°$ to $\tan 60° \cot 60°$?
52. From the statement $\tan 30° = \frac{1}{3}\sqrt{3}$ find $\cot 60°$.

11. Values of the Functions. The values of the functions have been computed and tables constructed giving these values. One of these tables is shown on page 11 and will suffice for the work required on the next few pages.

This table gives the values of the functions to four decimal places for every degree from 0° to 90°. All such values are only approximate, the values of the functions being, in general, incommensurable with unity and not being expressible by means of common fractions or by means of decimal fractions with a finite number of decimal places.

12. Arrangement of the Table. As explained in § 8, $\cos 45° = \sin 45°$, $\cos 46° = \sin 44°$, $\cos 47° = \sin 43°$, and so on. Hence the column of sines from 0° to 45° is the same as the column of cosines from 45° to 90°. Therefore

In finding the functions of angles from 0° to 45° read from the top down; in finding the functions of angles from 45° to 90° read from the bottom up.

Exercise 4. Use of the Table

From the table on page 11 find the values of the following:

1. sin 5°.	9. cos 6°.	17. cot 5°.	25. sec 0°.
2. sin 14°.	10. sin 84°.	18. tan 85°.	26. csc 90°.
3. sin 21°.	11. cos 14°.	19. cot 11°.	27. sec 15°.
4. sin 30°.	12. sin 76°.	20. tan 79°.	28. csc 75°.
5. cos 85°.	13. cos 24°.	21. tan 21°.	29. csc 12°.
6. cos 76°.	14. sin 66°.	22. cot 69°.	30. sec 78°.
7. cos 69°.	15. cos 35°.	23. tan 45°.	31. csc 44°.
8. cos 60°.	16. sin 55°.	24. cot 45°.	32. sec 46°.

33. Find the difference between $2 \sin 9°$ and $\sin (2 \times 9°)$.

34. Find the difference between $3 \tan 5°$ and $\tan (3 \times 5°)$.

35. Which is the larger, $2 \sec 10°$ or $\sec (2 \times 10°)$?

36. Which is the larger, $2 \csc 10°$ or $\csc (2 \times 10°)$?

37. Which is the larger, $2 \cos 15°$ or $\cos (2 \times 15°)$?

38. Compare $3 \sin 20°$ with $\sin (3 \times 20°)$; with $\sin (2 \times 20°)$.

39. Compare $3 \tan 10°$ with $\tan (3 \times 10°)$; with $\tan (2 \times 10°)$.

40. Compare $3 \cos 10°$ with $\cos (3 \times 10°)$; with $\cos (2 \times 10°)$.

41. Is $\sin (10° + 20°)$ equal to $\sin 10° + \sin 20°$?

42. When the angle is increased from 0° to 90° which of the six functions are increased and which are decreased?

TABLE OF TRIGONOMETRIC FUNCTIONS FOR EVERY DEGREE FROM 0° TO 90°

Angle	sin	cos	tan	cot	sec	csc	
0°	.0000	1.0000	.0000	∞	1.0000	∞	**90°**
1°	.0175	.9998	.0175	57.2900	1.0002	57.2987	89°
2°	.0349	.9994	.0349	28.6363	1.0006	28.6537	88°
3°	.0523	.9986	.0524	19.0811	1.0014	19.1073	87°
4°	.0698	.9976	.0699	14.3007	1.0024	14.3356	86°
5°	.0872	.9962	.0875	11.4301	1.0038	11.4737	**85°**
6°	.1045	.9945	.1051	9.5144	1.0055	9.5668	84°
7°	.1219	.9925	.1228	8.1443	1.0075	8.2055	83°
8°	.1392	.9903	.1405	7.1154	1.0098	7.1853	82°
9°	.1564	.9877	.1584	6.3138	1.0125	6.3925	81°
10°	.1736	.9848	.1763	5.6713	1.0154	5.7588	**80°**
11°	.1908	.9816	.1944	5.1446	1.0187	5.2408	79°
12°	.2079	.9781	.2126	4.7046	1.0223	4.8097	78°
13°	.2250	.9744	.2309	4.3315	1.0263	4.4454	77°
14°	.2419	.9703	.2493	4.0108	1.0306	4.1336	76°
15°	.2588	.9659	.2679	3.7321	1.0353	3.8637	**75°**
16°	.2756	.9613	.2867	3.4874	1.0403	3.6280	74°
17°	.2924	.9563	.3057	3.2709	1.0457	3.4203	73°
18°	.3090	.9511	.3249	3.0777	1.0515	3.2361	72°
19°	.3256	.9455	.3443	2.9042	1.0576	3.0716	71°
20°	.3420	.9397	.3640	2.7475	1.0642	2.9238	**70°**
21°	.3584	.9336	.3839	2.6051	1.0711	2.7904	69°
22°	.3746	.9272	.4040	2.4751	1.0785	2.6695	68°
23°	.3907	.9205	.4245	2.3559	1.0864	2.5593	67°
24°	.4067	.9135	.4452	2.2460	1.0946	2.4586	66°
25°	.4226	.9063	.4663	2.1445	1.1034	2.3662	**65°**
26°	.4384	.8988	.4877	2.0503	1.1126	2.2812	64°
27°	.4540	.8910	.5095	1.9626	1.1223	2.2027	63°
28°	.4695	.8829	.5317	1.8807	1.1326	2.1301	62°
29°	.4848	.8746	.5543	1.8040	1.1434	2.0627	61°
30°	.5000	.8660	.5774	1.7321	1.1547	2.0000	**60°**
31°	.5150	.8572	.6009	1.6643	1.1666	1.9416	59°
32°	.5299	.8480	.6249	1.6003	1.1792	1.8871	58°
33°	.5446	.8387	.6494	1.5399	1.1924	1.8361	57°
34°	.5592	.8290	.6745	1.4826	1.2062	1.7883	56°
35°	.5736	.8192	.7002	1.4281	1.2208	1.7434	**55°**
36°	.5878	.8090	.7265	1.3764	1.2361	1.7013	54°
37°	.6018	.7986	.7536	1.3270	1.2521	1.6616	53°
38°	.6157	.7880	.7813	1.2799	1.2690	1.6243	52°
39°	.6293	.7771	.8098	1.2349	1.2868	1.5890	51°
40°	.6428	.7660	.8391	1.1918	1.3054	1.5557	**50°**
41°	.6561	.7547	.8693	1.1504	1.3250	1.5243	49°
42°	.6691	.7431	.9004	1.1106	1.3456	1.4945	48°
43°	.6820	.7314	.9325	1.0724	1.3673	1.4663	47°
44°	.6947	.7193	.9657	1.0355	1.3902	1.4396	46°
45°	.7071	.7071	1.0000	1.0000	1.4142	1.4142	**45°**
	cos	**sin**	**cot**	**tan**	**csc**	**sec**	**Angle**

13. Reciprocal Functions. Considering the definitions of the six functions, we see that, since

$$\sin A = \frac{a}{c}, \qquad \cos A = \frac{b}{c}, \qquad \tan A = \frac{a}{b},$$

$$\csc A = \frac{c}{a}, \qquad \sec A = \frac{c}{b}, \qquad \cot A = \frac{b}{a},$$

The sine is the reciprocal of the cosecant, the cosine is the reciprocal of the secant, and the tangent is the reciprocal of the cotangent.

That is,

$$\sin A = \frac{1}{\csc A}, \qquad \cos A = \frac{1}{\sec A}, \qquad \tan A = \frac{1}{\cot A},$$

$$\csc A = \frac{1}{\sin A}, \qquad \sec A = \frac{1}{\cos A}, \qquad \cot A = \frac{1}{\tan A}.$$

Hence $\sin A \csc A = 1$, $\cos A \sec A = 1$, and $\tan A \cot A = 1$. For example, from the table on page 11 we find $\sin 27° \csc 27°$ thus:

$$\sin 27° = 0.4540.$$

$$\csc 27° = 2.2027.$$

Therefore $\sin 27° \csc 27° = 0.4540 \times 2.2027$

$= 1.00002580$, or approximately 1.

We have shown that $\sin A \csc A = 1$ exactly, but the numbers given in the table are, as before stated, correct only to four decimal places.

Exercise 5. Use of the Table

Using the values given in the table on page 11, show as above that the following are reciprocals:

1. $\sin 30°$, $\csc 30°$.
2. $\sin 25°$, $\csc 25°$.
3. $\cos 35°$, $\sec 35°$.
4. $\sin 10°$, $\csc 10°$.
5. $\tan 10°$, $\cot 10°$.
6. $\cos 10°$, $\sec 10°$.
7. $\sin 75°$, $\csc 75°$.
8. $\cos 75°$, $\sec 75°$.
9. $\tan 75°$, $\cot 75°$.

10. From the table show that the ratio of $\sin 20° \csc 20°$ to $\tan 50° \cot 50°$ is 1.

11. Similarly, show that $\cos 40° \sec 40° : \tan 70° \cot 70° = 1$.

In the right triangle ACB, as shown in § 7:

12. Find the length of side a if $A = 30°$, and $c = 75.2$.

13. Find the length of side a if $A = 45°$, and $c = 1.414$.

14. Find the length of side b if $A = 30°$, and $c = 115.47$.

15. Find the length of side a if $A = 60°$, and $b = 34.64$.

16. Find the length of side b if $A = 60°$, and $c = 25.72$.

17. Find the length of side a if $A = 30°$, and $c = 45.28$.

14. Other Relations of Functions. Since, from the figure in § 7, $a^2 + b^2 = c^2$, we have

$$\frac{a^2}{c^2} + \frac{b^2}{c^2} = 1,$$

or

$$\sin^2 A + \cos^2 A = 1.$$

It is customary to write $\sin^2 A$ for $(\sin A)^2$, and similarly for the other functions.

This formula is one of the most important in trigonometry and should be memorized. From it we see that

$$\sin A = \sqrt{1 - \cos^2 A}, \qquad \cos A = \sqrt{1 - \sin^2 A}.$$

Furthermore, since $\tan A = \frac{a}{b}$, $\sin A = \frac{a}{c}$, and $\cos A = \frac{b}{c}$, it follows that

$$\tan A = \frac{\sin A}{\cos A}.$$

This is also an important formula to be memorized. From it we see that $\tan A \cos A = \sin A$, and, in general, that we can find any one of the functions, sine, cosine, or tangent, given the other two.

Furthermore, from the same equation $a^2 + b^2 = c^2$ we see that $1 + \frac{a^2}{b^2} = \frac{c^2}{b^2}$. Hence we see that

$$1 + \tan^2 A = \sec^2 A.$$

In a similar manner we may prove that $1 + \frac{b^2}{a^2} = \frac{c^2}{a^2}$; whence we have the formula

$$1 + \cot^2 A = \csc^2 A.$$

These two formulas should be memorized.

From these formulas the following relations can easily be deduced:

$$\sin x = \cos x \tan x = \cos x / \cot x = \tan x / \sec x.$$
$$\cos x = \cot x \sin x = \cot x / \csc x = \sin x / \tan x.$$
$$\tan x = \sin x \sec x = \sin x / \cos x = \sec x / \csc x.$$
$$\cot x = \csc x \cos x = \csc x / \sec x = \cos x / \sin x.$$
$$\sec x = \tan x \csc x = \tan x / \sin x = \csc x / \cot x.$$
$$\csc x = \sec x \cot x = \sec x / \tan x = \cot x / \cos x.$$

It is often convenient to recall these relations, and this can be done by the aid of a simple mnemonic:

$$\begin{array}{ccc} & \tan x & \\ \sin x & & \sec x \\ \cos x & & \csc x \\ & \cot x & \end{array}$$

In the above diagram, *any function is equal to the product of the two adjacent functions, or to the quotient of either adjacent function divided by the one beyond it.*

15. Practical Use of the Sine. Since by definition we have

$$\frac{a}{c} = \sin A,$$

we see that $$a = c \sin A.$$

We might also derive the equation

$$c = \frac{a}{\sin A}.$$

But since $\frac{1}{\sin A} = \csc A$ (§ 13), it is easier at present to use

$$c = a \csc A,$$

and this will be considered when we come to study the cosecant.

1. Given $c = 38$ and $A = 40°$, find a.

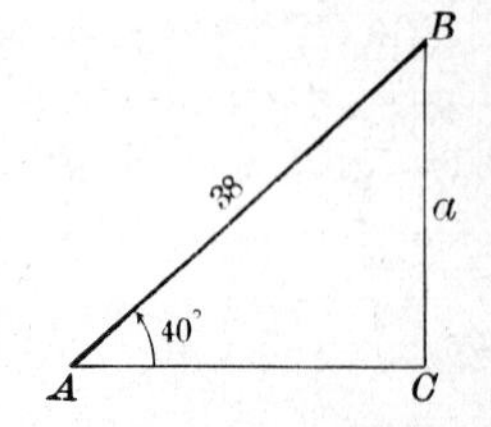

As above, $$a = c \sin A.$$

From the table, $$\sin 40° = 0.6428$$

and $$c = 38$$

$$\begin{array}{r} 5\,1424 \\ 19\,284 \\ \hline c \sin A = 24.4264 \end{array}$$

But since the table on page 11 gives only the first four figures of sin 40°, *we can expect only the first four figures of the result to be correct.* We therefore say that $a = 24.43-$. If the third decimal place were less than 5, the value of a would be written $24.42+$.

Some check should always be applied to the result. In this case we may proceed as follows: $24.4264 \div 38 = 0.6428$, which is sin 40°.

2. Given $c = 10$ and $a = 6.293$, find A.

Since $$\frac{a}{c} = \sin A,$$

we have $$\frac{6.293}{10} = 0.6293 = \sin A.$$

Looking in the table we see that

$$0.6293 = \sin 39°;$$

whence $$A = 39°.$$

3. Given $a = 4.68\frac{1}{4}$ and $A = 22°$, find c.

As stated above, c may be found from the formula $a = c \sin A$ by using a and $\sin A$, although we shall later use the cosecant for this purpose. Substituting the given values, we have

$$4.68\tfrac{1}{4} = c \sin 22°,$$

or $$4.6825 = 0.3746\,c.$$

Dividing by 0.3746, $$12.5 = c.$$

What check should be applied here and in Ex. 2?

Exercise 6. Use of the Sine

Find a to four figures, given the following:

1. $c = 10$, $A = 10°$.
2. $c = 15$, $A = 15°$.
3. $c = 58$, $A = 45°$.
4. $c = 75$, $A = 50°$.

Find A, given the following:

5. $c = 10$, $a = 2.079$.
6. $c = 20$, $a = 6.840$.
7. $c = 2$, $a = 1.2586$.
8. $c = 50$, $a = 34.1$.

9. A 50-foot ladder resting against the side of a house reaches a point 25 ft. from the ground. What angle does it make with the ground?

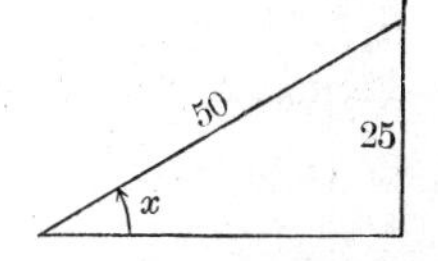

In all such cases the ground should be considered level and the side of the building should be considered vertical unless the contrary is expressly stated.

10. From the top of a rock a cord is stretched to a point on the ground, making an angle of 40° with the horizontal plane. The cord is 84 ft. long. Assuming the cord to be straight, how high is the rock?

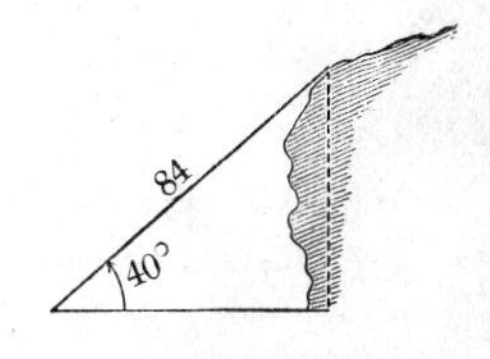

11. Find the side of a regular decagon inscribed in a circle of radius 7 ft.

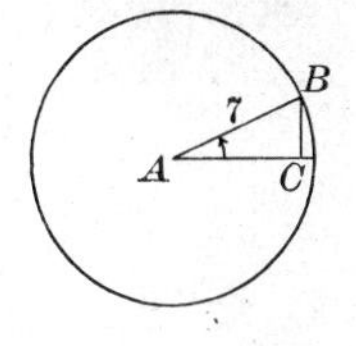

What is the central angle? What is half of this angle? Find BC and double it. By this plan we can find the perimeter of any inscribed regular polygon, given the radius of the circle. In this way we could approximate the value of π. For example, we see that the semiperimeter of a polygon of 90 sides in a unit circle is $90 \times \sin 2°$, or 90×0.0349, or 3.141.

12. The edge of the Great Pyramid is 609 ft. and makes an angle of 52° with the horizontal plane. What is the height of the pyramid?

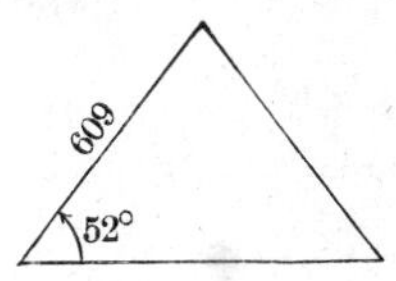

13. Wishing to measure BC, the length of a pond, a surveyor ran a line CA at right angles to BC. He measured AB and $\angle A$, finding that $AB = 928$ ft., and $A = 29°$. Find the length of BC.

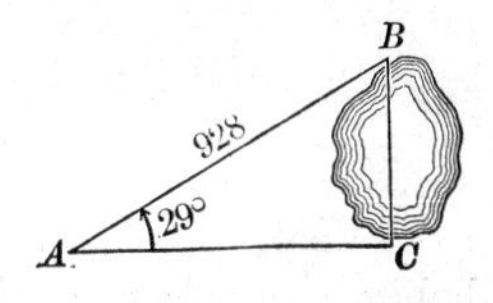

In practical surveying we would probably use an oblique triangle, although the work as given here is correct. The oblique triangle is considered later.

16. Practical Use of the Cosine. Since by definition we have

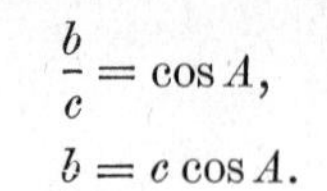

$$\frac{b}{c} = \cos A,$$

we see that

$$b = c \cos A.$$

1. Given $c = 28$ and $A = 46°$, find b.

From the table, $\cos 46° = 0.6947$

and $c = \quad 28$

$$\begin{array}{r} 5\,5576 \\ 13\,894 \\ \hline 19.4516 \end{array}$$

Hence, to four figures, $b = 19.45$.

2. Given $c = 2$ and $b = 1.9022$, find A.

Since $\frac{b}{c} = \cos A,$

we have $1.9022 \div 2 = 0.9511 = \cos A.$

From the table, $0.9511 = \cos 18°.$

Hence $A = 18°.$

What check should be applied here and in Ex. 1?

Exercise 7. Use of the Cosine

Find b to four figures, given the following:

1. $c = 11$, $A = 10°$.
2. $c = 14$, $A = 16°$.
3. $c = 28$, $A = 24°$.
4. $c = 41$, $A = 39°$.
5. $c = 75$, $A = 42°$.
6. $c = 2.8$, $A = 48°$.
7. $c = 9.7$, $A = 52°$.
8. $c = 11.2$, $A = 58°$.
9. $c = 12.5$, $A = 67°$.
10. $c = 28.25$, $A = 75°$.

Find A, given the following:

11. $c = 10$, $b = 9.848$.
12. $c = 20$, $b = 19.126$.
13. $c = 40$, $b = 35.952$.
14. $c = 17.6$, $b = 8.8$.
15. $c = 500$, $b = 227$.
16. $c = 600$, $b = 205.2$.
17. $c = 200$, $b = 117.56$.
18. $c = 187$, $b = 93\frac{1}{2}$.
19. $c = 300$, $b = 102\frac{3}{5}$.
20. $c = 1000$, $b = 104\frac{1}{2}$.

21. A flagstaff breaks off 22 ft. from the top and, the parts still holding together, the top of the staff reaches the earth 11 ft. from the foot. What angle does it make with the ground?

22. Wishing to measure the length of a pond, a class constructed a right triangle as shown in the figure. If $AB = 640$ ft. and $A = 50°$, required the distance AC.

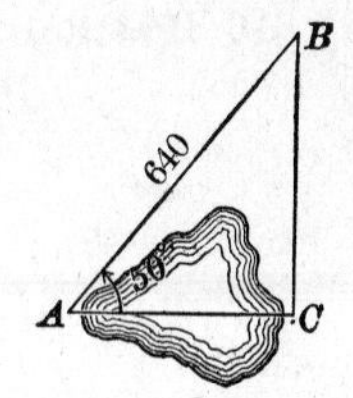

23. In the same figure what is the length of AC when $AB = 500$ ft. and $A = 40°$?

24. In the same figure, if $AC = 731.4$ ft. and $AB = 1000$ ft., what is the size of angle A?

25. A regular hexagon is inscribed in a circle of radius 9 in. How far is it from the center to a side?

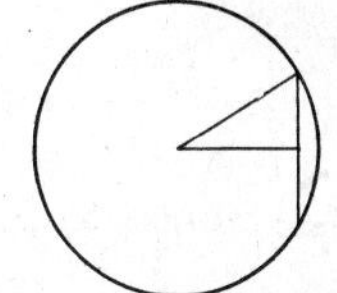

Having found this distance, the *apothem*, and knowing that a side of the regular hexagon equals the radius, we can find the area, as required in Ex. 26.

26. What is the area of a regular hexagon inscribed in a circle of radius 8 in.?

27. A ship sails northeast 8 mi. It is then how many miles to the east of the starting point?

Northeast is 45° east of north. In all such cases in plane trigonometry the figure is supposed to be a plane. For long distances it would be necessary to consider a spherical triangle.

28. Some 16-foot roof timbers make an angle of 30° with the horizontal in an A-shaped roof, as shown in the figure. Find AA', the span of the roof.

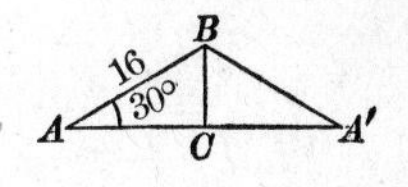

29. An equilateral triangle is inscribed in a circle of radius 12 in. How far is it from the center to a side?

30. A crane AB, 30 ft. long, makes an angle of x degrees with the horizontal line AC. Find the distance AC when $x = 20$; when $x = 45$; when $x = 65$; when $x = 0$; when $x = 90$.

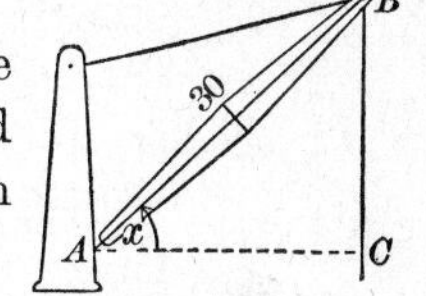

31. In Ex. 30 what angle does the crane make with the horizontal when $AC = 15$ ft.? when $AC = 30$ ft.?

32. The square AN, of which the side is 200 ft., is inscribed in the square CM. AC is 181.26 ft. Required the angles that the sides of the small square make with the large one.

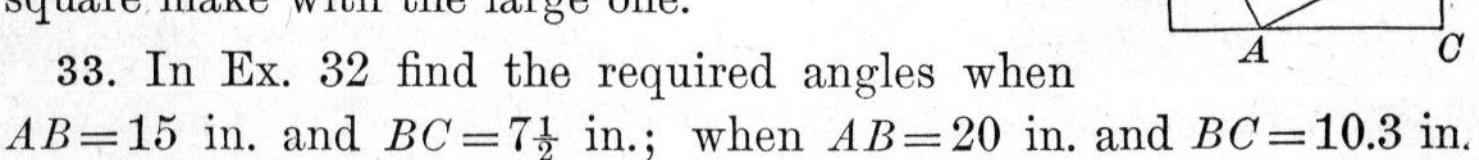

33. In Ex. 32 find the required angles when $AB = 15$ in. and $BC = 7\frac{1}{2}$ in.; when $AB = 20$ in. and $BC = 10.3$ in.

34. The edge of the Great Pyramid is 609 ft., and it makes an angle of 52° with the horizontal plane. What is the diagonal of the base?

17. Practical Use of the Tangent. Since by definition we have

$$\frac{a}{b} = \tan A,$$

we see that $$a = b \tan A.$$

Given $b = 12$ and $A = 35°$, find a.

From the table,

$$\begin{array}{rr} \tan 35° = & 0.7002 \\ b = & 12 \\ \hline & 1\,4004 \\ & 7\,002 \\ \hline & 8.4024 \end{array}$$

Hence, to four figures, $$a = 8.402.$$

The figures 1, 2, $\cdots$, 9 are often spoken of as *significant figures*. In 8.402 the zero is, however, looked upon as a significant figure, but not in a case like 12,550. The first four significant figures in 0.6705067 are 6705.

18. Angles of Elevation and Depression. The *angle of elevation*, or the *angle of depression*, of an object is the angle which a line from the eye to the object makes with a horizontal line in the same vertical plane.

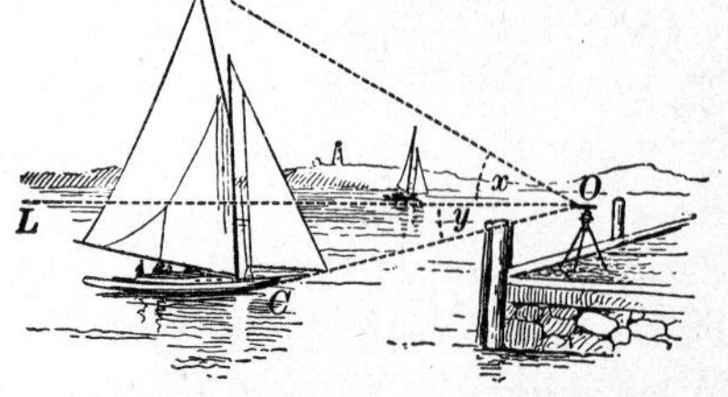

Thus, if the observer is at O, x is the angle of elevation of B, and y is the angle of depression of C.

In measuring angles with a transit the height of the instrument must always be taken into account. In stating problems, however, it is not convenient to consider this every time, and hence the angle is supposed to be taken from the level on which the instrument stands, unless otherwise stated.

1. From a point 5 ft. above the ground and 150 ft. from the foot of a tree the angle of elevation of the top is observed to be 20°. How high is the tree?

We have

$$\begin{aligned} a &= b \tan A \\ &= 150 \tan 20° \\ &= 150 \times 0.3640 \\ &= 54.6. \end{aligned}$$

Hence the height of the tree is 54.6 ft. + 5 ft., or 59.6 ft.

2. From a point A on a cliff 60 ft. high, including the instrument, the angle of depression of a boat B on a lake is observed to be 25°. How far is the boat from C, the foot of the cliff?

We have $\angle BAC = 65°$. Hence $BC = 60 \tan 65°$. From the table, $\tan 65° = 2.1445$. Hence $BC = 60 \times 2.1445 = 128.67$.

Exercise 8. Use of the Tangent

Find a to four significant figures, given the following:

1. $b = 37$, $A = 18°$.
2. $b = 26$, $A = 23°$.
3. $b = 48$, $A = 31°$.
4. $b = 62$, $A = 36°$.
5. $b = 98$, $A = 45°$.
6. $b = 4.8$, $A = 51°$.
7. $b = 9.6$, $A = 57°$.
8. $b = 23.4$, $A = 62°$.
9. $b = 28.7$, $A = 75°$.
10. $b = 39.7$, $A = 85°$.

Find A, given the following:

11. $a = 6$, $b = 6$.
12. $a = 0.281$, $b = 2$.
13. $a = 4.752$, $b = 30$.
14. $a = 13.772$, $b = 40$.
15. $a = 2.424$, $b = 6$.
16. $a = 20.503$, $b = 10$.

17. A man standing 120 ft. from the foot of a church spire finds that the angle of elevation of the top is 50°. If his eye is 5 ft. 8 in. from the ground, what is the height of the spire?

18. When a flagstaff 55.43 ft. high casts a shadow 100 ft. long on a horizontal plane, what is the angle of elevation of the sun?

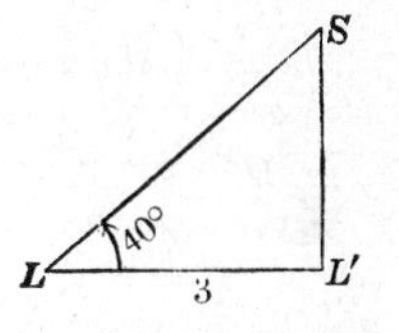

19. A ship S is observed at the same instant from two lighthouses, L and L', 3 mi. apart. $\angle L'LS$ is found to be 40° and $\angle LL'S$ is found to be 90°. What is the distance of the ship from L'? What is its distance from L?

20. From the top of a rock which rises vertically, including the instrument, 134 ft. above a river bank the angle of depression of the opposite bank is found to be 40°. How wide is the river?

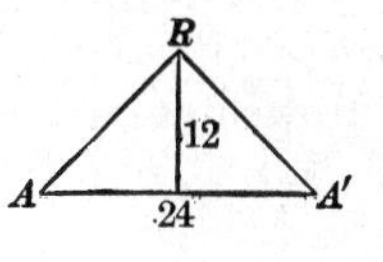

21. An A-shaped roof has a span AA' of 24 ft. The ridgepole R is 12 ft. above the horizontal line AA'. What angle does AR make with AA'? with RA'? with the perpendicular from R on AA'?

22. The foot of a ladder is 17 ft. 6 in. from a wall, and the ladder makes an angle of 42° with the horizontal when it leans against the wall. How far up the wall does it reach?

23. A post subtends an angle of 7° from a point on the ground 50 ft. away. What is the height of the post?

24. The diameter of a one-cent piece is $\frac{3}{4}$ in. If the coin is held so that it subtends an angle of 40° at the eye, what is its distance from the eye?

19. Practical Use of the Cotangent. Since by definition we have

$$\frac{b}{a} = \cot A,$$

we see that $$b = a \cot A.$$

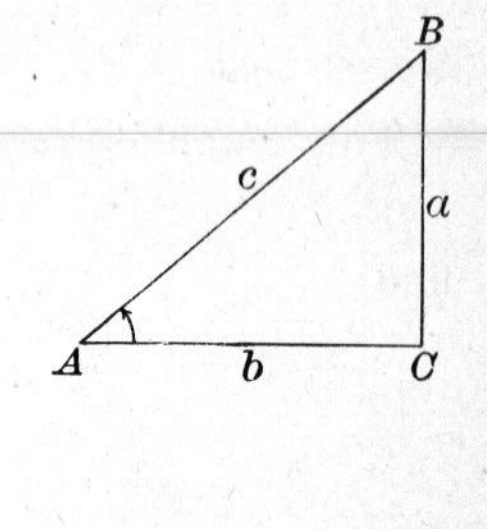

For example, given $a = 71$ and $A = 28°$, find b.

From the table, $\cot 28° = 1.8807$

and $a = 71$

$$\begin{array}{r} 1.8807 \\ 71 \\ \hline 1\ 8807 \\ 131\ 649 \\ \hline 133.5297 \end{array}$$

Hence, to four significant figures, $b = 133.5$.

What check should be applied in this case?

Exercise 9. Use of the Cotangent

Find b to four significant figures, given the following:

1. $a = 29$, $A = 48°$.
2. $a = 38$, $A = 72°$.
3. $a = 56$, $A = 19°$.
4. $a = 72$, $A = 40°$.
5. $a = 425$, $A = 38°$.
6. $a = 19\frac{1}{2}$, $A = 36°$.
7. $a = 24.8$, $A = 43°$.
8. $a = 256.8$, $A = 75°$.

Find A, given the following:

9. $a = 72$, $b = 72$.
10. $a = 60$, $b = 128.67$.

11. How far from a tree 50 ft. high must a person lie in order to see the top at an angle of elevation of 60°?

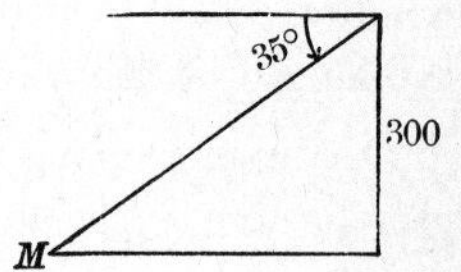

12. From the top of a tower 300 ft. high, including the instrument, a point on the ground is observed to have an angle of depression of 35°. How far is the point from the tower?

13. From the extremity of the shadow cast by a church spire 150 ft. high the angle of elevation of the top is 53°. What is the length of the shadow?

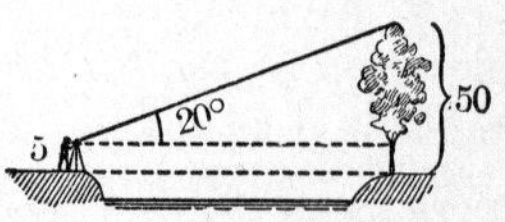

14. A tree known to be 50 ft. high, standing on the bank of a stream, is observed from the opposite bank to have an angle of elevation of 20°. The angle is measured on a line 5 ft. above the foot of the tree. How wide is the stream?

20. Practical Use of the Secant. Since by definition we have

$$\frac{c}{b} = \sec A,$$

we see that $c = b \sec A.$

For example, given $b = 15$ and $A = 30°$, find c.

From the table, $\sec 30° = 1.1547$

and $b = 15$

$$\begin{array}{r} 1.1547 \\ 15 \\ \hline 5\,7735 \\ 11\,547 \\ \hline 17.3205 \end{array}$$

Hence, to four significant figures, $c = 17.32$.

Exercise 10. Use of the Secant

Find c to four significant figures, given the following:

1. $b = 36,\ A = 27°$.
2. $b = 48,\ A = 39°$.
3. $b = 74,\ A = 43°$.
4. $b = 22\frac{1}{2},\ A = 48°$.
5. $b = 33.4,\ A = 53°$.
6. $b = 148.8,\ A = 64°$.

Find A, given the following:

7. $b = 10,\ c = 13\frac{1}{4}$.
8. $b = 17.8,\ c = 35.6$.

9. A ladder rests against the side of a building, and makes an angle of 28° with the ground. The foot of the ladder is 20 ft. from the building. How long is the ladder?

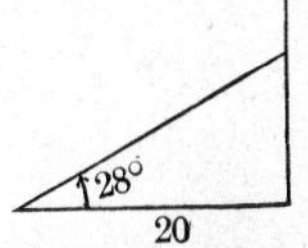

10. From a point 50 ft. from a house a wire is stretched to a window so as to make an angle of 30° with the horizontal. Find the length of the wire, assuming it to be straight.

11. In measuring the distance AB a surveyor ran the line AC, making an angle of 50° with AB, and the line BC perpendicular to AC. He measured AC and found that it was 880 ft. Required the distance AB.

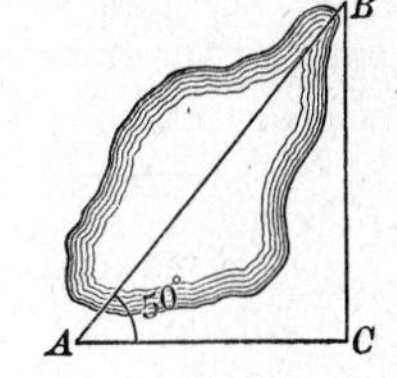

12. From the extremity of the shadow cast by a tree the angle of elevation of the top is 47°. The shadow is 62 ft. 6 in. long. How far is it from the top of the tree to the extremity of the shadow?

13. The span of this roof is 40 ft., and the roof timbers AB make an angle of 40° with the horizontal. Find the length of AB.

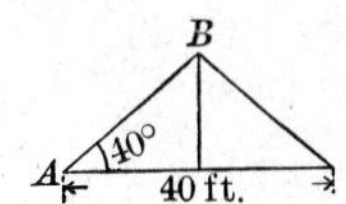

21. Practical Use of the Cosecant. Since by definition we have

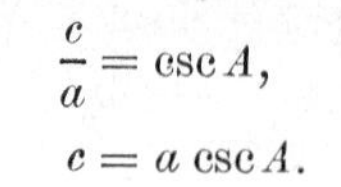

$$\frac{c}{a} = \csc A,$$

we see that

$$c = a \csc A.$$

For example, given $a = 22$ and $A = 35°$, find c.

From the table, $\csc 35° = 1.7434$

and $a = 22$

$$\begin{array}{r} 3\,4868 \\ 34\,868 \\ \hline 38.3548 \end{array}$$

Hence, to four significant figures, $c = 38.35$.

Check. Since $\frac{a}{c} = \sin A$, $22 \div 38.35 = 0.5736 = \sin 35°$.

Exercise 11. Use of the Cosecant

Find c to four significant figures, given the following:

1. $a = 24$, $A = 29°$.
2. $a = 36$, $A = 41°$.
3. $a = 56$, $A = 44°$.
4. $a = 56\frac{1}{2}$, $A = 61°$.
5. $a = 75.8$, $A = 69°$.
6. $a = 146.9$, $A = 74°$.

Find A, given the following:

7. $a = 10$, $c = 11.126$.
8. $a = 13$, $c = 27.6913$.
9. $a = 5\frac{1}{2}$, $c = 6.0687$.
10. $a = 75$, $c = 106.065$.

11. Seen from a point on the ground the angle of elevation of an aeroplane is 64°. If the aeroplane is 1000 ft. above the ground, how far is it in a straight line from the observer?

12. A ship sailing 47° east of north changes its latitude 28 mi. in 3 hr. What is its rate of sailing per hour?

13. A ship sailing 63° east of south changes its latitude 45 mi. in 5 hr. What is its rate of sailing per hour?

14. From the top of a lighthouse 100 ft., including the instrument, above the level of the sea a boat is observed under an angle of depression of 22°. How far is the boat from the point of observation?

15. Seen from a point on the ground the angle of elevation of the top of a telegraph pole 27 ft. high is 28°. How far is it from the point of observation to the top of the pole?

16. What is the length of the hypotenuse of a right triangle of which one side is $11\frac{3}{4}$ in. and the opposite angle 43°?

22. Functions as Lines. The functions of an angle, being ratios, are *numbers*; but we may represent them by *lines* if we first choose a unit of length, and then construct right triangles, such that the denominators of the ratios shall be equal to this unit.

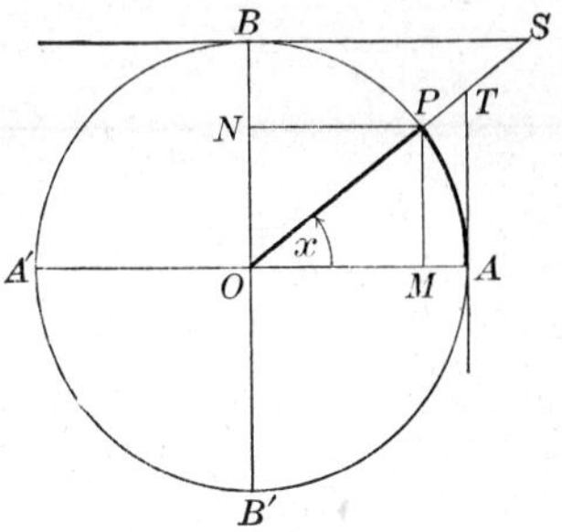

Thus in the annexed figure the radius is taken as 1, the circle then being spoken of as a *unit circle*. Then

$$OA = OP = OB = 1.$$

Drawing the four perpendiculars as shown, we have:

$$\sin x = \frac{MP}{OP} = MP; \qquad \cos x = \frac{OM}{OP} = OM;$$

$$\tan x = \frac{AT}{OA} = AT; \qquad \cot x = \frac{BS}{OB} = BS;$$

$$\sec x = \frac{OT}{OA} = OT; \qquad \csc x = \frac{OS}{OB} = OS.$$

In each case we have arranged the fraction so that the denominator is 1. For example, instead of taking $\frac{MP}{OM}$ for $\tan x$ we have taken the equal ratio $\frac{AT}{OA}$, because $OA = 1$.

Similarly, instead of taking $\frac{OP}{PM}$ for $\csc x$ we have taken the equal ratio $\frac{OS}{OB}$, because $OB = 1$.

This explains the use of the names *tangent* and *secant*, AT being a tangent to the circle, and OT being a secant.

Formerly the functions were considered as lines instead of ratios and received their names at that time. The word *sine* is from the Latin *sinus*, a translation of an Arabic term for this function.

We see from the figure that the sine of the complement of x is NP, which equals OM; also that the tangent of the complement of x is BS, and that the secant of the complement of x is OS.

Exercise 12. Functions as Lines

1. Represent by lines the functions of 45°.

2. Represent by lines the functions of an acute angle greater than 45°.

Using the above figure, determine which is the greater:

3. $\sin x$ or $\tan x$.

4. $\sin x$ or $\sec x$.

5. $\sec x$ or $\tan x$.

6. $\csc x$ or $\cot x$.

7. $\cos x$ or $\cot x$.

8. $\cos x$ or $\csc x$.

Construct the angle x, given the following:

9. $\tan x = 3$.
10. $\csc x = 2$.
11. $\cos x = \frac{1}{2}$.
12. $\sin x = \cos x$.
13. $\sin x = 2 \cos x$.
14. $4 \sin x = \tan x$.

15. Show that the sine of an angle is equal to one half the chord of twice the angle in a unit circle.

16. Find x if $\sin x$ is equal to one half the side of a regular decagon inscribed in a unit circle.

Given x and y, x + y being less than 90°, construct a line equal to

17. $\sin (x + y) - \sin x$.
18. $\tan (x + y) - \tan x$.
19. $\sec (x + y) - \sec x$.
20. $\cos x - \cos (x + y)$.
21. $\cot x - \cot (x + y)$.
22. $\csc x - \csc (x + y)$.
23. $\tan (x + y) - \sin (x + y) + \tan x - \sin x$.

Given an angle x, construct an angle y such that:

24. $\sin y = 2 \sin x$.
25. $\cos y = \frac{1}{2} \cos x$.
26. $\sin y = \cos x$.
27. $\tan y = \cot x$.
28. $\tan y = 3 \tan x$.
29. $\sec y = \csc x$.
30. $\sin y = \frac{1}{2} \tan x$.
31. $\sin y = \frac{2}{3} \tan x$.

32. Show by construction that $2 \sin A > \sin 2A$, when $A < 45°$.

33. Show by construction that $\cos A < 2 \cos 2A$, when $A < 30°$.

34. Given two angles A and B, $A + B$ being less than 90°; show that $\sin(A + B) < \sin A + \sin B$.

35. Given $\sin x$ in a unit circle; find the length of a line in a circle of radius r corresponding in position to $\sin x$.

36. In a right triangle, given the hypotenuse c, and $\sin A = m$; find the two sides.

37. In a right triangle, given the side b, and $\tan A = m$; find the other side and the hypotenuse.

Construct, or show that it is impossible to construct, the angle x, given the following:

38. $\sin x = \frac{1}{2}$.
39. $\sin x = 1$.
40. $\sin x = \frac{5}{4}$.
41. $\cos x = 0$.
42. $\cos x = \frac{4}{3}$.
43. $\cos x = \frac{1}{3}$.
44. $\tan x = \frac{4}{3}$.
45. $\cot x = \frac{1}{2}$.
46. $\sec x = \frac{1}{2}$.

47. Using a protractor, draw the figure to show that $\sin 60° = \cos (\frac{1}{2} \text{ of } 60°)$, and $\sin 30° = \cos (2 \times 30°)$.

23. Changes in the Functions. If we suppose $\angle AOP$, or x, to increase gradually to 90°, the sine MP increases to $M'P'$, $M''P''$, and so on to OB.

That is, the sine increases from 0 for the angle 0°, to 1 for the angle 90°. Hence 0 and 1 are called the *limiting values* of the sine.

Similarly, AT and OT gradually increase in length, while OM, BS, and OS gradually decrease. That is,

As an acute angle increases to 90°, its sine, tangent, and secant also increase, while its cosine, cotangent, and cosecant decrease.

If we suppose x to decrease to 0°, OP coincides with OA and is parallel to BS. Therefore MP and AT vanish, OM becomes equal to OA, while BS and OS are each infinitely long and are represented in value by the symbol ∞. Similarly, we may consider the changes as x increases from 0° to 90°.

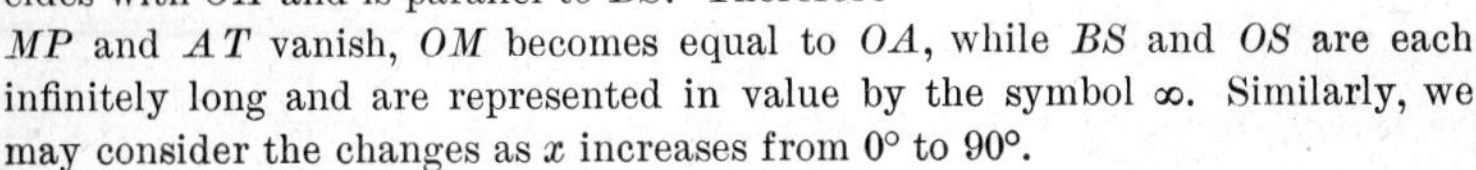

Hence, as the angle x increases from 0° to 90°, we see that

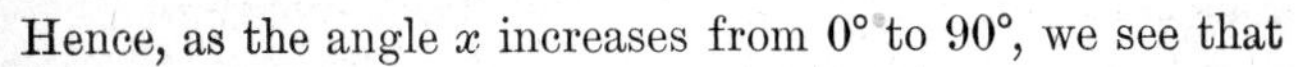

$\sin x$ increases from 0 to 1,
$\cos x$ decreases from 1 to 0,
$\tan x$ increases from 0 to ∞,
$\cot x$ decreases from ∞ to 0,
$\sec x$ increases from 1 to ∞,
$\csc x$ decreases from ∞ to 1.

We also see that

sines and cosines are never greater than 1;
secants and cosecants are never less than 1;
tangents and cotangents may have any values from 0 to ∞.

In particular, for the angle 0°, we have the following values:

$\sin 0° = 0$, $\tan 0° = 0$, $\sec 0° = 1$,
$\cos 0° = 1$, $\cot 0° = \infty$, $\csc 0° = \infty$.

For the angle 90° we have the following values:

$\sin 90° = 1$, $\tan 90° = \infty$, $\sec 90° = \infty$,
$\cos 90° = 0$, $\cot 90° = 0$, $\csc 90° = 1$.

By reference to the figure and the table it is apparent that the functions of 45° are never equal to half of the corresponding functions of 90°. Thus,

$\sin 45° = 0.7071$, $\tan 45° = 1$, $\sec 45° = 1.4142$,
$\cos 45° = 0.7071$. $\cot 45° = 1$, $\csc 45° = 1.4142$.

Exercise 13. Functions as Lines

1. Draw a figure to show that $\sin 90° = 1$.

2. What is the value of $\cos 90°$? Draw a figure to show this.

3. What is the value of $\sec 0°$? Draw a figure to show this.

4. What is the value of $\tan 90°$? Draw a figure to show this.

5. What is the value of $\cot 90°$? Draw a figure to show this.

6. As the angle increases, which increases the more rapidly, the sine or the tangent? Show this by reference to the figure.

7. If you double an angle, does this double the sine? Show this by reference to the figure.

8. If you bisect an angle, does this bisect the tangent? Prove it.

9. State the angle for which these relations are true:

$$\sin x = \cos x, \qquad \tan x = \cot x, \qquad \sec x = \csc x.$$

Show this by reference to the figure.

10. If you know that $\sin 40° 15' = 0.6461$, and $\cos 40° 15' = 0.7632$, and that the difference between each of these and the sine and cosine of $40° 15' 30''$ is 0.0001, what is $\sin 40° 15' 30''$? $\cos 40° 15' 30''$?

11. If you know that $\tan 20° 12'$ is 0.3679, and that the difference between this and $\tan 20° 12' 15''$ is 0.0001, what is $\tan 20° 12' 15''$?

12. If you know that $\cot 20° 12'$ is 2.7179, and that the difference between this and $\cot 20° 12' 15''$ is 0.0006, what is $\cot 20° 12' 15''$?

13. If you know that $\tan 66.5°$ is 2.2998, and that the difference between this and $\tan 66.6°$ is 0.0111, what is $\tan 66.6°$?

14. If you know that $\cos 57.4°$ is 0.5388, and that the difference between this and $\cos 57.5°$ is 0.0015, what is $\cos 57.5°$?

Draw the angle x for which the functions have the following values and state (page 11) to the nearest degree the value of the angle:

15. $\sin x = 0.1$.	21. $\tan x = 0.1$.	27. $\sec x = 1.2$.
16. $\sin x = 0.4$.	22. $\tan x = 0.23$.	28. $\sec x = 1.3$.
17. $\sin x = 0.7$.	23. $\tan x = 0.4$.	29. $\sec x = 1.7$.
18. $\cos x = 0.9$.	24. $\cot x = 4.0$.	30. $\csc x = 2.0$.
19. $\cos x = 0.8$.	25. $\cot x = 2.9$.	31. $\csc x = 3.6$.
20. $\cos x = 0.7$.	26. $\cot x = 0.9$.	32. $\csc x = 1.66$.

33. Find the value of $\sin x$ in the equation $\sin x - \dfrac{1}{\sin x} + 1.5 = 0$. Which root is admissible? Why is the other root impossible?

CHAPTER II

USE OF THE TABLE OF NATURAL FUNCTIONS

24. Sexagesimal and Decimal Fractions. The ancients, not having developed the idea of the decimal fraction and not having any convenient notation for even the common fraction, used a system based upon sixtieths. Thus they had units, sixtieths, thirty-six hundredths, and so on, and they used this system in all kinds of theoretical work requiring extensive fractions.

For example, instead of $1\frac{7}{15}$ they would use $1\ 28'$, meaning $1\frac{28}{60}$; and instead of 1.51 they would use $1\ 30'\ 36''$, meaning $1\frac{30}{60}+\frac{36}{3600}$. The symbols for degrees, minutes, and seconds are modern.

We to-day apply these *sexagesimal* (scale of sixty) fractions only to the measure of time, angles, and arcs. Thus

$$3 \text{ hr. } 10 \text{ min. } 15 \text{ sec. means } (3+\tfrac{10}{60}+\tfrac{15}{3600}) \text{ hr.},$$

and $$3°\ 10'\ 15'' \text{ means } (3+\tfrac{10}{60}+\tfrac{15}{3600})°.$$

In medieval times the sexagesimal system was carried farther than this. For example, $3\ 10'\ 20''\ 30'''\ 45^{iv}$ was used for $3+\dfrac{10}{60}+\dfrac{20}{60^2}+\dfrac{30}{60^3}+\dfrac{45}{60^4}$. Some writers used sexagesimal fractions in which the denominators extended to 60^{12}

Since about the year 1600 we have had decimal fractions with which to work, and these have gradually replaced sexagesimal fractions in most cases. At present there is a strong tendency towards using decimal instead of sexagesimal fractions in angle measure. On this account it is necessary to be familiar with tables which give the functions of angles not only to degrees and minutes, but also to degrees and hundredths, with provision for finding the functions also to seconds and to thousandths of a degree. Hence the tables which will be considered and the problems which will be proposed will involve both sexagesimal and decimal fractions, but with particular attention to the former because they are the ones still commonly used.

The rise of the metric system in the nineteenth century gave an impetus to the movement to abandon the sexagesimal system. At the time the metric system was established in France, trigonometric tables were prepared on the decimal plan. It is only within recent years, however, that tables of this kind have begun to come into use.

25. Sexagesimal Table. The following is a portion of a page from the Wentworth-Smith Trigonometric Tables:

41°

′	sin	cos	tan	cot	′
0	6561	7547	8693	1.1504	**60**
1	6563	7545	8698	1.1497	59
2	6565	7543	8703	1.1490	58
3	6567	7541	8708	1.1483	57
4	6569	7539	8713	1.1477	56
5	6572	7538	8718	1.1470	**55**
...	...	...	...	...	...
′	cos	sin	cot	tan	′

48°

42°

′	sin	cos	tan	cot	′
0	6691	7431	9004	1.1106	**60**
1	6693	7430	9009	1.1100	59
2	6696	7428	9015	1.1093	58
3	6698	7426	9020	1.1087	57
4	6700	7424	9025	1.1080	56
5	6702	7422	9030	1.1074	**55**
...	...	...	...	...	...
′	cos	sin	cot	tan	′

47°

The functions of 41° and any number of minutes are found by reading down, under the abbreviations *sin, cos, tan, cot.*

For example, $\sin 41° = 0.6561$, $\sin 42° = 0.6691$,
$\cos 41° 2' = 0.7543$, $\cos 42° = 0.7431$,
$\tan 41° 4' = 0.8713$, $\tan 42° 3' = 0.9020$,
$\cot 41° 5' = 1.1470$, $\cot 42° 5' = 1.1074$.

Decimal points are usually omitted in the tables when it is obvious where they should be placed.

The secant and cosecant are seldom given in tables, being reciprocals of the cosine and sine. We shall presently see that we rarely need them.

Since $\sin 41° 2'$ is the same as $\cos 48° 58'$ (§ 8), we may use the same table for 48° and any number of minutes by reading up, above the abbreviations *cos, sin, cot, tan.*

For example, $\cos 48° 55' = 0.6572$, $\cos 47° 55' = 0.6702$,
$\sin 48° 56' = 0.7539$, $\sin 47° 56' = 0.7424$,
$\cot 48° 58' = 0.8703$, $\cot 47° 57' = 0.9020$,
$\tan 48° 59' = 1.1497$, $\tan 47° 59' = 1.1100$.

Trigonometric tables are generally arranged with the degrees from 0° to 44° at the top, the minutes being at the left; and with the degrees from 45° to 89° at the bottom, the minutes being at the right. Therefore, in looking for functions of an angle from 0° to 44° 59′, look at the top of the page for the degrees and in the left column for the minutes, reading the number below the proper abbreviation. For functions of an angle from 45° to 90° (89° 60′), look at the bottom of the page for the degrees and in the right-hand column for the minutes, reading the number above the proper abbreviation.

Exercise 14. Use of the Sexagesimal Table

From the table on page 28 find the values of the following:

1. $\cos 41°$.
2. $\tan 42°$.
3. $\cos 41° 1'$.
4. $\tan 42° 2'$.
5. $\cos 41° 5'$.
6. $\sin 48° 59'$.
7. $\sin 47° 58'$.
8. $\cos 48° 59'$.
9. $\cos 47° 59'$.
10. $\cos 48° 57'$.
11. $\sin 42° 4'$.
12. $\cos 47° 56'$.
13. $\tan 41° 3'$.
14. $\cot 48° 57'$.
15. $\tan 48° 57'$.

In the right triangle ACB, in which $C = 90°$:

16. Given $c = 27$ and $A = 41° 3'$, find a.
17. Given $c = 48$ and $A = 42° 4'$, find a.
18. Given $c = 61$ and $A = 41° 2'$, find b.
19. Given $c = 72$ and $A = 42° 3'$, find b.
20. Given $b = 24$ and $A = 41° 3'$, find a.
21. Given $b = 28$ and $A = 42° 4'$, find a.
22. Given $a = 42$ and $A = 41° 1'$, find b.
23. Given $a = 60$ and $A = 42° 4'$, find b.
24. Given $c = 86$ and $A = 48° 56'$, find a.
25. Given $c = 92$ and $A = 48° 57'$, find a.
26. Given $b = 45$ and $A = 47° 55'$, find a.
27. Given $b = 85$ and $A = 47° 59'$, find a.
28. Given $a = 86$ and $A = 48° 56'$, find b.
29. Given $a = 98$ and $A = 47° 58'$, find b.
30. Given $b = 67$ and $c = 100$, find A.

31. A hoisting crane has an arm 30 ft. long. When the arm makes an angle of $41° 3'$ with x, what is the length of y? what is the length of x?

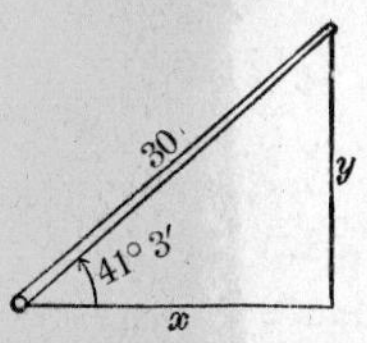

32. In Ex. 31 suppose the arm is raised until it makes an angle of $41° 5'$ with x, what are then the lengths of y and x?

33. From a point 128 ft. from a building the angle of elevation of the top is observed, by aid of an instrument 5 ft. above the ground, to be $42° 4'$. What is the height of the building?

34. From the top of a building 62 ft. 6 in. high, including the instrument, the angle of depression of the foot of an electric-light pole is observed to be $41° 3'$. How far is the pole from the building?

26. Decimal Table. It would be possible to have a decimal table of natural functions arranged as follows:

°	sin	cos	tan	cot	°
0.0	0000	1.0000	0000	∞	**90.0**
0.1	0017	1.0000	0017	573.0	89.9
0.2	0035	1.0000	0035	286.5	89.8
0.3	0052	1.0000	0052	191.0	89.7
0.4	0070	1.0000	0070	143.2	89.6
0.5	0087	1.0000	0087	114.6	**89.5**
...	...	...	...	...	...
°	cos	sin	cot	tan	°

°	sin	cos	tan	cot	°
4.0	0698	9976	0699	14.30	**86.0**
4.1	0715	9974	0717	13.95	85.9
4.2	0732	9973	0734	13.62	85.8
4.3	0750	9972	0752	13.30	85.7
4.4	0767	9971	0769	13.00	85.6
4.5	0785	9969	0787	12.71	**85.5**
...	...	...	...	...	...
°	cos	sin	cot	tan	°

Since, however, the decimal divisions of the angle have not yet become common, it is not necessary to have a special table of this kind. It is quite convenient to use the ordinary sexagesimal table for this purpose by simply referring to the Table of Conversion of sexagesimals to decimals and vice versa. This table is given with the other Wentworth-Smith tables prepared for use with this book. Thus if we wish to find $\sin 27.75°$, we see by the Table of Conversion that $0.75° = 45'$, so we simply look for $\sin 27° 45'$.

For example, using either the above table or, after conversion to sexagesimals, the common table, we see that:

$$\sin 0.4° = 0.0070, \qquad \sin 85.5° = 0.9969,$$
$$\cos 4.1° = 0.9974, \qquad \cos 85.5° = 0.0785,$$
$$\tan 0.5° = 0.0087, \qquad \tan 85.8° = 13.62,$$
$$\cot 4.3° = 13.30, \qquad \cot 85.9° = 0.0717.$$

Exercise 15. Use of the Decimal Table

From the above table find the values of the following:

1. $\sin 0.5°$.
2. $\tan 0.4°$.
3. $\sin 4°$.
4. $\cos 4.2°$.
5. $\tan 4.5°$.
6. $\sin 4.1°$.
7. $\cos 4.3°$.
8. $\tan 4.4°$.
9. $\cot 4.5°$.
10. $\cot 4.2°$.
11. $\sin 85.7°$.
12. $\sin 85.9°$.
13. $\cos 85.6°$.
14. $\tan 85.9°$.
15. $\cot 85.6°$.
16. $\sin 89.5°$.
17. $\cos 85.9°$.
18. $\tan 89.6°$.
19. $\cot 89.7°$.
20. $\cot 85.8°$.

21. The hypotenuse of a right triangle is 12.7 in., and one acute angle is 85.5°. Find the two perpendicular sides.

22. From a point on the top of a house the angle of depression of the foot of a tree is observed to be 4.4°. The house, including the instrument, is 30 ft. high. How far is the tree from the house?

23. A rectangle has a base 9.5 in. long, and the diagonal makes an angle of 4.5° with the base. Find the height of the rectangle and the length of the diagonal.

27. Interpolation. So long as we wish to find the functions of an acute angle expressed in degrees and minutes, or in degrees and tenths, the tables already explained are sufficient. But when the angle is expressed in degrees, minutes, and seconds, or in degrees and hundredths, we see that the tables do not give the values of the functions directly. It is then necessary to resort to a process called *interpolation.*

Briefly expressed, in the process of interpolation we assume that $\sin 42\frac{1}{2}°$ is found by adding to $\sin 42°$ half the difference between $\sin 42°$ and $\sin 43°$.

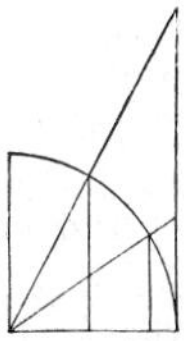

In general it is evident that this is not true. For example, in the annexed figure the line values of the functions of 30° and 60° are shown. It is clear that $\sin 30°$ is more than half $\sin 60°$, that $\tan 30°$ is less than half $\tan 60°$, and that $\sec 30°$ is more than half $\sec 60°$. This is also seen from the table on page 11, where

$$\sin 30° = 0.5000, \qquad \tan 30° = 0.5774, \qquad \sec 30° = 1.1547,$$
$$\sin 60° = 0.8660, \qquad \tan 60° = 1.7321, \qquad \sec 60° = 2.0000.$$

For angles in which the changes are very small, interpolation gives results which are correct to the number of decimal places given in the table.

For example, from the table on page 11 we have

$$\sin 42° = 0.6691$$
$$\sin 41° = 0.6561$$

Difference for 1°, or 60′, $= 0.0130$

Difference for $1' = \frac{1}{60}$ of 0.0130 $= 0.0002.$

Adding this to $\sin 41°$, we have

$$\sin 41° 1' = 0.6563,$$

a result given in the table on page 28.

But if we wish to find $\tan 89.6°$ from $\tan 89.5°$ and $\tan 89.7°$, we cannot use this method because here *the changes are very great*, as is always the case with the tangents and secants of angles near 90°, and with the cotangents and cosecants of angles near 0°. Thus, from the table on page 30,

$$\tan 89.7° = 191.0$$
$$\tan 89.5° = 114.6$$

Difference for 0.2° $= 76.4$

Difference for 0.1° $= 38.2$

Adding this to $\tan 89.5°$, $\tan 89.6° = 152.8,$

whereas the table shows the result to be 143.2.

When cases arise in which interpolation cannot safely be used, we resort to the use of special tables that give the required values. These tables are explained later. Interpolation may safely be used in all examples given in the early part of the work.

28. Interpolation applied. The following examples will illustrate the cases which arise in practical problems. The student should refer to the Wentworth-Smith Trigonometric Tables for the functions used in the problems.

1. Find $\sin 22° \, 10' \, 20''$.

From the tables,
$$\sin 22° \, 11' = 0.3776$$
$$\sin 22° \, 10' = 0.3773$$
Difference for 1′, or 60″, the *tabular difference* $= 0.0003$

Difference for 20″ is $\frac{20}{60}$ of 0.0003, or 0.0001

Adding this to $\sin 22° \, 10'$, we have
$$\sin 22° \, 10' \, 20'' = 0.3774$$

2. Find $\cos 64° \, 17' \, 30''$.

From the tables,
$$\cos 64° \, 17' = 0.4339$$
$$\cos 64° \, 18' = 0.4337$$
Tabular difference $= 0.0002$

Difference for 30″ is $\frac{30}{60}$ of 0.0002, or 0.0001

Since the cosine decreases as the angle increases we must subtract 0.0001 from $\cos 64° \, 17'$, which gives us
$$\cos 64° \, 17' \, 30'' = 0.4338$$

3. Find $\tan 37.54°$.

By the Table of Conversion, $0.54° = 32' \, 24''$.

From the tables,
$$\tan 37° \, 33' = 0.7687$$
$$\tan 37° \, 32' = 0.7683$$
Tabular difference $= 0.0004$

Difference for 24″ is $\frac{24}{60}$, or 0.4, of 0.0004 $= 0.0002$

Adding this to $\tan 37° \, 32'$, we have
$$\tan 37.54° = \tan 37° \, 32' \, 24'' = 0.7685$$

4. Given $\sin x = 0.6456$, find x.

Looking in the tables for the sine that is a little less than 0.6456, and for the next larger sine, we have
$$0.6457 = \sin 40° \, 13'$$
$$0.6455 = \sin 40° \, 12'$$
$$0.0002 = \text{tabular difference}$$

Therefore x lies between $40° \, 12'$ and $40° \, 13'$.

Furthermore,
$$0.6456 = \sin x$$
$$0.6455 = \sin 40° \, 12'$$
$$0.0001 = \text{difference}$$

But 0.0001 is $\frac{1}{2}$ of 0.0002, the tabular difference, so that x is halfway from $40° \, 12'$ to $40° \, 13'$. Therefore we add $\frac{1}{2}$ of 60″, or 30″, to $40° \, 12'$.

Hence $x = 40° \, 12' \, 30''$.

We interpolate in a similar manner when we use a decimal table.

Exercise 16. Use of the Table

Find the values of the following:

1. $\sin 27^\circ 10' 30''$.
2. $\sin 42^\circ 15' 30''$.
3. $\sin 56^\circ 29' 40''$.
4. $\sin 65^\circ 29' 40''$.
5. $\cos 36^\circ 14' 30''$.
6. $\cos 43^\circ 12' 20''$.
7. $\cos 64^\circ 18' 45''$.
8. $\tan 28^\circ 32' 20''$.
9. $\tan 32^\circ 41' 30''$.
10. $\tan 42^\circ 38' 30''$.
11. $\tan 52^\circ 10' 45''$.
12. $\tan 68^\circ 12' 45''$.
13. $\tan 72^\circ 15' 50''$.
14. $\tan 85^\circ 17' 45''$.
15. $\tan 86^\circ 15' 50''$.
16. $\cot 5^\circ 27' 30''$.
17. $\cot 6^\circ 32' 45''$.
18. $\cot 7^\circ 52' 50''$.
19. $\cot 8^\circ 40' 10''$.
20. $\cot 9^\circ 20' 10''$.

21. Given $\sin x = 0.6391$, find x. Then find $\cos x$.
22. Given $\sin x = 0.7691$, find x. Then find $\cos x$.
23. Given $\cos x = 0.3174$, find x. Then find $\sin x$.
24. Given $\tan x = 2.8649$, find x. Then find $\cot x$.
25. Given $\tan x = 5.3977$, find x. Then find $\cot x$.

First converting to sexagesimals, find the following:

26. $\sin 25.5^\circ$.
27. $\sin 25.55^\circ$.
28. $\sin 32.75^\circ$.
29. $\sin 41.65^\circ$.
30. $\sin 64.75^\circ$.
31. $\cos 78.52^\circ$.
32. $\tan 78.59^\circ$.
33. $\cos 81.43^\circ$.
34. $\tan 82.72^\circ$.
35. $\tan 84.68^\circ$.
36. $\cos 11.25^\circ$.
37. $\cot 12.32^\circ$.
38. $\cot 13.54^\circ$.
39. $\cot 15.48^\circ$.
40. $\cot 16.62^\circ$.

Find the value of x in each of the following equations:

41. $\sin x = 0.5225$.
42. $\sin x = 0.5771$.
43. $\sin x = 0.6601$.
44. $\sin x = 0.7023$.
45. $\cos x = 0.7853$.
46. $\cos x = 0.7716$.
47. $\cos x = 0.9524$.
48. $\cos x = 0.7115$.
49. $\tan x = 2.6395$.
50. $\tan x = 4.7625$.
51. $\tan x = 4.7608$.
52. $\cot x = 3.7983$.

53. If $\sin x = 0.6431$, what is the value of $\cos x$?
54. If $\cos x = 0.7652$, what is the value of $\sin x$?
55. If $\tan x = 0.6827$, what is the value of $\sin x$?
56. If $\tan x = 0.6537$, what is the value of x? of $\cot x$?
57. If $\cot x = 1.6550$, what is the value of x? of $\tan x$? Verify the second result by the relation $\tan x = 1/\cot x$.

29. Application to the Right Triangle. In §§ 15–21 we learned how to use the several functions in finding various parts of a right triangle from other given parts, the angles being in exact degrees. In §§ 25–28 we learned how to use the tables when the angles were not necessarily in exact degrees. We shall now review both of these phases of the work in connection with the solution of the right triangle.

In order to *solve* a right triangle, that is, to find both of the acute angles, the hypotenuse, and both of the sides, two independent parts besides the right angle must be given.

In speaking of the *sides* of a right triangle it should be repeated that we shall refer only to sides a and b, the sides which include the right angle, using the word *hypotenuse* to refer to c. It will be found that there is no confusion in thus referring to only two of the three sides by the special name *sides*.

By *independent parts* is meant parts that do not depend one upon another. For example, the two acute angles are not independent parts, for each is equal to 90° minus the other.

The two given parts may be:

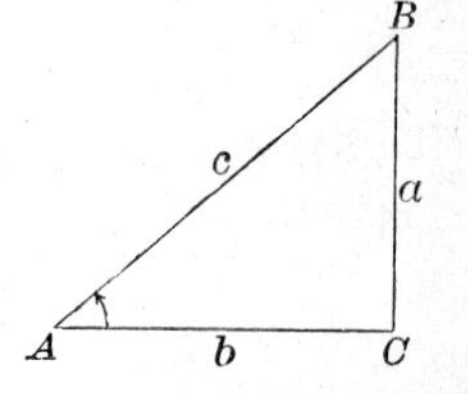

1. An acute angle and the hypotenuse.

That is, given A and c, or B and c. If A and c are given, we have to find a and b. The angle B is known from the relation $B = 90° - A$. If B is given, we can find A from the equation $A = 90° - B$.

2. An acute angle and the opposite side.

That is, given A and a, or B and b. If A and a are given, we have to find B, b, and c, and similarly for the other case.

3. An acute angle and the adjacent side.

That is, given A and b, or B and a. If A and b are given, we have to find B, a, and c, and similarly for the other case.

4. The hypotenuse and a side.

That is, given c and a, or c and b. If c and a are given, we have to find A, B, and b, and similarly for the other case.

5. The two sides.

That is, given a and b, to find A, B, and c. Using *side* to include hypotenuse, we might combine the fourth and fifth of these cases in one.

In each of these cases we shall consider right triangles which have their acute angles expressed in degrees and minutes, in degrees, minutes, and seconds, or in degrees and decimal parts of a degree. In this chapter the angles are given and required only to the nearest minute.

30. Given an Acute Angle and the Hypotenuse. For example, given $A = 43° 17'$, $c = 26$, find B, a, and b.

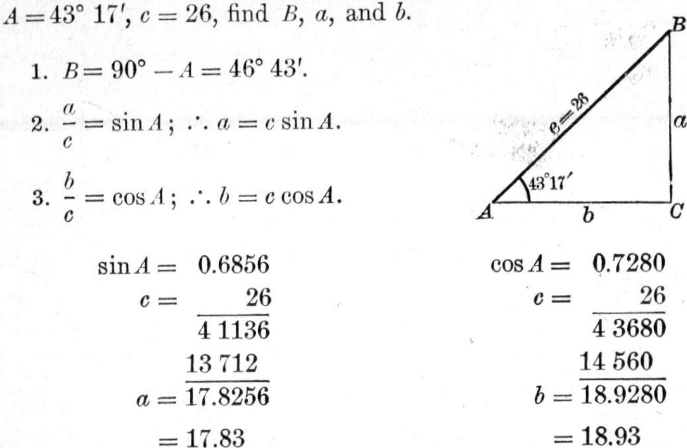

1. $B = 90° - A = 46° 43'$.

2. $\frac{a}{c} = \sin A$; $\therefore a = c \sin A$.

3. $\frac{b}{c} = \cos A$; $\therefore b = c \cos A$.

$$\begin{array}{rr} \sin A = & 0.6856 \\ c = & 26 \\ \hline & 4\,1136 \\ & 13\,712 \\ \hline a = & 17.8256 \\ = & 17.83 \end{array} \qquad \begin{array}{rr} \cos A = & 0.7280 \\ c = & 26 \\ \hline & 4\,3680 \\ & 14\,560 \\ \hline b = & 18.9280 \\ = & 18.93 \end{array}$$

As usual, when a four-place table is employed, the result is given to four figures only. The check is left for the student.

31. Given an Acute Angle and the Opposite Side. For example, given $A = 13° 58'$, $a = 15.2$, find B, b, and c.

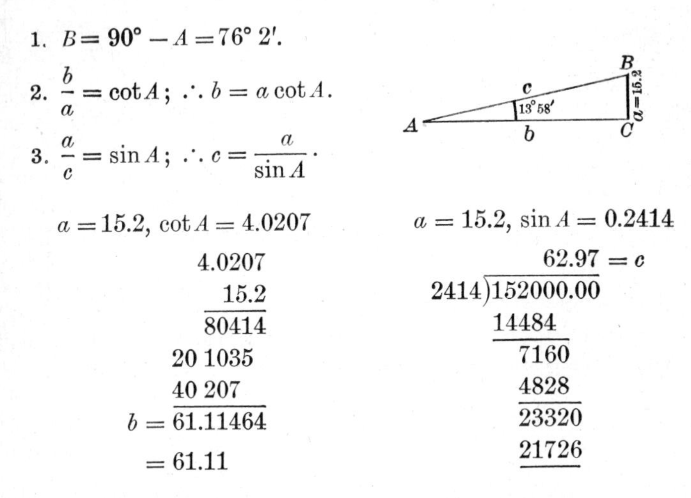

1. $B = 90° - A = 76° 2'$.

2. $\frac{b}{a} = \cot A$; $\therefore b = a \cot A$.

3. $\frac{a}{c} = \sin A$; $\therefore c = \frac{a}{\sin A}$.

$$\begin{array}{rr} a = 15.2, & \cot A = 4.0207 \\ & 4.0207 \\ & 15.2 \\ \hline & 80414 \\ & 20\,1035 \\ & 40\,207 \\ \hline b = & 61.11464 \\ = & 61.11 \end{array} \qquad \begin{array}{rl} a = 15.2, & \sin A = 0.2414 \\ & 62.97 = c \\ 2414) & 152000.00 \\ & 14484 \\ \hline & 7160 \\ & 4828 \\ \hline & 23320 \\ & 21726 \\ \hline \end{array}$$

In dividing 15.2 by 0.2414, we adopt the modern plan of first multiplying each by 10,000. Only part of the actual division is shown.

Instead of dividing a by $\sin A$ to find c, we might multiply a by $\csc A$, as on page 22, except that tables do not generally give the cosecants. It will be seen in Chapter III that, by the aid of logarithms, we can divide by $\sin A$ as readily as multiply by $\csc A$, and this is why the tables omit the cosecant.

32. Given an Acute Angle and the Adjacent Side. For example, given $A = 27° 12'$, $b = 31$, find B, a, and c.

1. $B = 90° - A = 62° 48'$.

2. $\frac{a}{b} = \tan A$; $\therefore a = b \tan A$.

3. $\frac{b}{c} = \cos A$; $\therefore c = \frac{b}{\cos A}\cdot$

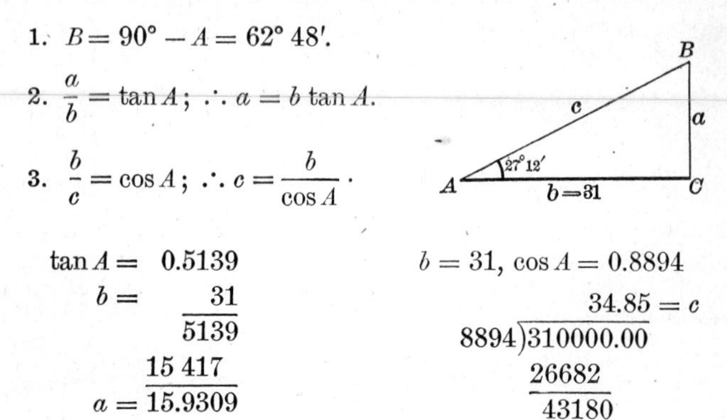

$$\begin{array}{rr} \tan A = & 0.5139 \\ b = & 31 \\ \hline & 5139 \\ & 15\,417 \\ \hline a = & 15.9309 \\ = & 15.93 \end{array}$$

$$b = 31,\ \cos A = 0.8894$$

$$\begin{array}{r} 34.85 = c \\ 8894\overline{)310000.00} \\ 26682 \\ \hline 43180 \\ 35576 \\ \hline \end{array}$$

We might multiply b by $\sec A$ instead of dividing by $\cos A$. The reason for not doing so is the same as that given in § 31 for not multiplying by $\csc A$.

33. Given the Hypotenuse and a Side. For example, given $a = 47$, $c = 63$, find A, B, and b.

1. $\sin A = \frac{a}{c}\cdot$

2. $B = 90° - A$.

3. $b = \sqrt{c^2 - a^2}$
$= \sqrt{(c + a)(c - a)}$.

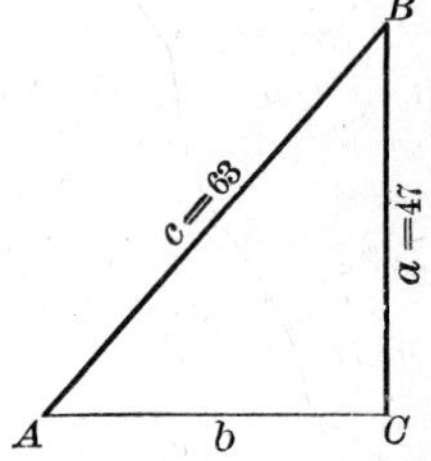

In the case of $\sqrt{c^2 - a^2}$ we can, of course, square c, square a, take the difference of these squares, and then extract the square root. It is, however, easier to proceed by factoring $c^2 - a^2$ as shown. This will be even more apparent when we come, in Chapter III, to the short methods of computing by logarithms.

$$a = 47,\ c = 63$$

$$\begin{array}{r} 0.7460 \\ 63\overline{)47.0000} \\ 44\,1 \\ \hline 2\,90 \\ 2\,52 \\ \hline 380 \\ 378 \\ \hline \end{array}$$

$$\sin A = 0.7460$$
$$\therefore A = 48° 15'$$
$$\therefore B = 41° 45'$$

$$\begin{array}{rr} c + a = & 110 \\ c - a = & 16 \\ \hline & 660 \\ & 110 \\ \hline c^2 - a^2 = & 1760 \\ \therefore b^2 = & 1760 \\ \therefore b = & \sqrt{1760} \\ = & 41.95 \end{array}$$

34. Given the Two Sides. For example, given $a = 40$, $b = 27$, find A, B, and c.

1. $\tan A = \frac{a}{b}$.

2. $B = 90° - A$.

3. $c = \sqrt{a^2 + b^2}$.

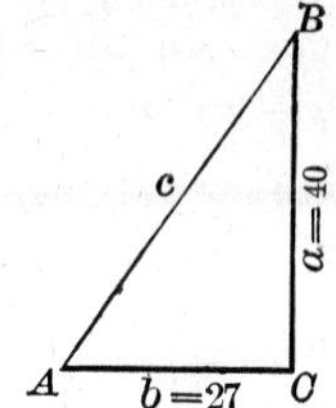

Of course c can be found in other ways. For example, after finding $\tan A$ we can find A, and hence can find $\sin A$. Then, because $\sin A = a/c$, we have $c = a/\sin A$. When the numbers are small, however, it is easy to find c from the relation given above.

$$a = 40,\ b = 27$$
$$\tfrac{40}{27} = 1.4815$$
$$\tan A = 1.4815$$
$$\therefore A = 55°\ 59'$$
$$\therefore B = 34°\ 1'$$

$$a^2 = 1600$$
$$b^2 = 729$$
$$c^2 = 2329$$
$$\therefore c = \sqrt{2329} = 48.26$$

35. Checks. As already stated, always apply some check to the results. For example, in § 34, we see at once that $a^2 = 1600$ and b^2 is less than 30^2, or 900, so that c^2 is less than 2500, and c is less than 50. Hence the result as given, 48.26, is probably correct.

We can also find B independently.

For since $\tan B = \frac{b}{a}$,

we see that $\tan B = \frac{27}{40} = 0.6750$,

and therefore that $B = 34°\ 1'$.

Exercise 17. The Right Triangle

Solve the right triangle ACB, in which $C = 90°$, given:

1. $a = 3$, $b = 4$.
2. $a = 7$, $c = 13$.
3. $a = 5.3$, $A = 12°\ 17'$.
4. $a = 10.4$, $B = 43°\ 18'$.
5. $c = 26$, $A = 37°\ 42'$.
6. $c = 140$, $B = 24°\ 12'$.
7. $b = 19$, $c = 23$.
8. $b = 98$, $c = 135.2$.
9. $b = 42.4$, $A = 32°\ 14'$.
10. $b = 200$, $B = 46°\ 11'$.
11. $a = 95$, $b = 37$.
12. $a = 6$, $c = 103$.
13. $a = 3.12$, $B = 5°\ 8'$.
14. $a = 17$, $c = 18$.
15. $c = 57$, $A = 38°\ 29'$.
16. $a + c = 18$, $b = 12$.
17. $a + c = 90$, $b = 30$.
18. $a + c = 45$, $b = 30$.

Solve the right triangle ACB, in which $C = 90°$, given:

19. $a = 2.5$, $A = 35° 10' 30''$.
20. $a = 5.7$, $A = 42° 12' 30''$.
21. $a = 6.4$, $B = 29° 18' 30''$.
22. $a = 7.9$, $B = 36° 20' 30''$.
23. $c = 6.8$, $A = 29° 42' 30''$.
24. $c = 360$, $A = 34° 20' 30''$.
25. $b = 250$, $A = 41° 10' 40''$.
26. $a = 48$, $A = 25.5°$.
27. $c = 25$, $A = 24.5°$.
28. $c = 40$, $A = 32.55°$.
29. $c = 80$, $A = 55.51°$.
30. $c = 75$, $A = 63.46°$.
31. $a = 45$, $B = 50.59°$.
32. $b = 90$, $A = 68.25°$.

33. Each equal side of an isosceles triangle is 16 in., and one of the equal angles is $24° 10'$. What is the length of the base?

34. Each equal side of an isosceles triangle is 25 in., and the vertical angle is $36° 40'$. What is the altitude of the triangle?

35. Each equal side of an isosceles triangle is 25 in., and one of the equal angles is $32° 20' 30''$. What is the length of the base?

36. Each equal side of an isosceles triangle is 60 in., and the vertical angle is $50° 30' 30''$. What is the altitude of the triangle?

37. Find the altitude of an equilateral triangle of which the side is 50 in. Show three methods of finding the altitude.

38. What is the side of an equilateral triangle of which the altitude is 52 in.?

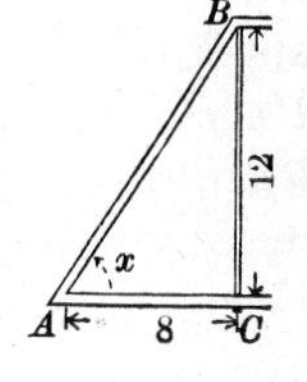

39. In planning a truss for a bridge it is necessary to have the upright $BC = 12$ ft., and the horizontal $AC = 8$ ft., as shown in the figure. What angle does AB make with AC? with BC?

40. In Ex. 39 what are the angles if $AB = 12$ ft. and $AC = 9$ ft.?

41. In the figure of Ex. 39, what is the length of BC if $AB = 15$ ft. and $x = 62° 10'$?

42. Two angles of a triangle are $42° 17'$ and $47° 43'$ respectively, and the included side is 25 in. Find the other two sides.

43. A tangent AB, drawn from a point A to a circle, makes an angle of $51° 10'$ with a line from A through the center. If $AB = 10$ ft., what is the length of the radius?

44. How far from the center of a circle of radius 12 in. will a tangent meet a diameter with which it makes an angle of $10° 20'$?

45. Two circles of radii 10 in. and 14 in. are externally tangent. What angle does their line of centers make with their common exterior tangent?

CHAPTER III

LOGARITHMS

36. Importance of Logarithms. It has already been seen that the trigonometric functions are, in general, incommensurable with unity. Hence they contain decimal fractions of an infinite number of places. Even if we express these fractions only to four or five decimal places, the labor of multiplying and dividing by them is considerable. For this reason numerous devices have appeared for simplifying this work. Among these devices are various calculating machines, but none of these can easily be carried about and they are too expensive for general use. There is also the slide rule, an inexpensive instrument for approximate multiplication and division, but for trigonometric work this is not of particular value because the tables must be at hand even when the slide rule is used. The most practical device for the purpose was invented early in the seventeenth century and the credit is chiefly due to John Napier, a Scotchman, whose tables appeared in 1614. These tables, afterwards much improved by Henry Briggs, a contemporary of Napier, are known as tables of logarithms, and by their use the operation of multiplication is reduced to that of addition; that of division is reduced to subtraction; raising to any power is reduced to one multiplication; and the extracting of any root is reduced to a single division.

For the ordinary purposes of trigonometry the tables of functions used in Chapter II are fairly satisfactory, the time required for most of the operations not being unreasonable. But when a problem is met which requires a large amount of computation, the tables of natural functions, as they are called, to distinguish them from the tables of logarithmic functions, are not convenient.

For example, we shall see that the product of 2.417, 3.426, 517.4, and 91.63 can be found from a table by adding four numbers which the table gives.

In the case of $\frac{4.27}{52.9} \times \frac{36.1}{5.28} \times \frac{5176}{9283}$ we shall see that the result can be found from a table by adding six numbers.

Taking a more difficult case, like that of $\sqrt[3]{\frac{523}{711} \times \frac{9.64}{0.379}}$, we shall see that it is necessary merely to take one third of the sum of four numbers, after which the table gives us the result.

37. Logarithm. The exponent of the power to which a given number, called the *base*, must be raised in order to be equal to another given number is called the *logarithm* of this second given number.

For example, since $10^2 = 100$,
we have, to the base 10, $2 =$ the logarithm of 100.
In the same way, since $10^3 = 1000$,
we have, to the base 10, $3 =$ the logarithm of 1000.
Similarly, $4 =$ the logarithm of 10,000,
$5 =$ the logarithm of 100,000,
and so on, whatever powers of 10 we take.
In general, if $b^x = N$,
then, to the base b, $x =$ the logarithm of N.

38. Symbolism. For "logarithm of N" it is customary to write "$\log N$." If we wish to specify $\log N$ to the base b, we write $\log_b N$, reading this "logarithm of N to the base b."

That is, as above, $\log 100 = 2$, $\log 10{,}000 = 4$,
$\log 1000 = 3$, $\log 100{,}000 = 5$,
and so on for the other powers of 10.

39. Base. Any positive number except unity may be taken as the base for a system of logarithms, but 10 is usually taken for purposes of practical calculation.

Thus, since $2^3 = 8$, $\log_2 8 = 3$;
since $3^4 = 81$, $\log_3 81 = 4$;
and since $5^4 = 625$, $\log_5 625 = 4$.

It is more convenient to take 10 as the base, however. For since

$$10^2 = 100 \text{ and } 10^3 = 1000,$$

we can tell at once that the logarithm of any number between 100 and 1000 must lie between 2 and 3, and therefore must be 2 + some fraction. That is, by using 10 as the base we know immediately the integral part of the logarithm.

When we write $\log 27$, we mean $\log_{10} 27$; that is, the base 10 is to be understood unless some other base is specified.

Since $\log 10 = 1$, because $10^1 = 10$,
and $\log 1 = 0$, because $10^0 = 1$,
and $\log \frac{1}{10} = -1$, because $10^{-1} = \frac{1}{10}$,
we see that *the logarithm of the base is always 1, the logarithm of 1 is always zero, and the logarithm of a proper fraction is negative.*

That this is true for any base is apparent from the fact that

$$b^1 = b, \quad \text{whence} \quad \log_b b = 1;$$
$$b^0 = 1, \quad \text{whence} \quad \log_b 1 = 0;$$
$$b^{-n} = \frac{1}{b^n}, \quad \text{whence} \quad \log_b \frac{1}{b^n} = -n.$$

Exercise 18. Logarithms

1. Since $2^5 = 32$, what is $\log_2 32$?
2. Since $4^2 = 16$, what is $\log_4 16$?
3. Since $10^4 = 10{,}000$, what is $\log 10{,}000$?

Write the following logarithms:

4. $\log_2 16$.	8. $\log_3 243$.	12. $\log_6 36$.	16. $\log 100$.
5. $\log_2 64$.	9. $\log_3 729$.	13. $\log_7 343$.	17. $\log 1000$.
6. $\log_2 128$.	10. $\log_4 256$.	14. $\log_8 512$.	18. $\log 100{,}000$.
7. $\log_2 256$.	11. $\log_5 125$.	15. $\log_9 6561$.	19. $\log 1{,}000{,}000$.

20. Since $10^{-1} = \frac{1}{10}$, or 0.1, what is $\log 0.1$?

21. What is $\log \frac{1}{100}$, or $\log 0.01$? $\log 0.001$? $\log 0.0001$?

22. Between what consecutive integers is $\log 52$? $\log 726$? $\log 2400$? $\log 24{,}000$? $\log 175{,}000$? $\log 175{,}000{,}000$?

23. Between what consecutive negative integers is $\log 0.08$? $\log 0.008$? $\log 0.0008$? $\log 0.1238$? $\log 0.0123$? $\log 0.002768$?

24. To the base 2, write the logarithms of 2, 4, 8, 64, 512, 1024, $\frac{1}{4}$, $\frac{1}{16}$, $\frac{1}{32}$, $\frac{1}{64}$, $\frac{1}{128}$, $\frac{1}{256}$.

25. To the base 3, write the logarithms of 3, 81, 729, 2187, 6561, $\frac{1}{3}$, $\frac{1}{9}$, $\frac{1}{27}$, $\frac{1}{81}$, $\frac{1}{243}$, $\frac{1}{729}$, $\frac{1}{2187}$.

26. To the base 10, write the logarithms of 1, 0.0001, 0.00001, 10,000,000, 100,000,000.

Write the consecutive integers between which the logarithms of the following numbers lie:

27. 75.	31. 642.	35. 7346.	39. 243,481.
28. 75.9.	32. 642.75.	36. 7346.9.	40. 5,276,192.
29. 75.05.	33. 642.005.	37. 7346.09.	41. 7,286,348.5
30. 82.95.	34. 793.175.	38. 9182.735.	42. 19,423,076.

Show that the following statements are true:

43. $\log_2 4 + \log_2 8 + \log_2 16 + \log_2 64 + \log_2 2 + \log_2 32 = 21$.

44. $\log_3 3 + \log_3 9 + \log_3 81 + \log_3 729 + \log_3 27 + \log_3 243 = 21$.

45. $\log_{11} 11 + \log_{11} 121 + \log_{11} 1331 + \log_{11} 14{,}641 = 10$.

46. $\log 1 + \log 10 + \log 1000 + \log 0.1 + \log 0.001 = 0$.

47. $\log 1 + \log 100 + \log 10{,}000 + \log 0.01 + \log 0.0001 = 0$.

48. $\log 10{,}000 - \log 1000 + \log 100{,}000 - \log 100 = 4$.

40. Logarithm of a Product. *The logarithm of the product of two numbers is equal to the sum of the logarithms of the numbers.*

Let A and B be the numbers, and x and y their logarithms. Then, taking 10 as the base and remembering that $x = \log A$, and $y = \log B$, we have

$$A = 10^x,$$

and

$$B = 10^y.$$

Therefore

$$AB = 10^{x+y},$$

and therefore

$$\log AB = x + y$$
$$= \log A + \log B.$$

The proof is the same if any other base is taken. For example,

if $x = \log_b A$, we have $A = b^x$;

and if $y = \log_b B$, we have $B = b^y$.

Therefore $AB = b^{x+y}$,

and

$$\log_b AB = x + y$$
$$= \log_b A + \log_b B.$$

The proposition is also true for the product of more than two numbers, the proof being evidently the same. Thus,

$$\log ABC = \log A + \log B + \log C,$$

and so on for any number of factors.

41. Logarithm of a Quotient. *The logarithm of the quotient of two numbers is equal to the logarithm of the dividend minus the logarithm of the divisor.*

For if

$$A = 10^x,$$

and

$$B = 10^y,$$

then

$$\frac{A}{B} = 10^{x-y},$$

and therefore

$$\log \frac{A}{B} = x - y$$
$$= \log A - \log B.$$

This proposition is true if any base b is taken. For, as in § 40,

$$\frac{A}{B} = b^{x-y},$$

and therefore

$$\log_b \frac{A}{B} = x - y$$
$$= \log_b A - \log_b B.$$

It is therefore seen from §§ 40 and 41 that if we know the logarithms of all numbers we can find the logarithm of a product by addition and the logarithm of a quotient by subtraction. If we can then find the numbers of which these results are the logarithms, we shall have solved our problems in multiplication and division by merely adding and subtracting.

42. Logarithm of a Power. *The logarithm of a power of a number is equal to the logarithm of the number multiplied by the exponent.*

For if $A = 10^x$,

raising to the pth power, $A^p = 10^{px}$.

Hence
$$\log A^p = px$$
$$= p \log A.$$

This is easily seen by taking special numbers. Thus if we take the base 2, we have the following relations:

Since $2^5 = 32$, then $\log_2 32 = 5$;

and since $(2^5)^2 = 32^2 = 1024$, then $\log_2 1024 = 2 \cdot 5$
$$= 2 \log_2 32.$$

That is, $\log_2 32^2 = 2 \log_2 32$.

43. Logarithm of a Root. *The logarithm of a root of a number is equal to the logarithm of the number divided by the index of the root.*

For if $A = 10^x$,

taking the rth root, $A^{\frac{1}{r}} = 10^{\frac{x}{r}}$.

Hence
$$\log A^{\frac{1}{r}} = \frac{x}{r}$$
$$= \frac{\log A}{r}.$$

The propositions of §§ 42 and 43 are true whatever base is taken, as may easily be seen by using the base b.

From §§ 42 and 43 we see that the raising of a number to any power, integral or fractional, reduces to the operation of multiplying the logarithm by the exponent (integral or fractional) and then finding the number of which the result is the logarithm.

Therefore the operations of multiplying, dividing, raising to powers, and extracting roots will be greatly simplified if we can find the logarithms of numbers, and this will next be considered.

44. Characteristic and Mantissa. Usually a logarithm consists of an integer plus a decimal fraction.

The integral part of a logarithm is called the *characteristic.*

The decimal part of a logarithm is called the *mantissa.*

Thus, if $\log 2353 = 3.37162$, the characteristic is 3 and the mantissa 0.37162. This means that $10^{3.37162} = 2353$, or that the 100,000th root of the 337,162d power of 10 is 2353, approximately.

It must always be recognized that the mantissa is only an approximation, correct to as many decimal places as are given in the table, but not exact. Computations made with logarithms give results which, in general, are correct only to a certain number of figures, but results which are sufficiently near the correct result to answer the purposes of the problem.

45. Finding the Characteristic. Since we know that

$$10^3 = 1000 \quad \text{and} \quad 10^4 = 10{,}000,$$

therefore $3 = \log 1000$ and $4 = \log 10{,}000.$

Hence the logarithm of a number between 1000 and 10,000 lies between 3 and 4, and so is 3 plus a fraction. Thus the characteristic of the logarithm of a number between 1000 and 10,000 is 3.

Likewise, since

$$10^{-3} = 0.001 \quad \text{and} \quad 10^{-2} = 0.01,$$

therefore $-3 = \log 0.001$ and $-2 = \log 0.01.$

Hence the logarithm of a number between 0.001 and 0.01 lies between -3 and -2, and so is -3 plus a fraction. Thus the characteristic of the logarithm of a number between 0.01 and 0.001 is -3.

Of course, instead of saying that log 1475 is 3 + a fraction, we might say that it is 4 − a fraction; and instead of saying that log 0.007 is − 3 + a fraction, we might say that it is − 2 − a fraction. For convenience, however, *the mantissa of a logarithm is always taken as positive*, but the characteristic may be either positive or negative.

46. Laws of the Characteristic. From the reasoning set forth in § 45 we deduce the following laws:

1. *The characteristic of the logarithm of a number greater than 1 is positive and is one less than the number of integral places in the number.*

For example, $\log 75 = 1 +$ some mantissa,

$\log 472.8 = 2 +$ some mantissa,

and $\log 14{,}800.75 = 4 +$ some mantissa.

2. *The characteristic of the logarithm of a number between 0 and 1 is negative and is one greater than the number of zeros between the decimal point and the first significant figure in the number.*

For example, $\log 0.02 = -2 +$ some mantissa,

and $\log 0.00076 = -4 +$ some mantissa.

The logarithm of a negative number is an imaginary number, and hence such logarithms are not used in computation.

47. Negative Characteristic. If $\log 0.02 = -2 + 0.30103$, we cannot write it -2.30103, because this would mean that both mantissa and characteristic are negative. Hence the form $\bar{2}.30103$ has been chosen, which means that only the characteristic 2 is negative.

That is, $\bar{2}.30103 = -2 + 0.30103$, and $\bar{5}.48561 = -5 + 0.48561$. We may also write $\bar{2}.30103$ as $0.30103 - 2$, or $8.30103 - 10$, or in any similar manner which will show that the characteristic is negative.

48. Mantissa independent of Decimal Point. It may be shown that

$$10^{3.37107} = 2350; \text{ whence } \log 2350 = 3.37107.$$

Dividing 2350 by 10, we have

$$10^{3.37107-1} = 10^{2.37107} = 235; \text{ whence } \log 235 = 2.37107.$$

Dividing 2350 by 10^4, or 10,000, we have

$$10^{3.37107-4} = 10^{\bar{1}.37107} = 0.235; \text{ whence } \log 0.235 = \bar{1}.37107.$$

That is, the mantissas are the same for log 2350, log 235, log 0.235, and so on, wherever the decimal points are placed.

The mantissa of the logarithm of a number is unchanged by any change in the position of the decimal point of the number.

This is a fact of great importance, for if the table gives us the mantissa of log 235, we know that we may use the same mantissa for log 0.00235, log 2.35, log 23,500, log 235,000,000, and so on.

Exercise 19. Logarithms

Write the characteristics of the logarithms of the following:

1. 75.	6. 2578.	11. 0.8.	16. 0.0007.
2. 75.4.	7. 257.8.	12. 0.08.	17. 0.0077.
3. 754.	8. 25.78.	13. 0.88.	18. 0.00007.
4. 7.54.	9. 2.578.	14. 0.885.	19. 0.10007.
5. 7540.	10. 25,780.	15. 0.005.	20. 0.07007.

Given 3.58681 as the logarithm of 3862, find the following:

21. log 38.62.	24. log 38,620.	27. log 0.3862.
22. log 3.862.	25. log 386,200.	28. log 0.03862.
23. log 386.2.	26. log 38,620,000.	29. log 0.0003862.

Given $\bar{1}.67724$ as the logarithm of 0.4756, find the following.

30. log 4756.	32. log 47,560.	34. log 0.04756.
31. log 4.756.	33. log 47,560,000.	35. log 0.00004756.

Given 3.40603 as the logarithm of 2547, find the following:

36. log 2.547.	38. log 0.2547.	40. log 25,470.
37. log 25.47.	39. log 0.002547.	41. log 25,470,000.

Given 1.39794 as the logarithm of 25, find the following:

42. log $2\frac{1}{2}$.	44. log 0.25.	46. log 25,000.
43. log $\frac{1}{4}$.	45. log 0.025.	47. log 25,000,000.

49. Using the Table. The following is a portion of a page taken from the Wentworth-Smith Logarithmic and Trigonometric Tables:

250 — 300

N	0	1	2	3	4	5	6	7	8	9
250	39 794	39 811	39 829	39 846	39 863	39 881	39 898	39 915	39 933	39 950
251	39 967	39 985	40 002	40 019	40 037	40 054	40 071	40 088	40 106	40 123
252	40 140	40 157	40 175	40 192	40 209	40 226	40 243	40 261	40 278	40 295
253	40 312	40 329	40 346	40 364	40 381	40 398	40 415	40 432	40 449	40 466
254	40 483	40 500	40 518	40 535	40 552	40 569	40 586	40 603	40 620	40 637
255	40 654	40 671	40 688	40 705	40 722	40 739	40 756	40 773	40 790	40 807

Only the mantissas are given; the characteristics are always to be determined by the laws stated in § 46. *Always write the characteristic at once, before writing the mantissa.*

For example, looking to the right of 251 and under 0, and writing the proper characteristics, we have

$$\log 251 = 2.39967, \qquad \log 25.1 = 1.39967,$$
$$\log 2510 = 3.39967, \qquad \log 0.0251 = \bar{2}.39967.$$

The first three significant figures of each number are given under **N**, and the fourth figure under the columns headed 0, 1, 2, . . ., 9.

For example, $\log 252.1 = 2.40157, \qquad \log 0.2547 = \bar{1}.40603,$

$$\log 25.25 = 1.40226, \qquad \log 2549 = 3.40637.$$

Furthermore, $\log 251.1 = 2.39985-$, the minus sign being placed beneath the final 5 in the table to show that if only a four-place mantissa is being used it should be written 3998 instead of 3999.

The logarithms of numbers of more than four figures are found by interpolation, as explained in § 27.

For example, to find log 25,314 we have

$$\begin{aligned} \log 25{,}320 &= 4.40346 \\ \log 25{,}310 &= \underline{4.40329} \\ \text{Tabular difference} &= 0.00017 \\ &\quad\ \ \underline{.4} \\ &\quad 0.000068 \\ \text{Difference to be added} &= 0.00007 \end{aligned}$$

Adding this to 4.40329, $\log 25314 = 4.40336$

In general, the tabular difference can be found so easily by inspection that it is unnecessary to multiply, as shown in this example. If any multiplication is necessary, it is an easy matter to turn to pages 46 and 47 of the tables, where will be found a table of proportional parts. On page 46, after the number 17 in the column of differences (**D**), and under 4 (for 0.4), is found 6.8. In the same way we can find any decimal part of a difference.

Exercise 20. Using the Table

Using the table, find the logarithms of the following:

1. 2.	9. 3485.	17. 0.7.	25. 12,340.
2. 20.	10. 4462.	18. 0.75.	26. 12,345.
3. 200.	11. 5581.	19. 0.756.	27. 12,347.
4. 0.002.	12. 7007.	20. 0.7567.	28. 123.47.
5. 2100.	13. 5285.	21. 0.0255.	29. 234.62.
6. 2150.	14. 68.48.	22. 0.0036.	30. 41.327.
7. 2156.	15. 7.926.	23. 0.0009.	31. 56.283.
8. 2.156.	16. 834.8.	24. 0.0178.	32. 0.41282.

33. In a certain computation it is necessary to find the sum of the logarithms of 45.6, 72.8, and 98.4. What is this sum?

34. In a certain computation it is necessary to subtract the logarithm of 3.84 from the sum of the logarithms of 52.8 and 26.5. What is the resulting logarithm?

Perform the following operations:

35. $\log 275 + \log 321 + \log 4.26 + \log 3.87 + \log 46.4$.

36. $\log 2643 + \log 3462 + \log 4926 + \log 5376 + \log 2194$.

37. $\log 51.82 + \log 7.263 + \log 5.826 + \log 218.7 + \log 3275$.

38. $\log 8263 + \log 2179 + \log 3972 - \log 2163 - \log 178$.

39. $\log 37.42 + \log 61.73 + \log 5.823 - \log 1.46 - \log 27.83$.

40. $\log 3.427 + \log 38.46 + \log 723.8 - \log 2.73 - \log 21.68$.

41. In a certain operation it is necessary to find three times log 41.75. What is the resulting logarithm?

42. In a certain operation it is necessary to find one fifth of log 254.8. What is the resulting logarithm?

Perform the following operations:

43. $2 \times \log 3$.	50. $\frac{1}{2} \log 2$.	57. $0.3 \log 431$.
44. $3 \times \log 2$.	51. $\frac{1}{2} \log 2000$.	58. $0.7 \log 43.19$.
45. $3 \times \log 25.6$.	52. $\frac{1}{3} \log 3460$.	59. $0.9 \log 4.007$.
46. $5 \times \log 3.76$.	53. $\frac{1}{3} \log 24.76$.	60. $1.4 \log 5.108$.
47. $4 \times \log 21.42$.	54. $\frac{1}{4} \log 368.7$.	61. $2.3 \log 7.411$.
48. $5 \times \log 346.8$.	55. $\frac{2}{3} \log 41.73$.	62. $\frac{5}{8} \log 16.05$.
49. $12 \times \log 42.86$.	56. $\frac{3}{4} \log 763.8$.	63. $\frac{7}{8} \log 23.43$.

50. Antilogarithm. The number corresponding to a given logarithm is called an *antilogarithm.*

For "antilogarithm of N" it is customary to write "antilog N."

Thus if log 25.31 = 1.40329, antilog 1.40329 = 25.31. Similarly, we see that antilog 5.40329 = 253,100, and antilog $\bar{2}$.40329 = 0.02531.

51. Finding the Antilogarithm. An antilogarithm is found from the tables by looking for the number corresponding to the given mantissa and placing the decimal point according to the characteristic. For example, consider the following portion of a table:

550 — 600

N	0	1	2	3	4	5	6	7	8	9
550	74 036	74 044	74 052	74 060	74 068	74 076	74 084	74 092	74 099	74 107
551	74 115	74 123	74 131	74 139	74 147	74 155	74 162	74 170	74 178	74 186

If the mantissa is given in the table, we find the sequence of the digits of the antilogarithm in the column under **N**. If the mantissa is not given in the table, we interpolate.

1. Find the antilogarithm of 5.74139.

We find 74139 in the table, opposite 551 and under 3. Hence the digits of the number are 5513. Since the characteristic is 5, there are six integral places, and hence the antilogarithm is 551,300. That is,

$$\log 551{,}300 = 5.74139,$$

or

$$\text{antilog } 5.74139 = 551{,}300.$$

2. Find the antilogarithm of $\bar{2}$.74166.

We find 74170 in the table, opposite 551 and under 7.

$$\begin{aligned} \log 0.05517 &= \bar{2}.74170 \\ \log 0.05516 &= \bar{2}.74162 \\ \text{Tabular difference} &= 0.00008 \end{aligned}$$

Subtracting, we see that, neglecting the decimal point, the tabular difference is 8, and the difference between $\log x$ and log 0.05516 is 4. Hence x is $\frac{4}{8}$ of the way from 0.05516 to 0.05517. Hence $x = 0.055165$.

3. Find the antilogarithm of 7.74053.

We find 74060 in the table, opposite 550 and under 3.

$$\begin{aligned} \log 55{,}030{,}000 &= 7.74060 \\ \log 55{,}020{,}000 &= 7.74052 \\ \text{Tabular difference} &= 0.00008 \end{aligned}$$

Reasoning as before, x is $\frac{1}{8}$ of the way from 55,020,000 to 55,030,000. Hence, to five significant figures, $x = 55{,}021{,}000$.

In general, the interpolation gives only one additional figure correct; that is, with a table like the one above, the sixth figure will not be correct if found by interpolation.

Exercise 21. Antilogarithms

Find the antilogarithms of the following:

1. 0.47712.
2. 3.47712.
3. $\bar{3}.47712$.
4. 2.48359.
5. 4.56844.
6. 1.66276.
7. 2.66978.
8. $\bar{5}.74819$.
9. 3.74076.
10. $\bar{2}.76305$.
11. $\bar{4}.78497$.
12. $\bar{1}.81954$.
13. 0.82575.
14. 0.88081.
15. 9.89237.
16. 7.90282.
17. 0.23305.
18. 1.43144.
19. 2.56838.
20. $\bar{1}.58041$.
21. $\bar{3}.63490$.
22. 4.63492.
23. 0.63994.
24. $\bar{2}.69085$.
25. 8.77425.
26. $\bar{4}.82966$.
27. 3.83547.
28. 2.83604.
29. 4.88960.
30. 2.89523.
31. 3.89858.
32. 0.93223.

33. If the logarithm of the product of two numbers is 2.94210, what is the product of the numbers?

34. If the logarithm of the quotient of two numbers is 0.30103, what is the quotient of the numbers?

35. If we wish to multiply 2857 by 2875, what logarithms do we need? What are these logarithms?

36. If we know that the logarithm of a result which we are seeking is 3.47056, what is that result?

37. If we know that log $\sqrt{0.000043641}$ is $\bar{3}.81995$, what is the value of $\sqrt{0.000043641}$?

38. If we know that log $\sqrt[6]{0.076553}$ is $\bar{1}.81400$, what is the value of $\sqrt[6]{0.076553}$?

39. The logarithm of $\sqrt{8322}$ is 1.96012. Find $\sqrt{8322}$ to three decimal places.

40. The logarithm of the cube of 376 is 7.72557. Find the cube of 376 to five significant figures.

41. If we know that log 0.003278^2 is $\bar{5}.03122$, what is the value of 0.003278^2?

42. Find twice log 731, and find the antilogarithm of the result.

43. Find the antilogarithm of the sum of $\log 27.8 + \log 34.6 + \log 367.8$.

Find the antilogarithms of the following:

44. $\log 7 + \log 2 - \log 1.934$.
45. $\log 63 + \log 5.8 - \log 3.415$.
46. $\log 728 + \log 96.8 - \log 2.768$.
47. $5 \log 27.83$.
48. $2.8 \log 5.683$.
49. $\frac{3}{4}(\log 2 + \log 4.2)$.

52. Multiplication by Logarithms. It has been shown (§ 40) that the logarithm of a product is equal to the sum of the logarithms of the numbers. This is of practical value in multiplication.

Find the product of 6.15×27.05.

From the tables,

$$\begin{aligned} \log 6.15 &= 0.78888 \\ \log 27.05 &= 1.43217 \\ \hline \log x &= 2.22105 \end{aligned}$$

Interpolating to find the value of x, we have

$$\begin{aligned} \log 166.4 &= 2.22115 \\ \log 166.3 &= 2.22089 \\ \hline & \quad 26 \end{aligned} \qquad \begin{aligned} \log x &= 2.22105 \\ \log 166.3 &= 2.22089 \\ \hline & \quad 16 \end{aligned}$$

Annexing to 166.3 the fraction $\frac{16}{26}$, we have

$$\begin{aligned} x &= 166.3\tfrac{16}{26} \\ &= 166.36, \end{aligned}$$

the interpolation not being exact beyond one figure.

If we perform the actual multiplication, we have $6.15 \times 27.05 = 166.3575$, or 166.36 to two decimal places.

Exercise 22. Multiplication by Logarithms

Using logarithms, find the following products:

1. 2×5.
2. 4×6.
3. 3×5.
4. 5×7.
5. 2×4.
6. 3×7.
7. 2×6.
8. 3×6.
9. 7×8.
10. 2×9.
11. 2×50.
12. 40×60.
13. 3×500.
14. 50×70.
15. 2×4000.
16. 30×700.
17. 200×60.
18. 30×600.
19. $7 \times 80,000$.
20. 200×900.
21. 35.8×28.9.
22. 52.7×41.6.
23. 2.75×4.84.
24. 5.25×3.86.
25. 14.26×42.35.
26. 43.28×29.64.
27. 529.6×348.7.
28. 240.8×46.09.
29. 34.81×46.25.
30. 5028×3.472.

31. Taking the circumference of a circle to be 3.14 times the diameter, find the circumference of a steel shaft of diameter 5.8 in.

32. Taking the ratio of the circumference to the diameter as given in Ex. 31, find the circumference of a water tank of diameter 36 ft.

Using logarithms, find the following products:

33. $2 \times 3 \times 5 \times 7$.
34. $3 \times 5 \times 7 \times 9$.
35. $5 \times 7 \times 11 \times 13$.
36. $43.8 \times 26.9 \times 32.8$.
37. $527.6 \times 283.4 \times 4.196$.
38. $7.283 \times 6.987 \times 5.437$.

53. Negative Characteristic. Since the mantissa is always positive (§ 45), care has to be taken in adding or subtracting logarithms in which a negative characteristic may occur. In all such cases it is better to separate the characteristics from the mantissas, as shown in the following illustrations:

1. Add the logarithms $\bar{2}.81764$ and 1.41283.

Separating the negative characteristic from its mantissa, we have

$$\bar{2}.81764 = 0.81764 - 2$$
$$1.41283 = 1.41283$$

Adding, we have

$$2.23047 - 2$$
$$= 0.23047$$

2. Add the logarithms $\bar{4}.21255$ and $\bar{2}.96245$.

Separating both negative characteristics from the mantissas, we have

$$\bar{4}.21255 = 0.21255 - 4$$
$$\bar{2}.96245 = 0.96245 - 2$$

Adding, we have

$$1.17500 - 6$$
$$= \bar{5}.17500$$

Exercise 23. Negative Characteristics

Add the following logarithms:

1. $2.41283 + 5.27681$.
2. $\bar{2}.41283 + 5.27681$.
3. $\bar{2}.41283 + \bar{5}.27681$.
4. $0.38264 + \bar{4}.71233$.
5. $0.57121 + \bar{1}.42879$.
6. $\bar{2}.63841 + 1.36158$.
7. $\bar{2}.41238 + \bar{3}.62701$.
8. $\bar{5}.58623 + 6.41387$.
9. $\bar{6}.41382 + 7.58617$.
10. $\bar{4}.22334 + 3.77666$.

Using logarithms, find the following products:

11. 256×4875.
12. 2.56×48.75.
13. 0.256×0.4875.
14. 0.0256×0.004875.
15. 0.1275×0.03428.
16. 0.2763×0.4134.
17. 0.00025×0.00125.
18. 0.725×0.3465.
19. 0.256×0.0875.
20. 0.037×0.00425.
21. 47.26×0.02755.
22. 296.8×0.1283
23. $45,650 \times 0.0725$.
24. $127,400 \times 0.00355$.
25. Given $\sin 25.75° = 0.4344$, find $52.8 \sin 25.75°$.
26. Given $\cos 37.25° = 0.7960$, find $42.85 \cos 37.25°$.
27. Given $\tan 30° 50' 30'' = 0.5971$, find $27.65 \tan 30° 50' 30''$.

54. Division by Logarithms. It has been shown (§ 41) that the logarithm of a quotient is equal to the logarithm of the dividend minus the logarithm of the divisor.

Care must be taken that the mantissa in subtraction does not become negative (§ 45).

1. Using logarithms, divide 17.28 by 1.44.

From the tables,

$$\begin{aligned} \log 17.28 &= 1.23754 \\ \log 1.44 &= \underline{0.15836} \\ &\ 1.07918 \\ &= \log 12 \end{aligned}$$

Hence $17.28 \div 1.44 = 12$.

2. Using logarithms, divide 2603.5 by 0.015998.

$$\begin{aligned} \log 2603.5 &= 3.41556 \\ \log 0.015998 &= \underline{\bar{2}.20407} \end{aligned}$$

Arranging these in a form more convenient for subtracting, we have

$$\begin{aligned} \log 2603.5 &= 3.41556 \\ \log 0.015998 &= \underline{0.20407 - 2} \\ &\ 3.21149 + 2 \\ &= 5.21149 = \log 162{,}740 \end{aligned}$$

Hence $2603.5 \div 0.015998 = 162{,}740$.

3. Using logarithms, divide 0.016502 by 127.41.

$$\begin{aligned} \log 0.016502 &= \bar{2}.21753 = 8.21753 - 10 \\ \log 127.41 &= 2.10520 = \underline{2.10520} \\ &\ 6.11233 - 10 \\ &= \bar{4}.11233 = \log 0.00012952 \end{aligned}$$

Hence $0.016502 \div 127.41 = 0.00012952$.

Here we increased $\bar{2}.21753$ by 10 and decreased the sum by 10. We might take any other number that would make the highest order of the minuend larger than the corresponding order of the subtrahend, but it is a convenient custom to take 10 or the smallest multiple of 10 that will serve the purpose.

4. Using logarithms, divide 0.000148 by 0.022922.

$$\begin{aligned} \log 0.000148 &= \bar{4}.17026 = 16.17026 - 20 \\ \log 0.022922 &= \bar{2}.36025 = \underline{\ \ 8.36025 - 10} \\ &\phantom{= \bar{2}.36025 =}\ \ 7.81001 - 10 \\ &\phantom{= \bar{2}.36025}= \ \ \bar{3}.81001 = \log 0.0064567 \end{aligned}$$

Hence $0.000148 \div 0.022922 = 0.0064567$.

5. Using logarithms, divide 0.2548 by 0.05513.

$$\begin{aligned} \log 0.2548 &= \bar{1}.40620 = 9.40620 - 10 \\ \log 0.05513 &= \bar{2}.74139 = \underline{8.74139 - 10} \\ &\phantom{= \bar{2}.74139 =}\ 0.66481 \\ &\phantom{= \bar{2}.74139}= \log 4.6218 \end{aligned}$$

Hence $0.2548 \div 0.05513 = 4.6218$.

Exercise 24. Division by Logarithms

Add the following logarithms:

1. $\bar{2}.14755 + 3.82764$.
2. $\bar{4}.07256 + 1.58822$.
3. $0.21783 + \bar{1}.46835$.
4. $0.41722 + \bar{3}.28682$.
5. $\bar{4}.18755 + \bar{2}.81245$.
6. $\bar{6}.28742 + \bar{3}.41258$.
7. $\bar{4}.21722 + \bar{4}.78278$.
8. $\bar{5}.28720 + \bar{3}.71280$.

9. Find the sum of $\bar{2}.41280$, $\bar{4}.17623$, $\bar{5}.26453$, 0.21020, 7.36423, 2.63577, $\bar{6}.41323$, and 3.28740.

From the first of these logarithms subtract the second:

10. 0.21250, $\bar{2}.21250$.
11. 0.17286, $\bar{3}.27286$.
12. 2.34222, $\bar{5}.44222$.
13. 3.14725, $\bar{1}.25625$.
14. $\bar{4}.17325$, $\bar{2}.17325$.
15. $\bar{5}.82340$, $\bar{3}.71120$.
16. $\bar{3}.14286$, $\bar{1}.14000$.
17. $\bar{3}.27283$, $\bar{5}.56111$.

Using logarithms, divide as follows:

18. $10 \div 2$.
19. $15 \div 3$.
20. $15 \div 5$.
21. $12 \div 3$.
22. $12 \div 4$.
23. $60 \div 12$.
24. $75 \div 25$.
25. $125 \div 25$.
26. $25{,}284 \div 301$.
27. $51{,}742 \div 631$.
28. $47{,}348 \div 623$.
29. $19{,}224 \div 540$.
30. $37{,}960 \div 520$.
31. $84{,}640 \div 920$.
32. $65{,}100 \div 620$.
33. $45{,}990 \div 730$.
34. $59.29 \div 0.77$.
35. $2.451 \div 190$.
36. $851.4 \div 0.66$.
37. $0.98902 \div 99$.
38. $0.41831 \div 5.9$.
39. $0.08772 \div 4.3$.
40. $0.02275 \div 0.35$.
41. $0.02736 \div 0.057$

Using logarithms, divide to four significant figures:

42. $15 \div 7$.
43. $7 \div 15$.
44. $0.7 \div 150$.
45. $26.4 \div 13.8$.
46. $4.21 \div 3.75$.
47. $63.25 \div 4.92$.
48. $17.625 \div 3.4$.
49. $43.826 \div 0.72$.
50. $5.483 \div 8.4$.

Taking log 3.1416 as 0.49715 and interpolating for six figures on the same principle as for five, find the diameters of circles with circumferences as follows:

51. 62.832.
52. 157.08.
53. 2199.12.
54. 2513.28.
55. 28,274.2.
56. 34,557.6.
57. 376,992
58. 0.031416.

59. By using logarithms find the product of 41.74×20.87, and the quotient of $41.74 \div 20.87$.

55. Cologarithm. The logarithm of the reciprocal of a number is called the *cologarithm* of the number.

For "cologarithm of N" it is customary to write "colog N."

By definition $\text{colog}\, x = \log \frac{1}{x} = \log 1 - \log x$ (§ 41). But $\log 1 = 0$.

Hence we have $\qquad \text{colog}\, x = -\log x.$

To avoid a negative mantissa (§ 45) it is customary to consider that

$$\text{colog}\, x = 10 - \log x - 10,$$

since $10 - \log x - 10$ is the same as $-\log x$.

For example, $\text{colog}\, 2 = -\log 2 = 10 - \log 2 - 10$
$= 10 - 0.30103 - 10$
$= 9.69897 - 10 = \bar{1}.69897.$

56. Use of the Cologarithm. Since to divide by a number is the same as to multiply by its reciprocal, *instead of subtracting the logarithm of a divisor we may add its cologarithm.*

The cologarithm of a number is easily written by looking at the logarithm in the table. Thus, since $\log 20 = 1.30103$, we find colog 20 by subtracting this from $10.00000 - 10$. To do this we begin at the left and subtract the number represented by each figure from 9, except the right-hand significant figure, which we subtract from 10. In full form we have

	$10.00000 - 10 =$	9.	9	9	9	9	10	-10	
$\log 20 =$	1.30103	$=$ 1.	3	0	1	0	3		
$\text{colog}\, 20 =$		8.	6	9	8	9	7	-10	$= \bar{2}.69897$

Similarly, we may find colog 0.03952 thus:

	$10.00000 - 10 =$	9.	9	9	9	9	10	-10	
$\log 0.03952 =$	$\bar{2}.59682$	$=$ 8.	5	9	6	8	2	-10	
$\text{colog}\, 0.03952 =$		1.	4	0	3	1	8		$= 1.40318$

Practically, of course, we would find log 0.03952 and subtract mentally.

Exercise 25. Cologarithms

Write the cologarithms of the following numbers:

1. 25.	5. 3751.	9. 0.5.	13. 3.007.
2. 130.	6. 427.3.	10. 0.72.	14. 62.09.
3. 27.4.	7. 51.61.	11. 0.083.	15. 0.0006.
4. 5.83.	8. 7.213.	12. 0.00726.	16. 0.00007.

17. What number has 0 for its cologarithm?
18. What number has 1 for its cologarithm?
19. What number has ∞ for its cologarithm?
20. Find the number whose cologarithm equals its logarithm.

57. Advantages of the Cologarithm. If, as is not infrequently the case in the computations of trigonometry and physics, we have the product of two or more numbers to be divided by the product of two or more different numbers, the cologarithm is of great advantage.

Using logarithms and cologarithms, simplify the expression

$$\frac{17.28 \times 6.25 \times 16.9}{1.44 \times 0.25 \times 1.3}.$$

This is so chosen that we can easily verify the answer by cancellation.
By logarithms we have,

$$\begin{aligned}
\log 17.28 &= 1.23754\\
\log 6.25 &= 0.79588\\
\log 16.9 &= 1.22789\\
\operatorname{colog} 1.44 &= 9.84164-10\\
\operatorname{colog} 0.25 &= 0.60206\\
\operatorname{colog} 1.3 &= \underline{9.88606-10}\\
& \ 3.59107 \qquad = \log 3900.1
\end{aligned}$$

In a long computation the fifth figure may be in error.

Exercise 26. Use of Cologarithms

Using cologarithms, find the value of the following to five figures:

1. $\frac{3 \times 2}{4 \times 1.5}$.
2. $\frac{8 \times 9}{3 \times 4}$.
3. $\frac{6 \times 12}{3 \times 8}$.
4. $\frac{4 \times 24}{12 \times 16}$.
5. $\frac{12 \times 15}{9 \times 20}$.
6. $\frac{12 \times 28}{8 \times 21}$.
7. $\frac{3 \times 22}{18 \times 33}$.
8. $\frac{11 \times 13}{17 \times 19}$.
9. $\frac{15 \times 17}{11 \times 13}$.
10. $\frac{172.8 \times 1.44}{0.288 \times 0.864}$.
11. $\frac{57.5 \times 0.64}{1.25 \times 320}$.
12. $\frac{1.28 \times 13.41}{1.49 \times 6.4}$.
13. $\frac{5.48 \times 0.198}{3.96 \times 27.4}$.
14. $\frac{1.176 \times 10.22}{14.6 \times 3.92}$.
15. $\frac{3 \times 11 \times 17}{7 \times 13}$.
16. $\frac{16 \times 23}{3 \times 7 \times 41}$.
17. $\frac{23 \times 39 \times 47}{17 \times 33 \times 53}$.
18. $\frac{0.2 \times 0.3}{0.11 \times 17\frac{1}{2}}$.
19. $\frac{435 \times 0.2751}{2.83 \times 1.045}$.
20. $\frac{50.05 \times 2.742}{381.4 \times 2.461}$.
21. $\frac{50730 \times 2.875}{34.48 \times 1.462}$.
22. $\frac{3.427 \times 0.7832}{3.1416 \times 0.0081}$.
23. $\frac{27.98 \times 32.05}{0.48 \times 0.00062}$.
24. $\frac{2.1 \times 0.3 \times 0.11}{17 \times 0.05}$.
25. $\frac{1.1 \times 3.003}{0.2 \times 0.07112}$.
26. $\frac{0.0347 \times 0.117}{3 \times 11 \times 170}$.
27. $\frac{528.4 \times 1.001}{7.03 \times 0.7281}$.

58. Raising to a Power. It has been shown (§ 42) that the logarithm of a power of a number is equal to the logarithm of the number multiplied by the exponent.

1. Find by logarithms the value of 11^3.

From the tables, $\log 11 = 1.04139$

Multiplying by 3, $\underline{\quad 3}$

$\log 11^3 = 3.12417$

$= \log 1331.0$

That is, $11^3 = 1331.0$, to five figures. Of course we see that $11^3 = 1331$ exactly, log 1331 being 3.12418. The last figure in $\log 11^3$ as found in the above multiplication is therefore not exact, as is frequently the case in such computations.

As usual, care must be taken when a negative characteristic appears.

2. Find by logarithms the value of 0.2413^5.

From the tables, $\log 0.2413 = 0.38256 - 1$

Multiplying by 5, $\underline{\quad 5}$

$\log 0.2413^5 = 1.91280 - 5$

$= \bar{4}.91280$

$= \log 0.00081808$

Hence $0.2413^5 = 0.00081808$, to five significant figures.

As on page 18, we use the expression "significant figures" to indicate the figures after the zeros at the left, even though some of these figures are zero.

Exercise 27. Raising to Powers

By logarithms, find the value of each of the following to five significant figures:

1. 2^2.	9. 1^{10}.	17. 25^3.	25. 1.1^8.	33. 12.55^2.
2. 2^3.	10. 7^9.	18. 25^7.	26. 2.1^7.	34. 34.75^3.
3. 2^5.	11. 9^7.	19. 125^2.	27. 0.1^{12}.	35. 1.275^3.
4. 2^{10}.	12. 8^8.	20. 625^3.	28. 0.2^{11}.	36. 0.1254^3.
5. 3^4.	13. 11^7.	21. 1750^5.	29. 0.7^8.	37. 0.4725^5.
6. 3^6.	14. 15^6.	22. 2775^2.	30. 0.07^6.	38. 0.01234^2.
7. 4^3.	15. 1.5^6.	23. 3146^3.	31. 0.37^4.	39. 0.00275^2.
8. 5^3.	16. 17^4.	24. 4135^4.	32. 5.37^3.	40. 0.000355^2.

41. If $\log \pi = 0.49715$, what is the value of π^2? of π^3?

42. Using $\log \pi$ as in Ex. 41, what is the value of πr when $r = 7$? of πr^2 when $r = 7$? of $\frac{4}{3}\pi r^3$ when $r = 9$?

59. Fractional Exponent. It has been shown (§ 43) that the logarithm of a root of a number is equal to the logarithm of the number divided by the index of the root. This law may, however, be combined with that of § 58, since $a^{\frac{1}{2}}$ means $\sqrt{a}$, and $a^{\frac{2}{3}}$ means $\sqrt[3]{a^2}$. The law of § 58 therefore applies to roots or to powers of roots, the exponent simply being considered fractional.

1. Find by logarithms the value of $\sqrt{4}$, or $4^{\frac{1}{2}}$.

From the tables, $\log 4 = 0.60206$

Dividing by 2, $2\overline{)0.60206}$

$\log \sqrt{4}$, or $\log 4^{\frac{1}{2}}$, $= 0.30103$

$= \log 2$

Hence $\sqrt{4}$, or $4^{\frac{1}{2}}$, is 2.

2. Find by logarithms the value of $8^{\frac{2}{3}}$.

From the tables, $\log 8 = 0.90309$

Multiplying by $\frac{2}{3}$, $\log 8^{\frac{2}{3}} = 0.60206$

$= \log 4$

Therefore $8^{\frac{2}{3}} = 4$.

3. Find by logarithms the value of $0.127^{\frac{1}{5}}$.

From the tables, $\log 0.127 = 0.10380 - 1$.

Since we cannot divide -1 by 5 and get an integral quotient for the new characteristic, we add 4 and subtract 4 and then have

$\log 0.127 = 4.10380 - 5$

Dividing by 5, $\log 0.127^{\frac{1}{5}} = 0.82076 - 1$

$= \log 0.66185$

Hence $0.127^{\frac{1}{5}}$, or $\sqrt[5]{0.127}$, is 0.66185.

We might have written $\log 0.127 = 9.10380 - 10$, $14.10380 - 15$, and so on.

Exercise 28. Extracting Roots

By logarithms, find the value of each of the following:

1. $\sqrt{2}$.	5. $2^{\frac{1}{5}}$.	9. $\sqrt{11}$.	13. $0.3^{\frac{1}{2}}$.	17. $127.8^{\frac{5}{8}}$.
2. $\sqrt[3]{5}$.	6. $3^{\frac{3}{4}}$.	10. $\sqrt[3]{3}$.	14. $0.05^{\frac{1}{3}}$.	18. $2.475^{\frac{3}{4}}$.
3. $\sqrt[7]{7}$.	7. $8^{\frac{5}{6}}$.	11. $\sqrt[3]{22}$.	15. $0.0175^{\frac{2}{3}}$.	19. $5.135^{\frac{5}{6}}$.
4. $\sqrt[15]{25}$.	8. $7^{\frac{4}{7}}$.	12. $\sqrt[25]{100}$.	16. $0.0325^{\frac{4}{5}}$.	20. $0.00125^{\frac{7}{8}}$.

21. If $\log \pi = 0.49715$, what is the value of $\sqrt{\pi}$? of $\sqrt[3]{\pi}$?

22. Using the value of $\log \pi$ given in Ex. 21, what is the value of $\pi^{\frac{1}{4}}$? of $\pi^{\frac{2}{3}}$? of $\pi^{\frac{3}{2}}$? of $\pi^{-\frac{3}{4}}$? of $\pi^{-\frac{4}{5}}$? of $\pi^{-0.2}$?

60. Exponential Equation. An equation in which the unknown quantity appears in an exponent is called an *exponential equation.*

Exponential equations may often be solved by the aid of logarithms.

1. Given $5^x = 625$, find by logarithms the value of x.

Taking the logarithms of both sides, we have (§ 42)

$$x \log 5 = \log 625$$

Whence
$$x = \frac{\log 625}{\log 5}$$
$$= \frac{2.79588}{0.69897} = 4$$

Check. $5^4 = 625$.

In all such cases bear in mind that one logarithm must actually be divided by the other. If we wished to perform this division by means of logarithms, we should have to take the logarithm of 2.79588 and the logarithm of 0.69897, subtract the second logarithm from the first, and then find the antilogarithm.

We may apply this principle to certain simultaneous equations.

2. Solve this pair of simultaneous equations

$$2^x \cdot 3^y = 72 \qquad (1)$$
$$4^x \cdot 27^y = 46{,}656 \qquad (2)$$

Taking the logarithms of both sides, we have (§§ 40, 42)

$$x \log 2 + y \log 3 = \log 72, \qquad (3)$$

and
$$x \log 4 + y \log 27 = \log 46{,}656. \qquad (4)$$

Then, since
$$\log 4 = \log 2^2 = 2 \log 2,$$

and
$$\log 27 = \log 3^3 = 3 \log 3,$$

we have
$$2x \log 2 + 3y \log 3 = \log 46{,}656. \qquad (5)$$

Eliminating x by multiplying equation (3) by 2 and subtracting from equation (5), we have

$$y = \frac{\log 46656 - 2 \log 72}{\log 3}$$
$$= \frac{4.66890 - 2 \times 1.85733}{0.47712}$$
$$= \frac{0.95424}{0.47712} = 2$$

We may substitute this value of y in (1), divide by 3^2, and then find x by taking the logarithms of both sides. It will be found that $x = 3$.

We may check by substituting in (2).

In the same way, equations involving three or more unknown quantities may be solved. Although the exponential equation is valuable in algebra, as in the solution of Exs. 22, 23, 25, and 26 of Exercise 29, we rarely have need of it in trigonometry.

Exercise 29. Exponential Equations

By logarithms, solve the following exponential equations:

1. $2^x = 8$.
2. $3^x = 81$.
3. $5^x = 625$.
4. $4^x = 256$.
5. $11^x = 1331$.
6. $2^x = 19$.
7. $3^x = 75$.
8. $5^x = 1000$.
9. $4^x = 2560$.
10. $11^x = 1500$.
11. $2^{-x} = \frac{1}{8}$.
12. $2^{-x} = 0.1$.
13. $0.3^{-x} = 0.9$.
14. $2^{x+1} = 3^{x-1}$.
15. $9^{x+5} = 53{,}143$.

Solve the following simultaneous equations:

16. $a^{x+y} = a^4$
 $a^{x-y} = a^2$
17. $m^{2x+y} = m^{11}$
 $n^{3x-y} = n^{14}$
18. $3^x \cdot 4^y = 12$
 $5^x \cdot 7^y = 35$
19. $2^x \cdot 3^y = 36$
 $4^x \cdot 5^y = 400$
20. $2^x \cdot 5^y = 200$
 $3^x \cdot 3^y = 243$
21. $2^x \cdot 8^y = 256$
 $8^x \cdot 32^y = 65{,}536$

Solve the following equations by logarithms:

22. $a = p(1+r)^x$.
23. $l = ar^{x-1}$.
24. $2^{x^2+2x} = 8$.
25. $a = p(1+rt)^x$.
26. $s(r-1) = ar^x - a$.
27. $3^{x^2-x+1} = 27$.

Perform the following operations by logarithms:

28. $\dfrac{2.47 \times 84.96}{34.8 \times 96.55}$.
29. $\sqrt[4]{\dfrac{42.4 \times 0.075}{3.64 \times 0.009}}$.
30. $\left(\dfrac{5.75 \times 3.428}{59.62 \times 48.08}\right)^{\frac{2}{3}}$.
31. $\sqrt[5]{\left(\dfrac{0.07 \times 0.00964}{3.426 \times 0.875}\right)^2}$.

32. To what power must 7 be raised to equal 117,649?

33. To what power must a be raised to equal b?

34. To what power must 5 be raised to equal n?

35. Find the value of x when $\sqrt[x]{9} = 3$; when $\sqrt[x]{2} = 1.1$; when $\sqrt[x]{2} = 1.414$; when $\sqrt[x]{3} = 1.73$.

36. Find the value of x when $\sqrt[x]{3} = 3$; when $\sqrt[x]{a} = b$; when $\sqrt[x]{a} = a$; when $\sqrt[x]{1331} = 11$; when $\sqrt[x]{20736} = 12$.

37. Solve the equations

$$\sqrt[x]{y} = a$$
$$\sqrt[x+1]{y} = b$$

38. What value of x satisfies the equation $a^{\frac{1}{x^2+2x+4}} = \sqrt[3]{a}$?

61. Logarithms of the Functions. Since computations involving trigonometric functions are often laborious, they are generally performed by the aid of logarithms. For this reason tables have been prepared giving the logarithms of the sine, cosine, tangent, and cotangent of the various angles from 0° to 90° at intervals of 1′. The functions of angles greater than 90° are defined and discussed later in this work when the need for them arises.

Logarithms of the secant and cosecant are usually not given for the reason that the secant is the reciprocal of the cosine, and the cosecant is the reciprocal of the sine. Instead of multiplying by $\sec x$, for example, we may divide by $\cos x$; and when we are using logarithms one operation is as simple as the other, since multiplication requires the addition of a logarithm and division requires the addition of a cologarithm.

In order to avoid negative characteristics the characteristic of every logarithm of a trigonometric function is printed 10 too large, and hence 10 must be subtracted from it.

Practically this gives rise to no confusion, for we can always tell by a result if a logarithm is 10 too large, since it would give an antilogarithm with 10 integral places more than it should have. For example, if we are measuring the length of a lake in miles, and find 10.30103 as the logarithm of the result, we see that the characteristic must be much too large, since this would make the lake 20,000,000,000 mi. long.

It would be possible to print $\bar{2}.97496$ for $\log \sin 5° \, 25'$, instead of 8.97496, which is 10 too large. It would be more troublesome, however, for the eye to detect the negative sign than it would be to think of the characteristic as 10 too large.

On pages 56–77 of the tables the characteristic remains the same throughout each column, and is therefore printed only at the top and bottom, except in the case of pages 58 and 77. Here the characteristic changes one unit at the places marked with the bars. By a little practice, such as is afforded on pages 61 and 62 of the text, the use of the tables will become clear.

On account of the rapid change of the sine and tangent for very small angles $\log \sin x$ is given for every second from 0″ to 3′ on page 49 of the tables, and $\log \tan x$ has identically the same values to five decimal places. The same table, read upwards, gives the $\log \cos x$ for every second from 89° 57′ to 90°. Also $\log \sin x$, $\log \tan x$, and $\log \cos x$ are given, on pages 50–55 of the tables, for every 10″ from 0″ to 2°. Reading from the foot of the page, the cofunctions of the complementary angles are given.

On pages 56–77 of the tables, $\log \sin x$, $\log \cos x$, $\log \tan x$, and $\log \cot x$ are given for every minute from 1° to 89°. Interpolation in the usual manner (page 31) gives the logarithmic functions for every second from 1° to 89°.

62. Use of the Tables. The tables are used in much the same way as the tables of natural functions.

For example,	$\log\sin\ 5^\circ\ 25'$	$= 8.97496 - 10$	Page 58
	$\log\tan 40^\circ\ 55'$	$= 9.93789 - 10$	Page 75
	$\log\cos 52^\circ\ 20'$	$= 9.78609 - 10$	Page 74
	$\log\cot 88^\circ\ 59'$	$= 8.24910 - 10$	Page 56
	$\log\sin\ 0^\circ\ 28'\ 40''$	$= 7.92110 - 10$	Page 51
	$\log\sin\ 0^\circ\ 1'\ 52''$	$= 6.73479 - 10$	Page 49

Furthermore, if $\log\cot x = 9.55910 - 10$, then $x = 70^\circ\ 5'$. Page 65

Interpolation is performed in the usual manner, whether the angles are expressed in the sexagesimal system or decimally.

1. Find $\log\sin 19^\circ\ 50'\ 30''$.

From the tables, $\log\sin 19^\circ\ 50' = 9.53056 - 10$, and the tabular difference is 36. We must therefore add $\frac{30}{60}$ of 36 to the mantissa, in the proper place. We therefore add 0.00018, and have $\log\sin 19^\circ\ 50'\ 30'' = 9.53074 - 10$.

2. Find $\log\tan 39.75^\circ$.

From the tables, $\log\tan 39.7^\circ = 9.91919 - 10$, and the tabular difference is 154. We therefore add 0.5 of 154 to the mantissa, in the proper place. Adding 0.00077, we have $\log\tan 39.75^\circ = 9.91996 - 10$.

Special directions in the case of very small angles are given on page 49 of the tables. It should be understood, however, that we rarely use angles involving seconds except in astronomy.

If the function is decreasing, care must be taken to subtract instead of add in making an interpolation.

3. Find $\log\cos 43^\circ\ 45'\ 15''$.

From the tables, $\log\cos 43^\circ\ 45' = 9.85876 - 10$, and the tabular difference is 12. Taking $\frac{15}{60}$ of 12, or $\frac{1}{4}$ of 12, we have 0.00003 to be *subtracted*.
Therefore $\log\cos 43^\circ\ 45'\ 15'' = 9.85873 - 10$.

4. Given $\log\cot x = 0.19268$, find x.

From the tables, $\log\cot 32^\circ\ 41' = 10.19275 - 10 = 0.19275$.
The tabular difference is 28, and the difference between the logarithm 0.19275 and the given logarithm is 7, in each case hundred-thousandths. Hence there is an angular difference of $\frac{7}{28}$ of $1'$, or $\frac{1}{4}$ of $1'$, or $15''$. Since the angle increases as the cotangent decreases, and 0.19268 is less than $10.19275 - 10$, we have to add $15''$ to $32^\circ\ 41'$, whence $x = 32^\circ\ 41'\ 15''$.

5. Given $\log\tan x = 0.26629$, find x.

From the tables, $\log\tan 61^\circ\ 33' = 10.26614 - 10 = 0.26614$.
The tabular difference is 30, and the difference between the logarithm 0.26614 and the given logarithm is 15, in each case hundred-thousandths. Hence there is an angular difference of $\frac{15}{30}$ of $1'$, or $30''$. Since $f(x)$ is increasing in this case, and x is also increasing, we add $30''$ to $61^\circ\ 33'$. Hence $x = 61^\circ\ 33'\ 30''$.

Exercise 30. Use of the Tables

Find the value of each of the following:

1. log sin 27°.
2. log sin 69°.
3. log cos 36°.
4. log cos 48°.
5. log tan 75°.
6. log tan 12°.
7. log cot 15°.
8. log cot 78°.
9. log sin 9° 15′.
10. log cos 8° 27′.
11. log tan 7° 56′.
12. log cot 82° 4′.
13. log sin 4.5°.
14. log cos 7.25°.
15. log tan 9.75°.
16. log cos 42° 45″.
17. log tan 26° 15″.
18. log cot 38° 30″.
19. log sin 21° 10′ 4″.
20. log sin 68° 49′ 56″.
21. log cos 15° 17′ 3″.
22. log cos 74° 42′ 57″.
23. log tan 17° 2′ 10″.
24. log tan 26° 3′ 4″.
25. log cot 48° 4′ 5″.
26. log cot 4° 10′ 7″.
27. log sin 34° 30″.
28. log sin 27.45°.
29. log tan 56.35°.
30. log cos 48.26°.
31. log sin 0° 1′ 7″.
32. log sin 1° 2′ 5″.
33. log tan 0° 2′ 8″.
34. log tan 2° 7′ 7″.
35. log cos 89° 50′ 10″.
36. log cos 89° 10′ 45″.
37. log cot 89° 15′ 12″
38. log cot 89° 25′ 15″
39. log sin 1° 1′ 1″.
40. log cos 88° 58′ 59″.
41. log tan 2° 27′ 25″.
42. log cot 87° 32′ 45″.
43. log sin 12° 12′ 12″.
44. log cos 77° 47′ 48″.
45. log tan 68° 6′ 43″.

Find the value of x, given the following logarithms, each of which is 10 too large:

46. $\log \sin x = 9.11570$.
47. $\log \sin x = 9.72843$.
48. $\log \sin x = 9.93053$.
49. $\log \sin x = 9.99866$.
50. $\log \cos x = 9.99866$.
51. $\log \cos x = 9.93053$.
52. $\log \cos x = 9.71705$.
53. $\log \cos x = 9.80320$.
54. $\log \tan x = 9.90889$.
55. $\log \tan x = 10.30587$.
56. $\log \tan x = 10.64011$.
57. $\log \cot x = 9.28865$.
58. $\log \cot x = 9.56107$.
59. $\log \sin x = 9.53871$.
60. $\log \sin x = 9.72868$.
61. $\log \sin x = 9.88150$.
62. $\log \sin x = 9.89530$.
63. $\log \cos x = 9.90151$.
64. $\log \cos x = 9.80070$.
65. $\log \cos x = 9.99483$.
66. $\log \tan x = 9.18854$.
67. $\log \tan x = 10.18750$.
68. $\log \tan x = 10.06725$.
69. $\log \cot x = 10.10134$.
70. $\log \cot x = 11.44442$.
71. $\log \cot x = 7.49849$.

CHAPTER IV

THE RIGHT TRIANGLE

63. Given an Acute Angle and the Hypotenuse. In § 30 the solution of the right triangle was considered when an acute angle and the hypotenuse are given. We may now consider this case and the following cases with the aid of logarithms. For example,

given $A = 34° 28'$, $c = 18.75$, find B, a, and b.

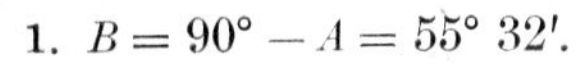

1. $B = 90° - A = 55° 32'$.

2. $\frac{a}{c} = \sin A$; $\therefore a = c \sin A$.

3. $\frac{b}{c} = \cos A$; $\therefore b = c \cos A$.

$\log a = \log c + \log \sin A$	$\log b = \log c + \log \cos A$
$\log c = 1.27300$	$\log c = 1.27300$
$\log \sin A = 9.75276 - 10$	$\log \cos A = 9.91617 - 10$
$\log a = 1.02576$	$\log b = 1.18917$
$\therefore a = 10.611$	$\therefore b = 15.459$
$= 10.61$	$= 15.46$

Check. $10.61^2 + 15.46^2 = 351.58$, and $18.75^2 = 351.56$.

This solution may be compared with the one on page 35. In this case there is a gain in using logarithms, since we avoid two multiplications by 18.75.

The result is given to four figures (two decimal places) only, the length of c having been given to four figures (two decimal places) only, and this probably being all that is desired. In general, *the result cannot be more nearly accurate than data derived from measurement.*

Consider also the case in which $A = 72° 27' 42''$, $c = 147.35$, to find B, a, and b as above.

$\log a = \log c + \log \sin A$	$\log b = \log c + \log \cos A$
$\log c = 2.16835$	$\log c = 2.16835$
$\log \sin A = 9.97933 - 10$	$\log \cos A = 9.47906 - 10$
$\log a = 2.14768$	$\log b = 1.64741$
$\therefore a = 140.50$	$\therefore b = 44.403$

Check. What convenient check can be applied in this case?

64. Given an Acute Angle and the Opposite Side. For example, given $A = 62° 10'$, $a = 78$, find B, b, and c.

1. $B = 90° - A = 27° 50'$.

2. $\frac{b}{a} = \cot A$; $\therefore b = a \cot A$.

3. $\frac{a}{c} = \sin A$;

$\therefore a = c \sin A$, and $c = \frac{a}{\sin A}$.

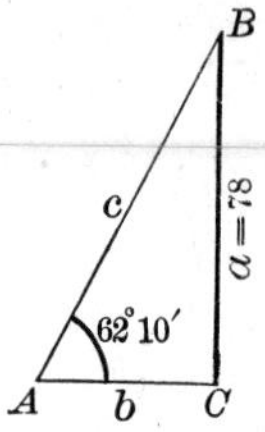

$$\begin{aligned} \log b &= \log a + \log \cot A \\ \log a &= 1.89209 \\ \log \cot A &= 9.72262 - 10 \\ \log b &= 1.61471 \\ \therefore b &= 41.182 \\ &= 41.18 \end{aligned}$$

$$\begin{aligned} \log c &= \log a + \operatorname{colog} \sin A \\ \log a &= 1.89209 \\ \operatorname{colog} \sin A &= 0.05340 \\ \log c &= 1.94549 \\ \therefore c &= 88.204 \\ &= 88.20 \end{aligned}$$

Check. $88.20^2 - 41.18^2 = 6083+$, and $78^2 = 6084$.

This solution should be compared with the one given in § 31, page 35. It will be seen that this is much shorter, especially as to that part in which c is found. The difference is still more marked if we remember that only part of the long division is given in § 31.

65. Given an Acute Angle and the Adjacent Side. For example, given $A = 50° 2'$, $b = 88$, find B, a, and c.

1. $B = 90° - A = 39° 58'$.

2. $\frac{a}{b} = \tan A$; $\therefore a = b \tan A$.

3. $\frac{b}{c} = \cos A$;

$\therefore b = c \cos A$, and $c = \frac{b}{\cos A}$.

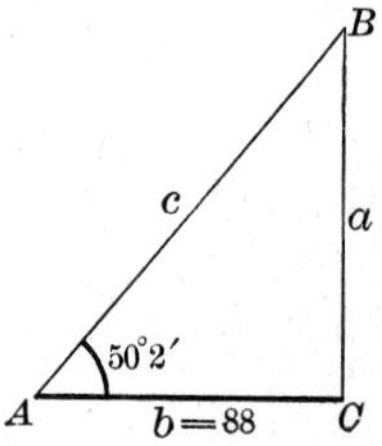

$$\begin{aligned} \log a &= \log b + \log \tan A \\ \log b &= 1.94448 \\ \log \tan A &= 10.07670 - 10 \\ \log a &= 2.02118 \\ \therefore a &= 105.00 \end{aligned}$$

$$\begin{aligned} \log c &= \log b + \operatorname{colog} \cos A \\ \log b &= 1.94448 \\ \operatorname{colog} \cos A &= 0.19223 \\ \log c &= 2.13671 \\ \therefore c &= 137.00 \end{aligned}$$

Check. $137^2 - 105^2 = 7744$, and $88^2 = 7744$.

This solution should be compared with the one given in § 32, page 36. Here again it will be seen that a noticeable gain is made by using logarithms, particularly in finding the value of c

66. Given the Hypotenuse and a Side. For example, given $a = 47.55$, $c = 58.4$, find A, B, and b.

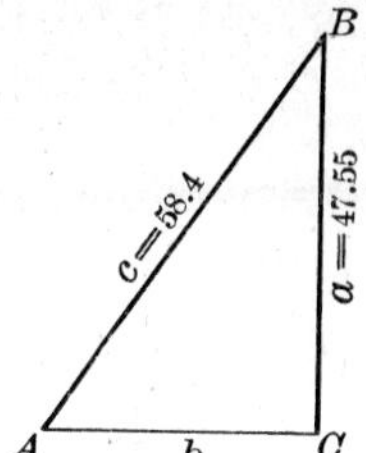

1. $\sin A = \frac{a}{c}$.

2. $B = 90° - A$.

3. $\frac{b}{a} = \cot A$; $\therefore b = a \cot A$.

We could, of course, find b from the equation $b = \sqrt{(c+a)(c-a)}$, as in § 33, page 36. By taking $b = a \cot A$, however, we save the trouble of first finding $c + a$ and $c - a$.

$$\begin{aligned} \log \sin A &= \log a + \text{colog}\, c \\ \log a &= 1.67715 \\ \text{colog}\, c &= 8.23359 - 10 \\ \log \sin A &= 9.91074 - 10 \\ \therefore A &= 54° \, 31' \\ \therefore B &= 35° \, 29' \end{aligned}$$

$$\begin{aligned} \log b &= \log a + \log \cot A \\ \log a &= 1.67715 \\ \log \cot A &= 9.85300 - 10 \\ \log b &= 1.53015 \\ \therefore b &= 33.896 \\ &= 33.90 \end{aligned}$$

Check. $58.4^2 - 33.9^2 = 2261+$, and $47.55^2 = 2261+$.

This solution should be compared with the one given in § 33, page 36.

67. Given the Two Sides. For example, given $a = 40$, $b = 27$, find A, B, and c.

1. $\tan A = \frac{a}{b}$.

2. $B = 90° - A$.

3. $\frac{a}{c} = \sin A$;

$\therefore a = c \sin A$, and $c = \frac{a}{\sin A}$.

$$\begin{aligned} \log \tan A &= \log a + \text{colog}\, b \\ \log a &= 1.60206 \\ \text{colog}\, b &= 8.56864 - 10 \\ \log \tan A &= 10.17070 - 10 \\ \therefore A &= 55° \, 59' \\ \therefore B &= 34° \, 1' \end{aligned}$$

$$\begin{aligned} \log c &= \log a + \text{colog} \sin A \\ \log a &= 1.60206 \\ \text{colog} \sin A &= 0.08151 \\ \log c &= 1.68357 \\ \therefore c &= 48.258 \\ &= 48.26 \end{aligned}$$

Check. $27^2 + 40^2 = 2329$, and $48.26^2 = 2329 +$.

This solution should be compared with the solution of the same problem given in § 34, page 37. There is not much gained in this particular example because the numbers are so small that the operations are easily performed.

68. Area of a Right Triangle. The area of a triangle is equal to one half the product of the base by the altitude; therefore, if a and b denote the two sides of a right triangle and S the area, then $S = \frac{1}{2}ab$.

Hence the area may be found when a and b are known.

Consider first the case in which an acute angle and the hypotenuse are given. For example, let $A = 34° 28'$ and $c = 18.75$. Then, finding $\log a$ and $\log b$ as in § 63, we have

$$\log S = \text{colog } 2 + \log a + \log b$$

$$\begin{aligned} \text{colog } 2 &= 9.69897 - 10 \\ \log a &= 1.02576 \\ \log b &= 1.18917 \\ \hline \log S &= 1.91390 \\ \therefore S &= 82.016 \\ &= 82.02 \end{aligned}$$

Next consider the case in which the hypotenuse and a side are given. For example, let $c = 58.4$ and $a = 47.55$. Then, finding $\log b$ as in § 66, we have

$$\log S = \text{colog } 2 + \log a + \log b$$

$$\begin{aligned} \text{colog } 2 &= 9.69897 - 10 \\ \log a &= 1.67715 \\ \log b &= 1.53015 \\ \hline \log S &= 2.90627 \\ \therefore S &= 805.88 \\ &= 805.9 \end{aligned}$$

Finally, consider the case in which an acute angle and the opposite side are given. For example, let $A = 62° 10'$ and $a = 78$. Then, finding $\log b$ as in § 64, we have

$$\log S = \text{colog } 2 + \log a + \log b$$

$$\begin{aligned} \text{colog } 2 &= 9.69897 - 10 \\ \log a &= 1.89209 \\ \log b &= 1.61471 \\ \hline \log S &= 3.20577 \\ \therefore S &= 1606.1 \\ &= 1606 \end{aligned}$$

We can easily verify this result, since, from § 64, $a = 78$ and $b = 41.18$; whence $\frac{1}{2}ab = 1606$, to four significant figures.

The case of an acute angle and the opposite side is treated in § 64; that of an acute angle and the adjacent side in § 65; and that of the two sides in § 67

Exercise 31. The Right Triangle

Using logarithms, solve the following right triangles, finding the sides and areas to four figures, and the angles to minutes:

1. $a = 6$, $c = 12$.
2. $b = 4$, $A = 60°$.
3. $a = 3$, $A = 30°$.
4. $a = 4$, $l = 4$.
5. $a = 2$, $c = 2.89$.
6. $c = 627$, $A = 23° 30'$.
7. $c = 2280$, $A = 28° 5'$.
8. $c = 72.15$, $A = 39° 34'$.
9. $c = 1$, $A = 36°$.
10. $c = 200$, $B = 21° 47'$.
11. $c = 93.4$, $B = 76° 25'$.
12. $a = 637$, $A = 4° 35'$.
13. $a = 48.53$, $A = 36° 44'$.
14. $a = 0.008$, $A = 86°$.
15. $b = 50.94$, $B = 43° 48'$.
16. $b = 2$, $B = 3° 38'$.
17. $a = 992$, $B = 76° 19'$.
18. $a = 73$, $B = 68° 52'$.
19. $a = 2.189$, $B = 45° 25'$.
20. $b = 4$, $A = 37° 56'$.
21. $c = 8590$, $a = 4476$.
22. $c = 86.53$, $a = 71.78$.
23. $c = 9.35$, $a = 8.49$.
24. $c = 2194$, $b = 1312.7$.
25. $c = 30.69$, $b = 18.25$.
26. $a = 38.31$, $b = 19.52$.
27. $a = 1.229$, $b = 14.95$.
28. $a = 415.3$, $b = 62.08$.
29. $a = 13.69$, $b = 16.92$.
30. $c = 91.92$, $a = 2.19$.

Compute the unknown parts and also the area, having given:

31. $a = 5$, $b = 6$.
32. $a = 0.615$, $c = 70$.
33. $b = \sqrt[3]{2}$, $c = \sqrt{3}$.
34. $a = 7$, $A = 18° 14'$.
35. $b = 12$, $A = 29° 8'$.
36. $c = 68$, $A = 69° 54'$.
37. $c = 27$, $B = 44° 4'$.
38. $a = 47$, $B = 48° 49'$.
39. $b = 9$, $B = 34° 44'$.
40. $c = 8.462$, $B = 86° 4'$.
41. Find the value of S in terms of c and A.
42. Find the value of S in terms of a and A.
43. Find the value of S in terms of b and A.
44. Find the value of S in terms of a and c.
45. Given $S = 58$ and $a = 10$, solve the right triangle.
46. Given $S = 18$ and $b = 5$, solve the right triangle.
47. Given $S = 12$ and $A = 29°$, solve the right triangle.
48. Given $S = 98$ and $c = 22$, solve the right triangle.
49. Find the two acute angles of a right triangle if the hypotenuse is equal to three times one of the sides.

50. The latitude of Washington is 38° 55′ 15″ N. Taking the radius of the earth as 4000 mi., what is the radius of the circle of latitude of Washington? What is the circumference of this circle?

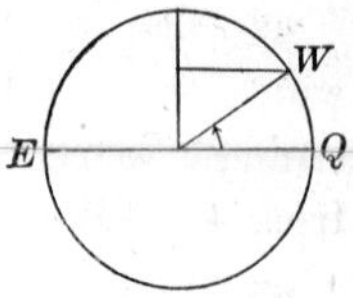

In all such examples the earth will be considered as a perfect sphere with the radius as above given, unless the contrary is stated. For more accurate data consult the Table of Constants.

W
E
Q

51. What is the difference between the length of a degree of latitude and the length of a degree of longitude at Washington?

Use the data given in Ex. 50.

52. From the top of a mountain 1 mi. high, overlooking the sea, an observer looks toward the horizon. What is the angle of depression of the line of sight?

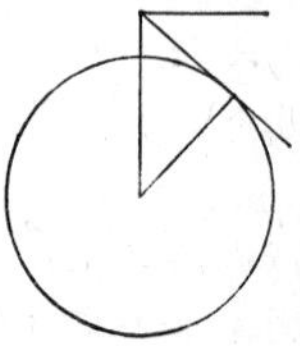

In the figure the height of the mountain is necessarily exaggerated. The angle is so small that the result can be found by five-place tables only between two limits which differ by 3′ 40″.

53. At a horizontal distance of 120 ft. from the foot of a steeple, the angle of elevation of the top is found to be 60° 30′. Find the height of the steeple above the instrument.

54. From the top of a rock which rises vertically 326 ft. out of the water, the angle of depression of a boat is found to be 24°. Find the distance of the boat from the base of the rock.

55. How far from the eye is a monument on a level plain if the height of the monument is 200 ft. and the angle of elevation of the top is 3° 30′?

56. A distance AB of 96 ft. is measured along the bank of a river from a point A opposite a tree C on the other bank. The angle ABC is 21° 14′. Find the breadth of the river.

57. What is the angle of elevation of an inclined plane if it rises 1 ft. in a horizontal distance of 40 ft.?

58. Find the angle of elevation of the sun when a tower 120 ft. high casts a horizontal shadow 70 ft. long.

59. How high is a tree which casts a horizontal shadow 80 ft. in length when the angle of elevation of the sun is 50°?

60. A rectangle 7.5 in. long has a diagonal 8.2 in. long. What angle does the diagonal make with the base?

61. A rectangle $8\frac{1}{4}$ in. long has an area of $49\frac{1}{2}$ sq. in. Find the angle which the diagonal makes with the base.

62. The length AB of a rectangular field $ABCD$ is 80 rd. and the width AD is 60 rd. The field is divided into two equal parts by a straight fence PQ starting from a point P on AD which is 15 rd. from A. What angle does PQ make with AD?

63. A ship is sailing due northeast at the rate of 10 mi. an hour. Find the rate at which she is moving due north, and also due east.

64. If the foot of a ladder 22 ft. long is 11 ft. from a house, how far up the side of the house does the ladder reach?

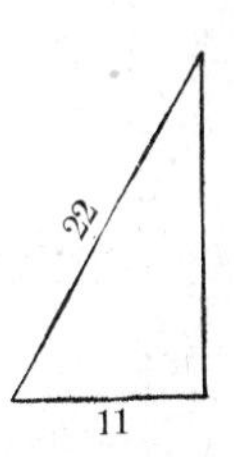

65. In front of a window 20 ft. from the ground there is a flower bed 6 ft. wide and close to the house. How long is a ladder which will just reach from the outside edge of the bed to the window?

66. A ladder 40 ft. long can be so placed that it will reach a window 33 ft. above the ground on one side of the street, and by tipping it back without moving its foot it will reach a window 21 ft. above the ground on the other side. Find the width of the street.

67. From the top of a hill the angles of depression of two successive milestones, on a straight, level road leading to the hill, are 5° and 15°. Find the height of the hill.

68. A stick 8 ft. long makes an angle of 45° with the floor of a room, the other end resting against the wall. How far is the foot of the stick from the wall?

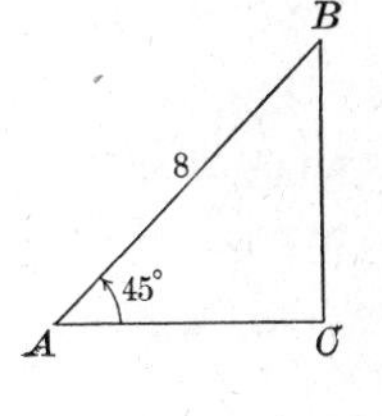

69. A building stands on a horizontal plain. The angle of elevation at a certain point on the plain is 30°, and at a point 100 ft. nearer the building it is 45°. How high is the building?

70. From a certain point on the ground the angles of elevation of the top of the belfry of a church and of the top of the steeple are found to be 40° and 51° respectively. From a point 300 ft. further off, on a horizontal line, the angle of elevation of the top of the steeple is found to be 33° 45′. Find the height of the top of the steeple above the top of the belfry.

71. The angle of elevation of the top C of an inaccessible fort observed from a point A is 12°. At a point B, 219 ft. from A and on a line AB perpendicular to AC, the angle ABC is 61° 45′. Find the height of the fort.

69. The Isosceles Triangle. Since an isosceles triangle is divided by the perpendicular from the vertex to the base into two congruent right triangles, an isosceles triangle is determined by any two parts which determine one of these right triangles.

In the examples which follow we shall represent the parts of the isosceles triangle ABC, among which the altitude CD is included, as follows:

$a =$ one of the equal sides,
$c =$ the base,
$h =$ the altitude,
$A =$ one of the equal angles,
$C =$ the angle at the vertex.

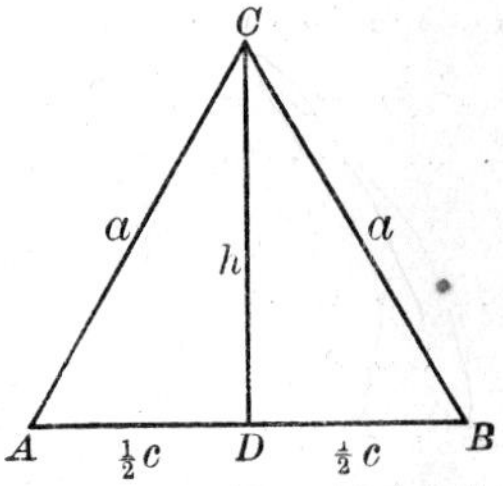

For example, given a and c, find A, C, and h.

1. $\cos A = \frac{\frac{1}{2}c}{a} = \frac{c}{2a}$.

2. $C + 2A = 180°$; $\therefore C = 180° - 2A = 2(90° - A)$.

3. h may be found by any one of the following equations:

$$h^2 + \tfrac{1}{4}c^2 = a^2,$$

whence $$h = \sqrt{(a + \tfrac{1}{2}c)(a - \tfrac{1}{2}c)};$$

or $$\frac{h}{a} = \sin A, \text{ whence } h = a \sin A;$$

or $$\frac{h}{\frac{1}{2}c} = \tan A, \text{ whence } h = \tfrac{1}{2}c \tan A.$$

When c and h are known, the area can be found by the formula

$$S = \tfrac{1}{2}ch$$

That is, $$S = \tfrac{1}{2}c \cdot a \sin A = \tfrac{1}{2}ac \sin A,$$

or $$S = \tfrac{1}{2}c \cdot \tfrac{1}{2}c \tan A = \tfrac{1}{4}c^2 \tan A,$$

or $$S = \tfrac{1}{2}c\sqrt{(a + \tfrac{1}{2}c)(a - \tfrac{1}{2}c)}.$$

Consider also the case in which a and h are given, to find A, C, c, and S.

1. $\sin A = \frac{h}{a}$, and hence A is known.

2. $C = 2(90° - A)$, as above, and hence C is known.

3. $\frac{1}{2}c = a \cos A$, and hence c is known.

4. $S = \frac{1}{2}ch$, and hence S is known.

We can also find S from any of its other equivalents, such as those given above, or $a^2 \sin \frac{1}{2}C \sin A$, each of which is easily deduced.

Exercise 32. The Isosceles Triangle

Solve the following isosceles triangles:

1. Given a and A, find C, c, and h.
2. Given a and C, find A, c, and h.
3. Given c and A, find C, a, and h.
4. Given c and C, find A, a, and h.
5. Given h and A, find C, a, and c.
6. Given h and C, find A, a, and c.
7. Given a and h, find A, C, and c.
8. Given c and h, find A, C, and a.
9. Given $a = 14.3$, $c = 11$, find A, C, and h.
10. Given $a = 0.295$, $A = 68° 10'$, find c, h, and S.
11. Given $c = 2.352$, $C = 69° 49'$, find a, h, and S.
12. Given $h = 7.4847$, $A = 76° 14'$, find a, c, and S.
13. Given $c = 147$, $S = 2572.5$, find A, C, a, and h.
14. Given $h = 16.8$, $S = 43.68$, find A, C, a, and c.
15. Given $a = 27.56$, $A = 75° 14'$, find c, h, and S.

Given an isosceles triangle, ABC:

16. Find the value of S in terms of a and C.
17. Find the value of S in terms of a and A.
18. Find the value of S in terms of h and C.
19. A barn is 40 ft. by 80 ft., the pitch of the roof is 45°; find the length of the rafters and the area of the whole roof.
20. In a unit circle what is the length of the chord subtending the angle 45° at the center?
21. The radius of a circle is 30 in., and the length of a chord is 44 in.; find the angle subtended at the center.
22. Find the radius of a circle if a chord whose length is 5 in. subtends at the center an angle of 133°.
23. What is the angle at the center of a circle if the subtending chord is equal to $\frac{2}{3}$ of the radius?
24. Find the area of a circular sector if the radius of the circle is 12 in., and the angle of the sector is 30°.
25. Find the tangent of the angle of the slope of an A-roof of a building which is 24 ft. 6 in. wide at the eaves, the ridgepole being 10 ft. 9 in. above the eaves.

70. The Regular Polygon. We have already considered a few cases involving the regular polygon. It is evident from geometry that if the polygon shown below has n sides, the angle of the right triangle which has its vertex at the center is equal to $\frac{1}{2}$ of $360°/n$, or $180°/n$. The triangle may evidently be solved if the radius of the circumscribed circle (r), the radius of the inscribed circle (h), or the side of the polygon (c) is given.

In the exercises we shall let

$n =$ number of sides,

$c =$ length of one side,

$r =$ radius of circumscribed circle,

$h =$ radius of inscribed circle,

$p =$ the perimeter,

$S =$ the area.

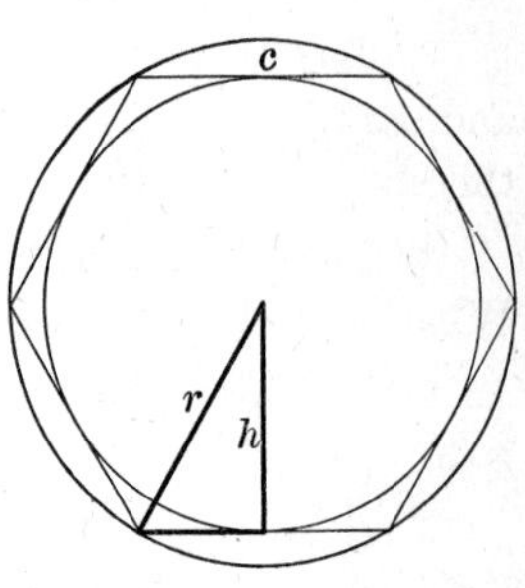

Then, by geometry,

$$S = \tfrac{1}{2}hp.$$

Exercise 33. The Regular Polygon

Find the remaining parts of a regular polygon, given:

1. $n = 10$, $c = 1$.
2. $n = 18$, $r = 1$.
3. $n = 20$, $r = 20$.
4. $n = 8$, $h = 1$.
5. $n = 11$, $S = 20$.
6. $n = 7$, $S = 7$.

7. The side of a regular inscribed hexagon is 1 in.; find the side of a regular inscribed dodecagon.

8. Given n and c, and represent by b the side of the regular inscribed polygon having $2n$ sides, find b in terms of n and c.

9. Compute the difference between the areas of a regular octagon and a regular nonagon if the perimeter of each is 16 in.

10. Compute the difference between the perimeters of a regular pentagon and a regular hexagon if the area of each is 12 sq. in.

11. Find the perimeter of a regular dodecagon circumscribed about a circle the circumference of which is 1 in.

12. What is the side of the regular inscribed polygon of 100 sides, the radius of the circle being unity? What is the perimeter?

13. What is the perimeter of the regular inscribed polygon of 360 sides, the radius of the circle being unity?

14. The area of a regular polygon of twenty-five sides is 40 sq. in; find the area of the ring included between the circumferences of the inscribed and circumscribed circles.

Exercise 34. Review Problems

1. Prove that the area of the parallelogram here shown is equal to $ab \sin A$.

2. Two sides of a parallelogram are 5 in. and 6 in. respectively, and their included angle is 82° 45′. What is the area?

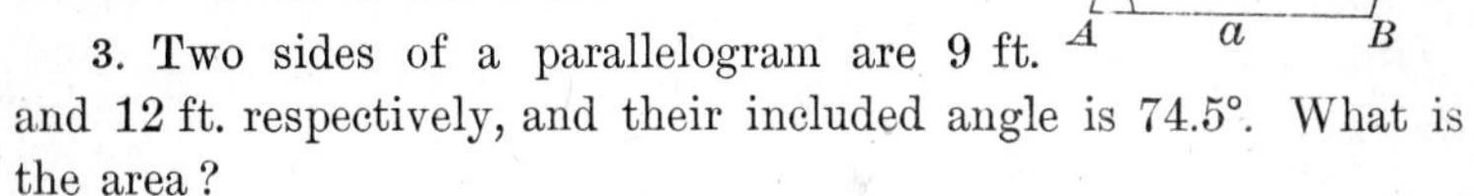

3. Two sides of a parallelogram are 9 ft. and 12 ft. respectively, and their included angle is 74.5°. What is the area?

4. Each side of a rhombus is 7.35 in., and one angle is 42° 27′. What is the area?

5. The area of a rhombus is 250 sq. in., and one of the angles is 37° 25′. What is the length of each side?

6. A pole BD stands on the top of a mound BC. From a point A the angles of elevation of the top and foot of the pole are 60° and 30° respectively. Prove that the height of the pole is twice the height of the mound.

7. A ladder 38 ft. long is resting against a wall. The foot of the ladder is 7 ft. 2 in. from the wall. What is the height of the top of the ladder above the ground?

8. From a boat 1325 ft. from the base of a vertical cliff the angle of elevation of the top of the cliff is observed to be 14° 30′. Find the height of the cliff.

9. On the top of a building 50 ft. high there is a flagstaff BD. From a point A on the ground the angles of elevation of B and D are 30° and 45° respectively. Find the length of the flagstaff and the distance AC of the observer from the building, as shown in the annexed figure.

Since $\frac{50}{x} = \tan 30°$ and $\frac{50 + y}{x} = \tan 45°$, x can evidently be eliminated.

10. A man whose eye is 5 ft. 8 in. above the ground stands midway between two telegraph poles which are 200 ft. apart. The elevation of the top of each pole is 48° 50′. What is the height of each?

11. The captain of a ship observed a lighthouse directly to the east. After sailing north 2 mi. he observed it to lie 55° 30′ east of south. How far was the ship from the lighthouse at the time of each observation?

12. A leveling instrument is placed at A on the slope MN, and the line $M'N'$ is sighted to two upright rods. By measurement MM' is found to be 12.8 ft., NN' to be 3.4 ft., and $M'N'$ to be 48.3 ft. Required the angle of the slope of MN and the distance MN.

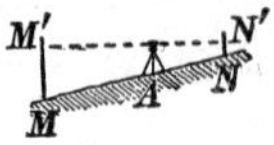

13. A wire stay is fastened to a telegraph pole 6.8 ft. from the ground and is stretched tightly so as to reach the ground 5.2 ft. from the foot of the pole. What angle does the wire stay make with the ground?

14. The top of a conical tent is 8 ft. 7 in. above the ground, and the diameter of the base is 9 ft. 8 in. Find the inclination of the side of the tent to the horizontal. Check the result by drawing the figure to scale and measuring the angle with a protractor.

15. In this piece of iron construction work $BC = 11$ in. and AB makes an angle of 30° with BC. What is the length of AC?

16. In Ex. 15 it is also known that BE and CD are each 9 in. long and make angles of 60° with BC produced. What is the length of ED?

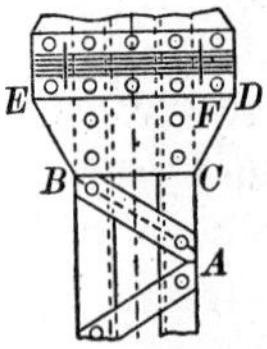

17. From the conditions given in Ex. 16, find the length of CF.

18. The base of a rectangle is $14\frac{5}{8}$ in. and the diagonal is $19\frac{1}{8}$ in. What angle does the diagonal make with the base? Check the result by drawing the figure to scale and measuring the angle with a protractor.

19. In constructing the spire represented in the figure below it is planned to have $AB = 42$ ft. and $PM = 92$ ft. What angle of slope must the builders give to AP?

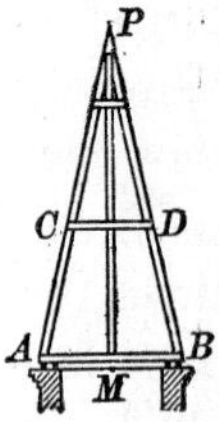

20. In Ex. 19 find the length of AP and find the angle P.

21. In the figure of Ex. 19 the brace CD is put in 38 ft. above AB. What is its length?

22. The spire of Ex. 19 rests on a tower. A man standing on the ground at a distance of 400 ft. from the base of the tower observes the angle of elevation of P to be 25° 38′, the instrument being 5 ft. above the ground. What is the height of P above the ground?

23. When the angle of elevation of the sun is 38.4°, what is the length of the shadow of a tower 175 ft. high?

24. Two men, M and N, 3200 ft. apart, observe an aeroplane A at the same instant, and at a time when the plane MNA is vertical. The angle of elevation at M is $41° 27'$ and the angle at N is $61° 42'$. Required AB, the height of the aeroplane.

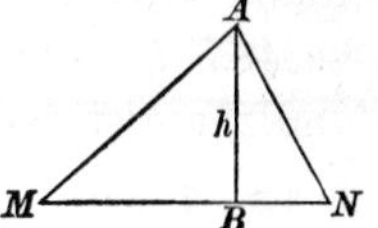

Show that $h \cot 41° 27' + h \cot 61° 42'$ is known, whence h can be found.

25. A kite string 475 ft. long makes an angle of elevation of $49° 40'$. Assuming the string to be straight, what is the altitude of the kite?

26. A steel bridge has a truss $ADEF$ in which it is given that $AD = 20$ ft., $BF = 6$ ft. 8 in., and $FE = 12$ ft., as shown in the figure. Required the angle of slope which AF makes with AD.

27. Two tangents are drawn from a point P to a circle and contain an angle of $37.4°$. The radius of the circle is 5 in. Find the length of each tangent and the distance of P from the center.

28. From the top of a cliff 95 ft. high, the angles of depression of two boats at sea are observed, by the aid of an instrument 5 ft. above the ground, to be 45° and 30° respectively. The boats are in a straight line with a point at the foot of the cliff directly beneath the observer. What is the distance between the boats?

29. A carpenter's square BCA is held against the vertical stick BD resting on a sloping roof AD, as in the figure. It is found that $AC = 24$ in. and $CD = 11.5$ in. Find the angle of slope of the roof with the horizontal.

30. In Ex. 29 find the length of AD.

31. A man 6 ft. tall stands 4 ft. 9 in. from a street lamp. If the length of his shadow is 19 ft., how high is the light above the street?

32. The shadow of a city building is observed to be 100 ft. long, and at the same time the shadow of a lamp-post 9 ft. high is observed to be 5.2 ft. long. Find the angle of elevation of the sun and the height of the building.

33. A man 5 ft. 10 in. tall walks along a straight line that passes at a distance of 2 ft. 9 in. from a street light. If the light is 9 ft. 6 in. above the ground, find the length of the man's shadow when his distance from the point on his path that is nearest to the lamp is 3 ft. 8 in.

34. A man on a bridge 35 ft. above a stream, using an instrument 5 ft. high, sees a rowboat at an angle of depression of 27° 30′. If the boat is approaching at the rate of $2\frac{3}{4}$ mi. an hour, in how many seconds will it reach the bridge?

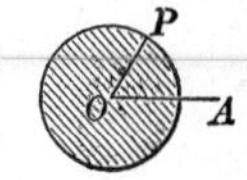

35. A shaft O, of diameter 4 in., makes 480 revolutions per minute. If the point P starts on the horizontal line OA, how far is it above OA after $\frac{1}{48}$ of a second?

36. Assuming the earth to be a sphere with radius 3957 mi., find the radius of the circle of latitude which passes through a place in latitude 47° 27′ 10″ N.

37. When a hoisting crane AB, 28 ft. long, makes an angle of 23° with the horizontal AC, what is the length of AC? Suppose that the angle CAB is doubled, what is then the length of AC?

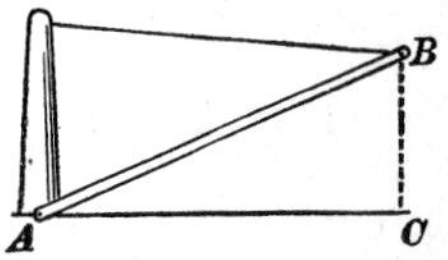

38. In Ex. 37 find the length of BC in each of the two cases.

39. Wishing to measure the distance AB, a man swings a 100-foot tape line about B, describing an arc on the ground, and then does the same about A. The arcs intersect at C, and the angle ACB is found to be 32° 10′. What is the length of AB?

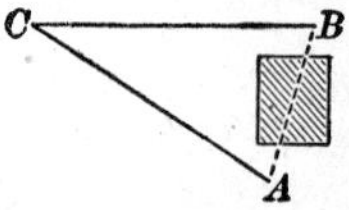

40. From the top of a mountain 15,250 ft. high, overlooking the sea to the south, over how many minutes of latitude can a person see if he looks southward? Use the assumption stated in Ex. 36.

41. The length of each blade of a pair of shears, from the screw to the point, is $5\frac{1}{4}$ in. When the points of the open shears are $3\frac{7}{8}$ in. apart, what angle do the blades make with each other?

42. In Ex. 41 how far apart are the points when the blades make an angle of 28° 45′ with each other?

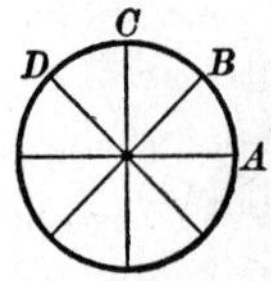

43. The wheel here represented has eight spokes, each being 19 in. long. How far is it from A to B? from B to D?

44. The angle of elevation of a balloon from a station directly south of it is 60°. From a second station lying 5280 ft. directly west of the first one the angle of elevation is 45°. The instrument being 5 ft. above the level of the ground, what is the height of the balloon?

CHAPTER V

TRIGONOMETRIC FUNCTIONS OF ANY ANGLE

71. Need for Oblique Angles. We have thus far considered only right triangles, or triangles which can readily be cut into right triangles for purposes of solution. There are, however, oblique triangles which cannot conveniently be solved by merely separating them into right triangles. We are therefore led to consider the functions of oblique angles, and to enlarge our idea of angles so as to include angles greater than 180°, angles greater than 360°, and even negative angles and the angle 0°.

72. Positive and Negative Angles. We have learned in algebra that we may distinguish between two lines which extend in opposite directions by calling one *positive* and the other *negative*.

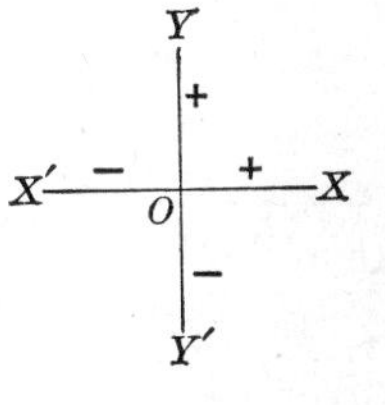

For example, in the annexed figure we consider OX as positive and therefore OX' as negative. We also consider OY as positive and hence OY' as negative. In general, horizontal lines extending to the right of a point which we select as zero are considered positive, and those to the left negative. Vertical lines extending upward from zero are considered positive, and those extending downward are considered negative.

With respect to angles, an angle is considered *positive* if the rotating line which describes it moves counterclockwise, that is, in the direction opposite to that taken by the hands of a clock. An angle is considered *negative* if the rotating line moves clockwise, that is, in the same direction as that taken by the hands of a clock.

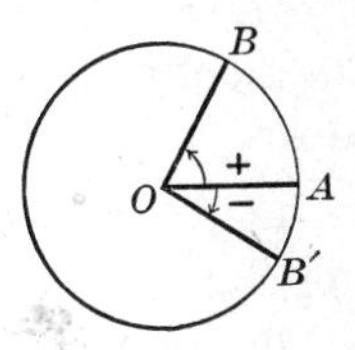

Arcs which subtend positive angles are considered *positive*, and arcs which subtend negative angles are considered *negative*. Thus $\angle AOB$ and arc AB are considered positive; $\angle AOB'$ and arc AB' are considered negative.

For example, we may think of a pendulum as swinging through a positive angle when it swings to the right, and through a negative angle when it swings to the left. We may also think of an angle of elevation as positive and an angle of depression as negative, if it appears to be advantageous to do so in the solution of a problem.

73. Coordinates of a Point. In trigonometry, as in work with graphs in algebra, we locate a point in a plane by means of its distances from two perpendicular lines.

These lines are lettered XX' and YY', and their point of intersection O. The lines are called the *axes* and the point of intersection the *origin*.

In some branches of mathematics it is more convenient to use oblique axes, but in trigonometry rectangular axes are used as here shown.

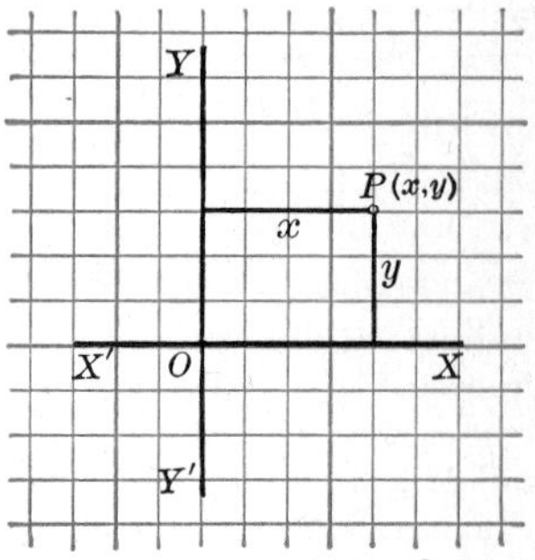

The distance of any point P from the axis XX', or the x-axis, is called the *ordinate* of the point. Its distance from the axis YY', or the y-axis, is called the *abscissa* of the point.

In the figure, y is the ordinate of P, and x is the abscissa of P. The point P is represented by the symbol (x, y). In the figure the side of each small square may be taken to represent one unit, in which case $P = (4, 3)$, because its abscissa is 4 and its ordinate 3. Following a helpful European custom, the points are indicated by small circles, so as to show more clearly when a line is drawn through them.

The abscissa and ordinate of a point are together called the *coordinates of the point.*

74. Signs of the Coordinates. From § 73 we see that *abscissas to the right of the y-axis are positive; abscissas to the left of the y-axis are negative; ordinates above the x-axis are positive; ordinates below the x-axis are negative.*

A point on the line YY' has zero for its abscissa, and hence the abscissa may be considered as either positive or negative and may be indicated by ± 0. Similarly, a point on the line XX' has ± 0 for its ordinate.

75. The Four Quadrants. The axes divide the plane into four parts known as *quadrants.*

Because angles are generally considered as generated by the rotating line moving counterclockwise, the four quadrants are named in a counterclockwise order. Quadrant XOY is spoken of as the first quadrant, YOX' as the second quadrant, $X'OY'$ as the third quadrant, and $Y'OX$ as the fourth quadrant.

76. Signs of the Coordinates in the Several Quadrants. From § 74 we have the following rule of signs:

In quadrant I the abscissa is positive, the ordinate positive;
In quadrant II the abscissa is negative, the ordinate positive;
In quadrant III the abscissa is negative, the ordinate negative;
In quadrant IV the abscissa is positive, the ordinate negative.

77. Plotting a Point. Locating a point, having given its coordinates, is called *plotting the point.*

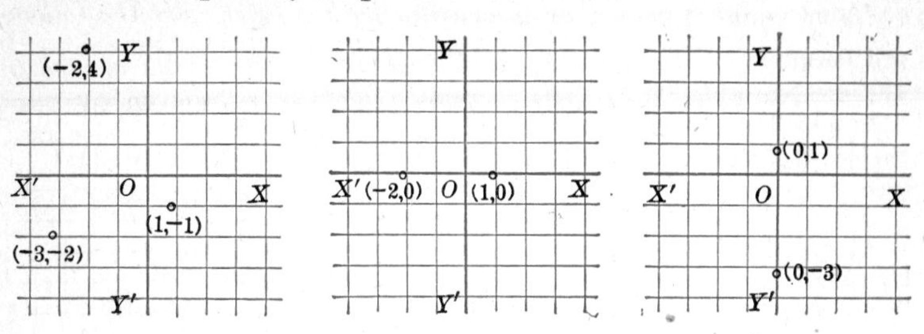

For example, in the first of these figures the point (− 2, 4) is shown in quadrant II, the point (− 3, − 2) in quadrant III, and the point (1, − 1) in quadrant IV.

In the second figure the point (− 2, 0) is shown on OX', between quadrants II and III, and the point (1, 0) on OX, between quadrants I and IV.

In the third figure the point (0, 1) is shown on OY, between quadrants I and II, and the point (0, − 3) on OY', between quadrants III and IV.

In every case the origin O may be designated as the point (0,0).

78. Distance from the Origin. The coordinates of P being x and y, we may form a right triangle the hypotenuse of which is the distance of P from O.

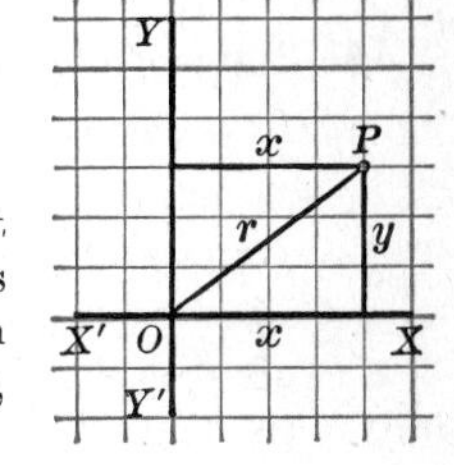

Representing OP by r, we have

$$r = \sqrt{x^2 + y^2}.$$

Since this may be written $r = \pm\sqrt{x^2+y^2}$, we see that r may be considered as either positive or negative. It is the custom, however, to consider the rotating line which forms the angle as positive. If r is produced through O, the production is considered as negative.

1. What is the distance of the point (3, 4) from the origin?

$$r = \sqrt{3^2 + 4^2} = \sqrt{25} = 5.$$

2. What is the distance of the point (− 3, − 2) from the origin?

$$r = \sqrt{(-3)^2 + (-2)^2} = \sqrt{9 + 4} = \sqrt{13} = 3.61.$$

3. What is the distance of the point (5, − 5) from the origin?

$$r = \sqrt{5^2 + (-5)^2} = \sqrt{50} = 7.07.$$

4. What is the distance of the point (− 2, 0) from the origin?

$$r = \sqrt{(-2)^2 + 0^2} = \sqrt{4} = 2,$$

as is evident from the conditions of the problem.

Exercise 35. Distances from the Origin

Using squared paper, or measuring with a ruler, plot the following points:

1. $(2, 3)$.
2. $(3, 5)$.
3. $(4, 4)$.
4. $(2\frac{1}{2}, 3)$.
5. $(3\frac{1}{2}, 4\frac{1}{2})$.
6. $(4\frac{1}{4}, 4\frac{1}{4})$.
7. $(5\frac{1}{2}, 3\frac{1}{2})$.
8. $(-3, 2)$.
9. $(-3, 4)$.
10. $(-5, 1)$.
11. $(-4, 6)$.
12. $(-2, -2)$.
13. $(-3, -5)$.
14. $(-5, -3)$.
15. $(3, -4)$.
16. $(4, -3)$.
17. $(5, -1)$.
18. $(0, 7)$.
19. $(3, 0)$.
20. $(0, -4)$.
21. $(-2, 0)$.
22. $(0, 0)$.
23. $(0, 2\frac{1}{2})$.
24. $(0, -3\frac{1}{2})$.
25. $(4\frac{1}{2}, 0)$.
26. $(5\frac{1}{2}, 0)$.
27. $(-2\frac{1}{2}, 0)$.
28. $(-3\frac{1}{4}, 0)$.

Find the distance of each of the following points from the origin:

29. $(6, 8)$.
30. $(9, 12)$.
31. $(5, 12)$.
32. $(1\frac{1}{2}, 2)$.
33. $(\frac{3}{4}, 1)$.
34. $(2\frac{1}{4}, 3)$.
35. $(2, \sqrt{5})$.
36. $(-3, 4)$.
37. $(0, 0)$.
38. $(0, 7)$.
39. $(5, 0)$.
40. $(-12, -9)$.

41. Find the distance from $(3, 2)$ to $(-2, 3)$.

42. Find the distance from $(-3, -2)$ to $(2, -3)$.

43. Find the distance from $(4, 1)$ to $(-4, -1)$.

44. Find the distance from $(0, 3)$ to $(-3, 0)$.

45. A point moves to the right 7 in., up 4 in., to the right 10 in., and up $18\frac{2}{3}$ in. How far is it then from the starting point?

46. A point moves to the right 9 in., up 5 in., to the left 4 in., and up 3 in. How far is it then from the starting point?

47. Find the distance from $(-\frac{1}{2}, \frac{1}{2}\sqrt{3})$ to $(\frac{1}{2}, -\frac{1}{2}\sqrt{3})$.

48. A triangle is formed by joining the points $(1, 0)$, $(-\frac{1}{2}, \frac{1}{2}\sqrt{3})$, and $(-\frac{1}{2}, -\frac{1}{2}\sqrt{3})$. Find the perimeter of the triangle. Draw the figure to scale.

49. Find the area of the triangle in Ex. 48.

50. A hexagon is formed by joining in order the points $(1, 0)$, $(\frac{1}{2}, \frac{1}{2}\sqrt{3})$, $(-\frac{1}{2}, \frac{1}{2}\sqrt{3})$, $(-1, 0)$, $(-\frac{1}{2}, -\frac{1}{2}\sqrt{3})$, $(\frac{1}{2}, -\frac{1}{2}\sqrt{3})$, and $(1, 0)$. Is the figure a regular hexagon? Prove it.

51. A polygon is formed by joining in order the points $(1, 0)$, $(\frac{1}{2}\sqrt{2}, \frac{1}{2}\sqrt{2})$, $(0, 1)$, $(-\frac{1}{2}\sqrt{2}, \frac{1}{2}\sqrt{2})$, $(-1, 0)$, $(-\frac{1}{2}\sqrt{2}, -\frac{1}{2}\sqrt{2})$, $(0, -1)$, $(\frac{1}{2}\sqrt{2}, -\frac{1}{2}\sqrt{2})$, and $(1, 0)$. Draw the figure, state the kind of polygon, and find its area.

79. Angles of any Magnitude. In the following figures, if the rotating line OP revolves about O from the position OX, in a counterclockwise direction, until it again coincides with OX, it will generate all angles in every quadrant from 0° to 360°.

The line OX is called the *initial side* of the angle, and the line OP the *terminal side* of the angle.

An angle is said to be an angle of that quadrant in which its terminal side lies.

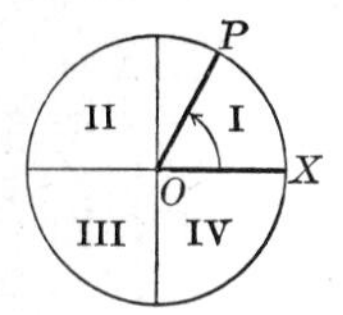

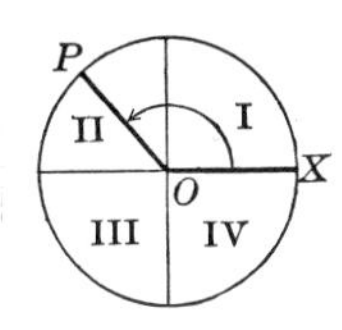

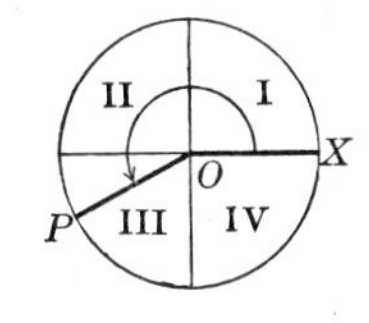

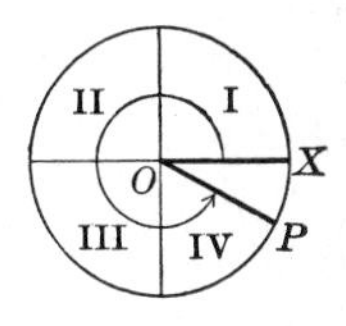

Angles between 0° and 90° are angles of quadrant I.
Angles between 90° and 180° are angles of quadrant II.
Angles between 180° and 270° are angles of quadrant III.
Angles between 270° and 360° are angles of quadrant IV.

The rotating line may also pass through 360°, forming angles from 360° to 720°. It may then make another revolution, forming angles greater than 720°, and so on indefinitely.

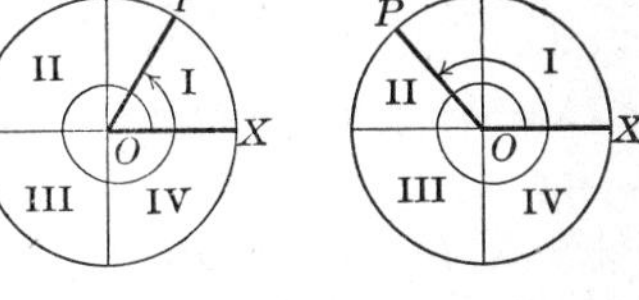

For example, in using a screwdriver we turn through angles of 360°, 720°, 1080°, and so on, depending upon the number of revolutions. In the same way, the minute hand of a clock turns through 8640° in a day, and the drive wheel of an engine may turn through thousands of degrees in an hour.

We might, if necessary, speak of an angle of 400° as an angle of quadrant I, because its terminal side is in that quadrant, but we have no occasion to do so in practical cases.

As stated in § 72, if the line OP is rotated clockwise, it generates negative angles.

In this way we may form angles of – 40° or – 140°, as here shown, and the rotation may continue until we have angles of – 360°, – 720°, – 1080°, – 1440°, and so on indefinitely.

We shall have but little need for the negative angle in the practical work of trigonometry, but we shall make extensive use of angles between 0° and 180°, and some use of those between 180° and 360°.

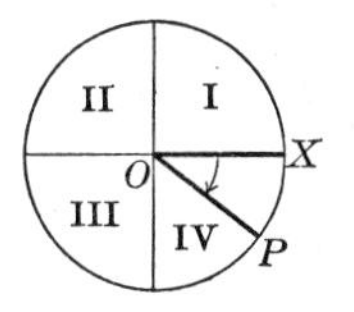

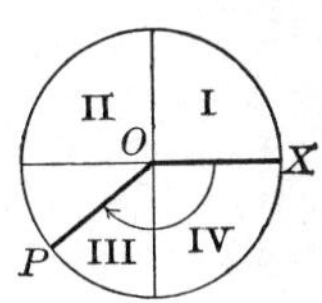

80. Functions of Any Angle. Since we have now seen that we may have angles of any magnitude, it is necessary to consider their functions. Although we must define these functions anew, it will be seen that the definitions hold for the acute angles which we have already considered.

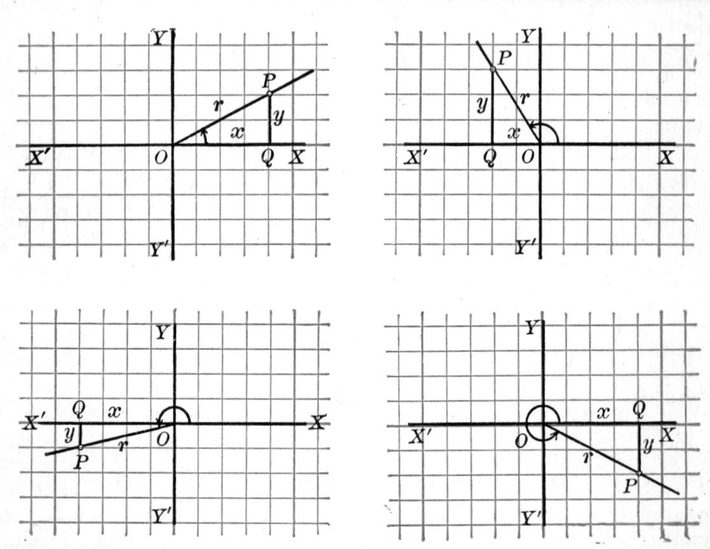

In whatever quadrant the angle is, we designate it by A. We take a point P, or (x, y), on the rotating line, and let $OP = r$. Then the angle XOP, read counterclockwise, is the angle A. We then define the functions as follows:

$$\sin A = \frac{y}{r} = \frac{\text{ordinate}}{\text{distance}}, \qquad \csc A = \frac{1}{\sin A} = \frac{r}{y} = \frac{\text{distance}}{\text{ordinate}},$$

$$\cos A = \frac{x}{r} = \frac{\text{abscissa}}{\text{distance}}, \qquad \sec A = \frac{1}{\cos A} = \frac{r}{x} = \frac{\text{distance}}{\text{abscissa}},$$

$$\tan A = \frac{y}{x} = \frac{\text{ordinate}}{\text{abscissa}}, \qquad \cot A = \frac{1}{\tan A} = \frac{x}{y} = \frac{\text{abscissa}}{\text{ordinate}}.$$

It will be seen that these definitions are practically the same as those already learned for angles in quadrant I. Their application to the other quadrants is apparent. The general definitions might have been given at first, but this plan offers difficulties for a beginner which make it undesirable.

By counting the squares on squared paper and thus getting the lengths of certain lines, the approximate values of the functions of any given angle may be found, but the exercise has no practical significance. The values of the functions are determined by series, these being explained in works on the calculus.

81. Angles determined by Functions. Given any function of an angle, it is possible to construct the angle or angles which satisfy the value of the function.

1. Given $\sin A = \frac{3}{5}$, construct the angle A.

If we take a line parallel to $X'X$ and 3 units above it, and then rotate a line OP, 5 units long, about O until P rests upon this parallel, we shall have in the annexed figure

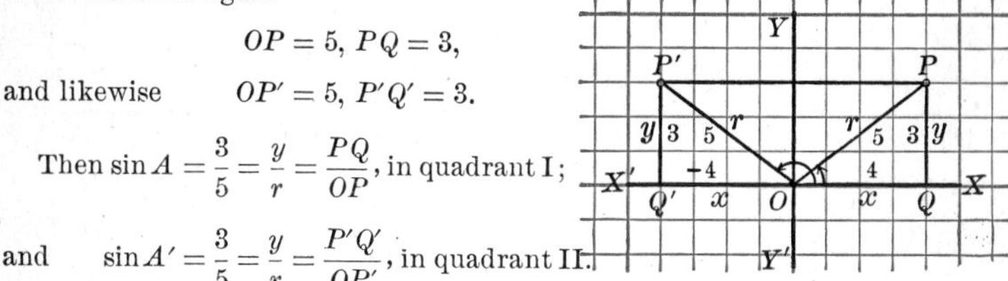

$$OP = 5,\ PQ = 3,$$

and likewise $$OP' = 5,\ P'Q' = 3.$$

Then $\sin A = \dfrac{3}{5} = \dfrac{y}{r} = \dfrac{PQ}{OP}$, in quadrant I;

and $\sin A' = \dfrac{3}{5} = \dfrac{y}{r} = \dfrac{P'Q'}{OP'}$, in quadrant II.

In other words, we have constructed two angles, each of which has $\frac{3}{5}$ for its sine.

Furthermore, we could construct an infinite number of such angles, for we see that $360° + A$ terminates in OP and has the same sine that A has, and that the same may be said of $360° + A'$, $720° + A$, $720° + A'$, $1080° + A$, and so on.

In general, therefore, the angle $n \times 360° + A$ has the same functions as A, n being any integer. Hence if we know the value of any particular function of an angle, the angle cannot be uniquely determined; that is, there is more than one angle which satisfies the condition. In general, as we see, an infinite number of angles will satisfy the given condition, although this gives no trouble because only two of these angles can be less than 360°.

2. Given $\tan A = \frac{3}{4}$, construct the angle A.

If we take an abscissa 4 and an ordinate 3, as in quadrant I of the figure, we locate the point (3, 4). Then angle XOP has for its tangent $\frac{3}{4}$. But it is evident that we may also locate the point $(-3, -4)$ in quadrant III, and thus find an angle between 180° and 270° whose tangent is $\frac{3}{4}$.

82. Functions found from Other Functions. Given any function of an angle, it is possible not only to construct the angle but also to find the other functions.

For in Ex. 1 above, after constructing angles A and A', we see that

$$\sin A = \frac{3}{5}, \qquad \csc A = \frac{5}{3},$$

$$\cos A = \frac{4}{5} \text{ or } \frac{-4}{5}, \qquad \sec A = \frac{5}{4} \text{ or } \frac{5}{-4},$$

$$\tan A = \frac{3}{4} \text{ or } \frac{3}{-4}, \qquad \cot A = \frac{4}{3} \text{ or } \frac{-4}{3}.$$

That is, if $\sin A = \frac{3}{5}$, then $\cos A = \pm \frac{4}{5}$, $\tan A = \pm \frac{3}{4}$, $\csc A = \frac{5}{3}$, $\sec A = \pm \frac{5}{4}$, and $\cot A = \pm \frac{4}{3}$.

Exercise 36. Construction of Angles and Functions

Using the protractor, construct the following angles:

1. 30°.	4. 150°.	7. 270°.	10. 405°.	13. – 45°.
2. 60°.	5. 180°.	8. 300°.	11. 450°.	14. – 90°.
3. 80°.	6. 200°.	9. 360°.	12. 720°.	15. – 180°.

State the quadrants in which the terminal sides of the following angles lie:

16. 45°.	19. 150°.	22. 390°.	25. 660°.	28. 930°.
17. 75°.	20. 210°.	23. 495°.	26. 765°.	29. 990°.
18. 120°.	21. 315°.	24. 570°.	27. 820°.	30. 1080°.

Construct two angles A, given the following:

31. $\sin A = \frac{1}{2}$.	36. $\sin A = -\frac{3}{4}$.	41. $\sin A = -1$.
32. $\cos A = \frac{1}{2}$.	37. $\cos A = -\frac{4}{5}$.	42. $\cos A = -1$.
33. $\tan A = \frac{1}{2}$.	38. $\tan A = -\frac{2}{3}$.	43. $\tan A = -1$.
34. $\cot A = \frac{1}{2}$.	39. $\cot A = -\frac{4}{5}$.	44. $\cot A = -1$.
35. $\sec A = 2$.	40. $\sec A = -1$.	45. $\sec A = -2$.

Given the following functions of angle A, construct the other functions:

46. $\sin A = \frac{2}{3}$.	51. $\sin A = -\frac{4}{5}$.	56. $\sin A = -\frac{1}{2}$.
47. $\cos A = \frac{3}{4}$.	52. $\cos A = -1$.	57. $\cos A = -\frac{1}{2}$.
48. $\tan A = \frac{4}{5}$.	53. $\tan A = -\frac{3}{8}$.	58. $\tan A = -\frac{1}{2}$.
49. $\cot A = \frac{3}{8}$.	54. $\sec A = -2$.	59. $\cot A = -\frac{1}{2}$.
50. $\csc A = 3$.	55. $\csc A = -1$.	60. $\sec A = -2\frac{1}{2}$.

61. If $\tan A = \sqrt{2}$, show that $\cot A$ is half as large. What are the values of $\sin A$, $\cos A$, $\sec A$, and $\csc A$?

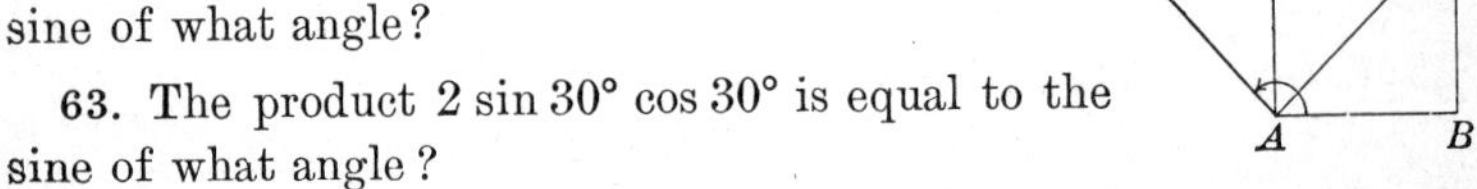

62. The product $2 \sin 45° \cos 45°$ is equal to the sine of what angle?

63. The product $2 \sin 30° \cos 30°$ is equal to the sine of what angle?

64. To the diagonal AC of a square $ABCD$ a perpendicular AM is drawn. Find the values of the six functions of angle BAM.

65. In the figure of Ex. 64, suppose AM rotates further, until it is in line with BA. What are then the six functions of angle BAM?

83. Line Values of the Functions. As in the case of acute angles (§ 22) we may represent the trigonometric functions of any angle by means of lines in a circle of radius unity.

Thus in each of the following figures

$$\sin x = MP, \quad \tan x = AT, \quad \sec x = OT,$$
$$\cos x = OM, \quad \cot x = BS, \quad \csc x = OS.$$

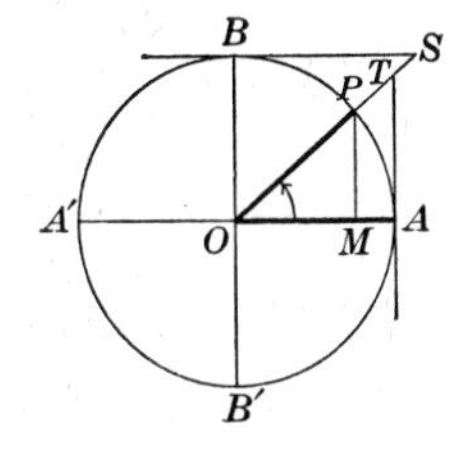

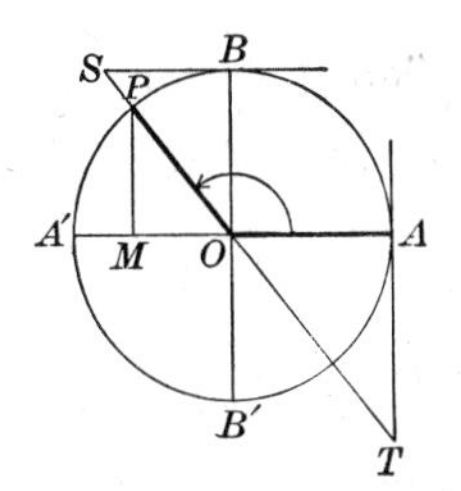

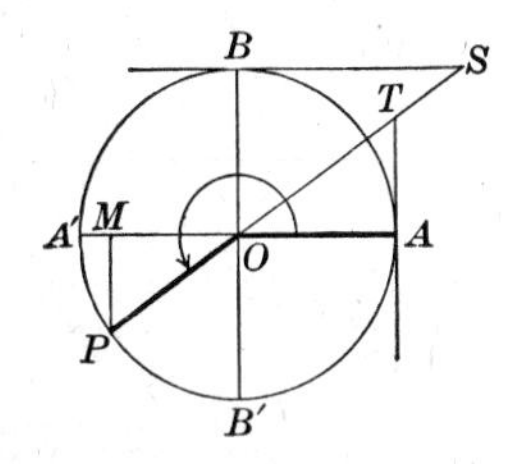

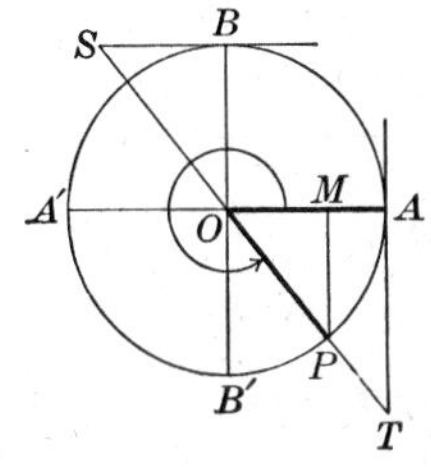

By examining the figures we see that

In quadrant I *all* the functions are positive;
In quadrant II the *sine and cosecant only* are positive;
In quadrant III the *tangent and cotangent only* are positive;
In quadrant IV the *cosine and secant only* are positive.

It will be seen as we proceed that the laws and relations which have been found for the functions of acute angles hold for the functions of angles greater than 90°. For example, it is apparent from the above figures that, in every quadrant,

$$\overline{MP}^2 + \overline{OM}^2 = \overline{OP}^2 = 1,$$

and hence that $\sin^2 A + \cos^2 A = 1,$

as shown in § 14. It is also evident that

$$\frac{AT}{1} = \frac{MP}{OM},$$

and hence that $\tan A = \dfrac{\sin A}{\cos A}.$

Other similar relations are easily proved by reference to the figures.

84. Variations in the Functions. A study of the line values of the functions shows how they change as the angle increases from 0° to 360°.

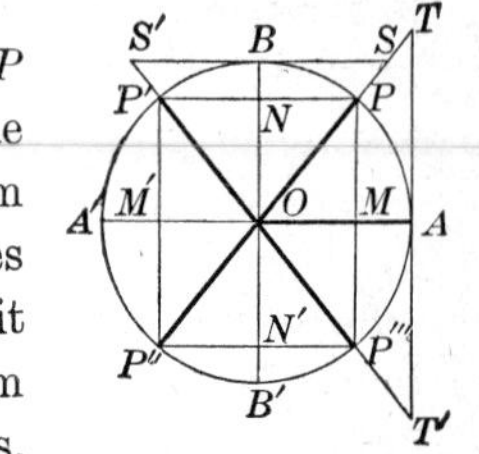

1. *The Sine.* In the first quadrant the sine MP is positive, and increases from 0 to 1; in the second it remains positive, and decreases from 1 to 0; in the third it is negative, and increases in absolute value from 0 to 1; in the fourth it is negative, and decreases in absolute value from 1 to 0. The absolute value of the sine varies, therefore, from 0 to 1, and its total range of values is from $+1$ to -1.

In the third quadrant the sine *decreases* from 0 to -1, but the *absolute value* (the value without reference to its sign) *increases* from 0 to 1, and similarly for other cases on this page in which the absolute value is mentioned.

2. *The Cosine.* In the first quadrant the cosine OM is positive, and decreases from 1 to 0; in the second it becomes negative, and increases in absolute value from 0 to 1; in the third it is negative, and decreases in absolute value from 1 to 0; in the fourth it is positive, and increases from 0 to 1. The absolute value of the cosine varies, therefore, from 0 to 1.

3. *The Tangent.* In the first quadrant the tangent AT is positive, and increases from 0 to ∞; in the second it becomes negative, and decreases in absolute value from ∞ to 0; in the third it is positive, and increases from 0 to ∞; in the fourth it is negative, and decreases in absolute value from ∞ to 0.

4. *The Cotangent.* In the first quadrant the cotangent BS is positive, and decreases from ∞ to 0; in the second it is negative, and increases in absolute value from 0 to ∞; in the third and fourth quadrants it has the same sign, and undergoes the same changes as in the first and second quadrants respectively. The tangent and cotangent may therefore have any values whatever, positive or negative.

5. *The Secant.* In the first quadrant the secant OT is positive, and increases from 1 to ∞; in the second it is negative, and decreases in absolute value from ∞ to 1; in the third it is negative, and increases in absolute value from 1 to ∞; in the fourth it is positive, and decreases from ∞ to 1.

6. *The Cosecant.* In the first quadrant the cosecant OS is positive, and decreases from ∞ to 1; in the second it is positive, and increases from 1 to ∞; in the third it is negative, and decreases in absolute value from ∞ to 1; in the fourth it is negative, and increases in absolute value from 1 to ∞.

It is evident, therefore, that the sine can never be greater than 1 nor less than -1, and that it has these limiting values at 90° and 270° respectively. We may also say that its absolute value can never be greater than 1, and that it has its limiting value 0 at 0° and 180°, and its limiting absolute value 1 at 90° and 270°.

If we have an equation in which the value of the sine is found to be greater than 1 or less than -1, we know either that the equation is wrong or that an error has been made in the solution.

Of course the values of the functions of 360° are the same as those of 0°, since the moving radius has returned to its original position and the initial and terminal sides of the angle coincide.

In the same way, the absolute value of the cosine cannot be greater than 1, and it has its limiting value 0 at 90° and 270°, and its limiting absolute value 1 at 0° and 180°. Similarly we can find the limiting values of all the other functions.

For convenience we speak of ∞ as a limiting value, although the function increases without limit, the meaning of the expression in this case being clear.

Summarizing these results, we have the following table:

Function	0°	90°	180°	270°	360°
Sine	∓ 0	$+1$	± 0	-1	∓ 0
Cosine	$+1$	± 0	-1	∓ 0	$+1$
Tangent	∓ 0	$\pm \infty$	∓ 0	$\pm \infty$	∓ 0
Cotangent	$\mp \infty$	± 0	$\mp \infty$	± 0	$\mp \infty$
Secant	$+1$	$\pm \infty$	-1	$\mp \infty$	$+1$
Cosecant	$\mp \infty$	$+1$	$\pm \infty$	-1	$\mp \infty$

Sines and cosines vary in value from $+1$ to -1; tangents and cotangents, from $+\infty$ to $-\infty$; secants and cosecants, from $+\infty$ to $+1$, and from -1 to $-\infty$.

In the table given above the double sign $\pm$ or $\mp$ is placed before 0 and ∞. From the preceding investigation it appears that the functions *always change sign in passing through 0 or through* ∞; and the sign $\pm$ or $\mp$ prefixed to 0 or ∞ simply shows the direction from which the value is reached. For example, at 0° the sine is passing from $-$ (in quadrant IV) to $+$ (in quadrant I). At 90° the tangent is passing from $+$ (in quadrant I) to $-$ (in quadrant II).

85. Functions of Angles Greater than 360°. The functions of $360° + x$ are the same in sign and in absolute value as those of x. If n is a positive integer,

The functions of $(n \times 360° + x)$ *are the same as those of* x.

For example, the functions of 2200°, or $6 \times 360° + 40°$, are the same in sign and in absolute value as the functions of 40°.

Exercise 37. Variations in the Functions

Represent the following functions by lines in a unit circle:

1. sin 135°.	7. sin 210°.	13. sin 300°.	19. sin 270°.
2. cos 120°.	8. cos 225°.	14. cos 315°.	20. cos 180°.
3. tan 150°.	9. tan 240°.	15. tan 330°.	21. tan 180°.
4. cot 135°.	10. cot 210°.	16. cot 300°.	22. cot 270°.
5. sec 120°.	11. sec 225°.	17. sec 315°.	23. sec 180°.
6. csc 150°.	12. csc 240°.	18. csc 330°.	24. csc 270°.

25. Prepare a table showing the signs of all the functions in each of the four quadrants.

26. Prepare a table showing which functions always have the minus sign in each of the four quadrants.

Represent the following functions by lines in a unit circle:

27. sin 390°.	30. cos 390°.	33. sin 460°.	36. tan 475°.
28. tan 405°.	31. cot 405°.	34. sin 570°.	37. sec 705°.
29. sec 420°.	32. csc 420°.	35. sin 720°.	38. csc 810°.

Show by lines in a unit circle that:

39. $\sin 150^\circ = \sin 30^\circ$.

40. $\cos 150^\circ = -\cos 30^\circ$.

41. $\sin 210^\circ = -\sin 30^\circ$.

42. $\cos 210^\circ = -\cos 30^\circ$.

43. $\sin 330^\circ = -\sin 30^\circ$.

44. $\cos 330^\circ = \cos 30^\circ$.

45. $\tan 120^\circ = -\tan 60^\circ$.

46. $\cot 120^\circ = -\cot 60^\circ$.

47. $\tan 240^\circ = \tan 60^\circ$.

48. $\cot 240^\circ = \cot 60^\circ$.

49. $\tan 300^\circ = -\tan 60^\circ$.

50. $\cot 300^\circ = -\cot 60^\circ$.

51. Write the signs of the functions of the following angles: 340°, 239°, 145°, 400°, 700°, 1200°, 3800°.

52. How many values less than 360° can the angle x have if $\sin x = +\frac{5}{7}$, and in what quadrants do the angles lie? Draw a figure.

53. How many values less than 720° can the angle x have if $\cos x = +\frac{2}{3}$, and in what quadrants do the angles lie? Draw a figure.

54. If we take into account only angles less than 180°, how many values can x have if $\sin x = \frac{5}{7}$? if $\cos x = \frac{1}{5}$? if $\cos x = -\frac{4}{5}$? if $\tan x = \frac{2}{3}$? if $\cot x = -7$?

55. Within what limits between 0° and 360° must the angle x lie if $\cos x = -\frac{2}{9}$? if $\cot x = 4$? if $\sec x = 80$? if $\csc x = -3$?

56. Why may cot 360° be considered as either $+\infty$ or $-\infty$?

57. Find the values of sin 450°, tan 540°, cos 630°, cot 720°, sin 810°, csc 900°, cos 1800°, sin 3600°.

58. What functions of an angle of a triangle may be negative? In what cases are they negative?

59. In what quadrant does an angle lie if sine and cosine are both negative? if cosine and tangent are both negative?

60. Between 0° and 3600° how many angles are there whose sines have the absolute value $\frac{3}{5}$? Of these sines how many are positive?

Compute the values of the following expressions:

61. $a \sin 0° + b \cos 90° - c \tan 180°$.

62. $a \cos 90° - b \tan 180° + c \cot 90°$.

63. $a \sin 90° - b \cos 360° + (a - b) \cos 180°$.

64. $(a^2 - b^2) \cos 360° - 4ab \sin 270° + \sin 360°$.

65. $(a^2 + b^2) \cos 180° + (a^2 + b^2) \sin 180° + (a^2 + b^2) \tan 135°$.

66. $(a^2 + 2ab + b^2) \sin 90° + (a^2 - 2ab + b^2) \cos 180° - 4ab \tan 225°$.

67. $(a - b + c - d) \sin 270° - (a - b + c - d) \cos 180° + a \tan 360°$.

State the sign of each of the six functions of the following angles:

68. 75°. **70.** 155°. **72.** 275°. **74.** 355°.

69. 125°. **71.** 185°. **73.** 325°. **75.** $-65°$.

Find the four smallest angles that satisfy the following conditions:

76. $\sin A = \frac{1}{2}$. **78.** $\sin A = \frac{1}{2}\sqrt{3}$. **80.** $\tan A = \frac{1}{3}\sqrt{3}$.

77. $\cos A = \frac{1}{2}\sqrt{3}$. **79.** $\cos A = \frac{1}{2}$. **81.** $\tan A = \sqrt{3}$.

Find two angles less than 360° that satisfy the following conditions:

82. $\sin A = -\frac{1}{2}$. **84.** $\sin A = -\frac{1}{2}\sqrt{2}$. **86.** $\tan A = -1$.

83. $\cos A = -\frac{1}{2}$. **85.** $\cos A = -\frac{1}{2}\sqrt{2}$. **87.** $\cot A = -1$.

If A, B, and C are the angles of any triangle ABC, prove that:

88. $\cos \frac{1}{2}A = \sin \frac{1}{2}(B + C)$. **90.** $\cos \frac{1}{2}B = \sin \frac{1}{2}(A + C)$.

89. $\sin \frac{1}{2}C = \cos \frac{1}{2}(A + B)$. **91.** $\sin \frac{1}{2}A = \cos \frac{1}{2}(B + C)$.

As angle A increases from 0° to 360°, trace the changes in sign and magnitude of the following:

92. $\sin A \cos A$. **94.** $\sin A - \cos A$. **96.** $\tan A + \cot A$.

93. $\sin A + \cos A$. **95.** $\sin A \div \cos A$. **97.** $\tan A - \cot A$.

86. Reduction of Functions to the First Quadrant. In the annexed figure BB' is perpendicular to the horizontal diameter AA', and the diameters PR and QS are so drawn as to make $\angle AOP = \angle SOA$. It therefore follows from geometry that △ MOP, MOS, NOQ, and NOR are congruent.

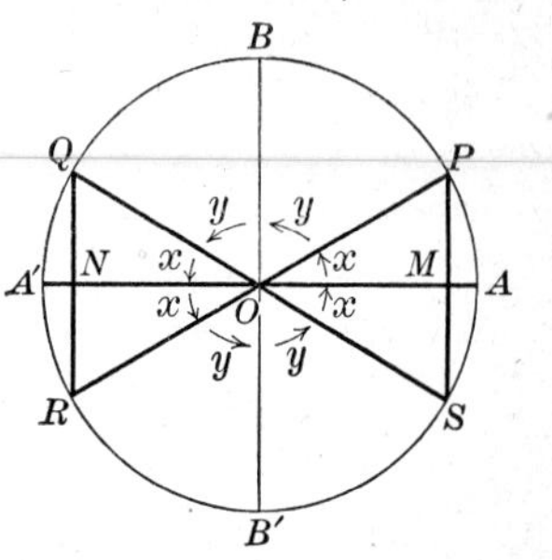

Considering, therefore, only the *absolute values* of the functions, we have

$\sin AOP = \sin AOQ = \sin AOR = \sin AOS,$
$\cos AOP = \cos AOQ = \cos AOR = \cos AOS,$

and so on for the other functions.

Hence, *For every acute angle there is an angle in each of the higher quadrants whose functions, in absolute value, are equal to those of this acute angle.*

If we let $\angle AOP = x$ and $\angle POB = y$, noticing that $\angle AOP = \angle QOA' = \angle A'OR = \angle SOA = x$, and $\angle POB = \angle BOQ = \angle ROB' = \angle B'OS = y$, and prefixing the proper signs to the functions (§ 83), we have:

ANGLE IN QUADRANT II

$\sin(180° - x) = \sin x \qquad \sin(90° + y) = \cos y$
$\cos(180° - x) = -\cos x \qquad \cos(90° + y) = -\sin y$
$\tan(180° - x) = -\tan x \qquad \tan(90° + y) = -\cot y$
$\cot(180° - x) = -\cot x \qquad \cot(90° + y) = -\tan y$

ANGLE IN QUADRANT III

$\sin(180° + x) = -\sin x \qquad \sin(270° - y) = -\cos y$
$\cos(180° + x) = -\cos x \qquad \cos(270° - y) = -\sin y$
$\tan(180° + x) = \tan x \qquad \tan(270° - y) = \cot y$
$\cot(180° + x) = \cot x \qquad \cot(270° - y) = \tan y$

ANGLE IN QUADRANT IV

$\sin(360° - x) = -\sin x \qquad \sin(270° + y) = -\cos y$
$\cos(360° - x) = \cos x \qquad \cos(270° + y) = \sin y$
$\tan(360° - x) = -\tan x \qquad \tan(270° + y) = -\cot y$
$\cot(360° - x) = -\cot x \qquad \cot(270° + y) = -\tan y$

For example, $\sin 127° = \sin(180° - 53°) = \sin 53° = \cos 37°,$
$\sin 210° = \sin(180° + 30°) = -\sin 30° = -\cos 60°,$
and $\sin 350° = \sin(360° - 10°) = -\sin 10° = -\cos 80°.$

It appears from the results set forth on page 90 that *the functions of any angle, however great, can be reduced to the functions of an angle in the first quadrant.*

For example, suppose that we have a polygon with a reëntrant angle of 247° 30′, and we wish to find the tangent of this angle. We may proceed by finding $\tan(180° + x)$ or by finding $\tan(270° - x)$. We then have

$$\tan 247° 30' = \tan(180° + 67° 30') = \tan 67° 30',$$

and

$$\tan 247° 30' = \tan(270° - 22° 30') = \cot 22° 30'.$$

That these two results are equal is apparent, for

$$\tan 67° 30' = \cot(90° - 67° 30') = \cot 22° 30'.$$

It also appears that, *for angles less than 180°, a given value of a sine or cosecant determines two supplementary angles, one acute, the other obtuse; a given value of any other function determines only one angle, this angle being acute if the value is positive and obtuse if the value is negative.*

For example, if we know that $\sin x = \frac{1}{2}$, we cannot tell whether $x = 30°$ or 150°, since the sine of each of these angles is $\frac{1}{2}$. But if we know that $\tan x = 1$, we know that $x = 45°$.

Similarly, if we know that $\cot x = -1$, we know that $x = 135°$, there being no other angle less than 180° whose cotangent is -1.

Since $\sec x$ is the reciprocal of $\cos x$ and $\csc x$ is the reciprocal of $\sin x$, and since by the aid of logarithms we can divide by $\cos x$ or $\sin x$ as easily as we can multiply by $\sec x$ or $\csc x$, we shall hereafter pay but little attention to the secant and cosecant. Since the invention of logarithms these functions have been of little practical importance in the work of ordinary mensuration.

Exercise 38. Reduction to the First Quadrant

Express the following as functions of angles less than 90°:

1. $\sin 170°$.
2. $\cos 160°$.
3. $\tan 148°$.
4. $\cot 156°$.
5. $\sin 180°$.
6. $\tan 180°$.
7. $\sin 200°$.
8. $\cos 225°$.
9. $\tan 258°$.
10. $\cot 262°$.
11. $\sin 275°$.
12. $\sin 345°$.
13. $\tan 282°$.
14. $\tan 325°$.
15. $\cos 290°$.
16. $\cos 350°$.
17. $\cot 295°$.
18. $\cot 347°$.
19. $\sin 360°$.
20. $\cos 360°$.
21. $\sin 148° 10'$.
22. $\cos 192° 20'$.
23. $\tan 265° 30'$.
24. $\cot 287° 40'$.
25. $\sin 187° 10' 3''$.
26. $\cos 274° 5' 14''$.
27. $\tan 322° 8' 15''$.
28. $\cot 375° 10' 3''$.
29. $\sin 147.75°$.
30. $\cos 232.25°$.

87. Functions of Angles Differing by 90°. It was shown in the case of acute angles that the function of any angle is equal to the co-function of its complement (§ 8).

That is, $\tan 28° = \cot (90° - 28°) = \cot 62°$,
$\sin x = \cos (90° - x)$, and so on.

It will now be shown for all angles that *if two angles differ by 90°, the functions of either are equal in absolute value to the co-functions of the other.*

In the annexed figure the diameters PR and QS are perpendicular to each other, and from P, Q, R, and S perpendiculars are drawn to AA'. Then from the congruent triangles OMP, QHO, OKR, and SNO we see that

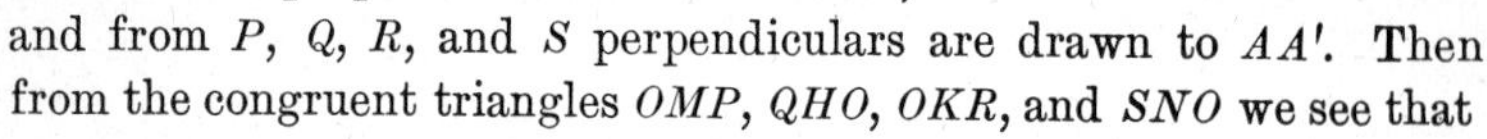

$$OM = QH = OK = SN,$$

and $$MP = OH = KR = ON.$$

Hence, considering the proper signs (§ 83),

$$\sin AOQ = \cos AOP, \quad \cos AOQ = -\sin AOP,$$
$$\sin AOR = \cos AOQ, \quad \cos AOR = -\sin AOQ,$$
$$\sin AOS = \cos AOR, \quad \cos AOS = -\sin AOR.$$

In all these equations, if x denotes the angle on the right-hand side, the angle on the left-hand side is $90° + x$.

Therefore, if x is an angle in any one of the four quadrants,

$$\sin (90° + x) = \cos x, \quad \cos (90° + x) = -\sin x;$$

and hence $$\tan (90° + x) = -\cot x, \quad \cot (90° + x) = -\tan x.$$

It is therefore seen that the algebraic sign of the function of the resulting angle is the same as that found in the similar case in § 86.

88. Functions of a Negative Angle. If the angle x is generated by the radius moving clockwise from the initial position OA to the terminal position OS, it will be negative (§ 72), and its terminal side will be identical with that for the angle $360° - x$. Therefore the functions of the angle $-x$ are the same as those of the angle $360° - x$; or

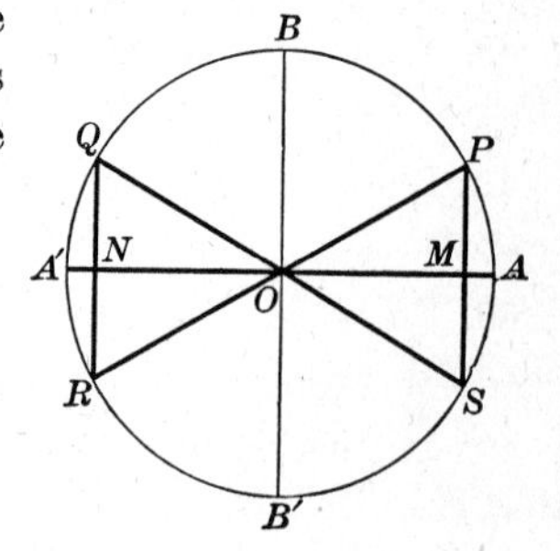

$$\sin (-x) = -\sin x,$$
$$\cos (-x) = \cos x,$$
$$\tan (-x) = -\tan x,$$
$$\cot (-x) = -\cot x.$$

Exercise 39. Reduction of Functions

Express the following as functions of angles less than 45° :

1. $\sin 100°$.
2. $\sin 120°$.
3. $\sin 110°$.
4. $\sin 130°$.
5. $\cos 95°$.
6. $\cos 97°$.
7. $\cos 111°$.
8. $\cos 127°$.
9. $\tan 91°$.
10. $\tan 99°$.
11. $\tan 119°$.
12. $\tan 129°$.
13. $\cot 94° 1'$.
14. $\cot 97° 2'$.
15. $\cot 98° 3'$.
16. $\cot 99° 9'$.

Express the following as functions of positive angles :

17. $\sin(-3°)$.
18. $\sin(-9°)$.
19. $\sin(-86°)$.
20. $\cos(-75°)$.
21. $\cos(-87°)$.
22. $\cos(-95°)$.
23. $\tan(-100°)$.
24. $\tan(-150°)$.
25. $\tan(-200°)$.
26. $\cot(-1.5°)$.
27. $\cot(-7.8°)$.
28. $\cot(-9.1°)$.

Find the following by aid of the tables :

29. $\sin 178° 30'$.
30. $\cos 236° 45'$.
31. $\tan 322° 18'$.
32. $\cot 423° 15'$.
33. $\sin(-7° 29' 30'')$.
34. $\cos(-29° 42' 19'')$.
35. $\tan(-172° 16' 14'')$.
36. $\cot(-262° 17' 15'')$.
37. $\log \sin 127.5°$.
38. $\log \cos 226.4°$.
39. $\log \tan 327.8°$.
40. $\log \cot 343.3°$.
41. $\log \sin 236° 13' 5''$.
42. $\log \cos 327° 5' 11''$.
43. $\log \tan(-125° 27')$.
44. $\log \cot(-236° 15')$.

45. Show that the angles 42°, 138°, − 318°, 402°, and − 222° all have the same sine.

46. Find four angles between 0° and 720° which satisfy the equation $\sin x = -\frac{1}{2}\sqrt{2}$.

47. Draw a circle with unit radius, and represent by lines the sine, cosine, tangent, and cotangent of − 325°.

48. Show by drawing a figure that $\sin 195° = \cos(-105°)$, and that $\cos 300° = \sin(-210°)$.

49. Show by drawing a figure that $\cos 320° = -\cos(-140°)$, and that $\sin 320° = -\sin 40°$.

50. Show by drawing a figure that $\sin 765° = \frac{1}{2}\sqrt{2}$, and that $\tan 1395° = -1$.

51. In the triangle ABC show that $\cos A = -\cos(B + C)$, and that $\cos B = -\cos(A + C)$.

89. Relations of the Functions. Certain relations between the functions have already been proved to exist in the case of acute angles (§§ 13, 14), and since the relations of the functions of any angle to the functions of an acute angle have also been considered (§§ 80, 85, 86, 88), it is evident that the laws are true for any angle. These laws are so important that they will now be summarized, and others of a similar kind will be added.

These laws should be memorized. They will be needed frequently in the subsequent work. The proof of each should be given, as required in § 14. The $\pm$ sign is placed before the square root sign, since we have now learned the meaning of negative functions.

To find the sine we have:

$$\sin x = \frac{1}{\csc x} \qquad \sin x = \pm\sqrt{1-\cos^2 x}$$

To find the cosine we have:

$$\cos x = \frac{1}{\sec x} \qquad \cos x = \pm\sqrt{1-\sin^2 x}$$

To find the tangent we have:

$$\tan x = \frac{1}{\cot x} \qquad \tan x = \frac{\sin x}{\cos x}$$

$$\tan x = \pm\frac{\sin x}{\sqrt{1-\sin^2 x}} \qquad \tan x = \pm\frac{\sqrt{1-\cos^2 x}}{\cos x}$$

$$\tan x = \pm\sqrt{\sec^2 x - 1} \qquad \tan x = \sin x \sec x$$

To find the cotangent we have:

$$\cot x = \frac{1}{\tan x} \qquad \cot x = \frac{\cos x}{\sin x}$$

$$\cot x = \pm\frac{\cos x}{\sqrt{1-\cos^2 x}} \qquad \cot x = \pm\frac{\sqrt{1-\sin^2 x}}{\sin x}$$

$$\cot x = \pm\sqrt{\csc^2 x - 1} \qquad \cot x = \cos x \csc x$$

To find the secant we have:

$$\sec x = \frac{1}{\cos x} \qquad \sec x = \pm\sqrt{1+\tan^2 x}$$

To find the cosecant we have:

$$\csc x = \frac{1}{\sin x} \qquad \csc x = \pm\sqrt{1+\cot^2 x}$$

Exercise 40. Relations of the Functions

1. Prove each of the formulas given in § 89.

Prove the following relations:

2. $\sin x = \pm \dfrac{\tan x}{\sqrt{1 + \tan^2 x}}$.

3. $\cos x = \pm \dfrac{\cot x}{\sqrt{1 + \cot^2 x}}$.

4. $\tan x = \pm \dfrac{1}{\sqrt{\csc^2 x - 1}}$.

5. $\cot x = \pm \dfrac{1}{\sqrt{\sec^2 x - 1}}$.

6. Find $\sin x$ in terms of $\cot x$.

7. Find $\cos x$ in terms of $\tan x$.

8. Find $\sec x$ in terms of $\sin x$.

9. Find $\csc x$ in terms of $\cos x$.

Prove the following relations:

10. $\tan x \cos x = \sin x$.

11. $\cos^2 x = \cot^2 x - \cot^2 x \cos^2 x$.

12. $\tan^2 x = \sin^2 x + \sin^2 x \tan^2 x$.

13. $\cos^2 x + 2 \sin^2 x = 1 + \sin^2 x$.

14. $\cot^2 x = \cos^2 x + \cos^2 x \cot^2 x$.

15. $\cot^2 x \sec^2 x = 1 + \cot^2 x$.

16. $\csc^2 x - \cot^2 x = 1$.

17. $\sec^2 x + \csc^2 x = \sec^2 x \csc^2 x$.

18. Show that the sum of the tangent and cotangent of an angle is equal to the product of the secant and cosecant of the angle.

Recalling the values given on page 8, find the value of x when:

19. $2 \cos x = \sec x$.

20. $4 \sin x = \csc x$.

21. $\sin^2 x = 3 \cos^2 x$.

22. $2 \sin^2 x + \cos^2 x = \frac{3}{2}$.

23. $3 \tan^2 x - \sec^2 x = 1$.

24. $\tan x + \cot x = 2$.

25. $\tan x = 2 \sin x$.

26. $\sec x = \sqrt{2} \tan x$.

27. $\sin^2 x - \cos x = \frac{1}{4}$.

28. $\tan^2 x - \sec x = 1$.

29. $\tan^2 x + \csc^2 x = 3$.

30. $\sin x + \sqrt{3} \cos x = 2$.

31. Given $(\sin x + \cos x)^2 - 1 = (\sin x - \cos x)^2 + 1$, find x.

32. Given $2 \sin x = \cos x$, find $\sin x$ and $\cos x$.

33. Given $4 \sin x = \tan x$, find $\sin x$ and $\tan x$.

34. Given $5 \sin x = \tan x$, find $\cos x$ and $\sec x$.

35. Given $4 \cot x = \tan x$, find the other functions.

36. Given $\sin x = 4 \cos x$, find $\sin x$ and $\cos x$.

37. If $\sin x : \cos x = 9 : 40$, find $\sin x$ and $\cos x$.

38. From the formula $\tan x = \pm \dfrac{\sin x}{\sqrt{1 - \sin^2 x}}$, find the condition under which $\tan x = \sin x$.

Solve the following equations; that is, find the value of x when:

39. $\cos x = \sec x$.
40. $\cos x = \tan x$.
41. $\cos x = \sin x$.
42. $\tan x = \cot x$.
43. $\sec x = \csc x$.
44. $2 \cos x + \sec x = 3$.
45. $\cos^2 x - \sin^2 x = \sin x$.
46. $2 \sin x + \cot x = 1 + 2 \cos x$.
47. $\sin^2 x + \tan^2 x = 3 \cos^2 x$.
48. $\tan x + 2 \cot x = \frac{5}{2} \csc x$.

Prove the following relations:

49. $\sin A + \cos A = (1 + \tan A) \cos A$.
50. $\frac{\cot x}{\cos x} = \sqrt{1 + \cot^2 x}$.
51. $\cos x : \cot x = \sqrt{1 - \cos^2 x}$.
52. $\tan^2 x = \frac{1}{\cos^2 x} - 1$.

Find the values of the other functions of A when:

53. $\sin A = \frac{2}{3}$.
54. $\cos A = \frac{3}{4}$.
55. $\tan A = 1.5$.
56. $\cot A = 0.75$.
57. $\sec A = 1.5$.
58. $\sin A = \frac{12}{13}$.
59. $\sin A = 0.8$.
60. $\cos A = \frac{60}{61}$.
61. $\cos A = 0.28$.
62. $\tan A = \frac{4}{3}$.
63. $\cot A = 1$.
64. $\cot A = 0.5$.
65. $\sec A = 2$.
66. $\csc A = \sqrt{2}$.
67. $\sin A = m$.
68. Given $\sin A = 2m : (1 + m^2)$, find the value of $\tan A$.
69. Given $\cos A = 2mn : (m^2 + n^2)$, find the value of $\sec A$.
70. Given $\sin 0° = 0$, find the other functions of 0°.
71. Given $\sin 90° = 1$, find the other functions of 90°.
72. Given $\tan 90° = \infty$, find the other functions of 90°.
73. Given $\cot 22° 30' = \sqrt{2} + 1$, find the other functions of 22° 30′.
74. Write $\tan^2 A + \cot^2 A$ so as to contain only $\cos A$.

In the triangle ABC, prove the following relations:

75. $\sin A = \sin(B + C)$.
76. $\cos A = -\cos(B + C)$.
77. $\tan A = -\tan(B + C)$.
78. $\cot A = -\cot(B + C)$.
79. $\sin A = -\sin(2A + B + C)$.
80. $\sin B = -\sin(A + 2B + C)$.
81. $\cos C = -\cos(A + B + 2C)$.
82. $\cot B = \cot(A + 2B + C)$.
83. $\sin A = -\cos(\frac{3}{2}A + \frac{1}{2}B + \frac{1}{2}C)$.
84. $\cos A = -\cos(2A + B + C)$.
85. $\cos A = \sin(\frac{3}{2}A + \frac{1}{2}B + \frac{1}{2}C)$.
86. $\sin(\frac{1}{2}A + B) = \cos(\frac{1}{2}B - \frac{1}{2}C)$
87. $\sin(\frac{1}{2}C - \frac{1}{2}A) = -\cos(\frac{1}{2}B + C)$
88. $\cos B = -\cos(A + 2B + C)$.
89. $\tan A = \tan(2A + B + C)$.
90. $\cot A = \tan(\frac{3}{2}B + \frac{3}{2}C + \frac{1}{2}A)$.

In the quadrilateral ABCD, prove the following relations:

91. $-\sin A = \sin(B + C + D)$.
92. $\cos A = \cos(B + C + D)$.
93. $-\tan A = \tan(B + C + D)$.
94. $-\cot A = \cot(B + C + D)$.

CHAPTER VI

FUNCTIONS OF THE SUM OR THE DIFFERENCE OF TWO ANGLES

90. Formula for $\sin(x+y)$. In this figure there are shown two acute angles, x and y, with $\angle AOC$ acute and equal to $x+y$; two perpendiculars are let fall from C, and two from D, as shown. Then by geometry the triangles CGD and EOD are similar and hence $\angle GCD = \angle EOD = x$. Considering the radius as unity, $OD = \cos y$ and $CD = \sin y$. Hence we have

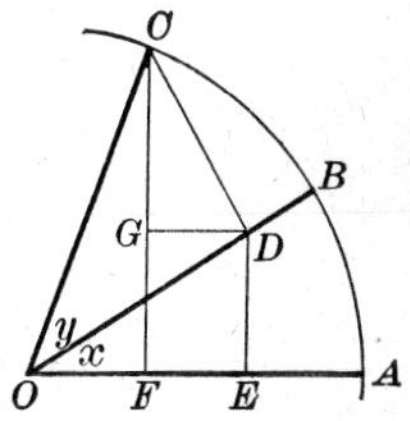

$$\sin(x+y) = CF = DE + CG.$$

But $\sin x = \dfrac{DE}{OD}$, whence $DE = \sin x \cdot OD$
$= \sin x \cos y$;

and $\cos x = \dfrac{CG}{CD}$, whence $CG = \cos x \cdot CD$
$= \cos x \sin y$.

Hence $$\mathbf{\sin(x+y) = \sin x \cos y + \cos x \sin y.}$$

This is one of the most important formulas and should be memorized.

For example, $\sin(30^\circ + 60^\circ) = \sin 30^\circ \cos 60^\circ + \cos 30^\circ \sin 60^\circ$

$$= \frac{1}{2}\cdot\frac{1}{2} + \frac{\sqrt{3}}{2}\cdot\frac{\sqrt{3}}{2} = \frac{1}{4} + \frac{3}{4} = 1,$$

which we have already found to be $\sin 90^\circ$.

91. Formula for $\cos(x+y)$. Using the above figure we see that

$$\cos(x+y) = OF = OE - DG.$$

But $\cos x = \dfrac{OE}{OD}$, whence $OE = \cos x \cdot OD = \cos x \cos y$;

and $\sin x = \dfrac{DG}{CD}$, whence $DG = \sin x \cdot CD = \sin x \sin y$.

Hence $$\mathbf{\cos(x+y) = \cos x \cos y - \sin x \sin y.}$$

This important formula should be memorized.

For example, $\cos(45^\circ + 45^\circ) = \cos 45^\circ \cos 45^\circ - \sin 45^\circ \sin 45^\circ$

$$= \frac{1}{\sqrt{2}}\cdot\frac{1}{\sqrt{2}} - \frac{1}{\sqrt{2}}\cdot\frac{1}{\sqrt{2}} = \frac{1}{2} - \frac{1}{2} = 0,$$

which we have already found to be $\cos 90^\circ$.

92. The Proofs continued. In the proofs given on page 97, x, y, and $x+y$ were assumed to be acute angles. If, however, x and y are acute but $x+y$ is obtuse, as shown in this figure, the proofs remain, word for word, the same as before, the only difference being that the sign of OF will be negative, as DG is now greater than OE. This, however, does not affect the proof. The above formulas, therefore, hold true for all acute angles x and y.

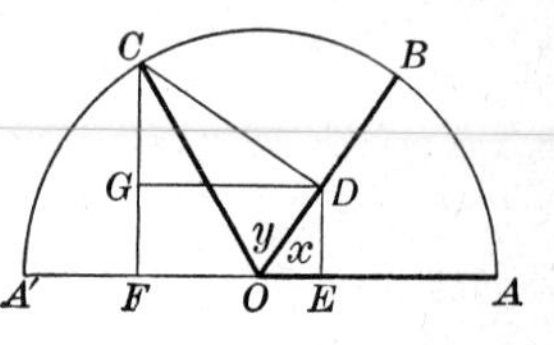

Furthermore, if these formulas hold true for any two acute angles x and y, they hold true when one of the angles is increased by 90°. Thus, if for x we write $x' = 90° + x$, then, by § 87,

$$\sin(x'+y) = \sin(90° + x + y) = \cos(x+y)$$
$$= \cos x \cos y - \sin x \sin y.$$

But by § 87, $\cos x = \sin(90° + x) = \sin x'$,

and $\sin x = -\cos(90° + x) = -\cos x'$.

Hence, by substituting these values,

$$\sin(x'+y) = \sin x' \cos y + \cos x' \sin y.$$

That is, § 90 holds true if either angle is repeatedly increased by 90°. It is therefore true for all angles.

Similarly, by § 87,

$$\cos(x'+y) = \cos(90° + x + y) = -\sin(x+y)$$
$$= -\sin x \cos y - \cos x \sin y$$
$$= \cos x' \cos y - \sin x' \sin y,$$

by substituting $\cos x'$ for $-\sin x$ and $\sin x'$ for $\cos x$ as above.

That is, § 91 also holds true if either angle is repeatedly increased by 90°. It is therefore true for all angles.

Exercise 41. Sines and Cosines

Given $\sin 30° = \cos 60° = \frac{1}{2}$, $\cos 30° = \sin 60° = \frac{1}{2}\sqrt{3}$, and $\sin 45° = \cos 45° = \frac{1}{2}\sqrt{2}$, find the values of the following:

1. sin 15°.	5. sin 90°.	9. sin 120°.	13. sin 150°.
2. cos 15°.	6. cos 90°.	10. cos 120°.	14. cos 150°.
3. sin 75°.	7. sin 105°.	11. sin 135°.	15. sin 165°.
4. cos 75°.	8. cos 105°.	12. cos 135°.	16. cos 165°.

93. Formula for $\tan(x+y)$. Since $\tan A = \frac{\sin A}{\cos A}$, therefore

$$\tan(x+y) = \frac{\sin(x+y)}{\cos(x+y)} = \frac{\sin x \cos y + \cos x \sin y}{\cos x \cos y - \sin x \sin y},$$

whatever the size of the angles x and y (§ 92).

Dividing each term of the numerator and denominator of the last of these fractions by $\cos x \cos y$, we have

$$\tan(x+y) = \frac{\frac{\sin x}{\cos x} + \frac{\sin y}{\cos y}}{1 - \frac{\sin x \sin y}{\cos x \cos y}}.$$

But since $\frac{\sin x}{\cos x} = \tan x$, and $\frac{\sin y}{\cos y} = \tan y$,

we have $$\tan(x+y) = \frac{\tan x + \tan y}{1 - \tan x \tan y}.$$

This important formula should be memorized.

94. Formula for $\cot(x+y)$. Since $\cot A = \frac{\cos A}{\sin A}$, therefore

$$\cot(x+y) = \frac{\cos(x+y)}{\sin(x+y)} = \frac{\cos x \cos y - \sin x \sin y}{\sin x \cos y + \cos x \sin y},$$

whatever the size of the angles x and y (§ 92).

Dividing each term of the numerator and denominator of the last of these fractions by $\sin x \sin y$, and then remembering that $\frac{\cos x}{\sin x} = \cot x$ and $\frac{\cos y}{\sin y} = \cot y$, we have

$$\cot(x+y) = \frac{\cot x \cot y - 1}{\cot y + \cot x}.$$

This important formula should be memorized.

Exercise 42. Tangents and Cotangents

Given $\tan 30° = \cot 60° = \frac{1}{3}\sqrt{3}$, $\cot 30° = \tan 60° = \sqrt{3}$, $\tan 45° = \cot 45° = 1$, find the values of the following:

1. $\tan 15°$.	5. $\tan 90°$.	9. $\tan 120°$.	13. $\tan 150°$.
2. $\cot 15°$.	6. $\cot 90°$.	10. $\cot 120°$.	14. $\cot 150°$.
3. $\tan 75°$.	7. $\tan 105°$.	11. $\tan 135°$.	15. $\tan 165°$.
4. $\cot 75°$.	8. $\cot 105°$.	12. $\cot 135°$.	16. $\cot 165°$

95. Formula for sin $(x-y)$. In this figure there are shown two acute angles, $AOB = x$ and $COB = y$, with $\angle AOC$ equal to $x - y$; two perpendiculars are let fall from C, and two from D.

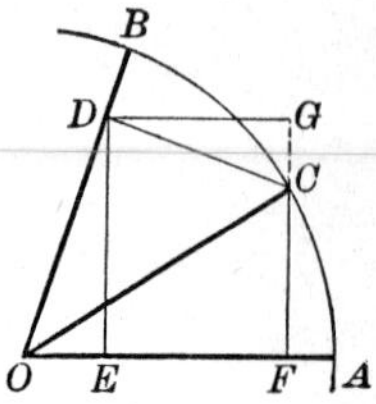

The perpendiculars from D are DE and DG, DG being drawn to FC produced.

Then, considering the radius as unity, we have

$$\sin(x-y) = CF = DE - CG.$$

But $$DE = \sin x \cdot OD = \sin x \cos y,$$

and $$GC = \cos x \cdot CD = \cos x \sin y.$$

Hence, by substituting these values of DE and GC,

$$\sin(x-y) = \sin x \cos y - \cos x \sin y.$$

This is one of the most important formulas and should be memorized.

96. Formula for cos $(x-y)$. Using the above figure we see that

$$\cos(x-y) = OF = OE + DG.$$

But $$OE = \cos x \cdot OD = \cos x \cos y,$$

and $$DG = \sin x \cdot CD = \sin x \sin y.$$

Hence it follows that

$$\cos(x-y) = \cos x \cos y + \sin x \sin y.$$

This important formula should be memorized. The proof in §§ 95 and 96 refers only to acute angles, but the formulas are entirely general if due regard is paid to the algebraic signs. The general proof may follow the method of § 92, or it may be based upon it; the latter plan is followed in § 97.

97. The Proofs continued. Since $x = (x-y) + y$, we see that

$$\sin x = \sin\{(x-y)+y\} = \sin(x-y)\cos y + \cos(x-y)\sin y,$$

$$\cos x = \cos\{(x-y)+y\} = \cos(x-y)\cos y - \sin(x-y)\sin y.$$

Multiplying the first equation by $\cos y$, and the second by $\sin y$,

$$\sin x \cos y = \sin(x-y)\cos^2 y + \cos(x-y)\sin y \cos y,$$

$$\cos x \sin y = -\sin(x-y)\sin^2 y + \cos(x-y)\sin y \cos y.$$

Hence $\sin x \cos y - \cos x \sin y = \sin(x-y)(\sin^2 y + \cos^2 y)$.

But by § 14 $\sin^2 y + \cos^2 y = 1$.

Therefore $\sin(x-y) = \sin x \cos y - \cos x \sin y$.

Similarly, $\cos(x-y) = \cos x \cos y + \sin x \sin y$.

Therefore the formulas of §§ 95 and 96 are universally true.

98. Formula for tan $(x-y)$. Since $\tan A = \dfrac{\sin A}{\cos A}$, we have

$$\tan(x-y) = \frac{\sin(x-y)}{\cos(x-y)}$$

$$= \frac{\sin x \cos y - \cos x \sin y}{\cos x \cos y + \sin x \sin y}.$$

Dividing numerator and denominator by $\cos x \cos y$, as in § 93, we obtain

$$\tan(x-y) = \frac{\dfrac{\sin x}{\cos x} - \dfrac{\sin y}{\cos y}}{1 + \dfrac{\sin x}{\cos x} \cdot \dfrac{\sin y}{\cos y}}.$$

That is, $$\tan(x-y) = \frac{\tan x - \tan y}{1 + \tan x \tan y}.$$

This important formula should be memorized.

99. Formula for cot $(x-y)$. Following the plan suggested in § 98, we may show that

$$\cot(x-y) = \frac{\cos(x-y)}{\sin(x-y)}$$

$$= \frac{\cos x \cos y + \sin x \sin y}{\sin x \cos y - \cos x \sin y}$$

$$= \frac{\dfrac{\cos x}{\sin x} \cdot \dfrac{\cos y}{\sin y} + 1}{\dfrac{\cos y}{\sin y} - \dfrac{\cos x}{\sin x}}.$$

That is, $$\cot(x-y) = \frac{\cot x \cot y + 1}{\cot y - \cot x}.$$

This important formula should be memorized.

100. Summary of the Addition Formulas. The formulas of §§ 90–99 may be combined as follows:

$$\sin(x \pm y) = \sin x \cos y \pm \cos x \sin y,$$

$$\cos(x \pm y) = \cos x \cos y \mp \sin x \sin y,$$

$$\tan(x \pm y) = \frac{\tan x \pm \tan y}{1 \mp \tan x \tan y},$$

$$\cot(x \pm y) = \frac{\cot x \cot y \mp 1}{\cot y \pm \cot x}.$$

When the signs $\pm$ and $\mp$ occur in the same formula we should be careful to take the $-$ of $\mp$ with the $+$ of $\pm$. That is, the upper signs are to be taken together, and the lower signs are to be taken together.

Exercise 43. The Addition Formulas

Given $\sin x = \frac{3}{5}$, $\cos x = \frac{4}{5}$, $\sin y = \frac{5}{13}$, $\cos y = \frac{12}{13}$, *find the value of:*

1. $\sin(x+y)$.
2. $\sin(x-y)$.
3. $\cos(x+y)$.
4. $\cos(x-y)$.
5. $\tan(x+y)$.
6. $\tan(x-y)$.

By letting $x = 90°$ *in the formulas, find the following:*

7. $\sin(90° - y)$.
8. $\cos(90° - y)$.
9. $\tan(90° - y)$.

Similarly, by substituting in the formulas, find the following:

10. $\sin(90° + y)$.
11. $\sin(180° - y)$.
12. $\sin(180° + y)$.
13. $\sin(270° - y)$.
14. $\sin(270° + y)$.
15. $\sin(360° - y)$.
16. $\sin(360° + y)$.
17. $\cos(x - 90°)$.
18. $\cos(x - 180°)$.
19. $\cos(x - 270°)$.
20. $\tan(x - 90°)$.
21. $\tan(x - 180°)$.
22. $\cot(x - 90°)$.
23. $\cot(x - 180°)$.
24. $\sin(-y)$.
25. $\sin(45° - y)$.
26. $\cos(45° - y)$.
27. $\tan(45° - y)$.
28. $\cot(30° + y)$.
29. $\cot(60° - y)$.
30. $\cot(90° - y)$.

31. If $\tan x = 0.5$ and $\tan y = 0.25$, find $\tan(x+y)$ and $\tan(x-y)$

32. If $\tan x = 1$ and $\tan y = \frac{1}{3}\sqrt{3}$, find $\tan(x+y)$ and $\tan(x-y)$.

33. If $\tan x = \frac{5}{6}$ and $\tan y = \frac{1}{11}$, find $\tan(x+y)$ and $\tan(x-y)$, and find the number of degrees in $x+y$.

34. If $\tan x = 2$ and $\tan y = \frac{1}{2}$, what is the nature of the angle $x+y$? Consider the same question when $\tan x = 3$ and $\tan y = \frac{1}{3}$, and when $\tan x = a$ and $\tan y = 1/a$.

35. Prove that the sum of $\tan(x - 45°)$ and $\cot(x + 45°)$ is zero.

36. Prove that the sum of $\cot(x - 45°)$ and $\tan(x + 45°)$ is zero.

37. If $\sin x = 0.2\sqrt{5}$ and $\sin y = 0.1\sqrt{10}$, prove that $x + y = 45°$ May $x+y$ have other values? If so, state two of these values.

38. Prove that if an angle x is decreased by 45° the cotangent of the resulting angle is equal to $-\dfrac{\cot x + 1}{\cot x - 1}$.

39. Prove that if an angle x is increased by 45° the cotangent of the resulting angle is equal to $\dfrac{\cot x - 1}{\cot x + 1}$.

40. If $\tan x = \dfrac{a}{1+a}$ and $\tan y = \dfrac{1}{1+2a}$, prove that $\tan(x+y) = 1$.

41. If a right angle is divided into any three angles x, y, z, prove that $\tan x = \dfrac{1 - \tan y \tan z}{\tan y + \tan z}$.

101. Functions of Twice an Angle. By substituting in the formulas for the functions of $x + y$ we obtain the following important formulas for the functions of twice an angle:

$$\sin 2x = 2 \sin x \cos x,$$

$$\cos 2x = \cos^2 x - \sin^2 x,$$

$$\tan 2x = \frac{2 \tan x}{1 - \tan^2 x},$$

$$\cot 2x = \frac{\cot^2 x - 1}{2 \cot x}.$$

Letting $2x = y$ we have the following useful formulas:

$$\sin y = 2 \sin \tfrac{1}{2} y \cos \tfrac{1}{2} y, \qquad \cos y = \cos^2 \tfrac{1}{2} y - \sin^2 \tfrac{1}{2} y,$$

$$\tan y = \frac{2 \tan \frac{1}{2} y}{1 - \tan^2 \frac{1}{2} y}, \qquad \cot y = \frac{\cot^2 \frac{1}{2} y - 1}{2 \cot \frac{1}{2} y}.$$

Exercise 44. Functions of Twice an Angle

As suggested above, deduce the formulas for the following:

1. $\sin 2x$. 2. $\cos 2x$. 3. $\tan 2x$. 4. $\cot 2x$.

Find $\sin 2x$, given the following values of $\sin x$ and $\cos x$:

5. $\sin x = \frac{1}{2}\sqrt{2}$, $\cos x = \frac{1}{2}\sqrt{2}$. 6. $\sin x = \frac{1}{2}$, $\cos x = \frac{1}{2}\sqrt{3}$.

Find $\cos 2x$, given the following values of $\sin x$ and $\cos x$:

7. $\sin x = \frac{1}{2}\sqrt{3}$, $\cos x = \frac{1}{2}$. 8. $\sin x = \frac{3}{5}$, $\cos x = \frac{4}{5}$.

Find $\tan 2x$, given the following values of $\tan x$:

9. $\tan x = 0.3673$. 10. $\tan x = 0.2701$.

Find $\cot 2x$, given the following values of $\cot x$ and $\tan x$:

11. $\cot x = 0.3673$. 12. $\tan x = 0.2701$.

Find $\sin 2x$, given the following values of $\sin x$:

13. $\sin x = \frac{5}{13}$. 14. $\sin x = \frac{12}{13}$.

15. As suggested in § 101, find $\sin 3x$ in terms of $\sin x$.

16. As suggested in § 101, find $\cos 3x$ in terms of $\cos x$.

102. Functions of Half an Angle. If we substitute $\frac{1}{2}z$ for x in the formulas $\cos^2 x + \sin^2 x = 1$ (§ 14) and $\cos^2 x - \sin^2 x = \cos 2x$ (§ 101), so as to find the functions of half an angle, we have

$$\cos^2 \tfrac{1}{2}z + \sin^2 \tfrac{1}{2}z = 1,$$

and $$\cos^2 \tfrac{1}{2}z - \sin^2 \tfrac{1}{2}z = \cos z.$$

Subtracting, $$2\sin^2 \tfrac{1}{2}z = 1 - \cos z;$$

whence $$\sin\frac{1}{2}z = \pm\sqrt{\frac{1-\cos z}{2}}.$$

In the above proof, if we add instead of subtract we have

$$2\cos^2 \tfrac{1}{2}z = 1 + \cos z;$$

whence $$\cos\frac{1}{2}z = \pm\sqrt{\frac{1+\cos z}{2}}.$$

Since $\tan\frac{1}{2}z = \frac{\sin\frac{1}{2}z}{\cos\frac{1}{2}z}$, and $\cot\frac{1}{2}z = \frac{\cos\frac{1}{2}z}{\sin\frac{1}{2}z}$, we have, by dividing,

$$\tan\frac{1}{2}z = \pm\sqrt{\frac{1-\cos z}{1+\cos z}},$$

and $$\cot\frac{1}{2}z = \pm\sqrt{\frac{1+\cos z}{1-\cos z}}.$$

These four formulas are important and should be memorized.

From the formula for $\tan\frac{1}{2}z$ can be derived a formula which is occasionally used in dealing with very small angles. In the triangle ACB we have

$$\tan\tfrac{1}{2}A = \pm\sqrt{\frac{1-\cos A}{1+\cos A}} = \pm\sqrt{\frac{1-\frac{b}{c}}{1+\frac{b}{c}}} = \pm\sqrt{\frac{c-b}{c+b}}.$$

Exercise 45. Functions of Half an Angle

Given $\sin 30° = \frac{1}{2}$, find the values of the following:

1. $\sin 15°$. 2. $\cos 15°$. 3. $\tan 15°$. 4. $\cot 15°$. 5. $\cot 7\frac{1}{2}°$.

Given $\tan 45° = 1$, find the values of the following:

6. $\sin 22.5°$. 7. $\cos 22.5°$. 8. $\tan 22.5°$. 9. $\cot 22.5°$. 10. $\cot 11\frac{1}{4}°$.

11. Given $\sin x = 0.2$, find $\sin\frac{1}{2}x$ and $\cos\frac{1}{2}x$.

12. Given $\cos x = 0.7$, find $\sin\frac{1}{2}x$, $\cos\frac{1}{2}x$, $\tan\frac{1}{2}x$, and $\cot\frac{1}{2}x$.

103. Sums and Differences of Functions. Since we have (§§ 92, 97)

$$\sin(x+y) = \sin x \cos y + \cos x \sin y,$$

and $$\sin(x-y) = \sin x \cos y - \cos x \sin y,$$

we find, by addition and subtraction, that

$$\sin(x+y) + \sin(x-y) = 2 \sin x \cos y,$$

and $$\sin(x+y) - \sin(x-y) = 2 \cos x \sin y.$$

Similarly, by using the formulas for $\cos(x \pm y)$, we obtain

$$\cos(x+y) + \cos(x-y) = 2 \cos x \cos y,$$

and $$\cos(x+y) - \cos(x-y) = -2 \sin x \sin y.$$

By letting $x + y = A$, and $x - y = B$, we have $x = \frac{1}{2}(A+B)$, and $y = \frac{1}{2}(A-B)$, whence

$$\sin A + \sin B = 2 \sin \tfrac{1}{2}(A+B) \cos \tfrac{1}{2}(A-B),$$

$$\sin A - \sin B = 2 \cos \tfrac{1}{2}(A+B) \sin \tfrac{1}{2}(A-B),$$

$$\cos A + \cos B = 2 \cos \tfrac{1}{2}(A+B) \cos \tfrac{1}{2}(A-B),$$

and $$\cos A - \cos B = -2 \sin \tfrac{1}{2}(A+B) \sin \tfrac{1}{2}(A-B).$$

By division we obtain

$$\frac{\sin A + \sin B}{\sin A - \sin B} = \tan \tfrac{1}{2}(A+B) \cot \tfrac{1}{2}(A-B);$$

and since $$\cot \tfrac{1}{2}(A-B) = \frac{1}{\tan \frac{1}{2}(A-B)},$$

we have $$\frac{\sin A + \sin B}{\sin A - \sin B} = \frac{\tan \frac{1}{2}(A+B)}{\tan \frac{1}{2}(A-B)}.$$

This is one of the most important formulas in the solution of oblique triangles.

Exercise 46. Formulas

Prove the following formulas:

1. $\sin 2x = \dfrac{2 \tan x}{1 + \tan^2 x}$.
2. $\cos 2x = \dfrac{1 - \tan^2 x}{1 + \tan^2 x}$.
3. $\tan \frac{1}{2} x = \dfrac{\sin x}{1 + \cos x}$.
4. $\cot \frac{1}{2} x = \dfrac{\sin x}{1 - \cos x}$.

If A, B, C are the angles of a triangle, prove that:

5. $\sin A + \sin B + \sin C = 4 \cos \frac{1}{2} A \cos \frac{1}{2} B \cos \frac{1}{2} C$.
6. $\cos A + \cos B + \cos C = 1 + 4 \sin \frac{1}{2} A \sin \frac{1}{2} B \sin \frac{1}{2} C$.
7. $\tan A + \tan B + \tan C = \tan A \tan B \tan C$.

8. Given $\tan \frac{1}{2}x = 1$, find $\cos x$.

9. Given $\cot \frac{1}{2}x = \sqrt{3}$, find $\sin x$.

10. Prove that $\tan 18^\circ = \dfrac{\sin 33^\circ + \sin 3^\circ}{\cos 33^\circ + \cos 3^\circ}$.

11. Prove that $\sin \frac{1}{2}x \pm \cos \frac{1}{2}x = \sqrt{1 \pm \sin x}$.

12. Prove that $\dfrac{\tan x \pm \tan y}{\cot x \pm \cot y} = \pm \tan x \tan y$.

13. Prove that $\tan(45^\circ - x) = \dfrac{1 - \tan x}{1 + \tan x}$.

14. In the triangle ABC prove that

$$\cot \tfrac{1}{2}A + \cot \tfrac{1}{2}B + \cot \tfrac{1}{2}C = \cot \tfrac{1}{2}A \cot \tfrac{1}{2}B \cot \tfrac{1}{2}C.$$

Change to a form involving products instead of sums, and hence more convenient for computation by logarithms:

15. $\cot x + \tan x$.

16. $\cot x - \tan x$.

17. $\cot x + \tan y$.

18. $\cot x - \tan y$.

19. $\dfrac{1 - \cos 2x}{1 + \cos 2x}$.

20. $1 + \tan x \tan y$.

21. $1 - \tan x \tan y$.

22. $\cot x \cot y + 1$.

23. $\cot x \cot y - 1$.

24. $\dfrac{\tan x + \tan y}{\cot x + \cot y}$.

25. Prove that $\tan x + \tan y = \dfrac{\sin(x + y)}{\cos x \cos y}$.

26. Prove that $\cot y - \cot x = \dfrac{\sin(x - y)}{\sin x \sin y}$.

27. Given $\tan(x + y) = 3$, and $\tan x = 2$, find $\tan y$.

28. Prove that $(\sin x + \cos x)^2 = 1 + \sin 2x$.

29. Prove that $(\sin x - \cos x)^2 = 1 - \sin 2x$.

30. Prove that $\tan x + \cot x = 2 \csc 2x$.

31. Prove that $\cot x - \tan x = 2 \cos 2x \csc 2x$.

32. Prove that $2 \sin^2(45^\circ - x) = 1 - \sin 2x$.

33. Prove that $\cos 45^\circ + \cos 75^\circ = \cos 15^\circ$.

34. Prove that $1 + \tan x \tan 2x = \tan 2x \cot x - 1$.

Prove the following formulas:

35. $(\cos x + \cos y)^2 + (\sin x + \sin y)^2 = 2 + 2 \cos(x - y)$.

36. $(\sin x + \cos y)^2 + (\sin y + \cos x)^2 = 2 + 2 \sin(x + y)$.

37. $\sin(x + y) + \cos(x - y) = (\sin x + \cos x)(\sin y + \cos y)$.

38. $\sin(x + y) \cos y - \cos(x + y) \sin y = \sin x$.

CHAPTER VII

THE OBLIQUE TRIANGLE

104. Geometric Properties of the Triangle. In solving an oblique triangle certain geometric properties are involved in addition to those already mentioned in the preceding chapters, and these should be recalled to mind before undertaking further work with trigonometric functions. These properties are as follows:

The angles opposite the equal sides of an isosceles triangle are equal.

If two angles of a triangle are equal, the sides opposite the equal angles are equal.

If two angles of a triangle are unequal, the greater side is opposite the greater angle.

If two sides of a triangle are unequal, the greater angle is opposite the greater side.

A triangle is determined, that is, it is completely fixed in form and size, if the following parts are given:

1. *Two sides and the included angle.*
2. *Two angles and the included side.*
3. *Two angles and the side opposite one of them.*
4. *Two sides and the angle opposite one of them.*
5. *Three sides.*

The fourth case, however, will be recalled as the *ambiguous case*, since the triangle is not in general completely determined. If we have given $\angle A$ and sides a and b in this figure, either of the triangles ABC and $AB'C$ will satisfy the conditions.

If a is equal to the perpendicular from C on AB, however, the points B and B' will coincide, and hence the two triangles become congruent and the triangle is completely determined.

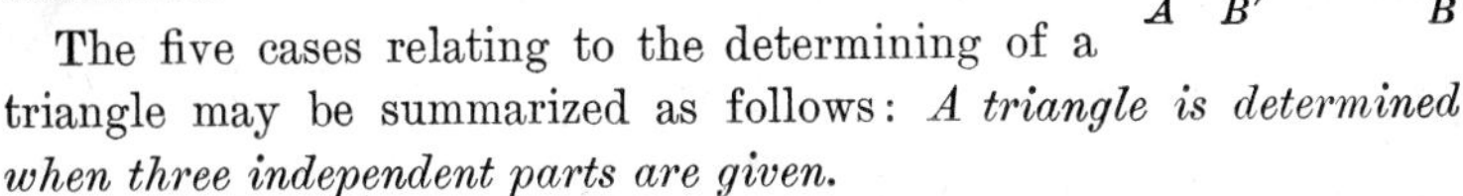

The five cases relating to the determining of a triangle may be summarized as follows: *A triangle is determined when three independent parts are given.*

This excludes the case of three angles, because they are not independent. That is, $A = 180° - (B + C)$, and therefore A depends upon B and C.

105. Law of Sines. In the triangle ABC, using either of the figures as here shown, we have the following relations.

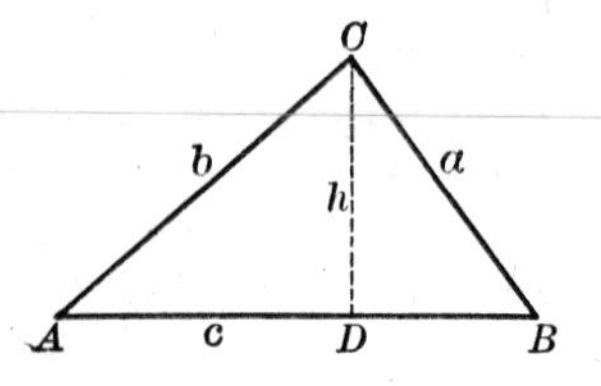

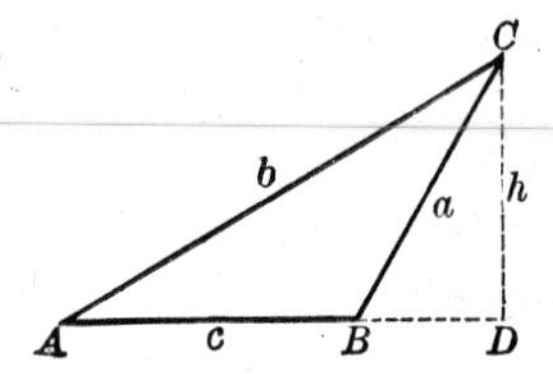

In either figure, $\frac{h}{b} = \sin A.$

In the first figure, $\frac{h}{a} = \sin B,$

and in the second figure,

$$\frac{h}{a} = \sin(180° - B)$$
$$= \sin B.$$

Therefore, whether h lies within or without the triangle, we obtain, by division, the following relation:

$$\frac{a}{b} = \frac{\sin A}{\sin B}.$$

In the same way, by drawing perpendiculars from the vertices A and B to the opposite sides, we may obtain the following relations:

$$\frac{b}{c} = \frac{\sin B}{\sin C},$$

and

$$\frac{a}{c} = \frac{\sin A}{\sin C}.$$

This relation between the sides and the sines of the opposite angles is called the Law of Sines and may be expressed as follows:

The sides of a triangle are proportional to the sines of the opposite angles.

If we multiply $\frac{a}{b} = \frac{\sin A}{\sin B}$ by b, and divide by $\sin A$, we have

$$\frac{a}{\sin A} = \frac{b}{\sin B}.$$

Similarly, we may obtain the following:

$$\frac{a}{\sin A} = \frac{b}{\sin B} = \frac{c}{\sin C},$$

and this is frequently given as the Law of Sines.

It is also apparent that $a \sin B = b \sin A$, $a \sin C = c \sin A$, and $b \sin C = c \sin B$, three relations which are still another form of the Law of Sines.

106. The Law of Sines extended. There is an interesting extension of the Law of Sines with respect to the diameter of the circle circumscribed about a triangle.

Circumscribe a circle about the triangle ABC and draw the radii OB, OC, as shown in the figure. Let R denote the radius. Draw OM perpendicular to BC. Since the angle BOC is a central angle intercepting the same arc as the angle A, the angle $BOC = 2A$; hence the angle $BOM = A$; then

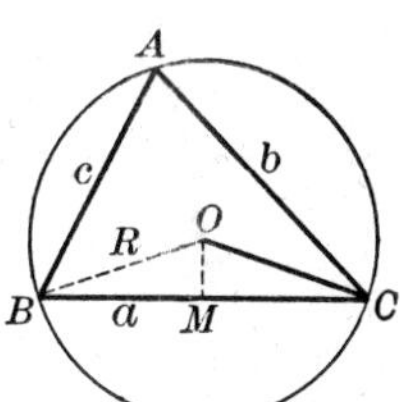

$$BM = R \sin BOM = R \sin A.$$

Therefore $$a = 2R \sin A.$$

In like manner, $$b = 2R \sin B,$$

and $$c = 2R \sin C.$$

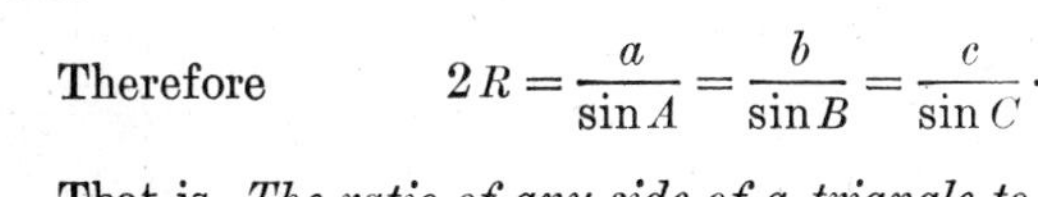

Therefore $$2R = \frac{a}{\sin A} = \frac{b}{\sin B} = \frac{c}{\sin C}.$$

That is, *The ratio of any side of a triangle to the sine of the opposite angle is numerically equal to the diameter of the circumscribed circle.*

Exercise 47. Law of Sines

1. Consider the formula $\frac{a}{b} = \frac{\sin A}{\sin B}$ when $B = 90°$; when $A = 90°$; when $A = B$; when $a = b$.

2. Prove by the Law of Sines that the bisector of an angle of a triangle divides the opposite side into parts proportional to the adjacent sides.

3. Prove Ex. 2 for the bisector of an exterior angle of a triangle.

4. The triangle ABC has $A = 78°$, $B = 72°$, and $c = 4$ in. Find the diameter of the circumscribed circle.

5. The triangle ABC has $A = 76° 37'$, $B = 81° 46'$, and $c = 368.4$ ft. Find the diameter of the circumscribed circle.

6. What is the diameter of the circle circumscribed about an equilateral triangle of side 7.4 in.? What is the diameter of the circle inscribed in the same triangle?

7. What is the diameter of the circle circumscribed about an isosceles triangle of base 4.8 in. and vertical angle 10°?

8. What is the diameter of the circle circumscribed about an isosceles triangle whose vertical angle is 18° and the sum of the two equal sides 18 in.?

107. Applications of the Law of Sines. If we have given any side of a triangle, and any two of the angles, we are able to solve the triangle by means of the Law of Sines. Thus, if we have given a, A, and B, in this triangle, we can find the remaining parts as follows:

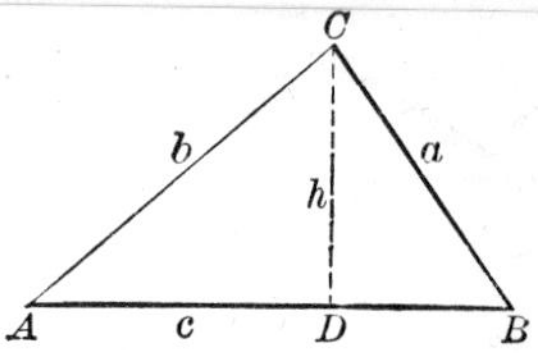

1. $C = 180° - (A + B)$.

2. $\frac{b}{a} = \frac{\sin B}{\sin A}$;

$$\therefore b = \frac{a \sin B}{\sin A} = \frac{a}{\sin A} \times \sin B.$$

3. $\frac{c}{a} = \frac{\sin C}{\sin A}$; $\quad \therefore c = \frac{a \sin C}{\sin A} = \frac{a}{\sin A} \times \sin C.$

For example, given $a = 24.31$, $A = 45° 18'$, and $B = 22° 11'$, solve the triangle.

The work may be arranged as follows:

$a = 24.31$	$\log a = 1.38578$	$= 1.38578$
$A = 45° 18'$	$\text{colog} \sin A = 0.14825$	$= 0.14825$
$B = 22° 11'$	$\log \sin B = 9.57700$	$\log \sin C = 9.96556$
$A + B = 67° 29'$	$\log b = 1.11103$	$\log c = 1.49959$
$\therefore C = 112° 31'$	$\therefore b = 12.913$	$\therefore c = 31.593$

When -10 is omitted after a logarithm or cologarithm to which it belongs, it must still be remembered that the logarithm or cologarithm is 10 too large.

The length of a having been given only to four significant figures, the values of b and c are to be depended upon only to the same number of significant figures in practical measurement. In the above example a is given to only four significant figures, and hence we say that $b = 12.91$, and $c = 31.59$.

Exercise 48. Law of Sines

Solve the triangle ABC, given the following parts:

1. $a = 500$, $A = 10° 12'$, $B = 46° 36'$.
2. $a = 795$, $A = 79° 59'$, $B = 44° 41'$.
3. $a = 804$, $A = 99° 55'$, $B = 45° 1'$.
4. $a = 820$, $A = 12° 49'$, $B = 141° 59'$.
5. $c = 1005$, $A = 78° 19'$, $B = 54° 27'$.
6. $b = 13.57$, $B = 13° 57'$, $C = 57° 13'$.
7. $a = 6412$, $A = 70° 55'$, $C = 52° 9'$.
8. $b = 999$, $A = 37° 58'$, $C = 65° 2'$.

Solve Exs. 9–14 without using logarithms:

9. Given $b = 7.071$, $A = 30°$, and $C = 105°$, find a and c.

10. Given $c = 9.562$, $A = 45°$, and $B = 60°$, find a and b.

11. The base of a triangle is 600 ft. and the angles at the base are 30° and 120°. Find the other sides and the altitude.

12. Two angles of a triangle are 20° and 40°. Find the ratio of the opposite sides.

13. The angles of a triangle are as $5:10:21$, and the side opposite the smallest angle is 3. Find the other sides.

14. Given one side of a triangle 27 in., and the adjacent angles each equal to 30°, find the radius of the circumscribed circle.

15. The angles B and C of a triangle ABC are $50° \, 30'$ and $122° \, 9'$ respectively, and BC is 9 mi. Find AB and AC.

16. In a parallelogram, given a diagonal d and the angles x and y which this diagonal makes with the sides, find the sides. Compute the results when $d = 11.2$, $x = 19° \, 1'$, and $y = 42° \, 54'$.

17. A lighthouse was observed from a ship to bear N. 34° E.; after the ship sailed due south 3 mi. the lighthouse bore N. 23° E. Find the distance from the lighthouse to the ship in each position.

The phrase *to bear N. 34° E.* means that the line of sight to the lighthouse is in the northeast quarter of the horizon and makes, with a line due north, an angle of 34°.

18. A headland was observed from a ship to bear directly east; after the ship had sailed 5 mi. N. 31° E. the headland bore S. 42° E. Find the distance from the headland to the ship in each position.

19. In a trapezoid, given the parallel sides a and b, and the angles x and y at the ends of one of the parallel sides, find the nonparallel sides. Compute the results when $a = 15$, $b = 7$, $x = 70°$, $y = 40°$.

20. Two observers 5 mi. apart on a plain, and facing each other, find that the angles of elevation of a balloon in the same vertical plane with themselves are 55° and 58° respectively. Find the distance from the balloon to each observer, and also the height of the balloon above the plain.

21. A balloon is directly above a straight road $7\frac{1}{4}$ mi. long, joining two towns. The balloonist observes that the first town makes an angle of 42° and the second town an angle of 38° with the perpendicular. Find the distance from the balloon to each town, and also the height of the balloon above the plain.

108. The Ambiguous Case. As mentioned in § 104, if two sides of a triangle and the angle opposite one of them are given, the solution will lead, in general, to two triangles. Thus, if we have the two sides a and b and the angle A given, we proceed to solve the triangle as follows:

$$C = 180° - (A + B);$$

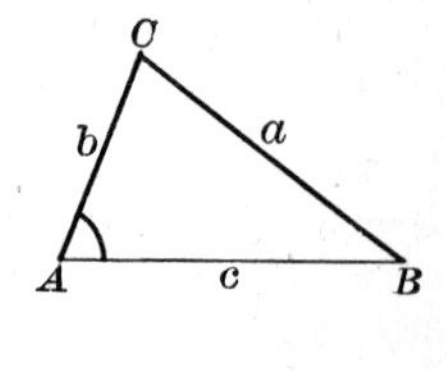

hence we can find C if we can find B.

Furthermore, $$\frac{c}{a} = \frac{\sin C}{\sin A},$$

whence $$c = \frac{a \sin C}{\sin A};$$

hence we can find c if we can find C, and we can also find c if we can find B. But to find B we have

$$\frac{\sin B}{\sin A} = \frac{b}{a},$$

whence $$\sin B = \frac{b \sin A}{a}.$$

Therefore we do not find B directly, but only $\sin B$. But when an angle is determined by its sine, it admits of two values which are supplements of each other (§ 86); hence either of the two values of B may be taken unless one of them is excluded by the conditions of the problem.

In general, therefore, either of the triangles ABC and $AB'C$ fulfills the given conditions.

Exercise 49. The Ambiguous Case

In the triangle ABC given a, b, and A, prove that:

1. If $a > b$, then $A > B$, B is acute, and there is one and only one triangle which will satisfy the given conditions.

2. If $a = b$, both A and B are acute, and there is one and only one triangle which will satisfy the given conditions, and this triangle is isosceles.

3. If $a < b$, then A must be acute to have the triangle possible, and there are in general two triangles which satisfy the given conditions.

4. If $a = b \sin A$, the required triangle is a right triangle.

5. If $a < b \sin A$, the triangle is impossible.

6. If $A = B$, there is one, and only one, triangle.

109. Number of Solutions to be expected. We may summarize the results found on page 112 as follows:

There are two solutions if A is acute and the value of a lies between b and $b \sin A$.

There is no solution if A is acute and $a < b \sin A$; or if A is obtuse and $a < b$, or $a = b$.

There is one solution in each of the other cases.

The number of solutions can often be determined by inspection. In case of doubt, find the value of $b \sin A$.

We can also determine the number of solutions by considering the value of $\log \sin B$. If $\log \sin B = 0$, then $\sin B = 1$ and $B = 90°$. Therefore the triangle required is a right triangle. If $\log \sin B > 0$, then $\sin B > 1$, and hence the triangle is impossible. If $\log \sin B < 0$, there is *one solution* when $a > b$; there are *two solutions* when $a < b$.

When there are two solutions, let B', C', c', denote the unknown parts of the second triangle; then

$$B' = 180° - B,$$

$$C' = 180° - (A + B') = B - A,$$

and

$$c' = \frac{a \sin C'}{\sin A}.$$

110. Illustrative Problems. The following may be taken as illustrative of the above cases:

1. Given $a = 16$, $b = 20$, and $A = 106°$, find the remaining parts.

In this case $a < b$ and $A > 90°$. Since $a < b$, it follows that $A < B$. Hence if $A > 90°$, B must also be greater than $90°$. But a triangle cannot have two obtuse angles. Therefore the triangle is impossible.

2. Given $a = 36$, $b = 80$, and $A = 30°$, find the remaining parts.

Here we have $b \sin A = 80 \times \frac{1}{2} = 40$; so that $a < b \sin A$ and the triangle is impossible. Draw the figure to illustrate this fact.

3. Given $a = 25$, $b = 50$, and $A = 30°$, find the remaining parts.

Here we have $b \sin A = 50 \times \frac{1}{2} = 25$; but a is also equal to 25. Hence B must be a right angle. ABC is therefore a right triangle and there is only one solution.

4. Given $a = 30$, $b = 30$, and $A = 60°$, find the remaining parts.

Here we have $a = b$, and A an acute angle. Hence there is one solution and only one. It is evident, also, that the triangle is not only isosceles but equilateral.

5. Given $a = 3.4$, $b = 3.4$, and $A = 45°$, find the remaining parts.

Here we have $a = b$, and A an acute angle. Hence there is one solution and only one. It is evident, also, that the triangle is not only isosceles but right.

6. Given $a = 72{,}630$, $b = 117{,}480$, and $A = 80° \, 0' \, 50''$, find B, C, and c.

$$\begin{aligned} \log b &= 5.06997 \\ \log \sin A &= 9.99337 \\ \text{colog}\, a &= 5.13888 \\ \hline \log \sin B &= 0.20222 \end{aligned}$$

Here $\log \sin B > 0$.
Therefore $\sin B > 1$, which is impossible.

Therefore there is *no solution.*

7. Given $a = 13.2$, $b = 15.7$, and $A = 57° \, 13' \, 15''$, find B, C, and c.

$$\begin{aligned} \log b &= 1.19590 \\ \log \sin A &= 9.92467 \\ \text{colog}\, a &= 8.87943 \\ \hline \log \sin B &= 0.00000 \\ \therefore B &= 90° \\ \therefore C &= 32° \, 46' \, 45'' \end{aligned}$$

$$\begin{aligned} c &= b \cos A \\ \log b &= 1.19590 \\ \log \cos A &= 9.73352 \\ \hline \log c &= 0.92942 \\ \therefore c &= 8.5 \end{aligned}$$

Therefore there is *one solution.*
Since $B = 90°$, the triangle is a right triangle.

8. Given $a = 767$, $b = 242$, and $A = 36° \, 53' \, 2''$, find B, C, and c.

$$\begin{aligned} \log b &= 2.38382 \\ \log \sin A &= 9.77830 \\ \text{colog}\, a &= 7.11520 \\ \hline \log \sin B &= 9.27732 \\ \therefore B &= 10° \, 54' \, 58'' \\ \therefore C &= 132° \, 12' \, 0'' \end{aligned}$$

$$\begin{aligned} \log a &= 2.88480 \\ \log \sin C &= 9.86970 \\ \text{colog} \sin A &= 0.22170 \\ \hline \log c &= 2.97620 \\ \therefore c &= 946.68 \\ &= 946.7 \end{aligned}$$

Here $a > b$, and $\log \sin B < 0$.
Therefore there is *one solution.*

9. Given $a = 177.01$, $b = 216.45$, and $A = 35° \, 36' \, 20''$, find the other parts.

$$\begin{aligned} \log b &= 2.33536 \\ \log \sin A &= 9.76507 \\ \text{colog}\, a &= 7.75200 \\ \hline \log \sin B &= 9.85243 \\ \therefore B &= 45° \, 23' \, 28'' \text{ or} \\ & \quad 134° \, 36' \, 32'' \\ \therefore C &= 99° \, 0' \, 12'' \text{ or} \\ & \quad 9° \, 47' \, 8'' \end{aligned}$$

$\log a =$	2.24800	2.24800
$\log \sin C =$	9.99462	9.23035
$\text{colog} \sin A =$	0.23493	0.23493
$\log c =$	2.47755	1.71328

$$\begin{aligned} \therefore c &= 300.29 \text{ or } 51.675 \\ &= 300.29 \text{ or } 51.68 \end{aligned}$$

Here $a < b$, and $\log \sin B < 0$.
Therefore there are *two solutions.*

Exercise 50. The Oblique Triangle

Find the number of solutions, given the following:

1. $a = 80$, $b = 100$, $A = 30°$.
2. $a = 50$, $b = 100$, $A = 30°$.
3. $a = 40$, $b = 100$, $A = 30°$.
4. $a = 100$, $b = 100$, $A = 30°$.
5. $a = 13.4$, $b = 11.46$, $A = 77° 20'$.
6. $a = 70$, $b = 75$, $A = 60°$.
7. $a = 134.16$, $b = 84.54$, $B = 52° 9'$.
8. $a = 200$, $b = 100$, $A = 30°$.

Solve the triangles, given the following:

9. $a = 840$, $b = 485$, $A = 21° 31'$.
10. $a = 9.399$, $b = 9.197$, $A = 120° 35'$.
11. $a = 91.06$, $b = 77.04$, $A = 51° 9'$.
12. $a = 55.55$, $b = 66.66$, $B = 77° 44'$.
13. $a = 309$, $b = 360$, $A = 21° 14'$.
14. $a = 34$, $b = 22$, $B = 30° 20'$.
15. $b = 19$, $c = 18$, $C = 15° 49'$.
16. $a = 8.716$, $b = 9.787$, $A = 38° 14' 12''$.
17. $a = 4.4$, $b = 5.21$, $A = 57° 37' 17''$.

18. Given $a = 75$, $b = 29$, and $B = 16° 15'$, find the difference between the areas of the two triangles which meet these conditions.

19. In a parallelogram, given the side a, a diagonal d, and the angle A made by the two diagonals, find the other diagonal. As a special case consider the parallelogram in which $a = 35$, $d = 63$, and $A = 21° 36'$.

20. In a parallelogram $ABCD$, given $AD = 3$ in., $BD = 2.5$ in., and $A = 47° 20'$, find AB.

21. In a quadrilateral $ABCD$, given $AC = 4$ in., $\angle BAC = 35°$, $\angle B = 75° 20'$, $\angle D = 38° 30'$, and $\angle BAD = 70° 40'$, find the length of each of the four sides.

22. In a pentagon $ABCDE$, given $\angle A = 110° 50'$, $\angle B = 106° 30'$, $\angle E = 104° 10'$, $\angle BAC = 30°$, $\angle DAE = 34° 56'$, $\angle ADC = 52° 30'$, and $AC = 6$ in., find the sides and the remaining angles of the pentagon.

111. Law of Cosines. This law gives the value of one side of a triangle in terms of the other two sides and the angle included between them.

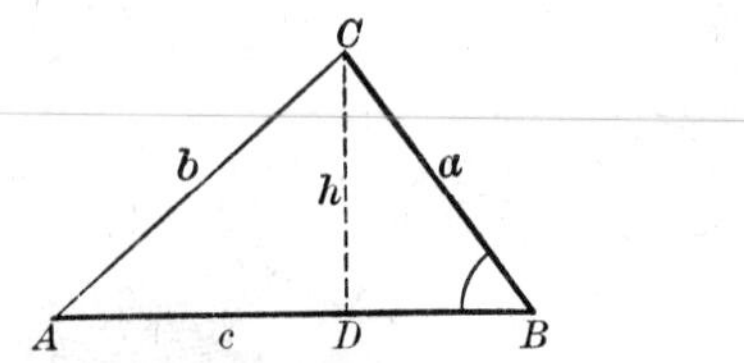

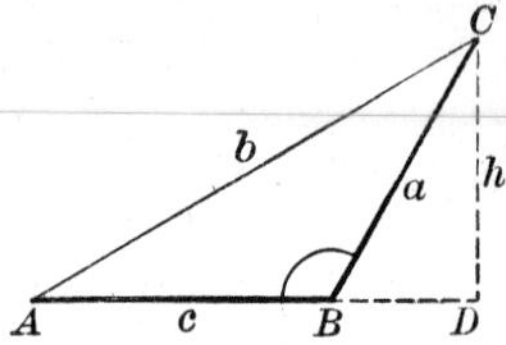

In either figure, $a^2 = h^2 + \overline{BD}^2$.

In the first figure, $BD = c - AD$.

In the second figure, $BD = AD - c$.

In either case, $\overline{BD}^2 = \overline{AD}^2 - 2c \times AD + c^2$.

Therefore, in all cases, $a^2 = h^2 + \overline{AD}^2 + c^2 - 2c \times AD$.

Now $h^2 + \overline{AD}^2 = b^2$,

and $AD = b \cos A$.

Therefore $\boldsymbol{a^2 = b^2 + c^2 - 2\,bc \cos A}$.

In like manner it may be proved that

$$b^2 = c^2 + a^2 - 2\,ca \cos B,$$

and

$$c^2 = a^2 + b^2 - 2\,ab \cos C.$$

The three formulas have precisely the same form, and the Law of Cosines may be stated as follows:

The square on any side of a triangle is equal to the sum of the squares on the other two sides diminished by twice their product into the cosine of the included angle.

It will be seen that if $A = 90°$, we have

$$a^2 = b^2 + c^2 - 2\,bc \cos 90°$$
$$= b^2 + c^2.$$

In other words we have the Pythagorean Theorem as a special case. Hence this is sometimes called the *Generalized Pythagorean Theorem.*

It will also be seen that the law includes two other familiar propositions of geometry, one of which is the following:

In an obtuse triangle the square on the side opposite the obtuse angle is equivalent to the sum of the squares on the other two sides increased by twice the product of one of those sides by the projection of the other upon that side.

This and the analogous proposition are given as exercises on page 117.

Exercise 51. Law of Cosines

1. Using the figures on page 116, prove that, whether the angle B is acute or obtuse, $c = a \cos B + b \cos A$.

2. What are the two symmetrical formulas obtained by changing the letters in Ex. 1? What does the formula in Ex. 1 become when $B = 90°$?

3. Show that the sum of the squares on the sides of a triangle is equal to $2(ab \cos C + bc \cos A + ca \cos B)$.

4. Consider the Law of Cosines in the case of the triangle $a = 5$, $b = 12$, $c = 6$.

5. Given $a = 5$, $b = 5$, and $C = 60°$, find c.

6. Given $a = 10$, $b = 10$, and $C = 45°$, find c.

7. Given $a = 8$, $b = 5$, and $C = 60°$, find c.

8. From the formula $a^2 = b^2 + c^2 - 2bc \cos A$ deduce a formula for $\cos A$. From this result find the value of A when $b^2 + c^2 = a^2$.

9. Prove that if $\dfrac{\cos A}{b} = \dfrac{\cos B}{a}$ the triangle is either isosceles or right.

10. Prove that $\dfrac{\cos A}{a} + \dfrac{\cos B}{b} + \dfrac{\cos C}{c} = \dfrac{a^2 + b^2 + c^2}{2abc}$.

11. Prove that $\dfrac{b^2}{a} \cos A + \dfrac{c^2}{b} \cos B + \dfrac{a^2}{c} \cos C = \dfrac{a^4 + b^4 + c^4}{2abc}$.

12. From the Law of Cosines prove that the square on the side opposite an acute angle of a triangle is equal to the sum of the squares on the other two sides minus twice the product of either side and the projection of the other side upon it.

13. As in Ex. 12, consider the geometric proposition relating to the square on the side opposite an obtuse angle.

14. In the parallelogram $ABCD$, given $AB = 4$ in., $AD = 5$ in., and $A = 38° 40'$, find the two diagonals.

15. In the parallelogram $ABCD$, given $AB = 7$ in., $AC = 10$ in., and $\angle BAC = 36° 7'$, find the side BC and the diagonal BD.

16. In the quadrilateral $ABCD$, given $AC = 3.6$ in., $AD = 4$ in., $BC = 2.4$ in., $\angle ACB = 29° 40'$, and $\angle CAD = 71° 20'$, find the other two sides and all four angles of the quadrilateral.

17. In the pentagon $ABCDE$, given $AB = 3.4$ in., $AC = 4.1$ in., $AD = 3.9$ in., $AE = 2.2$ in., $\angle BAC = 38° 7'$, $\angle CAD = 41° 22'$, and $\angle DAE = 32° 5'$, find the perimeter of the pentagon.

112. Law of Tangents. Since $\frac{a}{b} = \frac{\sin A}{\sin B}$, by the Law of Sines, it follows by the theory of proportion that

$$\frac{a-b}{a+b} = \frac{\sin A - \sin B}{\sin A + \sin B}.$$

This is easily seen without resorting to the theory of proportion. For, since $a \sin B = b \sin A$ (§ 105), we have

$$a \sin B - b \sin A = b \sin A - a \sin B$$

Adding,
$$a \sin A - b \sin B = a \sin A - b \sin B$$

$$a \sin A + a \sin B - b \sin A - b \sin B = a \sin A - a \sin B + b \sin A - b \sin B,$$

or
$$(a-b)(\sin A + \sin B) = (a+b)(\sin A - \sin B);$$

whence, by division,
$$\frac{a-b}{a+b} = \frac{\sin A - \sin B}{\sin A + \sin B}.$$

But by § 103,
$$\frac{\sin A - \sin B}{\sin A + \sin B} = \frac{\tan \frac{1}{2}(A-B)}{\tan \frac{1}{2}(A+B)}.$$

Therefore
$$\mathbf{\frac{a-b}{a+b} = \frac{\tan \frac{1}{2}(A-B)}{\tan \frac{1}{2}(A+B)}}.$$

By merely changing the letters,

$$\frac{a-c}{a+c} = \frac{\tan \frac{1}{2}(A-C)}{\tan \frac{1}{2}(A+C)},$$

and
$$\frac{b-c}{b+c} = \frac{\tan \frac{1}{2}(B-C)}{\tan \frac{1}{2}(B+C)}.$$

Hence the Law of Tangents:

The difference between two sides of a triangle is to their sum as the tangent of half the difference between the opposite angles is to the tangent of half their sum.

In the case of a triangle, if we know the two sides a and b and the included angle C, we have our choice of two methods of solving. From the Law of Cosines we can find c, and then, from the Law of Sines, we can find A and B. Or we can find $A + B$ by taking C from 180°, and then, since we also know $a + b$ and $a - b$, we can find $A - B$. From $A + B$ and $A - B$ we can find A and B. This second method is usually the simpler one.

If $b > a$, then $B > A$. The formula is still true, but to avoid negative numbers the formula in this case should be written

$$\frac{b-a}{b+a} = \frac{\tan \frac{1}{2}(B-A)}{\tan \frac{1}{2}(B+A)}.$$

Exercise 52. Law of Tangents

Find the form to which $\frac{a-b}{a+b}=\frac{\tan\frac{1}{2}(A-B)}{\tan\frac{1}{2}(A+B)}$ *reduces when:*

1. $C=90°$.
2. $a=b$.
3. $A=B=C$.
4. $A-B=90°$, and $B=C$.

Prove the following formulas:

5. $\frac{b-c}{b+c}=\tan\frac{1}{2}(B-C)\cot\frac{1}{2}(B+C)$.

6. $\tan\frac{1}{2}(B-C)=\frac{b-c}{b+c}\cot\frac{1}{2}A$.

7. $\frac{a+b}{a-b}=\frac{\cot\frac{1}{2}(A-B)}{\cot\frac{1}{2}(A+B)}$.

8. $\frac{\sin A+\sin B}{\sin A-\sin B}=\frac{\tan\frac{1}{2}(A+B)}{\tan\frac{1}{2}(A-B)}$.

9. $\frac{\sin B+\sin C}{\sin B-\sin C}=\frac{2\sin\frac{1}{2}(B+C)\cos\frac{1}{2}(B-C)}{2\cos\frac{1}{2}(B+C)\sin\frac{1}{2}(B-C)}$.

10. $\frac{\sin A+\sin B}{\sin A-\sin B}=\tan\frac{1}{2}(A+B)\cot\frac{1}{2}(A-B)$.

11. To what does the formula in Ex. 8 reduce when $A=B$?

12. To what does the formula in Ex. 9 reduce when $B=C=60°$?

13. To what does the formula in Ex. 10 reduce when the triangle is equilateral?

14. To what does the Law of Tangents, in the form stated at the top of this page, reduce in the case of an isosceles triangle in which $a=b$? What does this prove with respect to the angles opposite the equal sides?

15. By the help of the Law of Tangents prove that an equilateral triangle is also equiangular.

16. By the help of the Law of Tangents prove that an equiangular triangle is also equilateral.

17. Given any three sides and any three angles of a quadrilateral, show how the fourth side and the fourth angle can be found. Show also that it is not necessary to have so many parts given, and find the smallest number of parts that will solve the quadrilateral.

18. What sides, what diagonals, and what angles of a pentagon is it necessary to know in order, by the aid of the Law of Tangents alone, to solve the pentagon?

113. Applications to Triangles. The Law of Cosines and the Law of Tangents are frequently used in the solution of triangles. This is particularly the case when we have given two sides, a and b, and the included angle C.

There are two convenient ways of finding the angles A and B, the first being by the Law of Tangents. This law may be written

$$\tan \tfrac{1}{2}(A-B) = \frac{a-b}{a+b} \times \tan \tfrac{1}{2}(A+B).$$

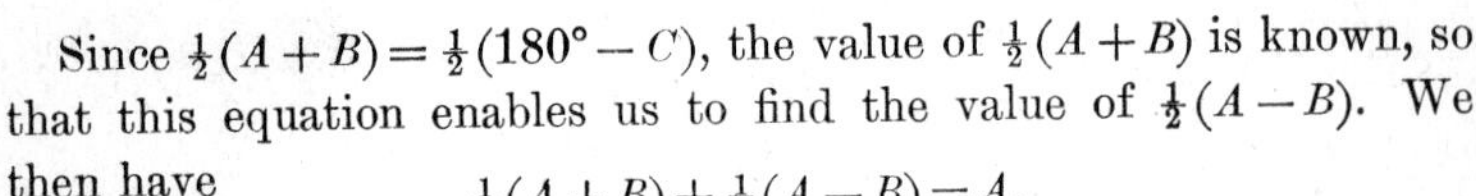

Since $\frac{1}{2}(A+B) = \frac{1}{2}(180° - C)$, the value of $\frac{1}{2}(A+B)$ is known, so that this equation enables us to find the value of $\frac{1}{2}(A-B)$. We then have

$$\tfrac{1}{2}(A+B) + \tfrac{1}{2}(A-B) = A,$$

and

$$\tfrac{1}{2}(A+B) - \tfrac{1}{2}(A-B) = B.$$

The second method of finding A and B is as follows: In the above figure let BD be perpendicular to AC.

Then
$$\tan A = \frac{BD}{AD} = \frac{BD}{AC - DC}.$$

Now
$$BD = a \sin C,$$

and
$$DC = a \cos C.$$

$$\therefore \tan A = \frac{a \sin C}{b - a \cos C}.$$

Since A and C are now known, B can be found.

This is not so convenient as the first method, because it is not so well adapted to work with logarithms.

The side c may now be found by the Law of Sines, thus:

$$c = \frac{a \sin C}{\sin A}, \quad \text{or} \quad c = \frac{b \sin C}{\sin B}.$$

Instead of finding A and B first, and from these values finding c, we may first find c and then find A and B. To find c first we may write the Law of Cosines (§ 111) as follows:

$$c = \sqrt{a^2 + b^2 - 2ab \cos C}.$$

Having thus found c, and already knowing a, b, and C, we have

$$\sin A = \frac{a \sin C}{c}, \quad \sin B = \frac{b \sin C}{c}.$$

In general this is not so convenient as the first method given above, because the formula for c is not so well adapted to work with logarithms.

114. Illustrative Problems. 1. Given $C = 63° 35' 30''$, $a = 748$, and $b = 375$, find A, B, and c.

We see that $a + b = 1123$, $a - b = 373$, and $A + B = 180° - C = 116° 24' 30''$. Hence $\frac{1}{2}(A + B) = 58° 12' 15''$.

$$\begin{aligned} \log(a - b) &= 2.57171 \\ \text{colog}(a + b) &= 6.94962 \\ \log\tan\tfrac{1}{2}(A + B) &= \underline{0.20766} \\ \log\tan\tfrac{1}{2}(A - B) &= 9.72899 \\ \therefore \tfrac{1}{2}(A - B) &= 28° 10' 54'' \end{aligned} \qquad \begin{aligned} \log b &= 2.57403 \\ \log\sin C &= 9.95214 \\ \text{colog}\sin B &= \underline{0.30073} \\ \log c &= 2.82690 \\ \therefore c &= 671.27 \end{aligned}$$

After finding $\frac{1}{2}(A - B)$ we combine this with $\frac{1}{2}(A + B)$ and find $A = 86° 23' 9''$ and $B = 30° 1' 21''$.

In the above example, in finding the side c we use the angle B rather than the angle A, because A is near 90°. The use of the sine of an angle near 90° should be avoided, because it varies so slowly that we cannot determine the angle accurately when the sine is given.

2. Given $a = 4$, $c = 6$, and $B = 60°$, find the third side b.

Here the Law of Cosines may be used to advantage, because the numbers are so small as to make the computation easy. We have

$$b = \sqrt{a^2 + c^2 - 2ac\cos B} = \sqrt{16 + 36 - 24} = \sqrt{28};$$

$$\log 28 = 1.44716, \qquad \log\sqrt{28} = 0.72358, \qquad \sqrt{28} = 5.2915;$$

that is, to three significant figures, $b = 5.292$.

Exercise 53. Solving Triangles

Solve these triangles, given the following parts:

1. $a = 77.99$, $b = 83.39$, $C = 72° 15'$.
2. $b = 872.5$, $c = 632.7$, $A = 80°$.
3. $a = 17$, $b = 12$, $C = 59° 17'$.
4. $b = \sqrt{5}$, $c = \sqrt{3}$, $A = 35° 53'$.
5. $a = 0.917$, $b = 0.312$, $C = 33° 7' 9''$.
6. $a = 13.715$, $c = 11.214$, $B = 15° 22' 36''$.
7. $b = 3000.9$, $c = 1587.2$, $A = 86° 4' 4''$.
8. $a = 4527$, $b = 3465$, $C = 66° 6' 27''$.
9. $a = 55.14$, $b = 33.09$, $C = 30° 24'$.
10. $a = 47.99$, $b = 33.14$, $C = 175° 19' 10''$.
11. $a = 210$, $b = 105$, $C = 36° 52' 12''$.
12. $a = 100$, $b = 900$, $C = 65°$.

Solve these triangles, given the following parts:

13. $a = 409$, $b = 169$, $C = 117.7°$.

14. $a = 6.25$, $b = 5.05$, $C = 105.77°$.

15. $a = 3718$, $b = 1507$, $C = 95.86°$.

16. $a = 46.07$, $b = 22.29$, $C = 66.36°$.

17. $b = 445$, $c = 624$, $A = 10.88°$.

18. $b = 15.7$, $c = 43.6$, $A = 57.22°$.

19. If two sides of a triangle are each equal to 6, and the included angle is 60°, find the third side by two different methods.

20. If two sides of a triangle are each equal to 6, and the included angle is 120°, find the third side by three different methods.

21. Apply the first method given on page 120 to the case in which a is equal to b; that is, the case in which the triangle is isosceles.

22. If two sides of a triangle are 10 and 11, and the included angle is 50°, find the third side.

23. If two sides of a triangle are 43.301 and 25, and the included angle is 30°, find the third side.

24. In order to find the distance between two objects, A and B, separated by a swamp, a station C was chosen, and the distances $CA = 3825$ yd., $CB = 3475.6$ yd., together with the angle $ACB = 62° 31'$, were measured. Find the distance from A to B.

B
C
A

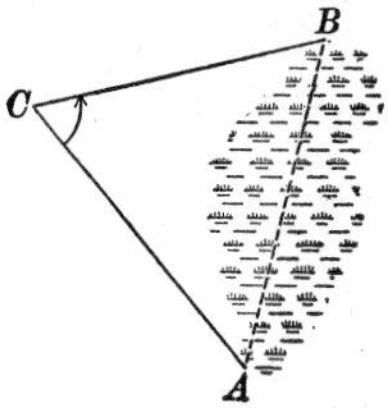

25. Two inaccessible objects, A and B, are each viewed from two stations, C and D, on the same side of AB and 562 yd. apart. The angle ACB is $62° 12'$, BCD $41° 8'$, ADB $60° 49'$, and ADC $34° 51'$. Required the distance AB.

26. In order to find the distance between two objects, A and B, separated by a pond, a station C was chosen, and it was found that $CA = 426$ yd., $CB = 322.4$ yd., and $ACB = 68° 42'$. Required the distance from A to B.

27. Two trains start at the same time from the same station and move along straight tracks that form an angle of 30°, one train at the rate of 30 mi. an hour, the other at the rate of 40 mi. an hour. How far apart are the trains at the end of half an hour?

28. In a parallelogram, given the two diagonals 5 and 6 and the angle which they form $49° 18'$, find the sides.

115. Given the Three Sides. Given the three sides of a triangle, it is possible to find the angles by the Law of Cosines. Thus, from

$$a^2 = b^2 + c^2 - 2\,bc \cos A,$$

we have

$$\cos A = \frac{b^2 + c^2 - a^2}{2\,bc}.$$

This formula is not, however, adapted to work with logarithms. In order to remedy this difficulty we shall now proceed to change its form.

Let s equal the semiperimeter of the triangle; that is,

let $a + b + c = 2\,s.$

Then

$$b + c - a = 2\,s - 2\,a = 2\,(s - a),$$

$$c + a - b = 2\,(s - b),$$

and

$$a + b - c = 2\,(s - c).$$

Hence

$$1 - \cos A = 1 - \frac{b^2 + c^2 - a^2}{2\,bc} = \frac{2\,bc - b^2 - c^2 + a^2}{2\,bc}$$

$$= \frac{a^2 - (b - c)^2}{2\,bc} = \frac{(a + b - c)(a - b + c)}{2\,bc}$$

$$= \frac{2\,(s - b)(s - c)}{bc}.$$

In the same way the value of $1 + \cos A$ is

$$1 + \frac{b^2 + c^2 - a^2}{2\,bc} = \frac{2\,bc + b^2 + c^2 - a^2}{2\,bc} = \frac{(b + c)^2 - a^2}{2\,bc}$$

$$= \frac{(b + c + a)(b + c - a)}{2\,bc} = \frac{2\,s\,(s - a)}{bc}.$$

But from § 102 we know that

$$1 - \cos A = 2 \sin^2 \tfrac{1}{2} A, \qquad \text{and} \qquad 1 + \cos A = 2 \cos^2 \tfrac{1}{2} A.$$

$$\therefore\ 2 \sin^2 \tfrac{1}{2} A = \frac{2\,(s - b)(s - c)}{bc}, \text{ and } 2 \cos^2 \tfrac{1}{2} A = \frac{2\,s\,(s - a)}{bc}.$$

It therefore follows that

$$\sin \tfrac{1}{2} A = \sqrt{\frac{(s - b)(s - c)}{bc}},$$

and

$$\cos \tfrac{1}{2} A = \sqrt{\frac{s\,(s - a)}{bc}}.$$

Furthermore, since $\tan x = \dfrac{\sin x}{\cos x}$, we have

$$\tan \tfrac{1}{2} A = \sqrt{\frac{(s - b)(s - c)}{s\,(s - a)}}.$$

By merely changing the letters in the formulas given on page 123, we have the following:

$$\sin \tfrac{1}{2} B = \sqrt{\frac{(s-a)(s-c)}{ac}}, \qquad \sin \tfrac{1}{2} C = \sqrt{\frac{(s-a)(s-b)}{ab}},$$

$$\cos \tfrac{1}{2} B = \sqrt{\frac{s(s-b)}{ac}}, \qquad \cos \tfrac{1}{2} C = \sqrt{\frac{s(s-c)}{ab}},$$

$$\tan \tfrac{1}{2} B = \sqrt{\frac{(s-a)(s-c)}{s(s-b)}}, \qquad \tan \tfrac{1}{2} C = \sqrt{\frac{(s-a)(s-b)}{s(s-c)}}.$$

There is then a choice of three different formulas for finding the value of each angle. If half the angle is very near 0°, the formula for the cosine will not give a very accurate result, because the cosines of angles near 0° differ little in value; and the same is true of the formula for the sine when half the angle is very near 90°. Hence in the first case the formula for the sine, and in the second that for the cosine, should be used.

But in general the formulas for the tangent are to be preferred, the tangent as a rule changing more rapidly than the sine or cosine.

It is not necessary to compute by the formulas more than two angles, for the third may then be found from the equation $A + B + C = 180°$. There is this advantage, however, in computing all three angles by the formulas, that we may then use the sum of the angles as a test of the accuracy of the results.

116. Checks on the Angles. In case it is desired to compute all the angles for the purpose of checking the work, the formulas for the tangent may be put in a more convenient form.

The formula for $\tan \frac{1}{2} A$ may be written thus:

$$\tan \tfrac{1}{2} A = \sqrt{\frac{(s-a)(s-b)(s-c)}{s(s-a)^2}}$$

$$= \frac{1}{s-a}\sqrt{\frac{(s-a)(s-b)(s-c)}{s}}.$$

Hence, if we put $$r = \sqrt{\frac{(s-a)(s-b)(s-c)}{s}},$$

we have $$\tan \tfrac{1}{2} A = \frac{r}{s-a}.$$

Likewise, $$\tan \tfrac{1}{2} B = \frac{r}{s-b}, \quad \tan \tfrac{1}{2} C = \frac{r}{s-c}.$$

For example, if $a = 3$, $b = 3.5$, and $c = 4.5$, we have $s = 5.5$, $s - a = 2.5$, $s - b = 2$, and $s - c = 1$.

$$\therefore r = \sqrt{\frac{2.5 \times 2 \times 1}{5.5}} = \sqrt{\frac{5}{5.5}} = \sqrt{\frac{10}{11}} = 0.9534.$$

$$\therefore \tan \tfrac{1}{2} A = 0.9534 \div 2.5 = 0.3814.$$

$$\therefore \tfrac{1}{2} A = 20° 53'.$$

$$\therefore A = 41° 46'.$$

Exercise 54. Formulas of the Triangle

1. Given $\tan \frac{1}{2} A = \sqrt{\frac{(s-b)(s-c)}{s(s-a)}}$, express the value of $\log \tan \frac{1}{2} A$.

2. Given $\sin \frac{1}{2} A = \sqrt{\frac{(s-b)(s-c)}{bc}}$, express the value of $\log \sin \frac{1}{2} A$.

3. Given $r = \sqrt{\frac{(s-a)(s-b)(s-c)}{s}}$, express the value of $\log r$.

4. Given $\tan \frac{1}{2} A = \frac{r}{s-a}$, express the value of $\log \tan \frac{1}{2} A$.

5. Given $\tan \frac{1}{2} A = \frac{r}{s-a}$, express the value of $\log r$.

6. Of the three values for $\tan \frac{1}{2} A$,

$$\sqrt{\frac{1-\cos A}{1+\cos A}}, \qquad (\S\ 102)$$

$$\sqrt{\frac{(s-b)(s-c)}{s(s-a)}}, \qquad (\S\ 115)$$

and

$$\frac{1}{s-a}\sqrt{\frac{(s-a)(s-b)(s-c)}{s}}, \qquad (\S\ 116)$$

which is the easiest to treat by logarithms? Express the logarithms of the results and show why your answer is correct.

7. Given $a = 4$, $b = 5$, and $c = 6$, find the value of $\tan \frac{1}{2} A$, and then find the value of A.

8. Deduce the equation

$$\tan \tfrac{1}{2} A = \sqrt{\frac{(s-b)(s-c)}{s(s-a)}}$$

from the equation

$$\tan \tfrac{1}{2} A = \sqrt{\frac{1-\cos A}{1+\cos A}}.$$

9. Discuss the formula

$$\tan \tfrac{1}{2} A = \sqrt{\frac{(s-b)(s-c)}{s(s-a)}}$$

$$= \frac{1}{s-a}\sqrt{\frac{(s-a)(s-b)(s-c)}{s}},$$

for the case of an equilateral triangle, say when $a = 4$.

117. Illustrative Problems. 1. Given $a = 3.41$, $b = 2.60$, $c = 1.58$, find the angles.

Since it is given that $a = 3.41$, $b = 2.60$, and $c = 1.58$, it follows that $2s = 7.59$ and $s = 3.795$. Therefore

$$s - a = 0.385, \qquad s - b = 1.195, \qquad s - c = 2.215.$$

Using the formula of § 115 and the corresponding formula for $\tan \frac{1}{2} B$, we may arrange the work as follows:

$$\begin{aligned} \text{colog}\, s &= 9.42079 \\ \text{colog}\,(s-a) &= 0.41454 \\ \log (s-b) &= 0.07737 \\ \log (s-c) &= 0.34537 \\ & 2\overline{)0.25807} \\ \log \tan \tfrac{1}{2} A &= 0.12903 \\ \therefore \tfrac{1}{2} A &= 53^\circ\, 23'\, 20'' \\ \therefore A &= 106^\circ\, 46'\, 40'' \end{aligned} \qquad \begin{aligned} \text{colog}\, s &= 9.42079 - 10 \\ \log (s-a) &= 9.58546 - 10 \\ \text{colog}\,(s-b) &= 9.92263 - 10 \\ \log (s-c) &= 0.34537 \\ & 2\overline{)19.27425 - 20} \\ \log \tan \tfrac{1}{2} B &= 9.63713 - 10 \\ \therefore \tfrac{1}{2} B &= 23^\circ\, 26'\, 37'' \\ \therefore B &= 46^\circ\, 53'\, 14'' \end{aligned}$$

$$\therefore A + B = 153^\circ\, 39'\, 54'', \text{ and } C = 26^\circ\, 20'\, 6''.$$

2. Solve the above problem by finding all three angles by the use of the formulas on page 124.

Since it is given that $a = 3.41$, $b = 2.60$, and $c = 1.58$, it follows that $2s = 7.59$ and $s = 3.795$. Therefore

$$s - a = 0.385, \qquad s - b = 1.195, \qquad s - c = 2.215.$$

Here the work may be compactly arranged as follows, if we find $\log \tan \frac{1}{2} A$, etc., by *subtracting* $\log (s - a)$, etc., from $\log r$ instead of adding the cologarithm.

$$\begin{aligned} \log (s-a) &= 9.58546 \\ \log (s-b) &= 0.07737 \\ \log (s-c) &= 0.34537 \\ \text{colog}\, s &= 9.42079 \\ \log r^2 &= 9.42899 \\ \log r &= 9.71450 \end{aligned} \qquad \begin{aligned} \log \tan \tfrac{1}{2} A &= 10.12903 \\ \log \tan \tfrac{1}{2} B &= 9.63713 \\ \log \tan \tfrac{1}{2} C &= 9.36912 \\ \tfrac{1}{2} A &= 53^\circ\, 23'\, 20'' \\ \tfrac{1}{2} B &= 23^\circ\, 26'\, 37'' \\ \tfrac{1}{2} C &= 13^\circ\, 10'\, 3'' \\ A &= 106^\circ\, 46'\, 40'' \\ B &= 46^\circ\, 53'\, 14'' \\ C &= 26^\circ\, 20'\, 6'' \\ \textit{Check.}\quad A + B + C &= 180^\circ\, 0'\, 0'' \end{aligned}$$

Even if no mistakes are made in the work, the sum of the three angles found as above may differ very slightly from 180° in consequence of the fact that computation with logarithms is at best only a method of close approximation. When a difference of this kind exists, it should be divided among the angles according to the probable amount of error for each angle.

Exercise 55. Finding the Angles

Find the three angles of a triangle, given the three sides as follows:

1. 51, 65, 20.
2. 78, 101, 29.
3. 111, 145, 40.
4. 21, 26, 31.
5. 19, 34, 49.
6. 43, 50, 57.
7. 37, 58, 79.
8. 73, 82, 91.
9. $\sqrt{5}$, $\sqrt{6}$, $\sqrt{7}$.
10. 21, 28, 35.
11. 6, 8, 10.
12. 6, 6, 10.
13. 6, 6, 6.
14. 6, 9, 12.
15. 3, 4, 5.

16. Given $a = 14.5$, $b = 55.4$, and $c = 66.9$, find A, B, and C.

17. Given $a = 2$, $b = \sqrt{6}$, and $c = \sqrt{3} - 1$, find A, B, and C.

18. Given $a = 2$, $b = \sqrt{6}$, and $c = \sqrt{3} + 1$, find A, B, and C.

19. The sides of a triangle are 78.9, 65.4, and 97.3 respectively. Find the largest angle.

20. The sides of a triangle are 487.25, 512.33, and 544.37 respectively. Find the smallest angle.

21. Find the angles of a triangle whose sides are $\frac{\sqrt{3}+1}{2\sqrt{2}}$, $\frac{\sqrt{3}-1}{2\sqrt{2}}$, and $\frac{\sqrt{3}}{2}$ respectively.

22. Of three towns, A, B, and C, A is found to be 200 mi. from B and 184 mi. from C, and B is found to be 150 mi. due north from C. How many miles is A north of C?

23. Under what visual angle is an object 7 ft. long seen by an observer whose eye is 5 ft. from one end of the object and 8 ft. from the other end?

24. The sides of a triangle are 14.6 in., 16.7 in., and 18.8 in. respectively. Find the length of the perpendicular from the vertex of the largest angle upon the opposite side.

25. The distances between three cities, A, B, and C, are measured and found to be as follows: $AB = 165$ mi., $AC = 72$ mi., and $BC = 185$ mi. B is due east from A. In what direction is C from A? What two answers are admissible?

26. In a quadrilateral $ABCD$, $AB = 2$ in., $BC = 3$ in., $CD = 3$ in., $DA = 4$ in., and $AC = 4$ in. Find the angles of the quadrilateral.

27. In a parallelogram $ABCD$, $AB = 2$ in., $AC = 3$ in., and $AD = 2.5$ in. Find $\angle CBA$.

28. In a rectangle $ABCD$, $AB = 3.3$ in., and $AC = 5\frac{1}{2}$ in. Find the angles that each diagonal makes with the sides.

118. Area of a Triangle. The area of a triangle may be found if the following parts are known:

1. Two sides and the included angle;
2. Two angles and any side;
3. The three sides.

These cases will now be considered.

CASE 1. *Given two sides and the included angle.*

Lettering the triangle as here shown, and designating CD by h and the area by S, we have

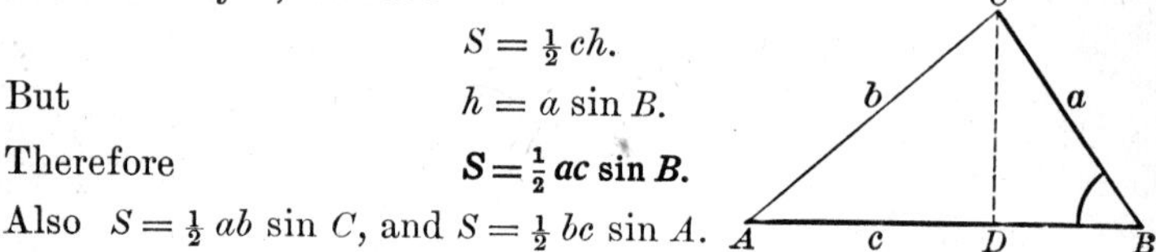

$$S = \tfrac{1}{2}ch.$$

But $$h = a \sin B.$$

Therefore $$\mathbf{S = \tfrac{1}{2}ac \sin B.}$$

Also $S = \frac{1}{2}ab \sin C$, and $S = \frac{1}{2}bc \sin A$.

Exercise 56. Area of a Triangle

Find the areas of the triangles in which it is given that:

1. $a = 27$, $c = 32$, $B = 40°$.
2. $a = 35$, $c = 43$, $B = 37°$.
3. $a = 4.8$, $c = 5.3$, $B = 39° \ 27'$.
4. $a = 9.8$, $c = 7.6$, $B = 48.5°$.
5. $a = 17.3$, $b = 19.4$, $C = 56.25°$.
6. $a = 48.35$, $b = 64.32$, $C = 62° \ 37'$.
7. $b = 127.8$, $c = 168.5$, $A = 72° \ 43'$.
8. $b = 423.9$, $c = 417.8$, $A = 68° \ 27'$.
9. $b = 32.78$, $c = 29.62$, $A = 57° \ 32' \ 20''$.
10. $b = 1487$, $c = 1634$, $A = 61° \ 30' \ 30''$.

11. Prove that the area of a parallelogram is equal to the product of the base, the diagonal, and the sine of the angle included by them.

12. Find the area of the quadrilateral $ABCD$, given $AB = 3$ in., $AC = 4.2$ in., $AD = 3.8$ in., $\angle BAD = 88° \ 10'$, $\angle BAC = 36° \ 20'$.

13. In a quadrilateral $ABCD$, $BC = 5.1$ in., $AC = 4.8$ in., $CD = 3.7$ in., $\angle ACB = 123° \ 42'$, and $\angle DCA = 117° \ 26'$. Draw the figure approximately and find the area.

14. In the pentagon $ABCDE$, $AB = 3.1$ in., $AC = 4.2$ in., $AD = 3.7$ in., $AE = 2.9$ in., $\angle A = 132° \ 18'$, $\angle BAC = 38° \ 16'$, and $\angle DAE = 53° \ 9'$. Find the area of the pentagon.

CASE 2. *Given two angles and any side.*

If two angles are known the third can be found, so we may consider that all three angles are given.

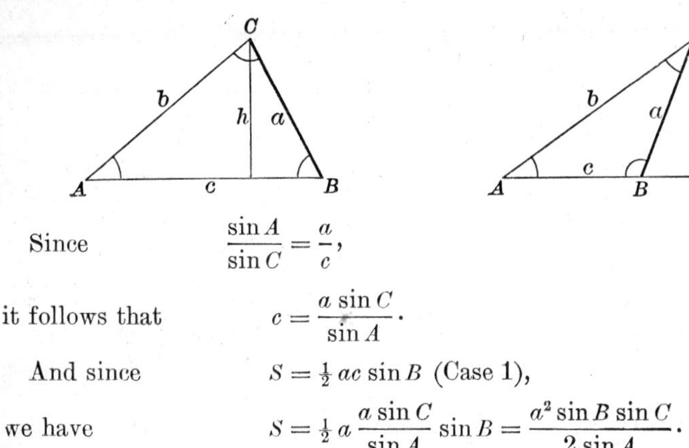

Since $$\frac{\sin A}{\sin C} = \frac{a}{c},$$

it follows that $$c = \frac{a \sin C}{\sin A}.$$

And since $$S = \tfrac{1}{2} ac \sin B \text{ (Case 1)},$$

we have $$S = \tfrac{1}{2} a \frac{a \sin C}{\sin A} \sin B = \frac{a^2 \sin B \sin C}{2 \sin A}.$$

Since all three angles are known we may use this formula; or, since $\sin(B + C) = \sin(180° - A) = \sin A$, we may write it as follows:

$$\boldsymbol{S = \frac{a^2 \sin B \sin C}{2 \sin (B + C)}}.$$

Exercise 57. Area of a Triangle

Find the areas of the triangles in which it is given that:

1. $a = 17$, $B = 48°$, $C = 52°$.
2. $a = 182$, $B = 63.5°$, $C = 78.4°$.
3. $a = 298$, $B = 78.8°$, $C = 95.5°$.
4. $a = 19.8$, $B = 39° 20'$, $C = 88° 40'$.
5. $a = 2487$, $B = 87° 28'$, $C = 69° 32'$.
6. $b = 483.7$, $A = 84° 32'$, $C = 78° 49'$.
7. $b = 527.4$, $A = 73° 42'$, $C = 63° 37'$.
8. $c = 296.3$, $A = 58° 35'$, $B = 42° 36'$.
9. $c = 17.48$, $A = 36° 27' 30''$, $B = 73° 50'$.
10. $c = 96.37$, $A = 42° 23' 35''$, $B = 69° 52' 50''$.

11. In a parallelogram $ABCD$ the diagonal AC makes with the sides the angles $27° 10'$ and $32° 43'$ respectively. AB is 2.8 in. long. What is the area of the parallelogram?

CASE 3. *Given the three sides.*

Since, by § 101, $\sin B = 2 \sin \frac{1}{2} B \cos \frac{1}{2} B$,

and, by § 115, $\sin \frac{1}{2} B = \sqrt{\frac{(s-a)(s-c)}{ac}}$,

and $\cos \frac{1}{2} B = \sqrt{\frac{s(s-b)}{ac}}$,

by substituting these values for $\sin \frac{1}{2} B$ and $\cos \frac{1}{2} B$ in the above equation, we have

$$\sin B = \frac{2}{ac} \sqrt{s(s-a)(s-b)(s-c)}.$$

By putting this value for $\sin B$ in the formula of Case 1, we have the following important formula for the area of a triangle:

$$S = \sqrt{s(s-a)(s-b)(s-c)}.$$

This is known as Heron's Formula for the area of a triangle, having been given in the works of this Greek writer. It is often given in geometry, but the proof by trigonometry is much simpler.

A special case of finding the area of a triangle when the three sides are given is that in which the radius of the circumscribed circle or the radius of the inscribed circle is also given.

If R denotes the radius of the circumscribed circle, we have, from § 106,

$$\sin B = \frac{b}{2R}.$$

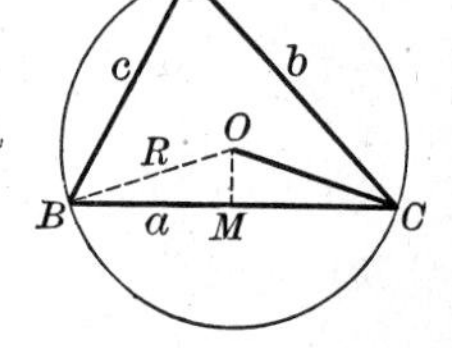

By putting this value of $\sin B$ in the formula of Case 1, we have

$$S = \frac{abc}{4R}.$$

If r denotes the radius of the inscribed circle, we may divide the triangle into three triangles by lines from the center of this circle to the vertices; then the altitude of each of the three triangles is equal to r. Therefore

$$S = \frac{1}{2} r(a+b+c) = rs.$$

By putting in this formula the value of S from Heron's Formula, we have

$$r = \sqrt{\frac{(s-a)(s-b)(s-c)}{s}}.$$

From this formula, r, as given in § 116, is seen to be equal to the radius of the inscribed circle.

Exercise 58. Area of a Triangle

Find the areas of the triangles in which it is given that:

1. $a = 3$, $b = 4$, $c = 5$.
2. $a = 15$, $b = 20$, $c = 25$.
3. $a = 10$, $b = 10$, $c = 10$.
4. $a = 1.8$, $b = 3.7$, $c = 2.1$.
5. $a = 5.3$, $b = 4.8$, $c = 4.6$.
6. $a = 7.1$, $b = 5.3$, $c = 6.4$.

7. There is a triangular piece of land with sides 48.5 rd., 52.3 rd., and 61.4 rd. Find the area in square rods; in acres.

Find the areas of the triangles in which it is given that:

8. $a = 2.4$, $b = 3.2$, $c = 4$, $R = 2$.
9. $a = 2.7$, $b = 3.6$, $c = 4.5$, $R = 2.25$.
10. $a = 3.9$, $b = 5.2$, $c = 6.5$, $R = 3.25$.
11. $a = 12$, $b = 12$, $c = 12$, $R = 6.928$.

12. Given $a = 60$, $B = 40° 35' 12''$, area $= 12$, find the radius of the inscribed circle.

Find the areas of the triangles in which it is given that:

13. $a = 40$, $b = 13$, $c = 37$.
14. $a = 408$, $b = 41$, $c = 401$.
15. $a = 624$, $b = 205$, $c = 445$.
16. $b = 8$, $c = 5$, $A = 60°$.
17. $a = 7$, $c = 3$, $A = 60°$.
18. $b = 21.66$, $c = 36.94$, $A = 66° 4' 19''$.
19. $a = 215.9$, $c = 307.7$, $A = 25° 9' 31''$.
20. $b = 149$, $A = 70° 42' 30''$, $B = 39° 18' 28''$.
21. $a = 4474.5$, $b = 2164.5$, $C = 116° 30' 20''$.
22. $a = 510$, $c = 173$, $B = 162° 30' 28''$.

23. If a is the side of an equilateral triangle, show that the area is $\frac{1}{4} a^2 \sqrt{3}$.

24. Two sides of a triangle are 12.38 ch. and 6.78 ch., and the included angle is 46° 24′. Find the area.

25. Two sides of a triangle are 18.37 ch. and 13.44 ch., and they form a right angle. Find the area.

26. Two angles of a triangle are 76° 54′ and 57° 33′ 12″, and the included side is 9 ch. Find the area.

27. The three sides of a triangle are 49 ch., 50.25 ch., and 25.69 ch. Find the area.

28. The three sides of a triangle are 10.64 ch., 12.28 ch., and 9 ch. Find the area.

29. The sides of a triangular field, of which the area is 14 A., are proportional to 3, 5, 7. Find the sides.

30. Two sides of a triangle are 19.74 ch. and 17.34 ch. The first bears N. 82° 30′ W.; the second S. 24° 15′ E. Find the area.

31. The base of an isosceles triangle is 20, and its area is $100 \div \sqrt{3}$; find its angles.

32. Two sides and the included angle of a triangle are 2416 ft., 1712 ft., and 30°; and two sides and the included angle of another triangle are 1948 ft., 2848 ft., and 150°. Find the sum of their areas.

33. Two adjacent sides of a rectangle are 52.25 ch. and 38.24 ch. Find the area.

34. Two adjacent sides of a parallelogram are 59.8 ch. and 37.05 ch., and the included angle is 72° 10′. Find the area.

35. Two adjacent sides of a parallelogram are 15.36 ch. and 11.46 ch., and the included angle is 47° 30′. Find the area.

36. Show that the area of a quadrilateral is equal to one half the product of its diagonals into the sine of the included angle.

37. The diagonals of a quadrilateral are 34 ft. and 56 ft., intersecting at an angle of 67°. Find the area.

38. The diagonals of a quadrilateral are 75 ft. and 49 ft., intersecting at an angle of 42°. Find the area.

39. In the quadrilateral $ABCD$ we have AB, 17.22 ch.; AD, 7.45 ch.; CD, 14.10 ch.; BC, 5.25 ch.; and the diagonal AC, 15.04 ch. Find the area.

40. Show that the area of a regular polygon of n sides, of which one side is a, is $\frac{na^2}{4} \cot \frac{180°}{n}$.

41. One side of a regular pentagon is 25. Find the area.

42. One side of a regular hexagon is 32. Find the area.

43. One side of a regular decagon is 46. Find the area.

44. If r is the radius of a circle, show that the area of the regular circumscribed polygon of n sides is $nr^2 \tan \frac{180°}{n}$, and the area of the regular inscribed polygon is $\frac{n}{2} r^2 \sin \frac{360°}{n}$.

45. Obtain a formula for the area of a parallelogram in terms of two adjacent sides and the included angle.

CHAPTER VIII

MISCELLANEOUS APPLICATIONS

119. Applications of the Right Triangle. Although the formulas for oblique triangles apply with equal force to right triangles, yet the formulas developed for the latter in Chapter IV are somewhat simpler and should be used when possible. It will be remembered that these formulas depend merely on the definitions of the functions.

Exercise 59. Right Triangles

1. If the sun's altitude is 30°, find the length of the longest shadow which can be cast on a horizontal plane by a stick 10 ft. in length.

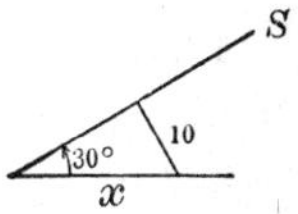

2. A flagstaff 90 ft. high, on a horizontal plane, casts a shadow of 117 ft. Find the altitude of the sun.

3. If the sun's altitude is 60°, what angle must a stick make with the horizon in order that its shadow in a horizontal plane may be the longest possible?

4. A tower 93.97 ft. high is situated on the bank of a river. The angle of depression of an object on the opposite bank is 25° 12′. Find the breadth of the river.

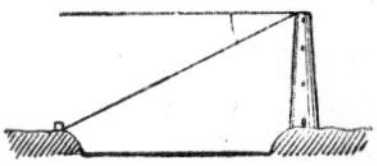

5. The angle of elevation of the top of a tower is 48° 19′, and the distance of the base from the point of observation is 95 ft. Find the height of the tower and the distance of its top from the point of observation.

6. From a tower 58 ft. high the angles of depression of two objects situated in the same horizontal line with the base of the tower, and on the same side, are 30° 13′ and 45° 46′. Find the distance between these two objects.

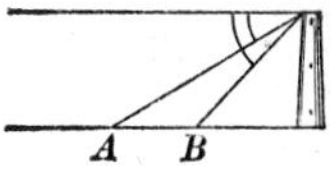

7. From one edge of a ditch 36 ft. wide the angle of elevation of the top of a wall on the opposite edge is 62° 39′. Find the length of a ladder that will just reach from the point of observation to the top of the wall.

8. The top of a flagstaff has been partly broken off and touches the ground at a distance of 15 ft. from the foot of the staff. If the length of the broken part is 39 ft., find the length of the whole staff.

9. From a balloon which is directly above one town the angle of depression of another town is observed to be $10° 14'$. The towns being 8 mi. apart, find the height of the balloon.

10. A ladder 40 ft. long reaches a window 33 ft. high, on one side of a street. Being turned over upon its foot, the ladder reaches another window 21 ft. high, on the opposite side of the street. Find the width of the street.

11. From a mountain 1000 ft. high the angle of depression of a ship is $27° 35' 11''$. Find the distance of the ship from the summit of the mountain.

12. From the top of a mountain 3 mi. high the angle of depression of the most distant object which is visible on the earth's surface is found to be $2° 13' 50''$. Find the diameter of the earth.

13. A lighthouse 54 ft. high is situated on a rock. The angle of elevation of the top of the lighthouse, as observed from a ship, is $4° 52'$, and the angle of elevation of the top of the rock is $4° 2'$. Find the height of the rock and its distance from the ship.

14. The latitude of Cambridge, Massachusetts, is $42° 22' 49''$. What is the length of the radius of that parallel of latitude?

15. At what latitude is the circumference of the parallel of latitude equal to half the equator?

16. In a circle with a radius of 6.7 is inscribed a regular polygon of thirteen sides. Find the length of one of its sides.

17. A regular heptagon, one side of which is 5.73, is inscribed in a circle. Find the radius of the circle.

18. When the moon is setting at any place, the angle at the moon subtended by the earth's radius passing through that place is $57' 3''$. If the earth's radius is 3956.2 mi., what is the moon's distance from the earth's center?

19. A man in a balloon observes the angle of depression of an object on the ground, bearing south, to be $35° 30'$; the balloon drifts $2\frac{1}{2}$ mi. east at the same height, when the angle of depression of the same object is $23° 14'$. Find the height of the balloon.

20. The angle at the earth's center subtended by the sun's radius is $16' 2''$, and the sun's distance is 92,400,000 mi. Find the sun's diameter in miles.

21. A man standing south of a tower and on the same horizontal plane observes its angle of elevation to be $54° 16'$; he goes east 100 yd. and then finds its angle of elevation is $50° 8'$. Find the height of the tower.

22. A regular pyramid, with a square base, has a lateral edge 150 ft. long, and the side of the base is 200 ft. Find the inclination of the face of the pyramid to the base.

23. The height of a house subtends a right angle at a window on the other side of the street, and the angle of elevation of the top of the house from the same point is 60°. The street is 30 ft. wide. How high is the house?

24. The perpendicular from the vertex of the right angle of a right triangle divides the hypotenuse into two segments 364.3 ft. and 492.8 ft. in length respectively. Find the acute angles of the triangle.

25. The bisector of the right angle of a right triangle divides the hypotenuse into two segments 431.9 ft. and 523.8 ft. in length respectively. Find the acute angles of the triangle.

26. Find the number of degrees, minutes, and seconds in an arc of a circle, knowing that the chord which subtends it is 238.25 ft., and that the radius is 196.27 ft.

27. Calculate to the nearest hundredth of an inch the chord which subtends an arc of $37° 43'$ in a circle having a radius of 542.35 in.

28. Calculate to the nearest hundredth of an inch the chord which subtends an arc of 14° in a circle having a radius of 475.23 in.

29. In an isosceles triangle ABC the base AB is 1235 in., and $\angle A = \angle B = 64° 22'$. Find the radius of the inscribed circle.

30. Find the number of degrees, minutes, and seconds in an arc of a circle, knowing that the chord which subtends it is two thirds of the diameter.

31. Find the number of degrees, minutes, and seconds in an arc of a circle, knowing that the chord which subtends it is three fourths of the diameter.

32. The radius of a circle being 2548.36 in., and the length of a chord BC being 3609.02 in., find the angle BAC made by two tangents drawn at B and C respectively.

33. Find the ratio of a chord to the diameter, knowing that the chord subtends an arc $27° 48'$. If the diameter is 8 in., how long is the chord? If the chord is 8 in., how long is the diameter?

34. Find the length of the diameter of a regular pentagon of which the side is 1 in., and the length of the side of a regular pentagon of which the diameter is 1 in.

35. Two circles of radii a and b are externally tangent. The common tangents AP, BP, and the line of centers $CC'P$ are drawn as shown in the figure. Find $\sin APC$.

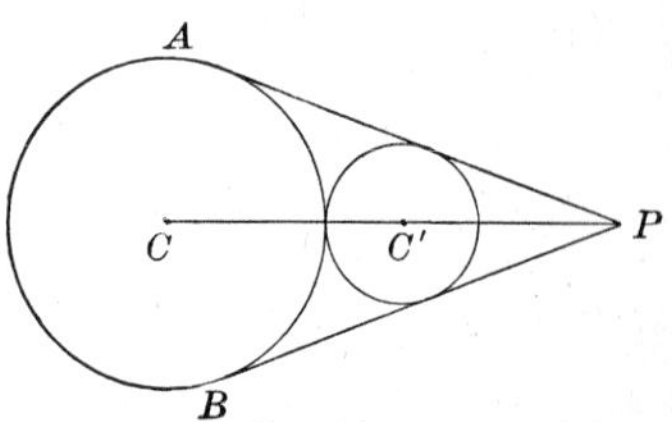

36. In Ex. 35 find $\angle APC$, knowing that $a = 3b$.

37. In $\triangle ABC$, $\angle A = 68° 26' 27''$, $\angle B = 75° 8' 23''$, and the altitude h, from C, is 148.17 in. Required the lengths of the three sides.

38. Two axes, OX and OY, form a right angle at O, the center of a circle of radius 1091 ft. Through P, a point on OX 1997 ft. from O, a tangent is drawn, meeting OY at C. Required OC and the angle CPO.

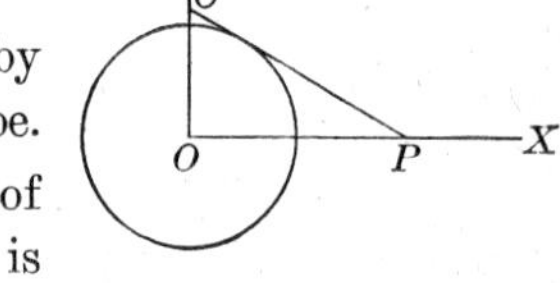

39. Find the sine of the angle formed by the intersection of the diagonals of a cube.

40. The angle of elevation of the top of a tower observed at a place A, south of it, is 30°; and at a place B, west of A, and at a distance of a from it, the angle of elevation is 18°. Show that the height of the tower is $\dfrac{a}{\sqrt{2 + 2\sqrt{5}}}$, the tangent of 18° being $\dfrac{\sqrt{5} - 1}{\sqrt{10 + 2\sqrt{5}}}$.

41. Standing directly in front of one corner of a flat-roofed house, which is 150 ft. in length, I observe that the horizontal angle which the length subtends has for its cosine $\sqrt{\frac{1}{5}}$, and that the vertical angle subtended by its height has for its sine $\dfrac{3}{\sqrt{34}}$. What is the height of the house?

42. At a distance a from the foot of a tower, the angle of elevation A of the top of the tower is the complement of the angle of elevation of a flagstaff on top of it. Show that the length of the staff is $2a \cot 2A$.

43. A rectangular solid is 4 in. long, 3 in. wide, and 2 in. high. Calculate the tangent of the angle formed by the intersection of any two of the diagonals.

44. Calculate the tangent as in Ex. 43, the solid being l units long, w units wide, and h units high.

120. Applications of the Oblique Triangle. As stated in § 119, when conditions permit of using a right triangle in making a trigonometric observation it is better to do so. Often, however, it is impossible or inconvenient to use the right triangle, as in the case of an observation on an inclined plane, and in such cases resort to the oblique triangle is necessary.

Exercise 60. Oblique Triangles

1. Show how to determine the height of an inaccessible object situated on a horizontal plane by observing its angles of elevation at two points in the same line with its base and measuring the distance between these two points.

2. Show how to determine the height of an inaccessible object standing on an inclined plane.

3. Show how to determine the distance between two inaccessible objects by observing angles at the ends of a line of known length.

4. The angle of elevation of the top of an inaccessible tower standing on a horizontal plain is $63° 26'$; at a point 500 ft. farther from the base of the tower the angle of elevation of the top is $32° 14'$. Find the height of the tower.

5. A tower stands on the bank of a river. From the opposite bank the angle of elevation of the top of the tower is $60° 13'$, and from a point 40 ft. further off the angle of elevation is $50° 19'$. Find the width of the river.

6. At the distance of 40 ft. from the foot of a vertical tower on an inclined plane, the tower subtends an angle of $41° 19'$; at a point 60 ft. farther away the angle subtended by the tower is $23° 45'$. Find the height of the tower.

7. A building makes an angle of $113° 12'$ with the inclined plane on which it stands; at a distance of 89 ft. from its base, measured down the plane, the angle subtended by the building is $23° 27'$. Find the height of the building.

8. A person goes 70 yd. up a slope of 1 in $3\frac{1}{2}$ from the bank of a river and observes the angle of depression of an object on the opposite bank to be $2\frac{1}{4}°$. Find the width of the river.

9. A tree stands on a declivity inclined $15°$ to the horizon. A man ascends the declivity 80 ft. from the foot of the tree and finds the angle then subtended by the tree to be $30°$. Find the height of the tree.

10. The angle subtended by a tree on an inclined plane is, at a certain point, 42° 17′, and 325 ft. further down it is 21° 47′. The inclination of the plane is 8° 53′. Find the height of the tree.

11. From a point B at the foot of a mountain, the angle of elevation of the top A is 60°. After ascending the mountain one mile, at an inclination of 30° to the horizon, and reaching a point C, an observer finds that the angle ACB is 135°. Find the number of feet in the height of the mountain.

12. The length of a lake subtends, at a certain point, an angle of 46° 24′, and the distances from this point to the two ends of the lake are 346 ft. and 290 ft. Find the length of the lake.

13. Along the bank of a river is drawn a base line of 500 ft. The angular distance of one end of this line from an object on the opposite side of the river, as observed from the other end of the line, is 53°; that of the second extremity from the same object, observed at the first, is 79° 12′. Find the width of the river.

14. Two observers, stationed on opposite sides of a cloud, observe its angles of elevation to be 44° 56′ and 36° 4′. Their distance from each other is 700 ft. What is the height of the cloud?

15. From the top of a house 42 ft. high the angle of elevation of the top of a pole is 14° 13′; at the bottom of the house it is 23° 19′. Find the height of the pole.

16. From a window on a level with the bottom of a steeple the angle of elevation of the top of the steeple is 40°, and from a second window 18 ft. higher the angle of elevation is 37° 30′. Find the height of the steeple.

17. The sides of a triangle are 17, 21, 28. Prove that the length of a line bisecting the longest side and drawn from the opposite angle is 13.

18. The sum of the sides of a triangle is 100. The angle at A is double that at B, and the angle at B is double that at C. Determine the sides.

19. A ship sailing north sees two lighthouses 8 mi. apart in a line due west; after an hour's sailing, one lighthouse bears S.W., and the other S. 22° 30′ W. (22° 30′ west of south). Find the ship's rate.

20. A ship, 10 mi. S.W. of a harbor, sees another ship sail from the harbor in a direction S. 80° E., at a rate of 9 mi. an hour. In what direction and at what rate must the first ship sail in order to catch up with the second ship in $1\frac{1}{2}$ hr.?

21. Two ships are a mile apart. The angular distance of the first ship from a lighthouse on shore, as observed from the second ship, is $35° 14' 10''$; the angular distance of the second ship from the lighthouse, observed from the first ship, is $42° 11' 53''$. Find the distance in feet from each ship to the lighthouse.

22. A lighthouse bears N. $11° 15'$ E., as seen from a ship. The ship sails northwest 30 mi., and then the lighthouse bears east. How far is the lighthouse from the second point of observation?

23. Two rocks are seen in the same straight line with a ship, bearing N. $15°$ E. After the ship has sailed N.W. 5 mi., the first rock bears E., and the second N.E. Find the distance between the rocks.

24. On the side OX of a given angle XOY a point A is taken such that $OA = d$. Deduce a formula for the length AB of a line from A to OY that makes a given angle a with OX. From this formula, x is a minimum when what sine is the maximum? Under those circumstances what is the sum of O and a? Then what is the size of $\angle B$? State the conclusion as to the size of $\angle a$ in order that x shall be the minimum.

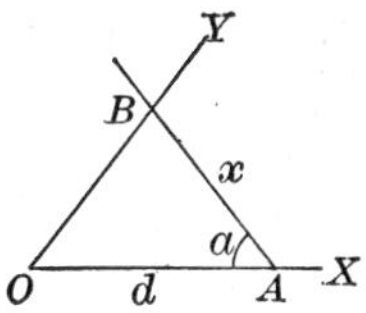

Y B x a O d A X

25. Three points, A, B, and C, form the vertices of an equilateral triangle, AB being 500 ft. Each of the two sides AB and AC is seen from a point P under an angle of $120°$; that is, $\angle APB = 120° = \angle CPA$. Find the length of AP.

26. A lighthouse facing south sends out its rays extending in a quadrant from S.E. to S.W. A steamer sailing due east first sees the light when 6 mi. away from the lighthouse and continues to see it for 45 min. At what rate is the ship sailing?

27. If two forces, represented in intensity by the lengths a and b, pull from P in the directions PC and PA, respectively, and if $\angle APC$ is known, the resultant force is represented in intensity and direction by f, the diagonal of the parallelogram $ABCP$. Show how to find f and $\angle APB$, given a, b, and $\angle APC$.

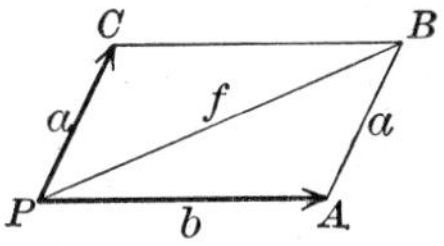

C B f a a P b A

28. Two forces, one of 410 lb. and the other of 320 lb., make an angle of $51° 37'$. Find the intensity and the direction of their resultant.

29. An unknown force combined with one of 128 lb. produces a resultant of 200 lb., and this resultant makes an angle of $18° 24'$ with the known force. Find the intensity and direction of the unknown force.

30. Wishing to determine the distance between a church A and a tower B, on the opposite side of a river, a man measured a line CD along the river (C being nearly opposite A), and observed the angles ACB, 58° 20′; ACD, 95° 20′; ADB, 53° 30′; BDC, 98° 45′. CD is 600 ft. What is the distance required?

31. Wishing to find the height of a summit A, a man measured a horizontal base line CD, 440 yd. At C the angle of elevation of A is 37° 18′, and the horizontal angle between D and the summit of the mountain is 76° 18′; at D the horizontal angle between C and the summit is 67° 14′. Find the height.

32. A balloon is observed from two stations 3000 ft. apart. At the first station the horizontal angle of the balloon and the other station is 75° 25′, and the angle of elevation of the balloon is 18°. The horizontal angle of the first station and the balloon, measured at the second station, is 64° 30′. Find the height of the balloon.

33. At two stations the height of a kite subtends the same angle A. The angle which the line joining one station and the kite subtends at the other station is B; and the distance between the two stations is a. Show that the height of the kite is $\frac{1}{2} a \sin A \sec B$.

34. Two towers on a horizontal plain are 120 ft. apart. A person standing successively at their bases observes that the angle of elevation of one is double that of the other; but when he is halfway between the towers, the angles of elevation are complementary. Prove that the heights of the towers are 90 ft. and 40 ft.

35. To find the distance of an inaccessible point C from either of two points A and B, having no instruments to measure angles. Prolong CA to a, and CB to b, and draw AB, Ab, and Ba. Measure AB, 500 ft.; aA, 100 ft.; aB, 560 ft.; bB, 100 ft.; and Ab, 550 ft. Compute the distances AC and BC.

36. To compute the horizontal distance between two inaccessible points A and B when no point can be found whence both can be seen. Take two points C and D, distant 200 yd., so that A can be seen from C, and B from D. From C measure CF, 200 yd. to F, whence A can be seen; and from D measure DE, 200 yd. to E, whence B can be seen. Measure AFC, 83°; ACD, 53° 30′; ACF, 54° 31′; BDE, 54° 30′; BDC, 156° 25′; DEB, 88° 30′. Compute the distance AB.

37. A column in the north temperate zone is S. 67° 30′ E. of an observer, and at noon the extremity of its shadow is northeast of him. The shadow is 80 ft. in length, and the elevation of the column at the observer's station is 45°. Find the height of the column.

121. Areas. In finding the areas of rectilinear figures the effort is made to divide any given figure into rectangles, parallelograms, triangles, or trapezoids, unless it already has one of these forms.

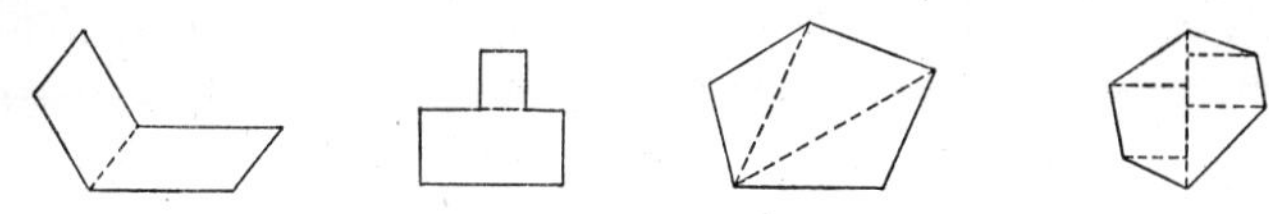

For example, the dotted lines show how the above figures may be divided for the purpose of computing the areas. A regular polygon would be conveniently divided into congruent isosceles triangles by the radii of the circumscribed circle.

Exercise 61. Miscellaneous Applications

1. In the trapezoid $ABCD$ it is known that $\angle A = 90°$, $\angle B = 32° 25'$, $AB = 324.35$ ft., and $CD = 208.15$ ft. Find the area.

2. Find the area of a regular pentagon of which each side is 4 in.

3. Find the area of a regular hexagon of which each side is 4 in.

4. The area of a regular polygon inscribed in a circle is to that of the circumscribed regular polygon of the same number of sides as 3 to 4. Find the number of sides.

5. The area of a regular polygon inscribed in a circle is the geometric mean between the areas of the inscribed and circumscribed regular polygons of half the number of sides.

6. Find the ratio of a square inscribed in a circle to a square circumscribed about the same circle. Find the ratio of the perimeters.

7. The square circumscribed about a circle is four thirds the inscribed regular dodecagon.

8. In finding the area of a field $ABCDE$ a surveyor measured the lengths of the sides and the angle which each side makes with the meridian (north and south) line through its extremities. AD happened to be a meridian line. Show how he could compute the area.

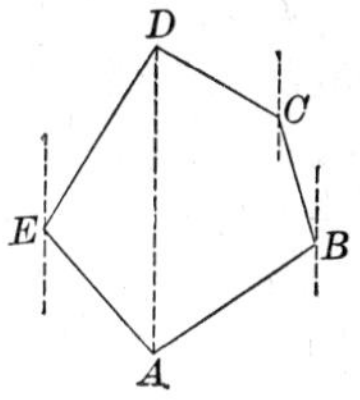

9. Two sides of a triangle are 3 and 12, and the included angle is 30°. Find the hypotenuse of the isosceles right triangle of equal area.

10. In the quadrilateral $ABCD$ we have given AB, BC, $\angle A$, $\angle B$, and $\angle C$. Show how to find the area of the quadrilateral.

11. In Ex. 10, suppose $AB = 175$ ft., $BC = 198$ ft., $\angle A = 95°$, $\angle B = 92° 15'$, and $\angle C = 96° 45'$. What is the area?

122. Surveyor's Measures. In measuring city lots surveyors commonly use feet and square feet, with decimal parts of these units. In measuring larger pieces of land the following measures are used:

$$16\frac{1}{2} \text{ feet (ft.)} = 1 \text{ rod (rd.)}$$
$$66 \text{ feet} = 4 \text{ rods} = 1 \text{ chain (ch.)}$$
$$100 \text{ links (li.)} = 1 \text{ chain}$$
$$10 \text{ square chains (sq. ch.)} = 160 \text{ square rods (sq. rd.)} = 1 \text{ acre (A.)}$$

We may write either 7 ch. 42 li. or 7.42 ch. for 7 chains and 42 links. The decimal fraction is rapidly replacing the old plan, in which the word *link* was used. Similarly, the parts of an acre are now written in the decimal form instead of, as formerly, in square chains or square rods.

Areas are computed as if the land were flat, or projected on a horizontal plane, no allowance being made for inequalities of surface.

123. Area of a Field. The areas of fields are found in various ways, depending upon the shape. In general, however, the work is reduced to the finding of the areas of triangles or trapezoids.

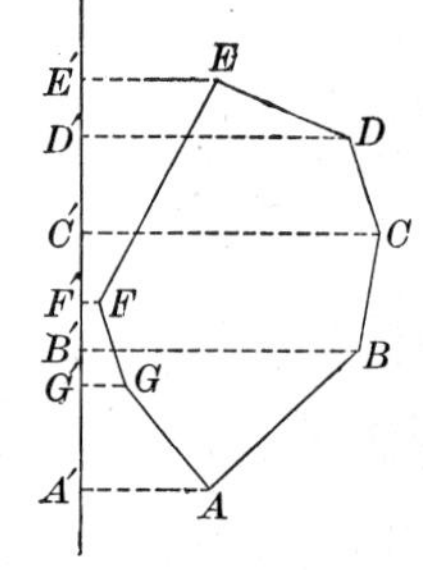

For example, in the case here shown we may draw a north and south line $E'A'$ and then find the sum of the areas of the trapezoids $ABB'A'$, $BCC'B'$, $CDD'C'$, and $DEE'D'$. From this we may subtract the sum of the trapezoids $AGG'A'$, $GFF'G'$ and $FEE'F'$. The result will be the area of the field.

Instead of running the imaginary line $E'A'$ outside the field, it would be quite as convenient to let it pass through F, A, E, or C. The method of computing the area is substantially the same in both cases.

For details concerning surveying, beyond what is here given and is included in Exercise 60, the student is referred to works upon the subject.

Exercise 62. Area of a Field

1. Find the number of acres in a triangular field of which the sides are 14 ch., 16 ch., and 20 ch.

2. Find the number of acres in a triangular field having two sides 16 ch. and 30 ch., and the included angle $64° 15'$.

3. Find the number of acres in a triangular field having two angles $68.4°$ and $47.2°$, and the included side 20 ch.

4. Required the area of the field described in § 123, knowing that $AA' = 8$ ch., $BB' = 12$ ch., $CC' = 13$ ch., $DD' = 12$ ch., $EE' = 8$ ch., $FF' = 1$ ch., $GG' = 2$ ch., $A'G' = 6$ ch., $G'B' = 1.5$ ch., $B'F' = 2.3$ ch., $F'C' = 3$ ch., $C'D' = 4$ ch., $D'E' = 2.9$ ch.

5. In a quadrangular field *ABCD*, *AB* runs N. 27° E. 12.5 ch., *BC* runs N. 30° W. 10 ch., *CD* runs S. 37° W. 15 ch., and *DA* runs S. 47° E. 11.5 ch. Find the area.

That *AB* is N. 27° E. means that it makes an angle of 27° east of the line running north through *A*.

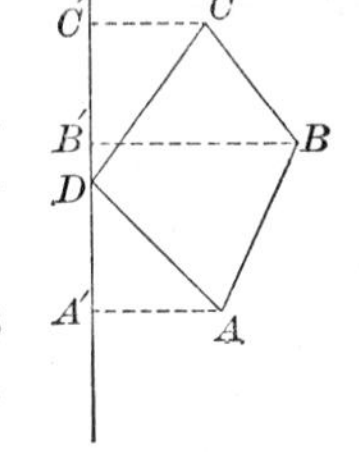

6. In a triangular field *ABC*, *AB* runs N. 10° E. 30 ch., *BC* runs S. 30° W. 20 ch., and *CA* runs S. 22° E. 13 ch. Find the area.

7. In a field *ABCD*, *AB* runs E. 10 ch., *BC* runs N. 12 ch., *CD* runs S. 68° 12′ W. 10.77 ch., and *DA* runs S. 8 ch. Find the area.

8. A field is in the form of a right triangle of which the sides are 15 ch., 20 ch., and 25 ch. From the vertex of the right angle a line is run to the hypotenuse, making an angle of 30° with the side that is 15 ch. long. Find the area of each of the triangles into which the field is divided.

Using a protractor, draw to scale the fields referred to in the following examples, and find the areas:

9. *AB*, N. 72° E. 18 ch., *BC*, N. 10° E. 12.5 ch., *CD*, N. 68° W. 21 ch., *DA*, S. 12° E. 26.3 ch.

10. *AB*, N. 45° E. 10 ch., *BC*, S. 75° E. 11.55 ch., *CD*, S. 15° W. 18.21 ch., *DA*, N. 45° W. 19.11 ch.

11. *AB*, N. 5° 30′ W. 6.08 ch., *BC*, S. 82° 30′ W. 6.51 ch., *CD*, S. 3° E. 5.33 ch., *DA*, E. 6.72 ch.

12. *AB*, N. 6° 15′ W. 6.31 ch., *BC*, S. 81° 50′ W. 4.06 ch., *CD*, S. 5° E. 5.86 ch., *DA*, N. 88° 30′ E. 4.12 ch.

13. A farm is bounded and described as follows: Beginning at the southwest corner of lot No. 13, thence N. $1\frac{1}{4}$° E. 132 rods and 23 links to a stake in the west boundary line of said lot; thence S. 89° E. 32 rods and $15\frac{4}{10}$ links to a stake; thence N. $1\frac{1}{4}$° E. 29 rods and 15 links to a stake in the north boundary line of said lot; thence S. 89° E. 61 rods and $18\frac{6}{10}$ links to a stake; thence S. $32\frac{1}{2}$° W. 54 rods to a stake; thence S. $35\frac{1}{4}$° E. 22 rods and 4 links to a stake; thence S. 48° E. 33 rods and 2 links to a stake; thence S. $7\frac{1}{2}$° W. 76 rods and 20 links to a stake in the south boundary line of said lot; thence N. 89° W. 96 rods and 10 links to the place of beginning. Containing 85.65 acres, more or less. Verify the area given and plot the farm.

This is a common way of describing a farm in a deed or a mortgage.

124. The Circle. It is learned in geometry that

$$c = 2\,\pi r, \quad \text{and} \quad a = \pi r^2,$$

where c = circumference, r = radius, a = area, and $\pi = 3.14159+$ $= 3.1416- =$ about $3\frac{1}{7}$. For practical purposes $\frac{22}{7}$ may be taken.

Furthermore, if we have a sector with angle n degrees, the area of the sector is evidently $\dfrac{n}{360}$ of πr^2.

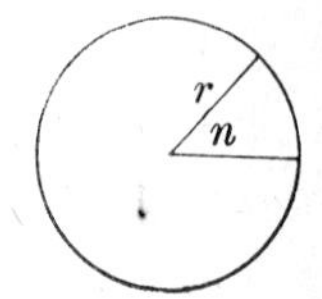

From these formulas we can, by the help of the formulas relating to triangles, solve numerous problems relating to the circle.

Exercise 63. The Circle

1. A sector of a circle of radius 8 in. has an angle of 62.5°. A chord joining the extremities of the radii forming the sector cuts off a segment. What is the area of this segment?

2. A sector of a circle of diameter 9.2 in. has an angle of 29° 42′. A chord joining the extremities of the radii forming the sector cuts off a segment. What is the area of the remainder of the circle?

3. In a circle of radius 3.5 in., what is the area included between two parallel chords of 6 in. and 5 in. respectively? (Give two answers.)

4. A regular hexagon is inscribed in a circle of radius 4 in. What is the area of that part of the circle not covered by the hexagon?

5. In a circle of radius 10 in. a regular five-pointed star is inscribed. What is the area of the star? What is the area of that part of the circle not covered by the star?

6. In a circle of diameter 7.2 in. a regular five-pointed star is inscribed. The points are joined, thus forming a regular pentagon. There is also a regular pentagon formed in the center by the crossing of the lines of the star. The small pentagon is what fractional part of the large one?

7. A circular hole is cut in a regular hexagonal plate of side 8 in. The radius of the circle is 4 in. What is the area of the rest of the plate?

8. A regular hexagon is formed by joining the mid-points of the sides of a regular hexagon. Find the ratio of the smaller hexagon to the larger.

CHAPTER IX

PLANE SAILING

125. Plane Sailing. A simple and interesting application of plane trigonometry is found in that branch of navigation in which the surface of the earth is considered a plane. This can be the case only when the distance is so small that the curvature of the earth may be neglected.

This chapter may be omitted if further applications of a practical nature are not needed.

126. Latitude and Departure. The *difference of latitude* between two places is the arc of a meridian between the parallels of latitude which pass through those places.

Thus the latitude of Cape Cod is 42° 2′ 21″ N. and the latitude of Cape Hatteras is 35° 15′ 14″ N. The difference of latitude is 6° 47′ 7″.

The *departure* between two meridians is the length of the arc of a parallel of latitude cut off by those meridians, measured in geographic miles.

The *geographic mile*, or *knot*, is the length of 1′ of the equator. Taking the equator to be 131,385,456 ft., $\frac{1}{60}$ of $\frac{1}{360}$ of this length is 6082.66 ft., and this is generally taken as the standard in the United States. The British Admiralty knot is a little shorter, being 6080 ft. The term "mile" in this chapter refers to the geographic mile, and there are 60 mi. in one degree of a great circle.

Calling the *course* the angle between the track of the ship and the meridian line, as in the case of N. 20° E., it will be evident by drawing a figure that the difference in latitude, expressed in distance, equals the distance sailed multiplied by the cosine of the course. That is

$$\text{diff. of latitude} = \text{distance} \times \cos C.$$

In the same way we can find the departure. This is evidently given by the equation

$$\text{departure} = \text{distance} \times \sin C.$$

For example, if a ship has sailed N. 30° E. 10 mi., the difference in latitude, expressed in miles, is

$$10 \cos 30° = 10 \times 0.8660 = 8.66,$$

and the departure is $10 \sin 30° = 10 \times 0.5 = 5.$

127. The Compass. The mariner divides the circle into 32 equal parts called *points*. There are therefore 8 points in a right angle, and a point is $11° 15'$. To sail two points east of north means, therefore, to sail $22° 30'$ east of north, or north-northeast (N.N.E.) as shown on the compass. Northeast (N.E.) is 45° east of north. One point east of north is called north by east (N. by E.) and one point east of south is called south by east (S. by E.). The other terms used, and their significance in angular measure, will best be understood from the illustration and the following table:

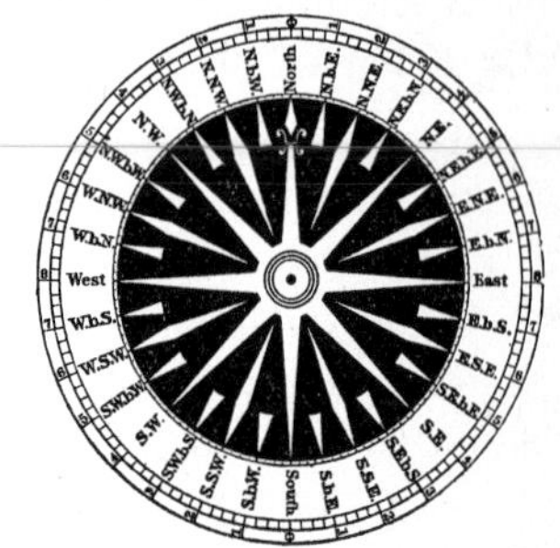

North		Points	° ′ ″	Points	South	
N. by E.	N. by W.	0-¼	2 48 45	0-¼	S. by E.	S. by W.
		0-½	5 37 30	0-½		
		0-¾	8 26 15	0-¾		
		1	11 15 0	1		
N.N.E.	N.N.W.	1-¼	14 3 45	1-¼	S.S.E.	S.S.W.
		1-½	16 52 30	1-½		
		1-¾	19 41 15	1-¾		
		2	22 30 0	2		
N.E. by N.	N.W. by N.	2-¼	25 18 45	2-¼	S.E. by S.	S.W. by S.
		2-½	28 7 30	2-½		
		2-¾	30 56 15	2-¾		
		3	33 45 0	3		
N.E.	N.W.	3-¼	36 33 45	3-¼	S.E.	S.W.
		3-½	39 22 30	3-½		
		3-¾	42 11 15	3-¾		
		4	45 0 0	4		
N.E. by E.	N.W. by W.	4-¼	47 48 45	4-¼	S.E. by E.	S.W. by W.
		4-½	50 37 30	4-½		
		4-¾	53 26 15	4-¾		
		5	56 15 0	5		
E.N.E.	W.N.W.	5-¼	59 3 45	5-¼	E.S.E.	W.S.W.
		5-½	61 52 30	5-½		
		5-¾	64 41 15	5-¾		
		6	67 30 0	6		
E. by N.	W. by N.	6-¼	70 18 45	6-¼	E. by S.	W. by S.
		6-½	73 7 30	6-½		
		6-¾	75 56 15	6-¾		
		7	78 45 0	7		
E.	W.	7-¼	81 33 45	7-¼	E.	W.
		7-½	84 22 30	7-½		
		7-¾	87 11 15	7-¾		
		8	90 0 0	8		

The compass varies in different parts of the earth; hence, in sailing, the compass course is not the same as the true course. The true course is the compass course, with allowances for variation of the needle in different parts of the earth, for deviation caused by the iron in the ship, and for leeway, the angle which the ship makes with her track.

Exercise 64. Plane Sailing

1. A ship sails from latitude 40° N. on a course N.E. 26 mi. Find the difference of latitude and the departure.

2. A ship sails from latitude 35° N. on a course S.W. 53 mi. Find the difference of latitude and the departure.

3. A ship sails from a point on the equator on a course N.E. by N. 62 mi. Find the difference of latitude and the departure.

4. A ship sails from latitude 43° 45′ S. on a course N. by E. 38 mi. Find the difference of latitude and the departure.

5. A ship sails from latitude 1° 45′ N. on a course S.E. by E. 25 mi. Find the difference of latitude and the departure.

6. A ship sails from latitude 13° 17′ S. on a course N.E. by E. $\frac{3}{4}$ E., until the departure is 42 mi. Find the difference of latitude and the latitude reached.

7. A ship sails from latitude 40° 20′ N. on a N.N.E. course for 92 mi. Find the departure.

8. If a steamer sails S.W. by W. 20 mi. what is the departure and the difference of latitude?

9. If a sailboat sails N. 25° W. until the departure is 25 mi., what distance does it sail?

10. A ship sails from latitude 37° 40′ N. on a N.E. by E. course for 122 mi. Find the departure.

11. A yacht sails $6\frac{1}{2}$ points west of north, the distance being 12 mi. What is the departure?

12. A steamer sails S.W. by W. 28 mi. It then sails N.W. 30 mi. How far is it then to the west of its starting point?

13. A ship sails on a course between S. and E. 24 mi., leaving latitude 2° 52′ S. and reaching latitude 2° 58′ S. Find the course and the departure.

14. A ship sails from latitude 32° 18′ N., on a course between N. and W., a distance of 34 mi. and a departure of 10 mi. Find the course and the latitude reached.

15. A ship sails on a course between S. and E., making a difference of latitude 13 mi. and a departure of 20 mi. Find the distance and the course.

16. A ship sails on a course between N. and W., making a difference of latitude 17 mi. and a departure of 22 mi. Find the distance and the course.

128. Parallel Sailing. Sailing due east or due west, remaining on the same parallel of latitude, is called *parallel sailing.*

129. Finding Difference in Longitude. In parallel sailing the distance sailed is, by definition (§ 126), the departure. From the departure the difference in longitude is found as follows:

Let AB be the departure. Then in rt. $\triangle OAD$

$$\angle AOD = 90° - \text{lat.}$$

Hence $$\frac{DA}{OA} = \sin(90° - \text{lat.}) = \cos \text{lat.}$$

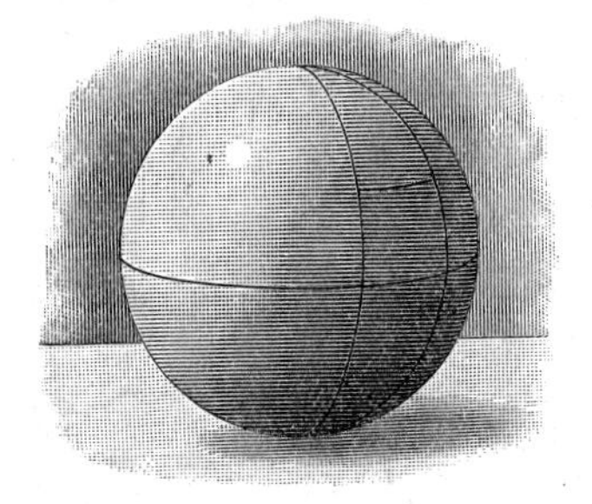

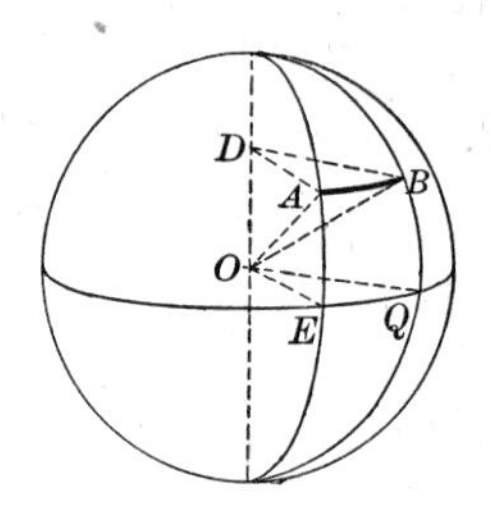

The triangles DAB and OEQ are similar, the arcs being (§ 125) considered straight lines.

Therefore $$\frac{DA}{OE} = \frac{AB}{EQ}, \quad \text{or} \quad \frac{DA}{OA} = \frac{AB}{EQ}.$$

Hence $$\cos \text{lat.} = \frac{AB}{EQ}.$$

Therefore $$EQ = \frac{AB}{\cos \text{lat.}} = AB \times \sec \text{lat.}$$

That is, **Diff. long. = depart. × sec lat.**

That is, the number of minutes in the difference in longitude is the product of the number of miles in the departure by the secant of the latitude, the nautical, or geographic, mile being a minute of longitude on the equator.

Exercise 65. Parallel Sailing

1. A ship in latitude 42° 16′ N., longitude 72° 16′ W., sails due east a distance of 149 mi. What is the position of the point reached?

2. A ship in latitude 44° 49′ S., longitude 119° 42′ E., sails due west until it reaches longitude 117° 16′ E. Find the distance made.

3. A ship in latitude 60° 15′ N., longitude 60° 15′ W., sails due west a distance of 60 mi. What is the position of the point reached?

130. Middle Latitude Sailing. Since a ship rarely sails for any length of time due east or due west, the difference in longitude cannot ordinarily be found as in parallel sailing (§§ 128, 129). Therefore, in plane sailing the departure between two places is measured generally on that parallel of latitude which lies midway between the

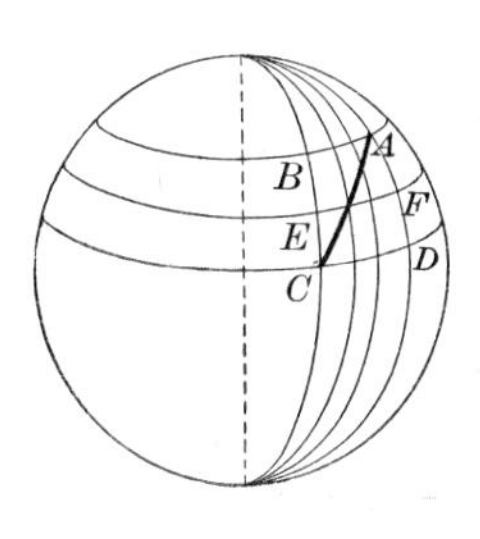

parallels of the two places. This is called the method of *middle latitude sailing*. Hence, in middle latitude sailing,

Diff. long. = depart. × sec mid. lat.

This assumption produces no great error, except in very high latitudes or excessive runs.

Exercise 66. Middle Latitude Sailing

1. A ship leaves latitude 31° 14′ N., longitude 42° 19′ W., and sails E.N.E. 32 mi. Find the position reached.

2. Leaving latitude 49° 57′ N., longitude 15° 16′ W., a ship sails between S. and W. till the departure is 38 mi. and the latitude is 49° 38′ N. Find the course, distance, and longitude reached.

3. Leaving latitude 42° 30′ N., longitude 58° 51′ W., a ship sails S.E. by S. 48 mi. Find the position reached.

4. Leaving latitude 49° 57′ N., longitude 30° W., a ship sails S. 39° W. and reaches latitude 49° 44′ N. Find the distance and the longitude reached.

5. Leaving latitude 37° N., longitude 32° 16′ W., a ship sails between N. and W. 45 mi. and reaches latitude 37° 10′ N. Find the course and the longitude reached.

6. A ship sails from latitude 40° 28′ N., longitude 74° W., on an E.S.E. course, 62 mi. Find the latitude and longitude reached.

7. A ship sails from latitude 42° 20′ N., longitude 71° 4′ W., on a N.N.E. course, 30 mi. Find the latitude and longitude reached.

131. Traverse Sailing. In case a ship sails from one point to another on two or more different courses, the departure and difference of longitude are found by reckoning each course separately and combining the results. For example, two such courses are shown in the figure. This is called the method of *traverse sailing*.

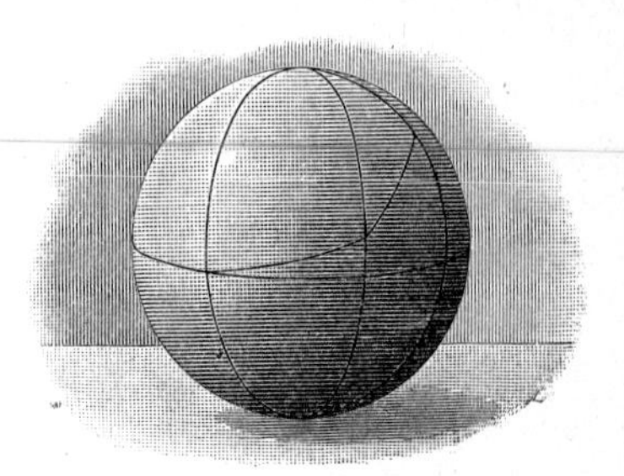

No new principles are involved in traverse sailing, as will be seen in solving Ex. 1, given below.

Exercise 67. Traverse Sailing

1. Leaving latitude 37° 16′ S., longitude 18° 42′ W., a ship sails N.E. 104 mi., then N.N.W. 60 mi., then W. by S. 216 mi. Find the position reached, and its bearing and distance from the point left.

For the first course we have difference of latitude 73.5 N., departure 73.5 E.; for the second course, difference of latitude 55.4 N., departure 23 W.; for the third course, difference of latitude 42.1 S., departure 211.8 W.

On the whole, then, the ship has made 128.9 mi. of north latitude and 42.1 mi. of south latitude. The place reached is therefore on a parallel of latitude 86.8 mi. to the north of the parallel left; that is, in latitude 35° 49.2′ S.

In the same way the departure is found to be 161.3 mi. W., and the middle latitude is 36° 32.6′. With these data we find the difference of longitude to be 201′, or 3° 21′ W. Hence the longitude reached is 22° 3′ W.

With the difference of latitude 86.8 mi. and the departure 161.3 mi., we find the course to be N. 61° 43′ W. and the distance 183.2 mi. The ship has reached the same point that it would have reached if it had sailed directly on a course N. 61° 43′ W. for a distance of 183.2 mi.

2. A ship leaves Cape Cod (42° 2′ N., 70° 3′ W.) and sails S.E. by S. 114 mi., then N. by E. 94 mi., then W.N.W. 42 mi. Find its position and the total distance.

3. A ship leaves Cape of Good Hope (34° 22′ S., 18° 30′ E.) and sails N.W. 126 mi., then N. by E. 84 mi., then W.S.W. 217 mi. Find its position and the total distance.

4. A ship in latitude 40° N. and longitude 67° 4′ W. sails N.W. 60 mi., then N. by W. 52 mi., then W.S.W. 83 mi. Find its position.

5. A ship sailed S.S.W. 48 mi., then S.W. by S. 36 mi., and then N.E. 24 mi. Find the difference in latitude and the departure.

6. A ship sailed S. ½ E. 18 mi., S.W. ½ S. 37 mi., and then S.S.W. ¼ W. 56 mi. Find the difference in latitude and the departure.

CHAPTER X

GRAPHS OF FUNCTIONS

132. Circular Measure. Besides the methods of measuring angles which have been discussed already and are generally used in practical work, there is another method that is frequently employed in the theoretical treatment of the subject. This takes for the unit the angle subtended by an arc which is equal in length to the radius, and is known as *circular measure.*

133. Radian. An angle subtended by an arc equal in length to the radius of the circle is called a *radian.*

The term "radian" is applied to both the angle and arc. In the annexed figure we may think of a radius bent around the arc AB so as to coincide with it. Then $\angle AOB$ is a radian.

134. Relation of the Radian to Degree Measure. The number of radians in 360° is equal to the number of times the length of the radius is contained in the length of the circumference. It is proved in geometry that this number is 2π for all circles, π being equal to 3.1416, nearly. Therefore the radian is the same angle in all circles.

The circumference of a circle is 2π times the radius.

Hence $\quad 2\pi$ radians $= 360°$, and π radians $= 180°$.

Therefore $\quad 1 \text{ radian} = \dfrac{180°}{\pi} = 57.29578° = 57°\,17'\,45'',$

and $\quad 1 \text{ degree} = \dfrac{\pi}{180} \text{ radian} = 0.017453 \text{ radian}.$

135. Number of Radians in an Angle. From the definition of radian we see that the number of radians in an angle is equal to the length of the subtending arc divided by the length of the radius.

Thus, if an arc is 6 in. long and the radius of the circle is 4 in., the number of radians in the angle subtended by the arc is 6 in. ÷ 4 in., or $1\frac{1}{2}$.

This may be reduced to degrees thus:

$$1\tfrac{1}{2} \times 57.29578° = 85.94367°,$$

or, for practical purposes, $\quad 1\frac{1}{2} \times 57.3° = 85.9° = 85°\,54'.$

136. Reduction of Radians and Degrees. From the values found in § 134 the following methods of reduction are evident:

To reduce radians to degrees, multiply 57° 17′ 45″, or 57 29578°, by the number of radians.

To reduce degrees to radians, multiply 0.017453 by the number of degrees.

These rules need not be learned, since we do not often have to make these reductions. It is essential, however, to know clearly the significance of radian measure, since we shall often use it hereafter. In solving the following problems the rules may be consulted as necessary.

In particular the student should learn the following:

$$360° = 2\pi \text{ radians}, \qquad 60° = \tfrac{1}{3}\pi \text{ radians},$$
$$180° = \pi \text{ radians}, \qquad 30° = \tfrac{1}{6}\pi \text{ radians},$$
$$90° = \tfrac{1}{2}\pi \text{ radians}, \qquad 15° = \tfrac{1}{12}\pi \text{ radians},$$
$$45° = \tfrac{1}{4}\pi \text{ radians}, \qquad 22.5° = \tfrac{1}{8}\pi \text{ radians}.$$

The word *radians* is usually understood without being written. Thus $\sin 2\pi$ means the sine of 2π radians, or $\sin 360°$; and $\tan \frac{1}{4}\pi$ means the tangent of $\frac{1}{4}\pi$ radians, or 45°. Also, $\sin 2$ means the sine of 2 radians, or $\sin 114.59156°$.

Exercise 68. Radians

Express the following in radians:

1. 270°.
2. 11.25°.
3. 56.25°.
4. 7.5°.
5. 196.5°.
6. 1440°.
7. 200°.
8. 3000°.

Express the following in degree measure:

9. $1\frac{1}{2}\pi$.
10. $1\frac{1}{3}\pi$.
11. $1\frac{1}{6}\pi$.
12. $1\frac{1}{4}\pi$.
13. $\frac{1}{24}\pi$.
14. 3π.
15. 6π.
16. 10π.

State the quadrant in which the following angles lie:

17. $\frac{2}{3}\pi$.
18. $\frac{4}{5}\pi$.
19. $1\frac{3}{8}\pi$.
20. $1\frac{4}{5}\pi$.
21. 2.5π.
22. -3.4π.
23. 1.
24. -2.

Express the following in degrees and also in radians:

25. $\frac{3}{5}$ of four right angles.
26. $\frac{5}{6}$ of four right angles.
27. $\frac{2}{3}$ of two right angles.
28. $\frac{3}{8}$ of one right angle.
29. What decimal part of a radian is 1°? 1′?
30. How many minutes in a radian? How many seconds?
31. Express in radians the angle of an equilateral triangle.
32. Over what part of a radian does the minute hand of a clock move in 15 min.?

137. Functions of Small Angles. Let AOP be any acute angle, and let x be its circular measure. Describe a circle of unit radius about O as center and take $\angle AOP' = -\angle AOP$. Draw the tangents to the circle at P and P', meeting OA in T. Then we see that

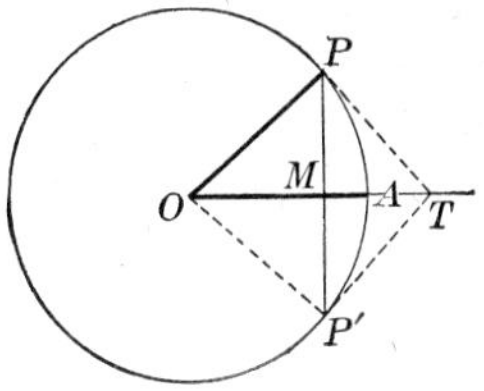

$$\text{chord } PP' < \text{arc } PP'$$
$$< PT + P'T.$$

Dividing by 2, $\quad MP < \text{arc } AP < PT,$

or $\quad \sin x < x < \tan x.$

Dividing by $\sin x$, $\quad 1 < \frac{x}{\sin x} < \sec x.$

Whence $\quad 1 > \frac{\sin x}{x} > \cos x.$

Therefore the value of $\frac{\sin x}{x}$ lies between $\cos x$ and 1.

If, now, the angle x is constantly diminished, $\cos x$ approaches the value 1.

Accordingly, the limit of $\frac{\sin x}{x}$, as x approaches 0, is 1.

Hence when x denotes the circular measure of an angle near 0° we may use x instead of $\sin x$ and instead of $\tan x$.

For example, required to find the sine and cosine of 1′.

If x is the circular measure of 1′,

$$x = \frac{2\pi}{360 \times 60} = \frac{3.14159+}{10800} = 0.00029088+,$$

the next figure in x being 8.

Now $\sin x > 0$ but $< x$; hence $\sin 1'$ lies between 0 and 0.000290889.

Again, $\cos 1' = \sqrt{1 - \sin^2 1'} > \sqrt{1 - (0.0003)^2} > 0.9999999.$

Hence $\quad \cos 1' = 0.9999999+.$

But, as above, $\quad \sin x > x \cos x.$

$$\therefore \sin 1' > 0.000290888 \times 0.9999999$$
$$> 0.000290888\,(1 - 0.0000001)$$
$$> 0.000290888 - 0.0000000000290888$$
$$> 0.000290887.$$

Hence $\sin 1'$ lies between 0.000290887 and 0.000290889; that is, to eight places of decimals,

$$\sin 1' = 0.00029088+,$$

the next figure being 7 or 8.

138. Angles having the Same Sine. If we let $\angle XOP = x$, in this figure, and let P' be symmetric to P with respect to the axis YY', we shall have $\angle XOP' = 180° - x$, or $\pi - x$. And since $\frac{a}{r} = \sin x = \sin(\pi - x)$ we see that x and $\pi - x$ have the same sine.

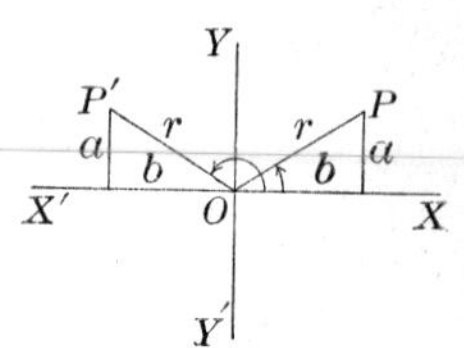

Furthermore, $\sin x = \sin(360° + x)$, and $\sin(180° - x) = \sin(360° + 180° - x)$. That is, we may increase any angle by 360° without changing the sine. Hence we have $\sin x = \sin(n \cdot 360° + x)$, and $\sin(180° - x) = \sin(n \cdot 360° + 180° - x)$. Using circular measure we may write these results as follows:

$$\sin x = \sin(2k\pi + x), \text{ and } \sin(\pi - x) = \sin(\overline{2k+1}\,\pi - x).$$

These may be simplified still more, thus:

$$\sin x = \sin[n\pi + (-1)^n x]$$

where n is any integer, positive or negative.

Thus if $n = 0$ we have $\sin x = \sin(0 \cdot \pi + (-1)^0 x) = \sin x$; if $n = 1$ we have $\sin x = \sin(\pi - x)$; if $n = 2$ we have $\sin x = \sin(2\pi + x)$; and so on.

Since the sine is the reciprocal of the cosecant, it is evident that x and $n\pi + (-1)^n x$ have the same cosecant.

To find four angles whose sine is 0.2588, we see by the tables that $\sin 15° = 0.2588$. Hence we have $\sin 15° = \sin[n\pi + (-1)^n \cdot 15°] = \sin(\pi - 15°) = \sin(2\pi + 15°) = \sin(3\pi - 15°)$; and so on.

Exercise 69. Sines and Small Angles

1. Find four angles whose sine is 0.2756.
2. Find six angles whose sine is 0.5000.
3. Find eight angles having the same sine as $\frac{1}{6}\pi$.
4. Find four angles having the same cosecant as $\frac{3}{8}\pi$.
5. Find four angles having the same cosecant as 0.1π.

Given $\pi = 3.141592653589$, compute to eleven decimal places:

6. $\cos 1'$.
7. $\sin 1'$.
8. $\tan 1'$.
9. $\sin 2'$.

10. From the results of Exs. 6 and 7, and by the aid of the formula $\sin 2x = 2\sin x \cos x$, compute $\sin 2'$, carrying the multiplication to six decimal places. Compare the result with that of Ex. 9.

11. Compute $\sin 1°$ to four decimal places.

12. From the formula $\cos x = 1 - 2\sin^2\frac{x}{2}$, show that $\cos x > 1 - \frac{x^2}{2}$.

139. Angles having the Same Cosine. If we let $\angle XOP = x$, in this figure, and let P' be symmetric to P with respect to the axis XX', we shall have $\angle XOP' = 360° - x$, or $-x$, depending on whether we think of it as a positive or a negative angle. In either case its cosine is $\frac{b}{r}$, the same as $\cos x$.

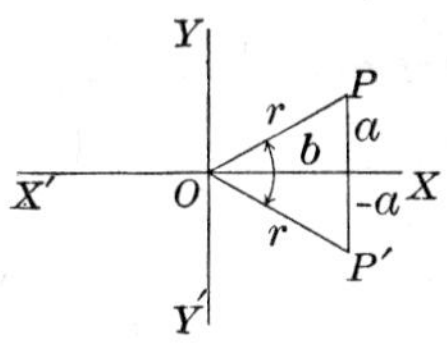

In either case $\cos x = \cos (n \cdot 360° - x)$.

In general, $\cos x = \cos (2\,n\pi \pm x)$,

where n is any integer, positive or negative.

Thus if $n = 0$, we have $\cos x = \cos (\pm x)$; if $n = 1$, we have $\cos x = \cos (2\pi \pm x)$; if $n = 2$, we have $\cos x = \cos (4\pi \pm x)$; and so on.

Since the cosine is the reciprocal of the secant, it is evident that x and $2\,n\pi \pm x$ have the same secant.

140. Angles having the Same Tangent. Since we have $\tan x = \frac{a}{b}$, and $\tan (180° + x) = \frac{-a}{-b}$, we see that $\tan x = \tan (180° + x)$. In general we may say that

$$\tan x = \tan (2\,k\pi + x) = \tan (2\,k\pi + \pi + x).$$

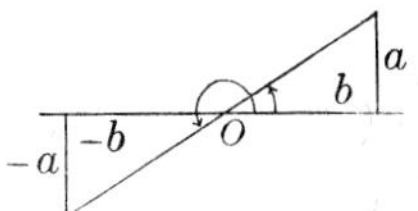

This may be written more simply thus:

$$\tan x = \tan (n\pi + x),$$

where n is any integer, positive or negative.

Thus if we have $\tan 20°$ given, we know that $n\pi + 20°$ has the same tangent. Writing both in degree measure, we may say that $n \cdot 180° + 20°$ has the same tangent. If $n = 1$, we have $200°$; if $n = 2$, we have $380°$; if $n = 3$, we have $560°$; and so on. Furthermore, if $n = -1$, we have $-160°$; and so on.

Since the cotangent is the reciprocal of the tangent, it is evident that x and $n\pi + x$ have the same cotangent.

Exercise 70. Angles having the Same Functions

1. Find two positive angles that have $\frac{1}{2}$ as their cosine.
2. Find two negative angles that have $\frac{1}{2}$ as their cosine.
3. Find four angles whose cosine is the same as the cosine of $25°$
4. Find four angles that have 2 as their secant.
5. Find two positive angles that have 1 as their tangent.
6. Find two negative angles that have 1 as their tangent.
7. Find four angles that have $\sqrt{3}$ as their tangent.
8. Find four angles that have $\sqrt{3}$ as their cotangent.
9. Find four angles that have 0.5000 as their tangent.
10. Find four negative angles whose cotangent is 0.5000.

141. Inverse Trigonometric Functions. If $y = \sin x$, then x is the angle whose sine is y. This is expressed by the symbols $x = \sin^{-1} y$, or $x = \text{arc} \sin y$.

In American and English books the symbol $\sin^{-1} y$ is generally used; on the continent of Europe the symbol arc sin y is the one that is met.

The symbol $\sin^{-1} y$ is read "the inverse sine of y," "the antisine of y," or "the angle whose sine is y." The symbol arc sin y is read "the arc whose sine is y," or "the angle whose sine is y."

The symbols $\cos^{-1} x$, $\tan^{-1} x$, $\cot^{-1} x$, and so on are similarly used.

The symbol $\sin^{-1} y$ must not be confused with $(\sin y)^{-1}$. The former means the angle whose sine is y; the latter means the reciprocal of $\sin y$.

We have seen (§ 138) that $\sin^{-1} 0.5000$ may be $30°, 150°, 390°, 510°$, and so on. In other words, there are many values for $\sin^{-1} x$; that is,

Inverse trigonometric functions are many-valued.

142. Principal Value of an Inverse Function. The smallest positive value of an inverse function is called its *principal value.*

For example, the principal value of $\sin^{-1} 0.5000$ is $30°$; the principal value of $\cos^{-1} 0.5000$ is $60°$; the principal value of $\tan^{-1}(-1)$ is $135°$; and so on.

Exercise 71. Inverse Functions

Prove the following formulas:

1. $\sin^{-1} x + \cos^{-1} x = \frac{1}{2}\pi$.
2. $\tan^{-1} x + \cot^{-1} x = \frac{1}{2}\pi$.
3. $\sec^{-1} x + \csc^{-1} x = \frac{1}{2}\pi$.
4. $\sin^{-1}(-x) = -\sin^{-1} x$.

Find two values of each of the following:

5. $\sin^{-1} \frac{1}{2}\sqrt{3}$.
6. $\csc^{-1} \sqrt{2}$.
7. $\tan^{-1} \frac{1}{3}\sqrt{3}$.
8. $\tan^{-1} \infty$.
9. $\sec^{-1} 2$.
10. $\cos^{-1}(-\frac{1}{2}\sqrt{2})$.

11. Find the value of the sine of the angle whose cosine is $\frac{1}{2}$; that is, the value of $\sin(\cos^{-1}\frac{1}{2})$.

Find the values of the following:

12. $\sin(\cos^{-1} \frac{1}{2}\sqrt{3})$.
13. $\sin(\tan^{-1} 1)$.
14. $\cos(\cot^{-1} 1)$.

Prove the following formulas:

15. $\tan(\tan^{-1} x + \tan^{-1} y) = \dfrac{x + y}{1 - xy}$.
16. $\tan^{-1}\left(\dfrac{x}{\sqrt{1 - x^2}}\right) = \sin^{-1} x$.
17. $\tan(2\tan^{-1} x) = \dfrac{2x}{1 - x^2}$.
18. $\sin(2\tan^{-1} x) = \dfrac{2x}{1 + x^2}$.

Find four values of each of the following:

19. $\tan^{-1} 0.5774$.
20. $\cot^{-1} 0.6249$.
21. $\sin^{-1} 0.9613$.
22. $\sin^{-1} 0.3256$.
23. $\cot^{-1} 0.2756$.
24. $\cos^{-1} 0.9455$.

25. Solve the equation $y = \sin^{-1} \frac{1}{3}$.
26. Find the value of $\sin(\tan^{-1} \frac{1}{2} + \tan^{-1} \frac{1}{3})$.
27. If $\sin^{-1} x = 2 \cos^{-1} x$, find the value of x.

Prove the following formulas:

28. $\cos(\sin^{-1} x) = \sqrt{1 - x^2}$.
29. $\cos(2 \sin^{-1} x) = 1 - 2x^2$.
30. $\sin(\sin^{-1} x) = x$.
31. $\sin(\sin^{-1} x + \sin^{-1} y) = x\sqrt{1 - y^2} + y\sqrt{1 - x^2}$.
32. $\tan^{-1} 2 + \tan^{-1} \frac{1}{2} = \frac{1}{2}\pi$.
33. $2 \tan^{-1} x = \tan^{-1}[2x : (1 - x^2)]$.
34. $2 \sin^{-1} x = \sin^{-1}(2x\sqrt{1 - x^2})$.
35. $2 \cos^{-1} x = \cos^{-1}(2x^2 - 1)$.
36. $3 \tan^{-1} x = \tan^{-1}[(3x - x^3) : (1 - 3x^2)]$.
37. $\sin^{-1}\sqrt{x : y} = \tan^{-1}\sqrt{x : (y - x)}$.
38. $\sin^{-1}\sqrt{(x - y) : (x - z)} = \tan^{-1}\sqrt{(x - y) : (y - z)}$
39. $\sin^{-1} x = \sec^{-1}(1 : \sqrt{1 - x^2})$.
40. $2 \sec^{-1} x = \tan^{-1}\left[2\sqrt{x^2 - 1} : (2 - x^2)\right]$.
41. $\tan^{-1} \frac{1}{2} + \tan^{-1} \frac{1}{3} = \frac{1}{4}\pi$.
42. $\tan^{-1} \frac{1}{3} + \tan^{-1} \frac{1}{5} = \tan^{-1} \frac{4}{7}$.
43. $\sin^{-1} \frac{3}{5} + \sin^{-1} \frac{12}{13} = \sin^{-1} \frac{63}{65}$.
44. $\sin^{-1} \frac{1}{82}\sqrt{82} + \sin^{-1} \frac{4}{41}\sqrt{41} = \frac{1}{4}\pi$.
45. $\sec^{-1} \frac{5}{3} + \sec^{-1} \frac{13}{12} = 75° 45'$.
46. $\tan^{-1}(2 + \sqrt{3}) - \tan^{-1}(2 - \sqrt{3}) = \sec^{-1} 2$.
47. $\tan^{-1} \frac{1}{3} + \tan^{-1} \frac{1}{5} + \tan^{-1} \frac{1}{7} + \tan^{-1} \frac{1}{8} = \frac{1}{4}\pi$.
48. $\sin^{-1} x + \sin^{-1}\sqrt{1 - x^2} = \frac{1}{2}\pi$.
49. $\sin^{-1} 0.5 + \sin^{-1} \frac{1}{2}\sqrt{3} = \sin^{-1} 1$.
50. $\tan^{-1} \frac{1}{2} = \tan^{-1} \frac{1}{4} + \tan^{-1} \frac{2}{9}$.
51. $\tan^{-1} 0.5 + \tan^{-1} 0.2 + \tan^{-1} 0.125 = \frac{1}{4}\pi$.
52. $\tan^{-1} 1 + \tan^{-1} 2 + \tan^{-1} 3 = \pi$.
53. $\tan^{-1} \frac{2}{3} + \tan^{-1} \frac{1}{4} + \tan^{-1} \frac{10}{11} = \frac{1}{2}\pi$.
54. $\cos^{-1} \frac{3}{10}\sqrt{10} + \sin^{-1} \frac{1}{5}\sqrt{5} = \frac{1}{4}\pi$.

143. Graph of a Function. As in algebra, so in trigonometry, it is possible to represent a function graphically. Before taking up the subject of graphs in trigonometry a few of the simpler cases from algebra will be considered.

Suppose, for example, we have the expression $3x + 2$. Since the value of this expression depends upon the value of x, it is called a *function* of x. This fact is indicated by the equation

$$f(x) = 3x + 2,$$

read "function $x = 3x + 2$." But since $f(x)$ is not so easily written as a single letter, it is customary to replace it by some such letter as y, writing the equation

$$y = 3x + 2.$$

If $x = 0$, we see that $y = 2$; if $x = 1$, then $y = 5$; and so on. We may form a table of such values, thus:

x	y	x	y
0	2	0	2
1	5	-1	-1
2	8	-2	-4
3	11	-3	-7
⋮	⋮	⋮	⋮

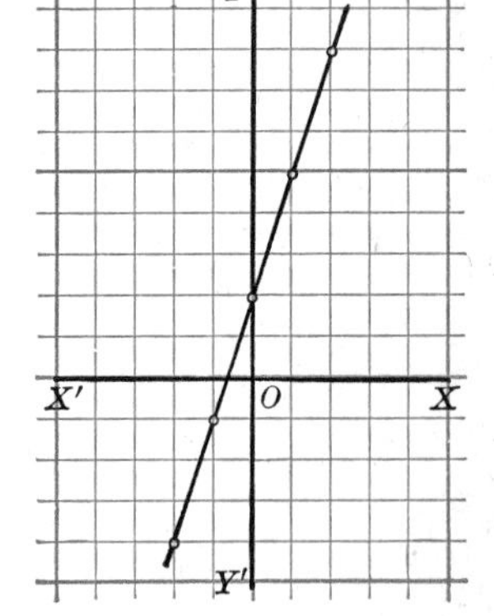

We may then plot the points (0, 2), (1, 5), (2, 8), $\cdots$, $(-1, -1)$, $(-2, -4)$, $\cdots$, as in § 77, and connect them. Then we have the graph of the function $3x + 2$.

The graph shows that the function, y or $f(x)$, changes in value much more rapidly than the variable, x. It also shows that the function does not become negative at the same time that the variable does, its value being 2 when $x = 0$, and $\frac{1}{2}$ when $x = -\frac{1}{2}$. This kind of function in which x is of the first degree only is called a *linear function* because its graph is a straight line.

Exercise 72. Graphs

Plot the graphs of the following functions:

1. $2x$.
2. $\frac{1}{2}x$.
3. $-x$.
4. $x + 1$.
5. $x - 1$.
6. $2x + 1$.
7. $3 - x$.
8. $4 - \frac{1}{2}x$.
9. $-2 - x$.
10. $2x + 3$.
11. $2x - 3$.
12. $3 - 2x$.
13. $0.5x + 1.5$.
14. $1.4x - 2.3$.
15. $-\frac{15}{4}x - 2\frac{1}{2}$.
16. $-\frac{29}{4}x + 3\frac{3}{4}$.

144. Graph of a Quadratic Function. We shall now consider functions of the second degree in the variable. Such a function is called a *quadratic function.*

Taking the function $x^2 + x - 2$, we write

$$y = x^2 + x - 2.$$

Preparing a table of values, as on page 158, we have

x	y	x	y
0	-2	0	-2
1	0	-1	-2
2	4	-2	0
3	10	-3	4
4	18	-4	10
⋮	⋮	⋮	⋮

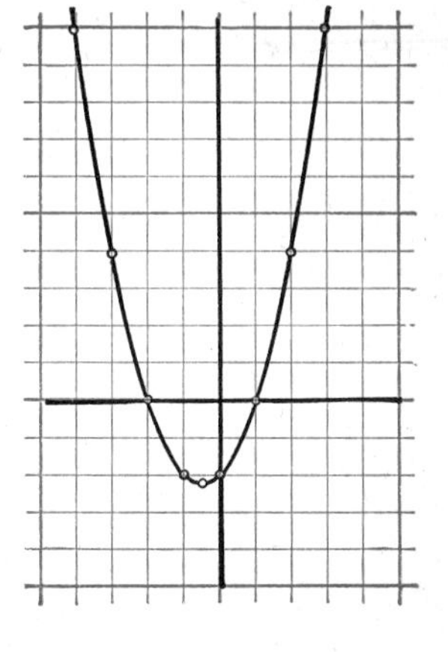

In order to see where the function lies between $y = -2$ and $y = -2$, we let $x = -\frac{1}{2}$. We find that when $x = -\frac{1}{2}$, $y = -2\frac{1}{4}$. Similarly if we give to x other values between 0 and -1, we shall find that y in every case lies between 0 and -2.

Plotting the points and drawing through them a smooth curve, we have the graph as here shown.

This curve is a *parabola.* All graphs of functions of the form $y = ax^2 + bx + c$ are parabolas.

Graphs of functions of the form $x^2 + y^2 = r^2$, or $y = \pm\sqrt{r^2 - x^2}$, are *circles* with their center at O.

Graphs of functions of the form $a^2x^2 + b^2y^2 = c^2$ are *ellipses*, these becoming circles if $a = b$.

Graphs of functions of the form $a^2x^2 - b^2y^2 = c^2$ are *hyperbolas.*

There are more general equations of all these *conic sections*, but these suffice for our present purposes. The graph of every quadratic function in x and y is always a conic section.

Exercise 73. Graphs of Quadratic Functions

Plot the graphs of the following functions:

1. x^2.	5. $x^2 - 1$.	9. $2x^2 + 3x$.	13. $\pm\sqrt{4 - 3x^2}$.
2. $2x^2$.	6. $x^2 + x + 1$.	10. $3x^2 - 4x$.	14. $\pm\sqrt{5 - 2x^2}$.
3. $\frac{1}{2}x^2$.	7. $x^2 - x + 1$.	11. $\pm\sqrt{4 - x^2}$.	15. $\pm\sqrt{4 + 3x^2}$.
4. $x^2 + 1$.	8. $x^2 + x - 1$.	12. $\pm\sqrt{9 - 4x^2}$.	16. $\pm\sqrt{5 + 2x^2}$.

145. Graph of the Sine. Since $\sin x$ is a function of x, we can plot the graph of $\sin x$. We may represent x, the arc (or angle), in degrees or in radians on the x-axis. Representing it in degrees, as more familiar, we may prepare a table of values as follows:

$x =$	0°	15°	30°	45°	60°	75°	90°	105°	120°	135°	150°	165°	180°	...
$y =$	0	.26	.5	.7	.87	.97	1	.97	.87	.7	.5	.26	0	...

If we represent each unit on the y-axis by $\frac{1}{5}$, and each unit on the x-axis by 30°, the graph is as follows:

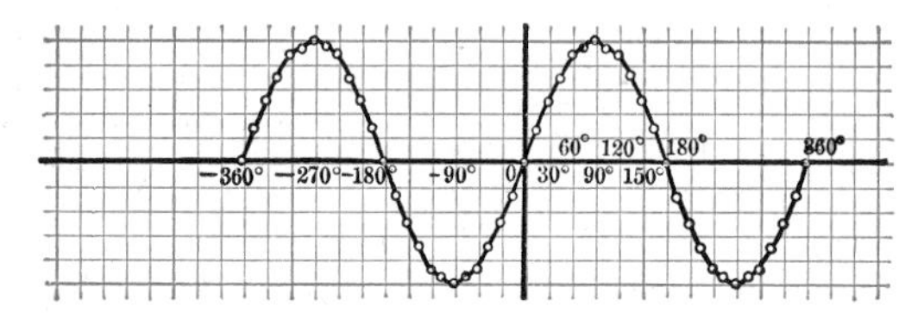

The graph shows very clearly that the sine of an angle x is positive between the values $x = 0°$ and $x = 180°$, and also between the values $x = -360°$ and $x = -180°$; that it is negative between the values $x = -180°$ and $x = 0°$, and also between the values $x = 180°$ and $x = 360°$. It also shows that the sine changes from positive to negative as the angle increases and passes through $-180°$ and 180°, and that the sine changes from negative to positive as the angle increases and passes through the values $-360°$, 0°, and 360°. These facts have been found analytically (§ 84), but they are seen more clearly by studying the graph.

If we use radian measure for the arc (angle), and represent each unit on the x-axis by $0.1\,\pi$, the graph is as follows:

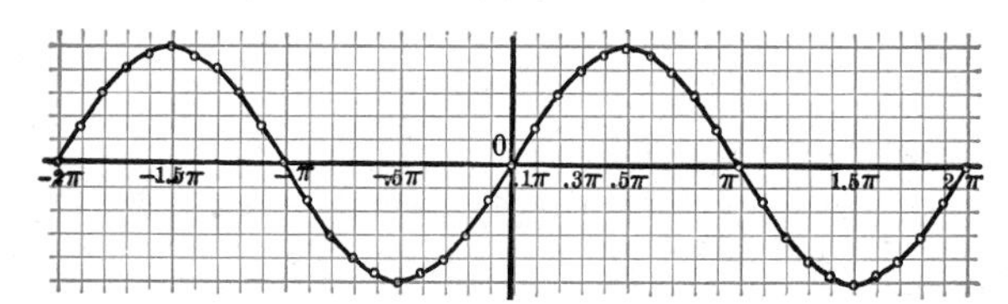

The nature of the curves is the same, the only difference being that we have used different units of measure on the x-axis, thus elongating the curve in the second figure.

146. Periodicity of Functions. This curve shows graphically what we have already found, that periodically the sine comes back to any given value.

Thus $\sin x = 1$ when $x = -270°$, 90°, 450°, $\cdots$, returning to this value for increase of the angle by every 360°, or $2\,\pi$ radians. The *period* of the sine is therefore said to be 360° or $2\,\pi$.

Exercise 74. Graphs of Trigonometric Functions

1. Verify the following plot of the graph of $\cos x$:

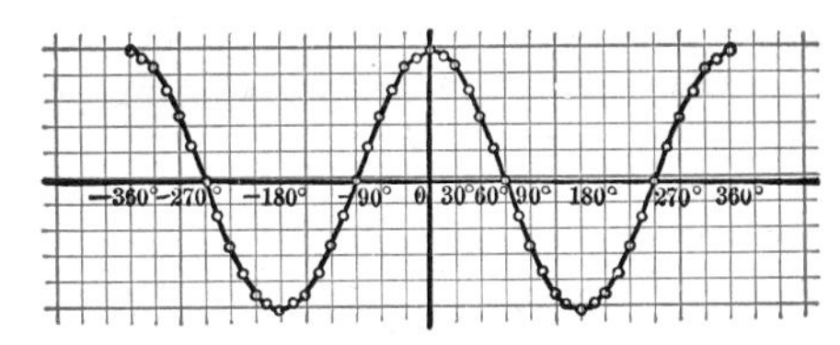

2. What is the period of $\cos x$?

3. Verify the following plot of the graph of $\tan x$:

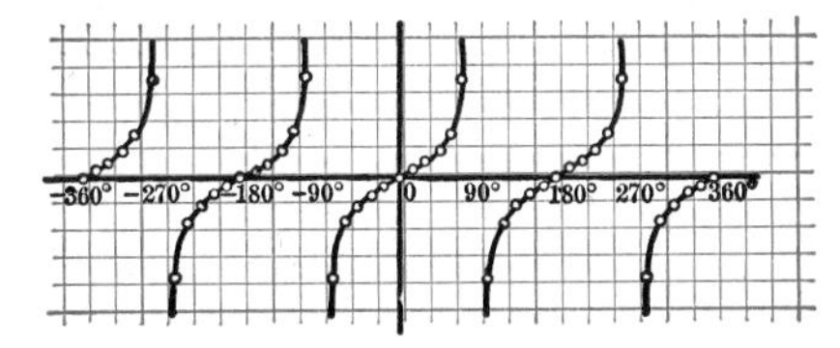

4. What is the period of $\tan x$?

5. Verify the following plot of the graph of $\cot x$:

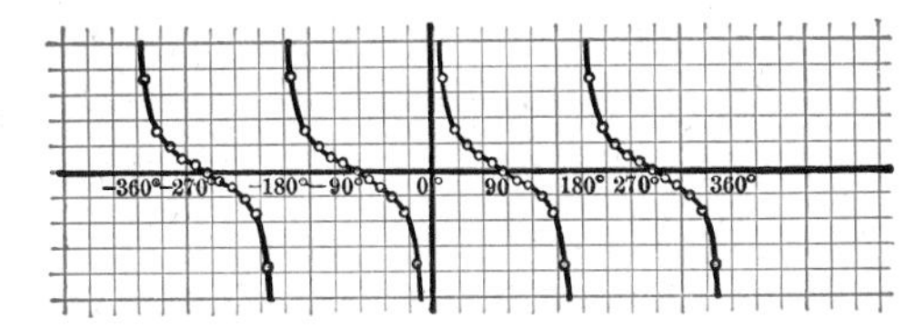

6. What is the period of $\cot x$?

7. Verify the following plot of the graph of $\sec x$:

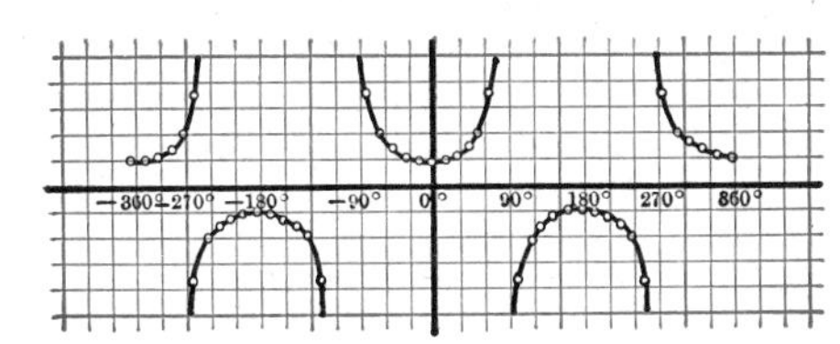

8. What is the period of $\sec x$?

9. Plot the graph of $\csc x$, and state the period. Also state at what values of x the sign of $\csc x$ changes.

10. Plot the graphs of $\sin x$ and $\cos x$ on the same paper. What does the figure tell as to the mutual relation of these functions?

Exercise 75. Miscellaneous Exercise

Find the areas of the triangles in which:

1. $a = 25$, $b = 25$, $c = 25$.
2. $a = 25$, $b = 33\frac{1}{3}$, $c = 41\frac{2}{3}$.
3. $a = 74$, $b = 75$, $c = 92$.
4. $a = 2\frac{1}{2}$, $b = 3\frac{1}{3}$, $c = 4\frac{1}{4}$.

5. Consider the area of a triangle with sides 17.2, 26.4, 43.6.

6. Consider the area of a triangle with sides 26.3, 42.4, 73.9.

7. Two inaccessible points A and B are visible from D, but no other point can be found from which both points are visible. Take some point C from which both A and D can be seen and measure CD, 200 ft.; angle ADC, 89°; and angle ACD, 50° 30′. Then take some point E from which both D and B are visible, and measure DE, 200 ft.; angle BDE, 54° 30′; and angle BED, 88° 30′. At D measure angle ADB, 72° 30′. Compute the distance AB.

8. Show by aid of the table of natural sines that $\sin x$ and x agree to four places of decimals for all angles less than 4° 40′.

9. If the values of $\log x$ and $\log \sin x$ agree to five decimal places, find from the table the greatest value x can have.

10. Find four angles whose cosine is the same as the cosine of 175°.

11. Find four angles whose cosine is the same as the cosine of 200°.

12. How many radians in the angle subtended by an arc 7.2 in. long, the radius being 3.6 in.? How many degrees?

13. How many radians in the angle subtended by an arc 1.62 in. long, the radius being 4.86 in.? How many degrees?

Draw the following angles:

14. $-\pi$.
15. -2.
16. $-\frac{1}{2}\pi$.
17. $-\frac{1}{2}$.
18. 2.7π.
19. $2\pi - 6$.
20. $3\pi - 9$.
21. $4 - \pi$.

22. Find four angles whose tangent is $\dfrac{1}{\sqrt{3}}$.

23. Find four angles whose cotangent is $\dfrac{1}{\sqrt{3}}$.

24. Plot the graphs of $\sin x$ and $\csc x$ on the same paper. What does the figure tell as to the mutual relation of these functions?

25. Plot the graphs of $\cos x$ and $\sec x$ on the same paper. What does the figure tell as to the mutual relation of these functions?

26. Plot the graphs of $\tan x$ and $\cot x$ on the same paper. What does the figure tell as to the mutual relation of these functions?

CHAPTER XI

TRIGONOMETRIC IDENTITIES AND EQUATIONS

147. Equation and Identity. An expression of equality which is true for one or more values of the unknown quantity is called an *equation.* An expression of equality which is true for all values of the literal quantities is called an *identity.*

For example, in algebra we may have the equation

$$4x - 3 = 7,$$

which is true only if $x = 2.5$. Or we may have the identity

$$(a + b)^2 = a^2 + 2ab + b^2,$$

which is true whatever values we may give to a and b.

Thus $\sin x = 1$ is a trigonometric equation. It is true for $x = 90°$ or $\frac{1}{2}\pi$, $x = 450°$ or $2\frac{1}{2}\pi$, $x = 810°$ or $4\frac{1}{2}\pi$, and so on, with a period of $360°$ or 2π. In general, therefore, the equation $\sin x = 1$ is true for $x = (2n + \frac{1}{2})\pi$. It is this general value that is required in solving a general trigonometric equation.

On the other hand, the equation $\sin^2 x = 1 - \cos^2 x$ is true for all values of x. It is therefore an identity.

The symbol $\equiv$ is often used instead of $=$ to indicate identity, but the sign of equality is very commonly employed unless special emphasis is to be laid upon the fact that the relation is an identity instead of an ordinary equation.

148. How to prove an Identity. A convenient method of proving a trigonometric identity is to substitute the proper ratios for the functions themselves.

Thus to prove that $\sin x = 1 : \csc x$ we have only to substitute $\frac{a}{c}$ for $\sin x$ and $\frac{c}{a}$ for $\csc x$. We then see that $\frac{a}{c} = 1 : \frac{c}{a}$. Similarly, to prove that $\tan x = \sin x \sec x$, we may substitute $\frac{a}{b}$ for $\tan x$, $\frac{a}{c}$ for $\sin x$, and $\frac{c}{b}$ for $\sec x$. We then have $\frac{a}{b} = \frac{a}{c} \cdot \frac{c}{b}$.

We can often prove a trigonometric identity by reference to formulas already proved.

This was done in proving the identity $\sin 2x = 2 \sin x \cos x$ (§ 101), and in proving $\tan(x + y) = \dfrac{\tan x + \tan y}{1 - \tan x \tan y}$ (§ 93).

In some cases it may be better to draw a figure and use a geometric proof, as was done in § 90.

Exercise 76. Identities

Prove the following identities:

1. $\tan x = \dfrac{2 \tan \frac{1}{2} x}{1 - \tan^2 \frac{1}{2} x}$.

2. $\sin x = \dfrac{2 \tan \frac{1}{2} x}{1 + \tan^2 \frac{1}{2} x}$.

3. $\sin 2x = \dfrac{2 \tan x}{1 + \tan^2 x}$.

4. $2 \sin x + \sin 2x = \dfrac{2 \sin^3 x}{1 - \cos x}$.

5. $\sin 3x = \dfrac{\sin^2 2x - \sin^2 x}{\sin x}$.

6. $\tan 3x = \dfrac{3 \tan x - \tan^3 x}{1 - 3 \tan^2 x}$.

7. $\dfrac{\tan 2x + \tan x}{\tan 2x - \tan x} = \dfrac{\sin 3x}{\sin x}$.

8. $\dfrac{3 \cos x + \cos 3x}{3 \sin x - \sin 3x} = \cot^3 x$.

9. $\dfrac{\sin 3x + \sin 5x}{\cos 3x - \cos 5x} = \cot x$.

10. $\dfrac{\sin 3x + \sin 5x}{\sin x + \sin 3x} = 2 \cos 2x$.

11. $\sin x + \sin 3x + \sin 5x = \dfrac{\sin^2 3x}{\sin x}$.

12. $\tan 2x + \sec 2x = \dfrac{\cos x + \sin x}{\cos x - \sin x}$.

13. $\tan x + \tan y = \dfrac{\sin (x + y)}{\cos x \cos y}$.

14. $\tan (x + y) = \dfrac{\sin 2x + \sin 2y}{\cos 2x + \cos 2y}$.

15. $\dfrac{\sin x + \cos y}{\sin x - \cos y} = \dfrac{\tan[\frac{1}{2}(x + y) + 45°]}{\tan[\frac{1}{2}(x - y) - 45°]}$.

16. $\sin 2x + \sin 4x = 2 \sin 3x \cos x$.

17. $\sin 4x = 4 \sin x \cos x - 8 \sin^3 x \cos x$.

18. $\sin 4x = 8 \cos^3 x \sin x - 4 \cos x \sin x$.

19. $\cos 4x = 1 - 8 \cos^2 x + 8 \cos^4 x = 1 - 8 \sin^2 x + 8 \sin^4 x$.

20. $\cos 2x + \cos 4x = 2 \cos 3x \cos x$.

21. $\sin 3x - \sin x = 2 \cos 2x \sin x$.

22. $\sin^3 x \sin 3x + \cos^3 x \cos 3x = \cos^3 2x$.

23. $\cos^4 x - \sin^4 x = \cos 2x$.

24. $\cos^4 x + \sin^4 x = 1 - \frac{1}{2} \sin^2 2x$.

25. $\cos^6 x - \sin^6 x = (1 - \sin^2 x \cos^2 x) \cos 2x$.

26. $\cos^6 x + \sin^6 x = 1 - 3 \sin^2 x \cos^2 x$.

27. $\csc x - 2 \cot 2x \cos x = 2 \sin x$.

Prove the following identities:

28. $(\sin 2x - \sin 2y)\tan(x+y) = 2(\sin^2 x - \sin^2 y)$.

29. $\sin 3x = 4\sin x \sin(60° + x)\sin(60° - x)$.

30. $\sin 4x = 2\sin x \cos 3x + \sin 2x$.

31. $\sin x + \sin(x - \frac{2}{3}\pi) + \sin(\frac{1}{3}\pi - x) = 0$.

32. $\cos x \sin(y - z) + \cos y \sin(z - x) + \cos z \sin(x - y) = 0$.

33. $\cos(x+y)\sin y - \cos(x+z)\sin z$
$= \sin(x+y)\cos y - \sin(x+z)\cos z$.

34. $\cos(x+y+z) + \cos(x+y-z) + \cos(x-y+z)$
$+ \cos(y+z-x) = 4\cos x \cos y \cos z$.

35. $\sin(x+y)\cos(x-y) + \sin(y+z)\cos(y-z)$
$+ \sin(z+x)\cos(z-x) = \sin 2x + \sin 2y + \sin 2z$.

36. $\sin(x+y) + \cos(x-y) = 2\sin(x + \frac{1}{4}\pi)\sin(y + \frac{1}{4}\pi)$.

37. $\sin(x+y) - \cos(x-y) = -2\sin(x - \frac{1}{4}\pi)\sin(y - \frac{1}{4}\pi)$.

38. $\cos(x+y)\cos(x-y) = \cos^2 x - \sin^2 y$.

39. $\sin(x+y)\sin(x-y) = \sin^2 x - \sin^2 y$.

40. $\sin x + 2\sin 3x + \sin 5x = 4\cos^2 x \sin 3x$.

If A, B, C are the angles of a triangle, prove that:

41. $\sin 2A + \sin 2B + \sin 2C = 4\sin A \sin B \sin C$.

42. $\cos 2A + \cos 2B + \cos 2C = -1 - 4\cos A \cos B \cos C$.

43. $\sin 3A + \sin 3B + \sin 3C = -4\cos\frac{3}{2}A \cos\frac{3}{2}B \cos\frac{3}{2}C$.

44. $\cos^2 A + \cos^2 B + \cos^2 C = 1 - 2\cos A \cos B \cos C$.

If $A + B + C = 90°$, prove that:

45. $\tan A \tan B + \tan B \tan C + \tan C \tan A = 1$.

46. $\sin^2 A + \sin^2 B + \sin^2 C = 1 - 2\sin A \sin B \sin C$.

47. $\sin 2A + \sin 2B + \sin 2C = 4\cos A \cos B \cos C$.

48. Prove that $\cot^{-1} 3 + \csc^{-1}\sqrt{5} = \frac{1}{4}\pi$.

49. Prove that $x + \tan^{-1}(\cot 2x) = \tan^{-1}(\cot x)$.

Prove the following statements:

50. $\dfrac{\sin 75° + \sin 15°}{\sin 75° - \sin 15°} = \tan 60°$.

51. $\sin 60° + \sin 120° = 2\sin 90° \cos 30°$.

52. $\cos 20° + \cos 100° + \cos 140° = 0$.

53. $\cos 36° + \sin 36° = \sqrt{2}\cos 9°$.

54. $\tan 11° 15' + 2\tan 22° 30' + 4\tan 45° = \cot 11° 15'$.

149. How to solve a Trigonometric Equation. To solve a trigonometric equation is to find for the unknown quantity the general value which satisfies the equation.

Practically it suffices to find the values between 0° and 360°, since we can then apply our knowledge of the periodicity of the various functions to give us the other values if we need them.

There is no general method applicable to all cases, but the following suggestions will prove of value:

1. *If functions of the sum or difference of two angles are involved, reduce such functions to functions of a single angle.*

Thus, instead of leaving $\sin(x+y)$ in an equation, substitute for $\sin(x+y)$ its equal $\sin x \cos y + \cos x \sin y$.

Similarly, replace $\cos 2x$ by $\cos^2 x - \sin^2 x$, and replace the functions of $\frac{1}{2}x$ by the functions of x.

2. *If several functions are involved, reduce them to the same function.*

This is not always convenient, but it is frequently possible to reduce the equation so as to involve only sines and cosines, or tangents and cotangents, after which the solution can be seen.

3. *If possible, employ the method of factoring in solving the final equation.*

4. *Check the results by substituting in the given equation.*

For example, solve the equation $\cos x = \sin 2x$.

By § 101, $$\sin 2x = 2 \sin x \cos x.$$

$$\therefore \cos x = 2 \sin x \cos x.$$

$$\therefore (1 - 2 \sin x) \cos x = 0.$$

$$\therefore \cos x = 0, \text{ or } 1 - 2 \sin x = 0.$$

$\therefore x = 90°$ or $270°$, $30°$ or $150°$, or these values increased by $2n\pi$.

Each of these values satisfies the given equation.

Exercise 77. Trigonometric Equations

Solve the following equations:

1. $\sin x = 2 \sin(\frac{1}{3}\pi + x)$.
2. $\sin 2x = 2 \cos x$.
3. $\cos 2x = 2 \sin x$.
4. $\sin x + \cos x = 1$.
5. $\sin x + \cos 2x = 4 \sin^2 x$.
6. $4 \cos 2x + 3 \cos x = 1$.
7. $\sin x = \cos 2x$.
8. $\tan x \tan 2x = 2$.
9. $\sec x = 4 \csc x$.
10. $\cos \theta + \cos 2\theta = 0$.
11. $\cot \frac{1}{2}\theta + \csc \theta = 2$.
12. $\cot x \tan 2x = 3$.

Solve the following equations:

13. $\sin x + \sin 2x = \sin 3x$.
14. $\sin 2x = 3\sin^2 x - \cos^2 x$.
15. $\cot\theta = \frac{1}{3}\tan\theta$.
16. $2\sin\theta = \cos\theta$.
17. $2\sin^2 x + 5\sin x = 3$.
18. $\tan x \sec x = \sqrt{2}$.
19. $\cos x - \cos 2x = 1$.
20. $\cos 3x + 8\cos^3 x = 0$.
21. $\tan x + \cot x = \tan 2x$.
22. $\tan x + \sec x = a$.
23. $\cos 2x = a(1 - \cos x)$.
24. $\sin^{-1}\frac{1}{2}x = 30°$.
25. $\tan^{-1}x + 2\cot^{-1}x = 135°$.
26. $\sec x - \cot x = \csc x - \tan x$.
27. $\tan 2x \tan x = 1$.
28. $\tan^2 x + \cot^2 x = \frac{10}{3}$.
29. $\sin x + \sin 2x = 1 - \cos 2x$.
30. $4\cos 2x + 6\sin x = 5$.
31. $\sin 4x - \sin 2x = \sin x$.
32. $2\sin^2 x + \sin^2 2x = 2$.
33. $\sin x \sec 2x = 1$.
34. $\sin^2 x + \sin 2x = 1$.
35. $\cos x \sin 2x \csc x = 1$.
36. $\cot x \tan 2x = \sec 2x$.
37. $\sin 2x = \cos 4x$.
38. $\sin 2z \cot z - \sin^2 z = \frac{1}{2}$.
39. $\tan^2 x = \sin 2x$.
40. $\sec 2x + 1 = 2\cos x$.
41. $\tan 2x + \tan 3x = 0$.
42. $\csc x = \cot x + \sqrt{3}$.
43. $\tan x \tan 3x = -\frac{2}{5}$.
44. $\cos 5x + \cos 3x + \cos x = 0$
45. $\sin^2 x - \cos^2 x = k$.
46. $\sin x + 2\cos x = 1$.
47. $\sin 4x - \cos 3x = \sin 2x$.
48. $\sin x + \cos x = \sec x$.
49. $2\cos x \cos 3x + 1 = 0$.
50. $\cos 3x - 2\cos 2x + \cos x = 0$
51. $\sin(x - 30°) = \frac{1}{2}\sqrt{3}\sin x$
52. $\sin^{-1}x + 2\cos^{-1}x = \frac{2}{3}\pi$.
53. $\sin^{-1}x + 3\cos^{-1}x = 210°$.
54. $\dfrac{1 - \tan x}{1 + \tan x} = \cos 2x$.
55. $\tan(\frac{1}{4}\pi + x) + \tan(\frac{1}{4}\pi - x) = 4$.
56. $\sqrt{1 + \sin x} - \sqrt{1 - \sin x} = 2\cos x$.
57. $\sin(45° + x) + \cos(45° - x) = 1$.
58. $(1 - \tan x)\cos 2x = a(1 + \tan x)$.
59. $\sin^6 x + \cos^6 x = \frac{7}{12}\sin^2 2x$.
60. $\sec(x + 120°) + \sec(x - 120°) = 2\cos x$.
61. $\sin^2 x \cos^2 x - \cos^2 x - \sin^2 x + 1 = 0$.
62. $\sin x + \sin 2x + \sin 3x = 0$.
63. $\sin\theta + 2\sin 2\theta + 3\sin 3\theta = 0$.
64. $\sin 3x = \cos 2x - 1$.
65. $\sin(x + 12°) + \sin(x - 8°) = \sin 20°$.

Solve the following equations:

66. $\tan(60° + x)\tan(60° - x) = -2.$

67. $\tan x + \tan 2x = 0.$

68. $\sin(x + 120°) + \sin(x + 60°) = \frac{3}{2}.$

69. $\sin(x + 30°)\sin(x - 30°) = \frac{1}{2}.$

70. $\sin 2\theta = \cos 3\theta.$

71. $\sin^4 x + \cos^4 x = \frac{5}{8}.$

72. $\sin^4 x - \cos^4 x = \frac{7}{25}.$

73. $\tan(x + 30°) = 2\cos x.$

74. $\sec x = 2\tan x + \frac{1}{4}.$

75. $\sin 11x \sin 4x + \sin 5x \sin 2x = 0.$

76. $\cos x + \cos 3x + \cos 5x + \cos 7x = 0.$

77. $\sin(x + 12°)\cos(x - 12°) = \cos 33° \sin 57$

78. $\sin^{-1} x + \sin^{-1} \frac{1}{2} x = 120°.$

79. $\tan^{-1} x + \tan^{-1} 2x = \tan^{-1} 3\sqrt{3}.$

80. $\tan^{-1}(x + 1) + \tan^{-1}(x - 1) = \tan^{-1} 2x.$

81. $(3 - 4\cos^2 x)\sin 2x = 0.$

82. $\cos 2\theta \sec\theta + \sec\theta + 1 = 0.$

83. $\sin x \cos 2x \tan x \cot 2x \sec x \csc 2x = 1.$

84. $\tan(\theta + 45°) = 8\tan\theta.$

85. $\tan(\theta + 45°)\tan\theta = 2.$

86. $\sin x + \sin 3x = \cos x - \cos 3x.$

87. $\sin \frac{1}{2} x(\cos 2x - 2)(1 - \tan^2 x) = 0.$

88. $\tan x + \tan 2x = \tan 3x.$

89. $\cot x - \tan x = \sin x + \cos x.$

Prove the following identities:

90. $(1 + \cot x + \tan x)(\sin x - \cos x) = \dfrac{\sec x}{\csc^2 x} - \dfrac{\csc x}{\sec^2 x}.$

91. $2\csc 2x \cot x = 1 + \cot^2 x.$

92. $\sin a + \sin b + \sin(a + b) = 4\cos\frac{1}{2}a \cos\frac{1}{2}b \sin\frac{1}{2}(a + b).$

93. $\tan(45° + x) - \tan(45° - x) = 2\tan 2x.$

94. $\cot^2 x - \cos^2 x = \cot^2 x \cos^2 x.$

95. $\tan^2 x - \sin^2 x = \tan^2 x \sin^2 x.$

96. $\cot^4 x + \cot^2 x = \csc^4 x - \csc^2 x.$

97. $\cos^2 x + \sin^2 x \cos^2 y = \cos^2 y + \sin^2 y \cos^2 x.$

150. Simultaneous Equations. Simultaneous trigonometric equations are solved by the same principles as simultaneous algebraic equations.

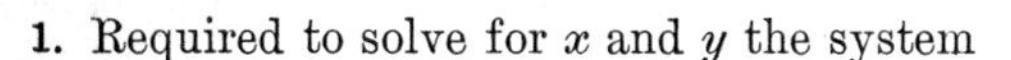

1. Required to solve for x and y the system

$$x \sin a + y \sin b = m \qquad (1)$$

$$x \cos a + y \cos b = n \qquad (2)$$

From (1), $x \sin a \cos a + y \sin b \cos a = m \cos a.$ (3)

From (2), $x \sin a \cos a + y \cos b \sin a = n \sin a.$ (4)

From (3) and (4), $y \sin b \cos a - y \cos b \sin a = m \cos a - n \sin a,$

or $y \sin (b - a) = m \cos a - n \sin a;$

whence $y = \dfrac{m \cos a - n \sin a}{\sin (b - a)}.$

Similarly, $x = \dfrac{n \sin b - m \cos b}{\sin (b - a)}.$

2. Required to solve for x and y the system

$$\sin x + \sin y = a \qquad (1)$$

$$\cos x + \cos y = b \qquad (2)$$

By § 103, $2 \sin \frac{1}{2}(x + y) \cos \frac{1}{2}(x - y) = a,$ (3)

and $2 \cos \frac{1}{2}(x + y) \cos \frac{1}{2}(x - y) = b.$

Dividing, $\tan \frac{1}{2}(x + y) = \dfrac{a}{b}.$ (4)

$$\therefore \sin \tfrac{1}{2}(x + y) = \frac{a}{\sqrt{a^2 + b^2}}.$$

Substituting the value of $\sin \frac{1}{2}(x + y)$ in (3),

$$\cos \tfrac{1}{2}(x - y) = \tfrac{1}{2}\sqrt{a^2 + b^2}. \qquad (5)$$

From (4), $x + y = 2 \tan^{-1} \dfrac{a}{b}.$ (6)

From (5), $x - y = 2 \cos^{-1} \frac{1}{2}\sqrt{a^2 + b^2}.$ (7)

From (6) and (7), $x = \tan^{-1} \dfrac{a}{b} + \cos^{-1} \frac{1}{2}\sqrt{a^2 + b^2},$

and $y = \tan^{-1} \dfrac{a}{b} - \cos^{-1} \frac{1}{2}\sqrt{a^2 + b^2}.$

3. Required to solve for x and y the system

$$y \sin x = a \qquad (1)$$

$$y \cos x = b \qquad (2)$$

Dividing, $\tan x = \dfrac{a}{b}.$

$$\therefore x = \tan^{-1} \frac{a}{b}.$$

Adding the squares of (1) and (2),

$$y^2 (\sin^2 x + \cos^2 x) = a^2 + b^2.$$

Therefore $y^2 = a^2 + b^2,$

and $y = \pm \sqrt{a^2 + b^2}.$

4. Required to solve for x and y the system

$$y \sin(x + a) = m \tag{1}$$

$$y \cos(x + b) = n \tag{2}$$

From (1), $y \sin x \cos a + y \cos x \sin a = m.$

From (2), $y \cos x \cos b - y \sin x \sin b = n.$

We may now solve for $y \sin x$ and $y \cos x$, and then solve for x and y.

5. Required to solve for r, x, and y the system

$$r \cos x \sin y = a \tag{1}$$

$$r \cos x \cos y = b \tag{2}$$

$$r \sin x = c \tag{3}$$

Dividing (1) by (2), $\tan y = \frac{a}{b}.$

$$\therefore y = \tan^{-1}\frac{a}{b}.$$

Squaring (1) and (2) and adding, $r^2 \cos^2 x = a^2 + b^2. \quad (4)$

Taking the square root, $r \cos x = \sqrt{a^2 + b^2}. \quad (5)$

Dividing (3) by (5), $\tan x = \frac{c}{\sqrt{a^2 + b^2}}.$

$$\therefore x = \tan^{-1}\frac{c}{\sqrt{a^2 + b^2}}.$$

Squaring (3) and adding to (4), $r^2 = a^2 + b^2 + c^2.$

$$\therefore r = \sqrt{a^2 + b^2 + c^2}.$$

Exercise 78. Simultaneous Equations

Solve the following systems for x and y:

1. $\sin x + \sin y = \sin a$
   $\cos x + \cos y = 1 + \cos a$

2. $\sin^2 x + \sin^2 y = a$
   $\cos^2 x - \cos^2 y = b$

3. $\sin x - \sin y = 0.7038$
   $\cos x - \cos y = -0.7245$

4. $x \sin 21° + y \cos 44° = 179.70$
   $x \cos 21° + y \sin 44° = 232.30$

5. $\sin^2 x + y = m$
   $\cos^2 x + y = n$

6. $\sin x + \sin y = 1$
   $\sin x - \sin y = 1$

7. $\cos x + \cos y = a$
   $\cos 2x + \cos 2y = b$

8. $\sin x + \sin y = 2m \sin a$
   $\cos x + \cos y = 2n \cos a$

9. Find two angles, x and y, knowing that the sum of their sines is a and the sum of their cosines is b.

Solve the following systems for r and x:

10. $r \sin x = 92.344$
    $r \cos x = 205.309$

11. $r \sin(x - 19° 18') = 59.4034$
    $r \cos(x - 30° 54') = 147.9347$

151. Additional Symbols and Functions. It is the custom in advanced trigonometry and in higher mathematics to represent angles by the Greek letters, and this custom will be followed in the rest of this work where it seems desirable.

The Greek letters most commonly used for this purpose are as follows:

α, alpha	θ, theta
β, beta	λ, lambda
γ, gamma	μ, mu
δ, delta	ϕ, phi
ϵ, epsilon	ω, omega

Besides the six trigonometric functions already studied, there are, as mentioned on page 4, two others that were formerly used and that are still occasionally found in books on trigonometry. These two functions are as follows:

$$\text{versed sine of } \alpha = 1 - \cos\alpha, \text{ written versin } \alpha;$$

$$\text{coversed sine of } \alpha = 1 - \sin\alpha, \text{ written coversin } \alpha.$$

Exercise 79. Simultaneous Equations

1. Solve for ϕ and x:

$$\text{versin } \phi = x$$
$$1 - \sin\phi = 0.5$$

2. Solve for θ and x:

$$1 - \sin\theta = x$$
$$1 + \sin\theta = a$$

3. Solve for λ and μ:

$$\sin\lambda = \sqrt{2}\sin\mu$$
$$\tan\lambda = \sqrt{3}\tan\mu$$

4. Solve for θ and ϕ:

$$\sin\theta + \cos\phi = a$$
$$\sin\phi + \cos\theta = b$$

5. Solve for θ and ϕ:

$$a\sin^4\theta - b\sin^4\phi = a$$
$$a\cos^4\theta - b\cos^4\phi = b$$

6. Solve for θ:

$$\sin^2\theta + 2\cos\theta = 2$$
$$\cos\theta - \cos^2\theta = 0$$

152. Eliminant. The equation resulting from the elimination of a certain letter, or of certain letters, between two or more given equations is called the *eliminant* of the given equations with respect to the letter or letters.

For example, if $ax = b$ and $a'x = b'$, it follows by division that $a : a' = b : b'$, or that $ab' = a'b$, and this equality, in which x does not appear, is the eliminant of the given equations with respect to x.

There is no definite rule for discovering the eliminant in trigonometric equations. The study of a few examples and the recalling of identities already considered will assist in the solutions of the problems that arise.

153. Illustrative Examples. The following examples will serve to illustrate the method of finding the eliminant:

1. Find the eliminant, with respect to ϕ, of

$$\sin\phi = a$$

$$\cos\phi = b$$

Since $\sin^2\phi + \cos^2\phi = 1$, we have $a^2 + b^2 = 1$, the eliminant.

2. Find the eliminant, with respect to λ, of

$$\sec\lambda = m$$

$$\tan\lambda = n$$

Since $\sec^2\lambda - \tan^2\lambda = 1$, we have $m^2 - n^2 = 1$, the eliminant.

3. Find the eliminant, with respect to μ, of

$$m\sin\mu + \cos\mu = 1$$

$$n\sin\mu - \cos\mu = 1$$

Writing the equations $m\sin\mu = 1 - \cos\mu$, $n\sin\mu = 1 + \cos\mu$, and multiplying, we have

$$mn\sin^2\mu = 1 - \cos^2\mu = \sin^2\mu.$$

Hence $mn = 1$ is the eliminant.

Exercise 80. Elimination

Find the eliminant with respect to α, θ, λ, μ, or ϕ of the following equations:

1. $\sin\phi + 1 = a$
   $\cos\phi - 1 = b$

2. $\tan\lambda - a = 0$
   $\cot\lambda - b = 0$

3. $\sin\alpha + m = n$
   $\cos\alpha + p = q$

4. $a + \sec\phi = b$
   $p \div \cot\phi = q$

5. $c\sin 2\phi + \cos 2\phi = 1$
   $b\sin 2\phi - \cos 2\phi = 1$

6. $x = r(\theta - \sin\theta)$
   $y = r(1 - \cos\theta)$
   $\theta = \text{versine}^{-1} y/r.$

7. $\sin\phi + \sin 2\phi = m$
   $\cos\phi + \cos 2\phi = n$

8. $a + \sin\theta = \csc\theta$
   $b + \cos\theta = \sec\theta$

9. $\tan\alpha + \sin\alpha = m$
   $\tan\alpha - \sin\alpha = n$

10. $p\sin^2\mu - p\cos^2\mu = r$
    $p'\cos^2\mu - p'\sin^2\mu = r'$

11. $\sin 2\phi + \tan 2\phi = k$
    $\sin 2\phi - \tan 2\phi = l$

12. $p = a\cos\theta\cos\phi$
    $q = b\cos\theta\sin\phi$
    $r = c\sin\theta$

CHAPTER XII

APPLICATIONS OF TRIGONOMETRY TO ALGEBRA

154. Extent of Applications. Trigonometry has numerous applications to algebra, particularly in the approximate solutions of equations and in the interpretation of imaginary roots.

These applications, however, are not essential to the study of spherical trigonometry, and hence this chapter may be omitted without interfering with the student's progress.

For example, if we had no better method of solving quadratic equations we could proceed by trigonometry, and in some cases it is even now advantageous to do so. Consider the equation $x^2 + px - q = 0$. Here the roots are

$$x_1 = -\tfrac{1}{2}p + \tfrac{1}{2}\sqrt{p^2 + 4q}, \quad x_2 = -\tfrac{1}{2}p - \tfrac{1}{2}\sqrt{p^2 + 4q}.$$

If we let $\dfrac{2\sqrt{q}}{p} = \tan\phi$, or $p = 2\sqrt{q}\cot\phi$, we have

$$\begin{aligned} x_1 &= -\sqrt{q}\cot\phi + \sqrt{q}\sqrt{\cot^2\phi + 1} \\ &= -\sqrt{q}\cot\phi + \frac{\sqrt{q}}{\sin\phi} = \sqrt{q}\left(\frac{1}{\sin\phi} - \cot\phi\right) \\ &= \sqrt{q}\,\frac{1 - \cos\phi}{\sin\phi} = \sqrt{q}\tan\tfrac{1}{2}\phi. \end{aligned}$$

Similarly,

$$x_2 = -\sqrt{q}\cot\tfrac{1}{2}\phi.$$

For example, if $x^2 + 1.1102x - 3.3594 = 0$ we have

$$\tan\phi = \frac{2\sqrt{3.3594}}{1.1102};$$

whence $\log\tan\phi = 0.51876,$

and $\phi = 73°\,9'\,2.6''.$

Therefore $\log\tan\tfrac{1}{2}\phi = 9.87041 - 10.$

and $\log\sqrt{q} = \log\sqrt{3.3594} = 0.26313.$

Hence $\log x_1 = 0.13354,$

and $x_1 = 1.360.$

Similarly, $x_2 = -2.470.$

155. De Moivre's Theorem. Expressions of the form

$$\cos x + i \sin x,$$

where $i = \sqrt{-1}$, play an important part in modern analysis.

Since $(\cos x + i \sin x)(\cos y + i \sin y)$

$$= \cos x \cos y - \sin x \sin y + i(\cos x \sin y + \sin x \cos y)$$
$$= \cos(x + y) + i \sin(x + y),$$

we have $(\cos x + i \sin x)^2 = \cos 2x + i \sin 2x;$

and again, $(\cos x + i \sin x)^3 = (\cos x + i \sin x)^2 (\cos x + i \sin x)$

$$= (\cos 2x + i \sin 2x)(\cos x + i \sin x)$$
$$= \cos 3x + i \sin 3x.$$

Similarly, $(\cos x + i \sin x)^n = \cos nx + i \sin nx.$

To find the nth power of $\cos x + i \sin x$, n being a positive integer, we have only to multiply the angle x by n in the expression.

This is known as De Moivre's Theorem, from the discoverer (c. 1725).

156. De Moivre's Theorem extended. Again, if n is a positive integer as before,

$$\left(\cos \frac{x}{n} + i \sin \frac{x}{n}\right)^n = \cos x + i \sin x.$$

$$\therefore (\cos x + i \sin x)^{\frac{1}{n}} = \cos \frac{x}{n} + i \sin \frac{x}{n}.$$

However, x may be increased by any integral multiple of 2π without changing the value of $\cos x + i \sin x$. Therefore the following n expressions are the nth roots of $\cos x + i \sin x$:

$$\cos \frac{x}{n} + i \sin \frac{x}{n}, \quad \cos \frac{x + 2\pi}{n} + i \sin \frac{x + 2\pi}{n},$$

$$\cos \frac{x + 4\pi}{n} + i \sin \frac{x + 4\pi}{n}, \cdots,$$

$$\cos \frac{x + (n-1)2\pi}{n} + i \sin \frac{x + (n-1)2\pi}{n}.$$

Hence, if n is a positive integer,

$$(\cos x + i \sin x)^{\frac{1}{n}}$$
$$= \cos \frac{x + 2k\pi}{n} + i \sin \frac{x + 2k\pi}{n} \quad (k = 0, 1, 2, \cdots, n-1).$$

Similarly, it may be shown that

$$(\cos x + i \sin x)^{\frac{m}{n}} = \cos \frac{m}{n}(x + 2k\pi) + i \sin \frac{m}{n}(x + 2k\pi).$$

($k = 0, 1, 2, \cdots, n-1$, m and n being integers, positive or negative.)

157. The Roots of Unity. If we have the binomial equation

$$x^n - 1 = 0,$$

we see that $$x^n = 1,$$

and $$x = \text{the } n\text{th root of } 1,$$

of which the simplest positive root is $\sqrt[n]{1}$ or 1. Since the equation is of the nth degree, there are n roots. In other words, 1 has n nth roots. These are easily found by De Moivre's Theorem.

There are no other roots than those in § 156. For, letting $k = n$, $n+1$, and so on, we have

$$\cos\frac{x + n(2\pi)}{n} + i\sin\frac{x + n(2\pi)}{n}$$

$$= \cos\left(\frac{x}{n} + 2\pi\right) + i\sin\left(\frac{x}{n} + 2\pi\right) = \cos\frac{x}{n} + i\sin\frac{x}{n},$$

and $$\cos\frac{x + (n+1)2\pi}{n} + i\sin\frac{x + (n+1)2\pi}{n}$$

$$= \cos\left(\frac{x + 2\pi}{n} + 2\pi\right) + i\sin\left(\frac{x + 2\pi}{n} + 2\pi\right)$$

$$= \cos\frac{x + 2\pi}{n} + i\sin\frac{x + 2\pi}{n},$$

and so on, all of which we found when $k = 0, 1, 2, \cdots, n-1$.

For example, required to find the three cube roots of 1.

If $$\cos\phi + i\sin\phi = 1, \text{ the given number,}$$

then $$\phi = 0, 2\pi, 4\pi, \cdots.$$

Also $$(\cos\phi + i\sin\phi)^{\frac{1}{3}} = 1^{\frac{1}{3}} = \text{the three cube roots of } 1.$$

But $$(\cos\phi + i\sin\phi)^{\frac{1}{3}} = \cos\frac{k(2\pi) + \phi}{3} + i\sin\frac{k(2\pi) + \phi}{3},$$

where $k = 0, 1$, or 2, and $\phi = 0, 2\pi, 4\pi, \cdots$.

Therefore $$1^{\frac{1}{3}} = \cos 2\pi + i\sin 2\pi = 1,$$

or $$1^{\frac{1}{3}} = \cos\tfrac{2}{3}\pi + i\sin\tfrac{2}{3}\pi = \cos 120^\circ + i\sin 120^\circ$$
$$= -\tfrac{1}{2} + \tfrac{1}{2}\sqrt{3}\cdot i = -0.5 + 0.8660\,i,$$

or $$1^{\frac{1}{3}} = \cos\tfrac{4}{3}\pi + i\sin\tfrac{4}{3}\pi = \cos 240^\circ + i\sin 240^\circ$$
$$= -\tfrac{1}{2} - \tfrac{1}{2}\sqrt{3}\cdot i = -0.5 - 0.8660\,i.$$

The three cube roots of 1 are therefore

$$1,\quad -\tfrac{1}{2} + \tfrac{1}{2}\sqrt{-3},\quad -\tfrac{1}{2} - \tfrac{1}{2}\sqrt{-3}.$$

These roots could, of course, be obtained algebraically, thus:

$$x^3 - 1 = 0,$$

whence $$(x-1)(x^2 + x + 1) = 0;$$

and either $$x - 1 = 0, \quad \text{whence } x = 1,$$

or $$x^2 + x + 1 = 0, \quad \text{whence } x = -\tfrac{1}{2} \pm \tfrac{1}{2}\sqrt{-3}.$$

Most equations like $x^n - a = 0$ cannot, however, be solved algebraically.

Required to find the seven 7th roots of -1; that is, to solve the equation $x^7 = -1$, or $x^7 + 1 = 0$.

If $\cos\phi + i\sin\phi = -1$, the given number,

then $\phi = \pi, 3\pi, 5\pi, \cdots$.

Also $$(\cos\phi + i\sin\phi)^{\frac{1}{7}} = \cos\frac{k(2\pi)+\phi}{7} + i\sin\frac{k(2\pi)+\phi}{7},$$

where $k = 0, 1, \cdots, 6$, and $\phi = \pi, 3\pi, \cdots$.

That is, in this case
$$(\cos\phi + i\sin\phi)^{\frac{1}{7}} = \cos\frac{(2k+1)\pi}{7} + i\sin\frac{(2k+1)\pi}{7}.$$

Hence the seven 7th roots of 1 are

$$\cos\frac{\pi}{7} + i\sin\frac{\pi}{7} = \cos 25^\circ\, 42'\, 51\tfrac{3}{7}'' + i\sin 25^\circ\, 42'\, 51\tfrac{3}{7}'',$$

$$\cos\frac{3\pi}{7} + i\sin\frac{3\pi}{7} = \cos 77^\circ\, 8'\, 34\tfrac{2}{7}'' + i\sin 77^\circ\, 8'\, 34\tfrac{2}{7}'',$$

and
$$\cos\frac{5\pi}{7} + i\sin\frac{5\pi}{7},\quad \cos\pi + i\sin\pi,\quad \cos\frac{9\pi}{7} + i\sin\frac{9\pi}{7},$$

$$\cos\frac{11\pi}{7} + i\sin\frac{11\pi}{7},\quad \cos\frac{13\pi}{7} + i\sin\frac{13\pi}{7}.$$

All these values may be found from the tables. For example,
$$\cos 25^\circ\, 42'\, 51\tfrac{3}{7}'' + i\sin 25^\circ\, 42'\, 51\tfrac{3}{7}'' = 0.9010 + 0.4339\sqrt{-1}.$$

Exercise 81. Roots of Unity

1. Find by De Moivre's Theorem the two square roots of 1.

2. Find by De Moivre's Theorem the four 4th roots of 1.

3. Find three of the nine 9th roots of 1.

4. Find the five 5th roots of 1.

5. Find the six 6th roots of $+1$ and of -1.

6. Find the four 4th roots of -1.

7. Show that the sum of the three cube roots of 1 is zero.

8. Show that the sum of the five 5th roots of 1 is zero.

9. From Exs. 7 and 8 infer the law as to the sum of the nth roots of 1 and prove this law.

10. From Ex. 9 infer the law as to the sum of the nth roots of k and prove this law.

11. Show that any power of any one of the three cube roots of 1 is one of these three roots.

12. Investigate the law implied in the statement of Ex. 11 for the four 4th roots and the five 5th roots of 1.

158. Roots of Numbers. We have seen that the three cube roots of 1 are

$$x_1 = \cos 120° + i \sin 120° = -\tfrac{1}{2} + \tfrac{1}{2}\sqrt{-3},$$
$$x_2 = \cos 240° + i \sin 240° = -\tfrac{1}{2} - \tfrac{1}{2}\sqrt{-3},$$

and
$$x_3 = \cos 360° + i \sin 360° = \cos 0° + i \sin 0° = 1.$$

Furthermore, x_2 is the square of x_1, because

$$(\cos 120° + i \sin 120°)^2 = \cos(2 \cdot 120°) + i \sin(2 \cdot 120°),$$

by De Moivre's Theorem. We may therefore represent the three cube roots by ω, ω^2, and either ω^3 or 1.

In the same way we may represent all n of the nth roots of 1 by $\omega, \omega^2, \omega^3, \cdots, \omega^n$ or 1.

If we have to extract the three cube roots of 8 we can see at once that they are

$$2, \quad 2\omega, \quad \text{and} \quad 2\omega^2,$$

because
$$2^3 = 8, \quad (2\omega)^3 = 2^3\omega^3 = 8 \cdot 1 = 8,$$

and
$$(2\omega^2)^3 = 2^3\omega^6 = 2^3(\omega^3)^2 = 2^3 1^2 = 8.$$

In general, to find the three cube roots of any number we may take the arithmetical cube root for one of them and multiply this by ω for the second and by ω^2 for the third.

The same is true for any root. For example, if ω, ω^2, ω^3, ω^4, and ω^5 or 1 are the five 5th roots of 1, the five 5th roots of 32 are 2ω, $2\omega^2$, $2\omega^3$, $2\omega^4$, and $2\omega^5$ or 2.

Exercise 82. Roots of Numbers

1. Find the three cube roots of 125.

2. Find the four 4th roots of -81 and verify the results.

3. Find three of the 6th roots of 729 and verify the results.

4. Find three of the 10th roots of 1024 and verify the results.

5. Find three of the 100th roots of 1.

6. Show that, if 2ω is one of the complex 7th roots of 128, two of the other roots are $2\omega^2$ and $2\omega^3$.

7. Show that either of the two complex cube roots of 1 is at the same time the square and the square root of the other.

8. Show that a result similar to the one stated in Ex. 7 can be found with respect to the four 4th roots of 1.

9. Show that the sum of all the nth roots of 1 is zero.

10. Show that the sum of the products of all the nth roots of 1, taken two by two, is zero.

159. Properties of Logarithms. The properties of logarithms have already been studied in Chapter III. These properties hold true whatever base is taken. They are as follows:

1. *The logarithm of 1 is 0.*
2. *The logarithm of the base itself is 1.*
3. *The logarithm of the reciprocal of a positive number is the negative of the logarithm of the number.*
4. *The logarithm of the product of two or more positive numbers is found by adding the logarithms of the several factors.*
5. *The logarithm of the quotient of two positive numbers is found by subtracting the logarithm of the divisor from the logarithm of the dividend.*
6. *The logarithm of a power of a positive number is found by multiplying the logarithm of the number by the exponent of the power.*
7. *The logarithm of the real positive value of a root of a positive number is found by dividing the logarithm of the number by the index of the root.*

160. Two Important Systems. Although the number of different systems of logarithms is unlimited, there are but two systems which are in common use. These are

1. The common system, also called the Briggs, denary, or decimal system, of which the base is 10.
2. The natural system, of which the base is the fixed value which the sum of the series

$$1+\frac{1}{1}+\frac{1}{1\cdot 2}+\frac{1}{1\cdot 2\cdot 3}+\frac{1}{1\cdot 2\cdot 3\cdot 4}+\cdots$$

approaches as the number of terms is indefinitely increased. This base, correct to seven places of decimals, is 2.7182818, and is denoted by the letter e.

Instead of writing $1\cdot 2$, $1\cdot 2\cdot 3$, $1\cdot 2\cdot 3\cdot 4$, and so on, we may write either $2!$, $3!$, $4!$, and so on, or $\underline{|2}$, $\underline{|3}$, $\underline{|4}$, and so on. The expression $2!$ is used on the continent of Europe, $\underline{|2}$ being formerly used in America and England. At present the expression $2!$ is coming to be preferred to $\underline{|2}$ in these two countries.

The common system of logarithms is used in actual calculation; the natural system is used in higher mathematics.

The natural logarithms are also known as Naperian logarithms, in honor of the inventor of logarithms, John Napier (1614), although these are not the ones used by him. They are also known as hyperbolic logarithms.

161. Exponential Series. By the binomial theorem we may expand $\left(1+\frac{1}{n}\right)^{nx}$ and have

$$\left(1+\frac{1}{n}\right)^{nx}=1+x+\frac{x\left(x-\frac{1}{n}\right)}{2!}+\frac{x\left(x-\frac{1}{n}\right)\left(x-\frac{2}{n}\right)}{3!}+\cdots. \quad (1)$$

This is true for all values of x and n, provided $n>1$. If n is not greater than 1 the series is not *convergent*; that is, the sum approaches no definite limit. The further discussion of convergency belongs to the domain of algebra.

When $x=1$ we have

$$\left(1+\frac{1}{n}\right)^{n}=1+1+\frac{1-\frac{1}{n}}{2!}+\frac{\left(1-\frac{1}{n}\right)\left(1-\frac{2}{n}\right)}{3!}+\cdots. \quad (2)$$

But

$$\left[\left(1+\frac{1}{n}\right)^{n}\right]^{x}=\left(1+\frac{1}{n}\right)^{nx}.$$

Hence, from (1) and (2),

$$\left[1+1+\frac{1-\frac{1}{n}}{2!}+\frac{\left(1-\frac{1}{n}\right)\left(1-\frac{2}{n}\right)}{3!}+\cdots\right]^{x}$$

$$=1+x+\frac{x\left(x-\frac{1}{n}\right)}{2!}+\frac{x\left(x-\frac{1}{n}\right)\left(x-\frac{2}{n}\right)}{3!}+\cdots. \quad (3)$$

If we take n infinitely large, (3) becomes

$$\left(1+1+\frac{1}{2!}+\frac{1}{3!}+\cdots\right)^{x}=1+x+\frac{x^2}{2!}+\frac{x^3}{3!}+\cdots; \quad (4)$$

that is,

$$e^{x}=1+x+\frac{x^2}{2!}+\frac{x^3}{3!}+\cdots.$$

In particular, if $x=1$ we have

$$e=1+1+\frac{1}{2!}+\frac{1}{3!}+\cdots.$$

We therefore see that we can compute the value of e by simply adding 1, 1, $\frac{1}{2}$ of 1, $\frac{1}{3}$ of $\frac{1}{2}$ of 1, and so on, indefinitely, and that to compute the value to only a few decimal places is a very simple matter. We have merely to proceed as here shown.

Here we take 1, 1, $\frac{1}{2}$ of 1, $\frac{1}{3}$ of $\frac{1}{2}$ of 1, $\frac{1}{4}$ of $\frac{1}{3}$ of $\frac{1}{2}$ of 1, and so on, and add them. The result given is correct to five decimal places. The result to ten decimal places is 2.7182818284.

	1.000000
2	1.000000
3	0.500000
4	0.166667
5	0.041667
6	0.008333
7	0.001388
8	0.000198
9	0.000025
	0.000003
$e=$	2.71828.

162. Expansion of $\sin x$, $\cos x$, and $\tan x$. Denote one radian by 1, and let

$$\cos 1 + i \sin 1 = k.$$

Then $$\cos x + i \sin x = (\cos 1 + i \sin 1)^x = k^x,$$

and, putting $-x$ for x,

$$\cos(-x) + i \sin(-x) = \cos x - i \sin x = k^{-x}.$$

That is, $$\cos x + i \sin x = k^x,$$

and $$\cos x - i \sin x = k^{-x}.$$

By taking the sum and difference of these two equations, and dividing the sum by 2 and the difference by $2i$, we have

$$\cos x = \frac{1}{2}(k^x + k^{-x}),$$

and $$\sin x = \frac{1}{2i}(k^x - k^{-x}).$$

But $$k^x = (e^{\log k})^x = e^{x \log k}, \text{ and } k^{-x} = e^{-x \log k}.$$

$$\therefore e^{x \log k} = 1 + x \log k + \frac{x^2 (\log k)^2}{2!} + \frac{x^3 (\log k)^3}{3!} + \cdots,$$

and $$e^{-x \log k} = 1 - x \log k + \frac{x^2 (\log k)^2}{2!} - \frac{x^3 (\log k)^3}{3!} + \cdots.$$

$$\therefore \cos x = \frac{1}{2}(k^x + k^{-x}) = 1 + \frac{x^2 (\log k)^2}{2!} + \frac{x^4 (\log k)^4}{4!} + \cdots,$$

and $$\sin x = \frac{1}{i}\left\{x \log k + \frac{x^3 (\log k)^3}{3!} + \frac{x^5 (\log k)^5}{5!} + \cdots\right\}.$$

Dividing the last equation by x, we have

$$\frac{\sin x}{x} = \frac{1}{i}\left\{\log k + \frac{x^2 (\log k)^3}{3!} + \frac{x^4 (\log k)^5}{5!} + \cdots\right\}.$$

But remembering that x represents radians, it is evident that the smaller x is, the nearer $\sin x$ comes to equaling x; that is, the more nearly the sine equals the arc.

Therefore the smaller x becomes, the nearer $\frac{\sin x}{x}$ comes to 1, and the nearer the second member of the equation comes to $\frac{1}{i} \log k$.

We therefore say that, as x approaches the limit 0, the limits of these two members are equal, and

$$1 = \frac{1}{i} \log k;$$

whence $$\log k = i,$$

and $$k = e^i.$$

Therefore, we have

$$\cos x = \frac{1}{2}(e^{xi} + e^{-xi}) = 1 - \frac{x^2}{2!} + \frac{x^4}{4!} - \frac{x^6}{6!} + \cdots,$$

$$\sin x = \frac{1}{2i}(e^{xi} - e^{-xi}) = x - \frac{x^3}{3!} + \frac{x^5}{5!} - \frac{x^7}{7!} + \cdots.$$

From the last two series we obtain, by division,

$$\tan x = \frac{\sin x}{\cos x} = x + \frac{x^3}{3} + \frac{2x^5}{15} + \frac{17x^7}{315} \cdots.$$

By the aid of these series, which rapidly converge, the trigonometric functions of any angle are readily calculated.

In the computation it must be remembered that x is the *circular measure* of the given angle.

Thus to compute $\cos 1$, that is, the cosine of 1 radian or $\cos 57.29578°$, or approximately $\cos 57.3°$, we have

$$\begin{aligned}\cos 1 &= 1 - \frac{1}{2!} + \frac{1}{4!} - \frac{1}{6!} + \frac{1}{8!} - \cdots\\ &= 1 - 0.5 + 0.04167 - 0.00139 + 0.00002 - \cdots\\ &= 0.5403 = \cos 57° 18'.\end{aligned}$$

163. Euler's Formula. An important formula discovered in the eighteenth century by the Swiss mathematician Euler will now be considered. We have, as in § 162,

$$\sin x = x - \frac{x^3}{3!} + \frac{x^5}{5!} - \frac{x^7}{7!} + \cdots,$$

and

$$\cos x = 1 - \frac{x^2}{2!} + \frac{x^4}{4!} - \frac{x^6}{6!} + \cdots.$$

By multiplying by i in the formula for $\sin x$, we have

$$i \sin x = ix - \frac{ix^3}{3!} + \frac{ix^5}{5!} - \frac{ix^7}{7!} + \cdots.$$

Adding,

$$\cos x + i \sin x = 1 + ix - \frac{x^2}{2!} - \frac{ix^3}{3!} + \frac{x^4}{4!} + \frac{ix^5}{5!} - \cdots.$$

By substituting ix for x in the formula for e^x, we see that

$$\begin{aligned}e^{ix} &= 1 + ix + \frac{i^2x^2}{2!} + \frac{i^3x^3}{3!} + \frac{i^4x^4}{4!} + \frac{i^5x^5}{5!} + \cdots\\ &= 1 + ix - \frac{x^2}{2!} - \frac{ix^3}{3!} + \frac{x^4}{4!} + \frac{ix^5}{5!} - \cdots.\end{aligned}$$

In other words,

$$e^{ix} = \cos x + i \sin x.$$

164. Deductions from Euler's Formula. Euler's formula is one of the most important formulas in all mathematics. From it several important deductions will now be made.

Since $e^{ix} = \cos x + i \sin x$, in which x may have any values, we may let $x = \pi$. We then have

$$e^{i\pi} = \cos \pi + i \sin \pi = -1 + 0,$$

or

$$e^{i\pi} = -1.$$

In this formula we have combined four of the most interesting numbers of mathematics, e (the natural base), i (the imaginary unit, $\sqrt{-1}$), π (the ratio of the circumference to the diameter), and -1 (the negative unit).

Furthermore, we see that a real number (e) may be affected by an imaginary exponent ($i\pi$) and yet have the power real (-1).

Taking the square root of each side of the equation $e^{i\pi} = -1$, we have

$$e^{\frac{i\pi}{2}} = \sqrt{-1} = i.$$

Taking the logarithm of each side of the equation $e^{i\pi} = -1$, we have

$$i\pi = \log(-1).$$

Hence we see that -1 has a logarithm, but that it is an imaginary number and is, therefore, not suitable for purposes of calculation.

Since $\cos \phi + i \sin \phi = \cos(2k\pi + \phi) + i \sin(2k\pi + \phi)$, we see that $e^{\phi i}$, which is equal to $\cos \phi + i \sin \phi$, may be written $e^{(2k\pi + \phi)i}$, or we may write

$$e^{\phi i} = e^{(2k\pi + \phi)i} = \cos \phi + i \sin \phi = \cos(2k\pi + \phi) + i \sin(2k\pi + \phi)$$

Hence $\quad (2k\pi + \phi)i = \log[\cos(2k\pi + \phi) + i \sin(2k\pi + \phi)].$

If $\phi = 0, \quad 2k\pi i = \log 1.$

If $k = 0$, this reduces to $0 = \log 1$.

If $k = 1$ we have $2\pi i = \log 1$; if $k = 2$, we have $4\pi i = \log 1$, and so on. In other words, $\log 1$ is multiple-valued, but only one of these values is real.

If $\phi = \pi, \quad (2k\pi + \pi)i = (2k + 1)\pi i = \log(-1).$

Hence the logarithms of negative numbers are always imaginary; for if $k = 0$ we have $\pi i = \log(-1)$; if $k = 1$ we have $3\pi i = \log(-1)$; and so on.

If we wish to consider the logarithm of some number N, we have

$$Ne^{2k\pi i} = N(\cos 2k\pi + i \sin 2k\pi).$$

Hence
$$\begin{aligned}\log N + 2k\pi i &= \log N + \log(\cos 2k\pi + i \sin 2k\pi) \\ &= \log N + \log 1 = \log N.\end{aligned}$$

That is, $\log N = \log N + 2k\pi i$. Hence the logarithm of a number is the logarithm given by the tables, $+ 2k\pi i$. If $k = 0$ we have the usual logarithm, but for other values of k we have imaginaries.

Exercise 83. Properties of Logarithms

Prove the following properties of logarithms as given in § 159, using b as the base:

1. Properties 1 and 2.
2. Property 3.
3. Property 4.
4. Property 5.
5. Property 6.
6. Property 7.

Find the value of each of the following:

7. 5!
8. 7!
9. 6!
10. 8!
11. 10!

Simplify the following:

12. $\frac{10!}{3!}$.
13. $\frac{10!}{8!}$.
14. $\frac{7!}{5!}$.
15. $\frac{15!}{14!}$.
16. $\frac{20!}{17!}$.

17. Find to five decimal places the value of $\left(1+1+\frac{1}{2!}+\frac{1}{3!}+\cdots\right)^2$.

18. Find to five decimal places the value of $\left(2+\frac{1}{2!}+\frac{1}{3!}+\cdots\right)^{\frac{1}{2}}$.

By the use of the series for cos x find the following:

19. $\cos \frac{1}{2}$.
20. $\cos \frac{1}{8}$.
21. $\cos 2$.
22. $\cos 0$.

By the use of the series for sin x find the following:

23. $\sin 1$.
24. $\sin \frac{1}{2}$.
25. $\sin 2$.
26. $\sin 0$.

By the use of the series for tan x find the following:

27. $\tan 0$.
28. $\tan 1$.
29. $\tan \frac{1}{2}$.
30. $\tan 2$.

Prove the following statements:

31. $e^{2\pi i} = 1$.
32. $e^{-\frac{\pi}{2}} = i^i$.
33. $e^{\pi} = \sqrt[i]{-1}$.
34. $e^{i} = \sqrt[\pi]{-1}$.

Given $\log_e 2 = 0.6931$, find two logarithms (to the base e) of:

35. 2.
36. 4.
37. $\sqrt{2}$.
38. -2.

Given $\log_e 5 = 1.609$, find three logarithms (to the base e) of:

39. 5.
40. 25.
41. 125.
42. -5.

Given $\log_e 10 = 2.302585$, find two logarithms (to the base e) of:

43. 100.
44. -10.
45. 1000.
46. $\sqrt{10}$.

47. From the series of § 162 show that $\sin(-\phi) = -\sin \phi$.

48. Prove that the ratio of the circumference of a circle to the diameter equals $-2\log(i^i) = -2i\log i$.

Exercise 84. Review Problems

1. The angle of elevation of the top of a vertical cliff at a point 575 ft. from the foot is $32° 15'$. Find the height of the cliff.

2. An aeroplane is above a straight road on which are two observers 1640 ft. apart. At a given signal the observers take the angles of elevation of the aeroplane, finding them to be 58° and 63° respectively. Find the height of the aeroplane and its distance from each observer.

3. Prove that $\left(\sqrt{\csc x + \cot x} - \sqrt{\csc x - \cot x}\right)^2 = 2(\csc x - 1)$.

4. Given $\sin x = 2m/(m^2+1)$ and $\sin y = 2n/(n^2+1)$, find the value of $\tan(x+y)$.

5. Find the least value of $\cos^2 x + \sec^2 x$.

6. Prove that $1 - \sin^2 x/\sin^2 y \doteq \cos^2 x(1 - \tan^2 x/\tan^2 y)$.

7. Prove this formula, due to Euler: $\tan^{-1}\frac{1}{2} + \tan^{-1}\frac{1}{3} = \frac{1}{4}\pi$.

8. Prove that $\cot\frac{1}{2}x - \cot x = \csc x$.

9. Prove that $(\sin x + i\cos x)^n = \cos n(\frac{1}{2}\pi - x) + i\sin n(\frac{1}{2}\pi - x)$.

10. Show that $\log i = \frac{1}{2}\pi i$ and that $\log(-i) = -\frac{1}{2}\pi i$.

11. Through the excenters of a triangle ABC lines are drawn parallel to the three sides, thus forming another triangle $A'B'C'$. Prove that the perimeter of $\triangle A'B'C'$ is $4r\cot\frac{1}{2}A\cot\frac{1}{2}B\cot\frac{1}{2}C$, where r is the radius of the circumcircle.

12. Given two sides and the included angle of a triangle, find the perpendicular drawn to the third side from the opposite vertex.

13. To find the height of a mountain a north-and-south base line is taken 1000 yd. long. From one end of this line the summit bears N. 80° E., and has an angle of elevation of $13° 14'$; from the other end it bears N. $43° 30'$ E. Find the height of the mountain.

14. The angle of elevation of a wireless telegraph tower is observed from a point on the horizontal plain on which it stands. At a point a feet nearer, the angle of elevation is the complement of the former. At a point b feet nearer still, the angle of elevation is double the first. Show that the height of the tower is $[(a+b)^2 - \frac{1}{4}a^2]^{\frac{1}{2}}$.

Prove the following formulas:

15. $2\cos^2 x = \cos 2x + 1$.

16. $2\sin^2 x = -\cos 2x + 1$.

17. $8\cos^4 x = \cos 4x + 4\cos 2x + 3$.

18. $4\cos^3 x = \cos 3x + 3\cos x$.

19. $4\sin^3 x = -\sin 3x + 3\sin x$.

20. $8\sin^4 x = \cos 4x - 4\cos 2x + 3$.

THE MOST IMPORTANT FORMULAS OF PLANE TRIGONOMETRY

Right Triangles (§§ 15–21)

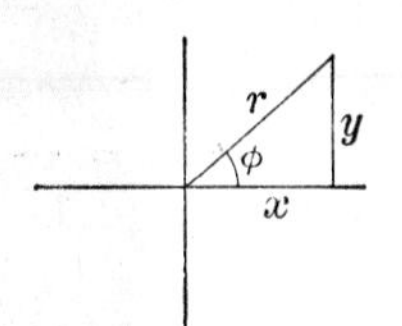

1. $y = r \sin \phi.$
2. $x = r \cos \phi.$
3. $y = x \tan \phi.$
4. $x = y \cot \phi.$
5. $r = x \sec \phi.$
6. $r = y \csc \phi.$

Relations of Functions (§§ 13, 14, 89)

7. $\sin \phi = \dfrac{1}{\csc \phi}.$
8. $\cos \phi = \dfrac{1}{\sec \phi}.$
9. $\tan \phi = \dfrac{1}{\cot \phi}.$
10. $\sin \phi \csc \phi = 1.$
11. $\cos \phi \sec \phi = 1.$
12. $\cot \phi = \dfrac{1}{\tan \phi}.$
13. $\sec \phi = \dfrac{1}{\cos \phi}.$
14. $\csc \phi = \dfrac{1}{\sin \phi}.$
15. $\tan \phi \cot \phi = 1.$
16. $\sin^2 \phi + \cos^2 \phi = 1.$
17. $\sin \phi = \dfrac{\cos \phi}{\cot \phi}.$
18. $\tan \phi = \dfrac{\sin \phi}{\cos \phi}.$
19. $\cot \phi = \dfrac{\cos \phi}{\sin \phi}.$
20. $1 + \tan^2 \phi = \sec^2 \phi.$
21. $1 + \cot^2 \phi = \csc^2 \phi.$

Functions of $x \pm y$ (§§ 90–100)

22. $\sin (x + y) = \sin x \cos y + \cos x \sin y.$
23. $\sin (x - y) = \sin x \cos y - \cos x \sin y.$
24. $\cos (x + y) = \cos x \cos y - \sin x \sin y.$
25. $\cos (x - y) = \cos x \cos y + \sin x \sin y.$
26. $\tan (x + y) = \dfrac{\tan x + \tan y}{1 - \tan x \tan y}.$
27. $\tan (x - y) = \dfrac{\tan x - \tan y}{1 + \tan x \tan y}.$
28. $\cot (x + y) = \dfrac{\cot x \cot y - 1}{\cot y + \cot x}$
29. $\cot (x - y) = \dfrac{\cot x \cot y + 1}{\cot y - \cot x}.$

Functions of Twice an Angle (§ 101)

30. $\sin 2\phi = 2 \sin \phi \cos \phi.$
31. $\tan 2\phi = \dfrac{2 \tan \phi}{1 - \tan^2 \phi}.$
32. $\cos 2\phi = \cos^2 \phi - \sin^2 \phi.$
33. $\cot 2\phi = \dfrac{\cot^2 \phi - 1}{2 \cot \phi}.$

Functions of Half an Angle (§ 102)

34. $\sin \frac{1}{2}\phi = \pm \sqrt{\dfrac{1 - \cos \phi}{2}}.$
35. $\cos \frac{1}{2}\phi = \pm \sqrt{\dfrac{1 + \cos \phi}{2}}.$
36. $\tan \frac{1}{2}\phi = \pm \sqrt{\dfrac{1 - \cos \phi}{1 + \cos \phi}}.$
37. $\cot \frac{1}{2}\phi = \pm \sqrt{\dfrac{1 + \cos \phi}{1 - \cos \phi}}.$

Functions involving Half Angles (§ 101)

38. $\sin x = 2 \sin \frac{x}{2} \cos \frac{x}{2}$.

39. $\tan x = \dfrac{2 \tan \frac{x}{2}}{1 - \tan^2 \frac{x}{2}}$.

40. $\cos x = \cos^2 \frac{x}{2} - \sin^2 \frac{x}{2}$.

41. $\cot x = \dfrac{\cot^2 \frac{x}{2} - 1}{2 \cot \frac{x}{2}}$.

Sums and Differences of Functions (§ 103)

42. $\sin A + \sin B = 2 \sin \frac{1}{2}(A + B) \cos \frac{1}{2}(A - B)$.

43. $\sin A - \sin B = 2 \cos \frac{1}{2}(A + B) \sin \frac{1}{2}(A - B)$.

44. $\cos A + \cos B = 2 \cos \frac{1}{2}(A + B) \cos \frac{1}{2}(A - B)$.

45. $\cos A - \cos B = - 2 \sin \frac{1}{2}(A + B) \sin \frac{1}{2}(A - B)$.

46. $\dfrac{\sin A + \sin B}{\sin A - \sin B} = \dfrac{\tan \frac{1}{2}(A + B)}{\tan \frac{1}{2}(A - B)}$.

Laws of Sines, Cosines, and Tangents (§§ 105, 111, 112)

47. Law of sines, $\dfrac{a}{b} = \dfrac{\sin A}{\sin B}$,

$$\frac{a}{\sin A} = \frac{b}{\sin B} = \frac{c}{\sin C}.$$

48. Law of cosines, $a^2 = b^2 + c^2 - 2\,bc \cos A$.

49. Law of tangents, $\dfrac{a - b}{a + b} = \dfrac{\tan \frac{1}{2}(A - B)}{\tan \frac{1}{2}(A + B)}$, if $a > b$;

$$\frac{b - a}{b + a} = \frac{\tan \frac{1}{2}(B - A)}{\tan \frac{1}{2}(B + A)}, \text{ if } a < b.$$

Formulas in Terms of Sides (§§ 115, 116)

50. $\dfrac{a + b + c}{2} = s$.

51. $\sin \frac{1}{2} A = \sqrt{\dfrac{(s - b)(s - c)}{bc}}$.

52. $\cos \frac{1}{2} A = \sqrt{\dfrac{s(s - a)}{bc}}$.

53. $\sqrt{\dfrac{(s - a)(s - b)(s - c)}{s}} = r$.

54. $\tan \frac{1}{2} A = \sqrt{\dfrac{(s - b)(s - c)}{s(s - a)}}$.

55. $\tan \frac{1}{2} A = \dfrac{r}{s - a}$.

Areas of Triangles (§ 118)

56. Area of triangle $ABC = \frac{1}{2}\,ac \sin B = \frac{1}{2}\,r(a + b + c) = rs =$
$\sqrt{s(s - a)(s - b)(s - c)} = \dfrac{abc}{4R} = \dfrac{a^2 \sin B \sin C}{2 \sin (B + C)}$.

INDEX

ANSWERS

ANSWERS

PLANE TRIGONOMETRY

Exercise 1. Page 5

1. $\cos B = \frac{a}{c}$; $\tan B = \frac{b}{a}$; $\cot B = \frac{a}{b}$; $\sec B = \frac{c}{a}$; $\csc B = \frac{c}{b}$.

3. $\tan A$. **4.** $\cot A$. **5.** $\sec A$. **6.** $\csc A$.

7. $\sin A = \frac{3}{5}$; $\cos A = \frac{4}{5}$; $\tan A = \frac{3}{4}$; $\cot A = \frac{4}{3}$; $\sec A = \frac{5}{4}$; $\csc A = \frac{5}{3}$.

8. $\sin A = \frac{5}{13}$; $\cos A = \frac{12}{13}$; $\tan A = \frac{5}{12}$; $\cot A = \frac{12}{5}$; $\sec A = \frac{13}{12}$; $\csc A = \frac{13}{5}$.

9. $\sin A = \frac{8}{17}$; $\cos A = \frac{15}{17}$; $\tan A = \frac{8}{15}$; $\cot A = \frac{15}{8}$; $\sec A = \frac{17}{15}$; $\csc A = \frac{17}{8}$.

10. $\sin A = \frac{9}{41}$; $\cos A = \frac{40}{41}$; $\tan A = \frac{9}{40}$; $\cot A = \frac{40}{9}$; $\sec A = \frac{41}{40}$; $\csc A = \frac{41}{9}$.

11. $\sin A = \frac{39}{89}$; $\cos A = \frac{80}{89}$; $\tan A = \frac{39}{80}$; $\cot A = \frac{80}{39}$; $\sec A = \frac{89}{80}$; $\csc A = \frac{89}{39}$.

12. $\sin A = \frac{119}{169}$; $\cos A = \frac{120}{169}$; $\tan A = \frac{119}{120}$; $\cot A = \frac{120}{119}$; $\sec A = \frac{169}{120}$;
$\csc A = \frac{169}{119}$.

13. $a^2 + b^2 = c^2$.

14. $\sin A = \frac{2n}{n^2+1}$; $\cos A = \frac{n^2-1}{n^2+1}$; $\tan A = \frac{2n}{n^2-1}$; $\cot A = \frac{n^2-1}{2n}$;
$\sec A = \frac{n^2+1}{n^2-1}$; $\csc A = \frac{n^2+1}{2n}$.

15. $\sin A = \frac{2n}{n^2+1}$; $\cos A = \frac{n^2-1}{n^2+1}$; $\tan A = \frac{2n}{n^2-1}$; $\cot A = \frac{n^2-1}{2n}$;
$\sec A = \frac{n^2+1}{n^2-1}$; $\csc A = \frac{n^2+1}{2n}$.

16. $\sin A = \frac{2mn}{m^2+n^2}$; $\cos A = \frac{m^2-n^2}{m^2+n^2}$; $\tan A = \frac{2mn}{m^2-n^2}$; $\cot A = \frac{m^2-n^2}{2mn}$;
$\sec A = \frac{m^2+n^2}{m^2-n^2}$; $\csc A = \frac{m^2+n^2}{2mn}$.

17. $\sin A = \frac{2mn}{m^2+n^2}$; $\cos A = \frac{m^2-n^2}{m^2+n^2}$; $\tan A = \frac{2mn}{m^2-n^2}$; $\cot A = \frac{m^2-n^2}{2mn}$;
$\sec A = \frac{m^2+n^2}{m^2-n^2}$; $\csc A = \frac{m^2+n^2}{2mn}$.

19. $\sin A = \frac{1}{2}\sqrt{2} = \cos A$; $\tan A = 1 = \cot A$; $\sec A = \sqrt{2} = \csc A$.

20. $\sin A = \frac{2}{5}\sqrt{5}$; $\cos A = \frac{1}{5}\sqrt{5}$; $\tan A = 2$; $\cot A = \frac{1}{2}$; $\sec A = \sqrt{5}$;
$\csc A = \frac{1}{2}\sqrt{5}$.

21. $\sin A = \frac{2}{3}$; $\cos A = \frac{1}{3}\sqrt{5}$; $\tan A = \frac{2}{5}\sqrt{5}$; $\cot A = \frac{1}{2}\sqrt{5}$; $\sec A = \frac{3}{5}\sqrt{5}$;
$\csc A = \frac{3}{2}$.

22. $\sin B = \frac{143}{145}$; $\cos B = \frac{24}{145}$; $\tan B = \frac{143}{24}$; $\cot B = \frac{24}{143}$; $\sec B = \frac{145}{24}$;
$\csc B = \frac{145}{143}$.

23. $\sin B = \frac{95}{193}$; $\cos B = \frac{168}{193}$; $\tan B = \frac{95}{168}$; $\cot B = \frac{168}{95}$; $\sec B = \frac{193}{168}$;
$\csc B = \frac{193}{95}$.

24. $\sin B = \frac{23}{265}$; $\cos B = \frac{264}{265}$; $\tan B = \frac{23}{264}$; $\cot B = \frac{264}{23}$; $\sec B = \frac{265}{264}$;
$\csc B = \frac{265}{23}$.

25. $\sin B = \frac{2\sqrt{pq}}{p+q}$; $\cos B = \frac{p-q}{p+q}$; $\tan B = \frac{2\sqrt{pq}}{p-q}$; $\cot B = \frac{p-q}{2pq}\sqrt{pq}$;
$\sec B = \frac{p+q}{p-q}$; $\csc B = \frac{p+q}{2pq}\sqrt{pq}$.

26. $\sin A = \frac{\sqrt{p^2+q^2}}{p+q} = \cos B$; $\cot A = \frac{\sqrt{2pq}}{\sqrt{p^2+q^2}} = \tan B$;
$\cos A = \frac{\sqrt{2pq}}{p+q} = \sin B$; $\sec A = \frac{p+q}{\sqrt{2pq}} = \csc B$;
$\tan A = \frac{\sqrt{p^2+q^2}}{\sqrt{2pq}} = \cot B$; $\csc A = \frac{p+q}{\sqrt{p^2+q^2}} = \sec B$.

27. $\sin A = \frac{\sqrt{p^2+p}}{p+1} = \cos B$; $\cot A = \frac{\sqrt{p}}{p} = \tan B$;
$\cos A = \frac{1}{\sqrt{p+1}} = \sin B$; $\sec A = \sqrt{p+1} = \csc B$;
$\tan A = \sqrt{p} = \cot B$; $\csc A = \frac{\sqrt{p^2+p}}{p} = \sec B$.

28. 12.3.
29. 1.54.
30. 9.
31. 6800.
32. 4000.
33. 227.84.
34. $3\sqrt{13}$; 9.
35. $\frac{7}{3}\sqrt{3}$; $\frac{7}{6}\sqrt{3}$.
36. 5; 3.
37. 2.5; 1.5.
38. 1.5 mi.; 2 mi.
40. $a = 0.342$; $b = 0.94$.
41. $a = 1.368$; $b = 3.76$.
42. $a = 1.197$; $b = 3.29$.
43. $a = 1.6416$; $b = 4.512$.
44. $a = 2.565$; $b = 7.05$.
45. $a = 0.643$; $b = 0.766$.
46. $a = 1.929$; $b = 2.298$.
47. $a = 4.501$; $b = 5.362$.
48. $a = 6.8801$; $b = 8.1962$.
49. $a = 160.75$; $b = 191.5$.
50. $a = 1.88$; $b = 0.684$.
51. $c = 2.128$; $b = 0.728$.
52. $c = 5.848$; $a = 5.494$.
53. $c = 26.6$; $b = 9.1$.
54. $a = 412.05$; $c = 438.6$.
55. 142.926 yd.
56. $1\frac{1}{7}$; 24 ft.

Exercise 2. Page 7

1. cos 60°.
2. sin 70°.
3. cot 50°.
4. csc 65°.
5. cos 40°.
6. cot 30°.
7. csc 15°.
8. sec 5°.
9. cos 30°.
10. sin 30°.
11. cot 45°.
12. csc 45°.
13. cos 14° 30′.
14. cot 7° 15′.
15. csc 21° 45′.
16. sin 1° 50′.
17. cos 25°.
18. cot 10°.
19. csc 13°.
20. sin 38°.
21. tan 29°.
22. sec 12°.
23. cos 1°.
24. sin 4°.
25. csc 2°.
26. cos $12\frac{1}{2}$°.
27. sin $7\frac{1}{2}$°.
28. cot 1.4°.
29. 45°.
30. 45°.
31. 30°.
32. 30°.

Exercise 3. Page 9

1. 0.5.
2. 0.8660.
3. 0.5773.
4. 1.7320.
5. 1.1547.
6. 2.
7. 0.8660.
8. 0.5.
9. 1.7320.
10. 0.5773.
11. 2.
12. 1.1547.
13. $\sqrt{2}$.
14. $\frac{1}{3}\sqrt{6}$.
15. $\sqrt{3}$.
16. $\frac{1}{3}\sqrt{3}$.
17. $\frac{1}{2}\sqrt{6}$.
18. $\frac{1}{2}\sqrt{2}$.
19. $\frac{1}{3}\sqrt{3}$.
20. $\sqrt{3}$.
21. $\frac{1}{3}$.
22. 3.
23. $\frac{1}{3}\sqrt{3}$.
24. $\sqrt{3}$.
25. cos 27° 42′ 20″.
26. cot 14° 31′ 25″.
27. csc 2° 27′ 9″.
28. sin 1° 59′ 33″.
29. cos 14.2°.
30. sin 7.25°.
31. cot 21.18°.
32. csc 4.05°.
33. 90°.
34. 60°.
35. 22° 30′.
36. 18°.
37. $\frac{90°}{n+1}$.
38. 90°.
39. 60°.
40. 22° 30′.
41. 18°.
42. $\frac{90°}{n+1}$.
43. $\frac{1}{3}\sqrt{6}$.
44. $\sqrt{2}$.
45. $\sqrt{6}$.
46. $\frac{2}{3}\sqrt{3}$.
47. $2\sqrt{3}$.
48. 2.
49. $\frac{1}{3}\sqrt{3}$.
50. $\frac{1}{3}\sqrt{3}$.
51. 1.
52. $\frac{1}{3}\sqrt{3}$.

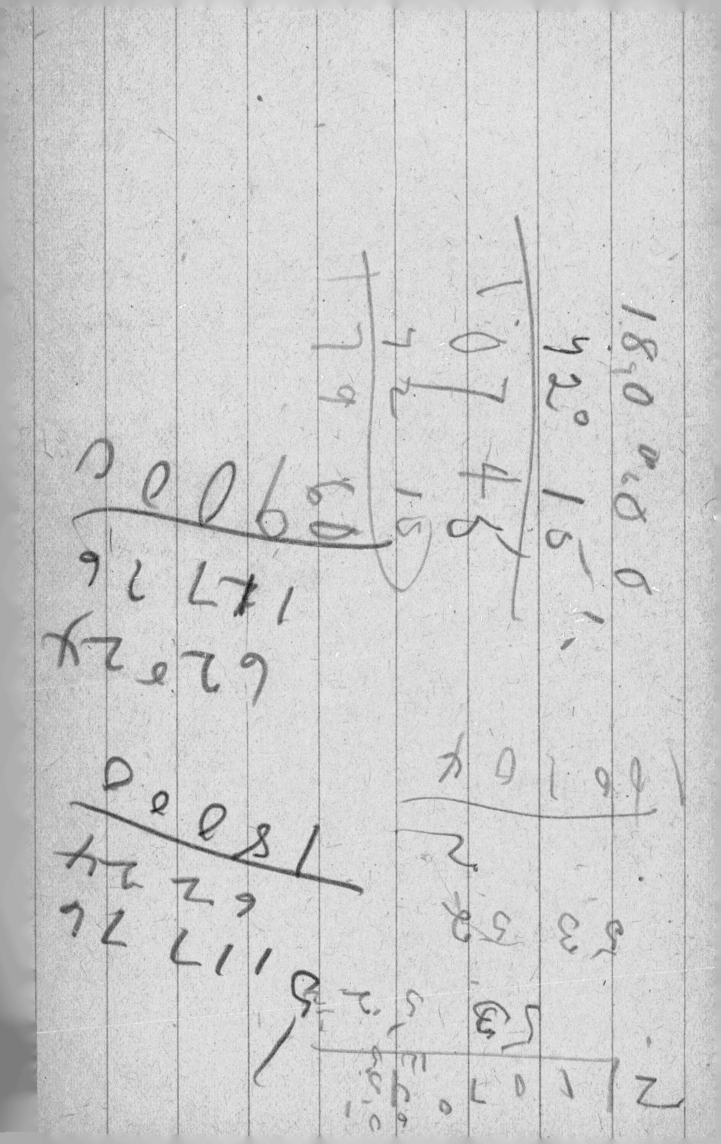

83.39
77.99

5.40

77.99
83.39

161.38

Exercise 4. Page 10

1. 0.0872. **2.** 0.2419. **3.** 0.3584. **4.** 0.5000. **5.** 0.0872. **6.** 0.2419.
7. 0.3584. **8.** 0.5000. **9.** 0.9945. **10.** 0.9945. **11.** 0.9703. **12.** 0.9703.
13. 0.9135. **14.** 0.9135. **15.** 0.8192. **16.** 0.8192. **17.** 11.4301. **18.** 11.4301.
19. 5.1446. **20.** 5.1446. **21.** 0.3839. **22.** 0.3839. **23.** 1.0000. **24.** 1.0000.
25. 1.0000. **26.** 1.0000. **27.** 1.0353. **28.** 1.0353. **29.** 4.8097. **30.** 4.8097.
31. 1.4396. **32.** 1.4396. **33.** 0.0038. **34.** 0.0054. **35.** 2 sec 10°. **36.** 2 csc 10°.

37. 2 cos 15°.
38. $3 \sin 20^\circ > \sin(3 \times 20^\circ)$ and $> \sin(2 \times 20^\circ)$.
39. $3 \tan 10^\circ < \tan(3 \times 10^\circ)$ and $> \tan(2 \times 10^\circ)$.
40. $3 \cos 10^\circ > \cos(3 \times 10^\circ)$ and $> \cos(2 \times 10^\circ)$.
41. No.
42. The sin, tan, sec increase and the cos, cot, csc decrease.

Exercise 5. Page 12

12. 37.6. **13.** 1. **14.** 100. **15.** 60. **16.** 12.86. **17.** 22.64.

Exercise 6. Page 15

1. 1.736. **2.** 3.882. **3.** 41.01.
4. 57.45. **5.** 12°. **6.** 20°.
7. 39°. **8.** 43°. **9.** 30°.
10. 54 ft. **11.** 4.326 ft. **12.** 479.9 ft.
13. 449.9 ft

Exercise 7. Page 16

1. 10.83. **2.** 13.46. **3.** 25.58. **4.** 31.86. **5.** 55.73. **6.** 1.873. **7.** 5.972.
8. 5.935. **9.** 4.884. **10.** 7.311. **11.** 10°. **12.** 17°. **13.** 26°. **14.** 60°.
15. 63°. **16.** 70°. **17.** 54°. **18.** 60°. **19.** 70°. **20.** 84°. **21.** 60°.
22. 411.4 ft. **23.** 383 ft. **24.** 43°. **25.** 7.794 in. **26.** 166.272 sq. in. **27.** 5.657. **28.** 27.71 ft.
29. 6 in.
30. 28.19 ft.; 21.21 ft.; 12.68 ft.; 30 ft.; 0 ft
31. 60°; 0°.
32. 25°; 65°.
33. 30° and 60°; 31° and 59°.
34. 749.9 ft.

Exercise 8. Page 19

1. 12.02. **2.** 11.04. **3.** 28.84. **4.** 45.04. **5.** 98.
6. 5.928. **7.** 14.78. **8.** 44.01. **9.** 107.1. **10.** 453.8.
11. 45°. **12.** 8°. **13.** 9°. **14.** 19°. **15.** 22°.
16. 64°. **17.** 148 ft. 8 in. **18.** 29°. **19.** 2.517 mi; 3.916 mi.
20. 159.7 ft. **21.** 45°; 90°; 45° **22.** 15.76 ft. **23.** 6.14 ft. **24.** 1.03 in.

Exercise 9. Page 20

1. 26.11. **2.** 12.35. **3.** 162.6.
4. 85.81. **5.** 544.0. **6.** 26.84.
7. 26.60. **8.** 68.80. **9.** 45°.
10. 25°. **11.** 28.87 ft. **12.** 428.4 ft.
13. 113 ft. **14.** 123.6 ft.

Exercise 10. Page 21

1. 40.40. **2.** 61.77. **3.** 101.2.
4. 33.63. **5.** 55.50. **6.** 339.4.
7. 41°. **8.** 60°. **9.** 22.65 ft.
10. 57.74 ft. **11.** 1369 ft. **12.** 91.64 ft.
13. 26.11 ft

Exercise 11. Page 22

1. 49.50. **3.** 80.62. **5.** 81.19. **7.** 64°. **9.** 65°. **11.** 1113 ft.
2. 54.87. **4.** 64.60. **6.** 152.8. **8.** 28°. **10.** 45°. **12.** 13.69 mi
13. 19.82 mi. **14.** 267.0 ft. **15.** 57.51 ft. **16.** 17.23 in.

Exercise 12. Page 23

3. $\tan x$. **4.** $\sec x$. **5.** $\sec x$. **6.** $\csc x$. **7.** $\cot x$. **8.** $\csc x$. **16.** 18°. **35.** $r \sin x$.
36. $a = cm$; $b = c\sqrt{1 - m^2}$. **37.** $a = bm$; $c = b\sqrt{m^2 + 1}$.

Exercise 13. Page 26

2. 0. **8.** No. **13.** 2.3109. **19.** 37°. **25.** 19°. **31.** 16°.
3. 1. **9.** 45°. **14.** 0.5373. **20.** 46°. **26.** 48°. **32.** 37°.
4. ∞. **10.** 0.6462; 0.7631. **15.** 6°. **21.** 6°. **27.** 34°. **33.** $\frac{1}{2}$.
5. 0. **16.** 24°. **22.** 13°. **28.** 40°.
6. The tangent. **11.** 0.3680. **17.** 44°. **23.** 22°. **29.** 54°.
7. No. **12.** 2.7173. **18.** 26°. **24.** 14°. **30.** 30°.

Exercise 14. Page 29

1. 0.7547. **7.** 0.7428. **13.** 0.8708. **19.** 53.47. **25.** 69.38. **31.** 19.70 ft.; 22.62 ft.
2. 0.9004. **8.** 0.6563. **14.** 0.8708. **20.** 20.90. **26.** 49.83.
3. 0.7545. **9.** 0.6693. **15.** 1.1483. **21.** 25.27. **27.** 94.35. **32.** 19.72 ft.; 22.61 ft.
4. 0.9015. **10.** 0.6567. **16.** 17.73. **22.** 48.29. **28.** 74.93.
5. 0.7538. **11.** 0.6700. **17.** 32.16. **23.** 66.48. **29.** 88.35. **33.** 120.5 ft.
6. 0.7545. **12.** 0.6700. **18.** 46.01. **24.** 64.84. **30.** 47° 56′. **34.** 71.77 ft.

Exercise 15. Page 30

1. 0.0087. **6.** 0.0715. **11.** 0.9972. **16.** 1.0000. **21.** 12.66 in.; 0.9970 in.
2. 0.0070. **7.** 0.9972. **12.** 0.9974. **17.** 0.0715.
3. 0.0698. **8.** 0.0769. **13.** 0.0767. **18.** 143.2. **22.** 390 ft.
4. 0.9973. **9.** 12.71. **14.** 13.95. **19.** 0.0052. **23.** 0.7477 in.; 9.530 in.
5. 0.0787. **10.** 13.62. **15.** 0.0769. **20.** 0.0734.

Exercise 16. Page 33

1. 0.4567. **14.** 12.1524. **24.** 70° 45′ 30″; 0.3490. **35.** 10.7389. **48.** 44° 38′ 30″.
2. 0.6725. **15.** 15.3140. **36.** 0.9808. **49.** 69° 15′.
3. 0.8338. **16.** 10.4652. **25.** 79° 30′ 15″; 0.1852. **37.** 4.5787. **50.** 78° 8′ 30″.
4. 0.9099. **17.** 8.7149. **38.** 4.1525. **51.** 78° 8′ 15″.
5. 0.8065. **18.** 7.2246. **26.** 0.4305. **39.** 3.6108. **52.** 14° 45′.
6. 0.7289. **19.** 6.5585. **27.** 0.4313. **40.** 3.3502. **53.** 0.7658.
7. 0.4335. **20.** 6.0826. **28.** 0.5410. **41.** 31° 30′. **54.** 0.6438.
8. 0.5438. **21.** 39° 43′ 30″; 0.7691. **29.** 0.6646. **42.** 35° 15′. **55.** 0.5639.
9. 0.6418. **30.** 0.9045. **43.** 41° 18′ 30″. **56.** 33° 10′ 15″; 1.5298.
10. 0.9209. **22.** 50° 16′ 30″; 0.6391. **31.** 0.1990. **44.** 44° 36′ 30″.
11. 1.2882. **32.** 4.9550. **45.** 38° 15′. **57.** 31° 8′ 30″; 0.6042.
12. 2.5018. **23.** 71° 29′ 40″; 0.9483. **33.** 0.1490. **46.** 39° 30′.
13. 3.1266. **34.** 7.8279. **47.** 17° 45′.

Exercise 17. Page 37

1. $A = 36° 52'$, $B = 53° 8'$, $c = 5$.
2. $A = 32° 35'$, $B = 57° 25'$, $b = 10.95$.
3. $B = 77° 43'$, $b = 24.34$, $c = 24.93$.
4. $A = 46° 42'$, $b = 9.801$, $c = 14.29$.
5. $B = 52° 18'$, $a = 15.90$, $b = 20.57$.
6. $A = 65° 48'$, $a = 127.7$, $b = 57.39$.
7. $A = 34° 18'$, $B = 55° 42'$, $a = 12.96$.
8. $A = 43° 33'$, $B = 46° 27'$, $a = 93.14$.
9. $B = 57° 46'$, $a = 26.73$, $c = 50.12$.
10. $A = 43° 49'$, $a = 191.9$, $c = 277.2$.
11. $A = 68° 43'$, $B = 21° 17'$, $c = 102.0$.
12. $A = 3° 20'$, $B = 86° 40'$, $b = 102.8$.
13. $A = 84° 52'$, $b = 0.2802$, $c = 3.133$.
14. $A = 70° 48'$, $B = 19° 12'$, $b = 5.916$.
15. $B = 51° 31'$, $a = 35.47$, $b = 44.62$.
16. $A = 22° 37'$, $B = 67° 23'$, $a = 5$, $c = 13$.
17. $A = 53° 8'$, $B = 36° 52'$, $a = 40$, $c = 50$.
18. $A = 22° 37'$, $B = 67° 23'$, $a = 12.5$, $c = 32.5$.
19. $B = 54° 49' 30''$, $b = 3.547$, $c = 4.340$.
20. $B = 47° 47' 30''$, $b = 6.284$, $c = 8.485$.
21. $A = 60° 41' 30''$, $b = 3.593$, $c = 7.339$
22. $A = 53° 39' 30''$, $b = 5.812$, $c = 9.808$
23. $B = 60° 17' 30''$, $a = 3.370$, $b = 5.906$.
24. $B = 55° 39' 30''$, $a = 203.08$, $b = 297.25$.
25. $B = 48° 49' 20''$, $a = 218.68$, $c = 332.14$.
26. $B = 64.5°$, $b = 100.6$, $c = 111.5$.
27. $B = 65.5°$, $a = 10.37$, $b = 22.75$.
28. $B = 57.45°$, $a = 21.52$, $b = 33.72$.
29. $B = 34.49°$, $a = 65.94$, $b = 45.30$.
30. $B = 26.54°$, $a = 67.10$, $b = 33.51$.
31. $A = 39.41°$, $b = 54.77$, $c = 70.88$.
32. $B = 21.75°$, $a = 225.6$, $c = 242.8$.
33. 29.20 in.
34. 23.73 in.
35. 42.25 in.
36. 54.26 in.
37. 43.30 in.
38. 60.05 in.
39. 56° 18′ 36″, 33° 41′ 24″.
40. $A = 41° 24' 30''$, $B = 48° 35' 30''$.
41. 13.26 ft.
42. 16.82 in.; 18.50 in.
43. 12.42 ft.
44. 66.89 in.
45. 9° 35′ 40″.

Exercise 18. Page 41

1. 5.
2. 2.
3. 4.
4. 4.
5. 6.
6. 7.
7. 8.
8. 5.
9. 6.
10. 4.
11. 3.
12. 2.
13. 3.
14. 3.
15. 4.
16. 2.
17. 3.
18. 5.
19. 6.
20. −1.
21. −2; −3; −4.
22. 1 and 2; 2 and 3; 3 and 4; 4 and 5; 5 and 6; 8 and 9.
23. −2 and −1; −3 and −2; −4 and −3; −1 and 0; −2 and −1; −3 and −2.
24. 1; 2; 3; 6; 9; 10; −2; −4; −5; −6; −7; −8.
25. 1; 4; 6; 7; 8; −1; −2; −3; −4; −5; −6; −7.
26. 0; −4; −5; 7; 8.
27. 1 and 2.
28. 1 and 2.
29. 1 and 2.
30. 1 and 2.
31. 2 and 3.
32. 2 and 3.
33. 2 and 3.
34. 2 and 3.
35. 3 and 4.
36. 3 and 4.
37. 3 and 4.
38. 3 and 4.
39. 5 and 6.
40. 6 and 7.
41. 6 and 7.
42. 7 and 8.

Exercise 19. Page 45

1. 1.
2. 1.
3. 2.
4. 0.
5. 3.
6. 3.
7. 2.
8. 1.
9. 0.
10. 4.
11. −1.
12. −2.
13. −1.
14. −1.
15. −3.
16. −4.
17. −3.
18. −5.
19. −1.
20. −2.
21. 1.58681.
22. 0.58681.
23. 2.58681.
24. 4.58681.
25. 5.58681.

26. 7.58681.
27. $\bar{1}$.58681.
28. $\bar{2}$.58681.
29. $\bar{4}$.58681.
30. 3.67724.
31. 0.67724.
32. 4.67724.
33. 7.67724.
34. $\bar{2}$.67724.
35. $\bar{5}$.67724.
36. 0.40603.
37. 1.40603.
38. $\bar{1}$.40603.
39. $\bar{3}$.40603.
40. 4.40603.
41. 7.40603.
42. 0.39794.
43. $\bar{1}$.39794.
44. $\bar{1}$.39794.
45. $\bar{2}$.39794.
46. 4.39794.
47. 7.39794.

Exercise 20. Page 47

1. 0.30103.
2. 1.30103.
3. 2.30103.
4. $\bar{3}$.30103.
5. 3.32222.
6. 3.33244.
7. 3.33365.
8. 0.33365.
9. 3.54220.
10. 3.64953.
11. 3.74671.
12. 3.84553.
13. 3.72304.
14. 1.83556.
15. 0.89905.
16. 2.92158.
17. $\bar{1}$.84510.
18. $\bar{1}$.87506.
19. $\bar{1}$.87852.
20. $\bar{1}$.87892.
21. $\bar{2}$.40654.
22. $\bar{3}$.55630.
23. $\bar{4}$.95424.
24. $\bar{2}$.25042.
25. 4.09132.
26. 4.09150.
27. 4.09157.
28. 2.09157.
29. 2.37037.
30. 1.61624.
31. 1.75037.
32. $\bar{1}$.61576.
33. 5.51409.
34. 2.56155.
35. 7.82948.
36. 17.72562.
37. 9.19605.
38. 5.26893.
39. 2.51989.
40. 3.20732.
41. 4.86198.
42. 0.48124.
43. 0.95424.
44. 0.90309.
45. 4.22472.
46. 2.87595.
47. 5.32328.
48. 12.70040.
49. 19.58460.
50. 0.15052.
51. 1.65052.
52. 1.17969.
53. 0.46458.
54. 0.64167.
55. 1.08030.
56. 2.16224.
57. 0.79034.
58. 1.14477.
59. 0.54254.
60. 0.99155.
61. 2.00072.
62. 0.75343.
63. 1.19855.

Exercise 21. Page 49

1. 3.
2. 3000.
3. 0.003.
4. 304.5.
5. 37,020.
6. 46.
7. 467.5.
8. 0.000056.
9. 5505.
10. 0.05795.
11. 0.0006095.
12. 0.66.
13. 6.695.
14. 7.6.
15. 7,805,000,000.
16. 79,950,000.
17. 1.7102.
18. 27.005.
19. 370.15.
20. 0.38055.
21. 0.0043142.
22. 43,144.
23. 4.3646.
24. 0.049074.
25. 594,640,000.
26. 0.00067555.
27. 6846.5.
28. 685.55.
29. 77,553.
30. 785.65.
31. 7917.3.
32. 8.5552.
33. 875.18.
34. 2.
35. 3.45591; 3.45864.
36. 2955.
37. 0.0066062.
38. 0.65163.
39. 91.226.
40. 53,159,000.
41. 0.000010745.
42. 5.72784; 534,360.
43. 353,780.
44. 7.2388.
45. 107.
46. 25,459.
47. 16,693,000.
48. 129.66.
49. 4.9341.

Exercise 22. Page 50

1. 10.
2. 24.
3. 15.
4. 35.
5. 8.
6. 21.
7. 12.
8. 18.
9. 56.
10. 18.
11. 100.
12. 2400.
13. 1500.
14. 3500.
15. 8000.
16. 21,000.
17. 12,000.
18. 18,000.
19. 560,000.
20. 180,000.
21. 1034.6.
22. 2192.3.
23. 13.31.
24. 20.265.
25. 603.9.
26. 1282.8.
27. 184,670.
28. 11,099.
29. 1609.9.
30. 17,458.
31. 18.212 in.
32. 113.04 ft.
33. 210.
34. 945.
35. 5005.
36. 38,645.
37. 627,400
38. 276.67.

Exercise 23. Page 51

1. 7.68964. **2.** 3.68964. **3.** $\bar{7}$.68964. **4.** $\bar{3}$.09497. **5.** 0.00000. **6.** $\bar{1}$.99999.
7. $\bar{4}$.03939. **8.** 2.00010. **9.** 1.99999. **10.** 0.00000. **11.** 1,248,000. **12.** 124.8.
13. 0.1248. **14.** 0.0001248. **15.** 0.0043707. **16.** 0.11422. **17.** 0.0000003125. **18.** 0.25121.
19. 0.02240. **20.** 0.00015725. **21.** 1.3020. **22.** 38.079. **23.** 3309.6. **24.** 452.27
25. 22.936. **26.** 34.108. **27.** 16.51.

Exercise 24. Page 53

1. 1.97519. **2.** $\bar{3}$.66078. **3.** $\bar{1}$.68618. **4.** $\bar{3}$.70404. **5.** $\bar{5}$.00000. **6.** $\bar{9}$.70000. **7.** $\bar{7}$.00000. **8.** $\bar{7}$.00000. **9.** $\bar{3}$.76439. **10.** 2.00000. **11.** 2.90000. **12.** 6.90000.
13. 3.89100. **14.** $\bar{2}$.00000. **15.** $\bar{2}$.11220. **16.** $\bar{2}$.00286. **17.** 1.71172. **18.** 5. **19.** 5. **20.** 3. **21.** 4. **22.** 3. **23.** 5. **24.** 3.
25. 5. **26.** 84. **27.** 82.002. **28.** 76. **29.** 35.6. **30.** 73.002. **31.** 92. **32.** 105. **33.** 63. **34.** 77. **35.** 0.0129. **36.** 1290.
37. 0.00999. **38.** 0.0709. **39.** 0.0204. **40.** 0.065. **41.** 0.48001. **42.** 2.143. **43.** 0.4667. **44.** 0.004667. **45.** 1.913. **46.** 1.123. **47.** 12.86. **48.** 5.184.
49. 60.87. **50.** 0.6527. **51.** 20. **52.** 50. **53.** 700. **54.** 800. **55.** 9000. **56.** 11,000. **57.** 120,000 **58.** 0.01. **59.** 871.1 ; 2.

Exercise 25. Page 54

1. $\bar{2}$.60206. **2.** $\bar{3}$.88606. **3.** $\bar{2}$.56225. **4.** $\bar{1}$.23433.
5. $\bar{4}$.42585. **6.** $\bar{3}$.36927. **7.** $\bar{2}$.28727. **8.** $\bar{1}$.14188.
9. 0.30103. **10.** 0.14267. **11.** 1.08092. **12.** 2.13906.
13. $\bar{1}$.52187. **14.** $\bar{2}$.20698. **15.** 3.22185. **16.** 4.15490.
17. 1. **18.** 0.1 **19.** 0. **20.** 1.

Exercise 26. Page 55

1. 1. **2.** 6. **3.** 3. **4.** 0.5. **5.** 1. **6.** 2. **7.** 0.11111.
8. 0.44272. **9.** 1.7833. **10.** 1000. **11.** 0.092. **12.** 1.8. **13.** 0.01. **14.** 0.21.
15. 6.1649. **16.** 0.42742. **17.** 1.4179. **18.** 0.031169. **19.** 40.464. **20.** 0.14621. **21.** 2893.2.
22. 105.47. **23.** 3,013,400. **24.** 0.081528. **25.** 232.24. **26.** 0.0000007237 **27.** 103.33.

Exercise 27. Page 56

1. 4. **2.** 8. **3.** 32. **4.** 1024. **5.** 80.998.
6. 728.98. **7.** 64. **8.** 125. **9.** 1. **10.** 40,355,000.
11. 4,782,800. **12.** 16,777,000. **13.** 19,486,000. **14.** 11,391,000. **15.** 11.391.
16. 83,522. **17.** 15,625. **18.** 6,103,600,000 **19.** 15,625. **20.** 244,140,000.

21. 16,413,000,000,000,000.
22. 7,700,500.
23. 31,137,000,000.
24. 292,360,000,000,000.
25. 2.1435.
26. 180.11.
27. 0.000000000001.
28. 0.00000002048.
29. 0.05765.
30. 0.00000011765.
31. 0.018741.
32. 154.85.
33. 157.5.
34. 41,961.
35. 2.0727.
36. 0.0019720.
37. 0.023551.
38. 0.00015228.
39. 0.0000075624.
40. 0.00000012603.
41. 9.8696 ; 31.006.
42. 21.991 ; 153.94
3053.6.

Exercise 28. Page 57

1. 1.4142.
2. 1.71.
3. 1.3205.
4. 1.2394.
5. 1.1487.
6. 2.2795.
7. 5.6569.
8. 3.0403.
9. 3.3166.
10. 1.4422.
11. 2.802.
12. 1.2023.
13. 0.54773.
14. 0.3684.
15. 0.067405.
16. 0.064491.
17. 20.729.
18. 1.9733.
19. 3.9095.
20. 0.0028827.
21. 1.7725 ; 1.4645.
22. 1.3313 ; 2.1450 ; 5.5684 ; 0.42378 ; 0.40020 ; 0.79537.

Exercise 29. Page 59

1. $x = 3$.
2. $x = 4$.
3. $x = 4$.
4. $x = 4$.
5. $x = 3$.
6. $x = 4.2479$.
7. $x = 3.9300$.
8. $x = 4.2920$.
9. $x = 5.6610$.
10. $x = 3.0499$.
11. $x = 3$.
12. $x = 3.3219$.
13. $x = -0.087515$.
14. $x = 4.4190$.
15. $x = -0.047954$.
16. $x = 3, y = 1$.
17. $x = 5, y = 1$.
18. $x = 1, y = 1$.
19. $x = 2, y = 2$.
20. $x = 3, y = 2$.
21. $x = 2, y = 2$.
22. $x = \dfrac{\log a - \log p}{\log(1+r)}$.
23. $x = \dfrac{\log r + \log l - \log a}{\log r}$.
24. $x = 1, -3$.
25. $x = \dfrac{\log a - \log p}{\log(1+rt)}$.
26. $x = \dfrac{\log[s(r-1)+a] - \log a}{\log r}$.
27. $x = 2, -1$.
28. 0.062457.
29. 3.1389.
30. 0.036161.
31. 0.03475.
32. 6.
33. $\dfrac{\log b}{\log a}$.
34. $\dfrac{\log n}{\log 5}$.
35. 2 ; 7.2730 ; 2.0009 ; 2.0043.
36. 1 ; $\dfrac{\log a}{\log b}$; 1 ; 3 ; 4
37. $x = \dfrac{\log b}{\log a - \log b}$.
38. -1.

Exercise 30. Page 62

1. 9.65705 – 10.
2. 9.97015 – 10.
3. 9.90796 – 10.
4. 9.82551 – 10.
5. 10.57195 – 10.
6. 9.32747 – 10.
7. 10.57195 – 10.
8. 9.32747 – 10.
9. 9.20613 – 10.
10. 9.99526 – 10.
11. 9.14412 – 10.
12. 9.14412 – 10.
13. 8.89464 – 10.
14. 9.99651 – 10.
15. 9.23510 – 10.
16. 9.87099 – 10.
17. 9.68826 – 10.
18. 10.10706 – 10.
19. 9.55763 – 10.
20. 9.96966 – 10.
21. 9.98436 – 10.
22. 9.42095 – 10.
23. 9.48632 – 10.
24. 9.68916 – 10.
25. 9.95340 – 10.
26. 11.13737 – 10.
27. 9.74766 – 10.
28. 9.66368 – 10.
29. 10.17675 – 10.
30. 9.82332 – 10.
31. 6.51165 – 10.
32. 8.25667 – 10.
33. 6.79257 – 10.
34. 8.56813 – 10.
35. 7.45643 – 10.
36. 8.15611 – 10.
37. 8.11503 – 10.
38. 8.00469 – 10.
39. 8.24915 – 10.
40. 8.24915 – 10.
41. 8.63254 – 10.
42. 8.63205 – 10.
43. 9.32507 – 10.
44. 9.32507 – 10.
45. 10.39604 – 10
46. 7° 30′.
47. 32° 21′.
48. 58° 27′.

49. 85° 30′.
50. 4° 30′.
51. 31° 33′.
52. 58° 35′.
53. 50° 32′.
54. 39° 2′.
55. 63° 41′ 23″.
56. 77° 6′.
57. 79°.
58. 70°.
59. 20° 13′ 30″.
60. 32° 22′ 15″.
61. 49° 34′ 12″.
62. 51° 47′ 36″.
63. 37° 8′ 48″.
64. 50° 48′ 15″.
65. 8° 49′ 30″.
66. 8° 46′ 30″.
67. 57° $4\frac{2}{7}$″.
68. 49° 25′ 7″.
69. 38° 22′ 30″.
70. 2° 3′ 30″.
71. 89° 49′ 10″.

Exercise 31. Page 67

1. $A = 30°$, $B = 60°$, $b = 10.39$, $S = 31.18$.
2. $B = 30°$, $a = 6.928$, $c = 8$, $S = 13.86$.
3. $B = 60°$, $b = 5.196$, $c = 6$, $S = 7.794$.
4. $A = 45°$, $B = 45°$, $c = 5.657$, $S = 8$.
5. $A = 43° 47'$, $B = 46° 13'$, $b = 2.086$, $S = 2.086$.
6. $B = 66° 30'$. $a = 250$, $b = 575$, $S = 71{,}880$.
7. $B = 61° 55'$, $a = 1073$, $b = 2012$, $S = 1{,}079{,}500$.
8. $B = 50° 26'$, $a = 45.96$, $b = 55.62$, $S = 1278$.
9. $B = 54°$, $a = 0.5878$, $b = 0.8090$, $S = 0.2378$.
10. $A = 68° 13'$, $a = 185.7$, $b = 74.22$, $S = 6892$.
11. $A = 13° 35'$, $a = 21.94$, $b = 90.79$, $S = 995.8$.
12. $B = 85° 25'$, $b = 7946$, $c = 7972$, $S = 2{,}531{,}000$.
13. $B = 53° 16'$, $b = 65.03$, $c = 81.14$, $S = 1578$.
14. $B = 4°$, $b = 0.0005594$, $c = 0.00802$, $S = 0.000002238$.
15. $A = 46° 12'$, $a = 53.12$, $c = 73.60$, $S = 1353$.
16. $A = 86° 22'$, $a = 31.50$, $c = 31.56$, $S = 31.50$.
17. $A = 13° 41'$, $b = 4075$, $c = 4194$, $S = 2{,}021{,}000$.
18. $A = 21° 8'$, $b = 188.9$, $c = 202.5$, $S = 6893$.
19. $A = 44° 35'$, $b = 2.221$, $c = 3.119$, $S = 2.431$.
20. $B = 52° 4'$, $a = 3.118$, $c = 5.071$, $S = 6.235$.
21. $A = 31° 24'$, $B = 58° 36'$, $b = 7333$, $S = 16{,}410{,}000$.
22. $A = 56° 3'$, $B = 33° 57'$, $b = 48.32$, $S = 1734$.
23. $A = 65° 14'$, $B = 24° 46'$, $b = 3.917$, $S = 16.63$.
24. $A = 53° 15'$, $B = 36° 45'$, $a = 1758$, $S = 1{,}154{,}000$.
25. $A = 53° 31'$, $B = 36° 29'$, $a = 24.68$, $S = 225.2$.
26. $A = 63°$, $B = 27°$, $c = 43$, $S = 373.9$.
27. $A = 4° 42'$, $B = 85° 18'$, $c = 15$, $S = 9.187$.
28. $A = 81° 30'$, $B = 8° 30'$, $c = 419.9$, $S = 12{,}890$.
29. $A = 38° 59'$, $B = 51° 1'$, $c = 21.76$, $S = 115.8$.
30. $A = 1° 22'$, $B = 88° 38'$, $b = 91.89$, $S = 100.6$.
31. $A = 39° 48'$, $B = 50° 12'$, $c = 7.811$, $S = 15$.
32. $A = 30' 12''$, $B = 89° 29' 48''$, $b = 70$, $S = 21.53$.
33. $A = 43° 20'$, $B = 46° 40'$, $a = 1.189$, $S = 0.7488$.
34. $B = 71° 46'$, $b = 21.25$, $c = 22.37$, $S = 74.37$.
35. $B = 60° 52'$, $a = 6.688$, $c = 13.74$, $S = 40.13$.
36. $B = 20° 6'$, $a = 63.86$, $b = 23.37$, $S = 746.15$.
37. $A = 45° 56'$, $a = 19.40$, $b = 18.78$, $S = 182.15$.
38. $A = 41° 11'$, $b = 53.72$, $c = 71.38$, $S = 1262.4$
39. $A = 55° 16'$, $a = 12.98$, $c = 15.80$, $S = 58.42$.
40. $A = 3° 56'$, $a = 0.5805$, $b = 8.442$, $S = 2.450$.

41. $S = \frac{1}{2} c^2 \sin A \cos A$.
43. $S = \frac{1}{2} b^2 \tan A$.
42. $S = \frac{1}{2} a^2 \cot A$.
44. $S = \frac{1}{2} a \sqrt{c^2 - a^2}$.
45. $A = 40° 45' 48''$, $B = 49° 14' 12''$, $b = 11.6$, $c = 15.315$.
46. $A = 55° 13' 20''$, $B = 34° 46' 40''$, $a = 7.2$, $c = 8.766$.
47. $B = 61°$, $a = 3.647$, $b = 6.58$, $c = 7.523$.
48. $A = 27° 2' 30''$, $B = 62° 57' 30''$, $a = 10.002$, $b = 19.595$.
49. 19° 28′ 17″; 70° 31′ 43″.
50. 3112 mi.; 19,553 mi.
51. 15.498 mi.
52. Between 1° 15′ 30″ and 1°19′ 10″.
53. 212.1 ft.
54. 732.2 ft.
55. 3270 ft.
56. 37.3 ft.
57. 1° 25′ 56″.
58. 59° 44′ 35″.
59. 95.34 ft.
60. 23° 50′ 40″.
61. 36° 1′ 42″.
62. 69° 26′ 38″.
63. 7.071 mi.; 7.071 mi.
64. 19.05 ft.
65. 20.88 ft.
66. 56.65 ft.
67. 685.9 ft.
68. 5.657 ft
69. 136.6 ft.
70. 140 ft.
71. 84.74 ft.

Exercise 32. Page 71

1. $C = 2(90° - A)$, $c = 2a \cos A$, $h = a \sin A$.
2. $A = 90° - \frac{1}{2} C$, $c = 2a \cos A$, $h = a \sin A$.
3. $C = 2(90° - A)$, $a = \frac{c}{2 \cos A}$, $h = a \sin A$.
4. $A = 90° - \frac{1}{2} C$, $a = \frac{c}{2 \cos A}$, $h = a \sin A$.
5. $C = 2(90° - A)$, $a = \frac{h}{\sin A}$, $c = 2a \cos A$.
6. $A = 90° - \frac{1}{2} C$, $a = \frac{h}{\sin A}$, $c = 2a \cos A$.
7. $\sin A = \frac{h}{a}$, $C = 2(90° - A)$, $c = 2a \cos A$.
8. $\tan A = \frac{2h}{c}$, $C = 2(90° - A)$, $a = \frac{h}{\sin A}$.
9. $A = 67° 22' 50''$, $C = 45° 14' 20''$, $h = 13.2$.
10. $c = 0.21943$, $h = 0.27384$, $S = 0.03004$.
11. $a = 2.055$, $h = 1.6852$, $S = 1.9819$.
12. $a = 7.706$, $c = 3.6676$, $S = 13.725$.
13. $A = 25° 27' 47''$, $C = 129° 4' 26''$, $a = 81.41$, $h = 35$.
14. $A = 81° 12' 9''$, $C = 17° 35' 42''$, $a = 17$, $c = 5.2$.
15. $c = 14.049$, $h = 26.649$, $S = 187.2$.
16. $S = a^2 \sin \frac{1}{2} C \cos \frac{1}{2} C$.
17. $S = a^2 \sin A \cos A$.
18. $S = h^2 \tan \frac{1}{2} C$.
19. 28.284 ft.; 4525.44 sq. ft.
20. 0.76536.
21. 94° 20′.
22. 2.7261.
23. 38° 56′ 33″.
24. 37.699 sq. in.
25. 0.8775.

Exercise 33. Page 72

1. $r = 1.618$, $h = 1.5388$, $S = 7.694$.
2. $h = 0.9848$, $p = 6.2514$, $S = 3.0782$.
3. $h = 19.754$, $c = 6.257$, $S = 1236$.
4. $r = 1.0824$, $c = 0.82842$, $S = 3.3137$.
5. $r = 2.5942$, $h = 2.4891$, $c = 1.461$.
6. $r = 1.5994$, $h = 1.441$, $p = 9.716$.
7. 0.51764 in.
8. $b = \dfrac{c}{2 \cos \frac{90°}{n}}$.
9. 0.2238 sq. in.
10. 0.310 in.
11. 1.0235 in.
12. 0.062821; 6.2821.
13. 6.283.
14. 0.635 sq. in.

Exercise 34. Page 73

2. 29.76 sq. in.
3. 104.07 sq. ft.
4. 36.463 sq. in.
5. 20.284 in.
7. 37.319 ft.
8. 342.67 ft.
9. 36.602 ft.; 86.602 ft.
10. 120.03 ft.
11. 2.9101 mi.; 3.531 mi.
12. $11° 47''$; 49.206 ft.
13. $52° 35' 42''$.
14. $60° 36' 58''$.
15. 6.3509 in.
16. 20 in.
17. 7.7942 in.
18. $40° 7' 6''$.
19. $77° 8' 31''$.
20. 94.368 ft.; $25° 42' 58''$.
21. 24.652 ft.
22. 196.93 ft.
23. 220.8 ft.
24. 1915.3 ft.
25. 362.09 ft.
26. $59° 2' 10''$.
27. 14.772 in.; 15.595 in.
28. 73.21 ft.
29. $25° 36' 9''$.
30. 26.613 in.
31. 7.5 ft.
32. $59° 58' 54''$; 173.08 ft.
33. 7.2917 ft.
34. 19.051.
35. 1.732 in.
36. 2675.8 mi.
37. 25.775 ft.; 19.45 ft.
38. 10.941 ft.; 20.141 ft.
39. 55.406 ft.
40. Between 131′ and 132′.
41. $43° 18' 48''$.
42. 2.6068 in.
43. 14.542 in.; 26.87 in.
44. 6471.7 ft.

Exercise 35. Page 80

29. 10.
30. 15.
31. 13.
32. $2\frac{1}{2}$.
33. $1\frac{1}{4}$.
34. $3\frac{3}{4}$.
35. 3.
36. 5.
37. 0.
38. 7.
39. 5.
40. 15.
41. 5.10.
42. 5.10.
43. 8.24.
44. 4.24.
45. $28\frac{1}{3}$ in.
46. 9.43 in.
47. 2.
48. $3\sqrt{3}$.
49. $\frac{3}{4}\sqrt{3}$.
50. Yes.
51. Octagon, 2.829.

Exercise 36. Page 84

16. I.
17. I.
18. II.
19. II.
20. III.
21. IV.
22. I.
23. II.
24. III.
25. IV.
26. I.
27. II.
28. III.
29. On OY'.
30. On OX.
61. $\frac{1}{3}\sqrt{6}$; $\frac{1}{3}\sqrt{3}$; $\sqrt{3}$; $\frac{1}{2}\sqrt{6}$.
62. 90°.
63. 60°.
64. $\sin = \frac{1}{2}\sqrt{2}$; $\cos = -\frac{1}{2}\sqrt{2}$; $\tan = -1$; $\csc = \sqrt{2}$; $\sec = -\sqrt{2}$; $\cot = -1$.
65. $\sin = 0$; $\cos = -1$; $\tan = 0$; $\csc = \infty$; $\sec = -1$; $\cot = \infty$.

Exercise 37. Page 88

52. 2; one in Quadrant I, one in Quadrant II.
53. 4; two in Quadrant I, two in Quadrant IV.
54. 2; 1; 1; 1; 1.
55. Between 90° and 270°; between 0° and 90° or between 180° and 270°; between 0° and 90° or between 270° and 360°; between 180° and 360°.
57. 1; 0; 0; ∞; 1; ∞; 1; 0.
59. III; II.
60. 40; 20.
61. 0.
62. 0.
63. 0.
64. $a^2 - b^2 + 4ab$.
65. $-2(a^2 + b^2)$.
66. 0.
67. 0.
76. 30°; 150°; 390°; 510°.
77. 30°; 330°; 390°; 690°.
78. 60°; 120°; 420°; 480°.
79. 60°; 300°; 420°; 660°.
80. 30°; 210°; 390°; 570°.
81. 60°; 240°; 420°; 600°.
82. 210°; 330°.
83. 120°; 240°.
84. 225°; 315°.
85. 135°; 225°.
86. 135°; 315°
87. 135°; 315°.

Exercise 38. Page 91

1. sin 10°.
2. – cos 20°.
3. – tan 32°.
4. – cot 24°.
5. sin 0°.
6. – tan 0°.
7. – sin 20°.
8. – cos 45°.
9. tan 78°.
10. cot 82°.
11. – sin 85°.
12. – sin 15°.
13. – tan 78°.
14. – tan 35°
15. cos 70°.
16. cos 10°.
17. – cot 65°.
18. – cot 13°.
19. – sin 0°.
20. cos 0°.
21. sin 31° 50′.
22. – cos 12° 20′.
23. tan 85° 30′.
24. – cot 72° 20′.
25. – sin 7° 10′ 3″.
26. cos 85° 54′ 46″.
27. – tan 37° 51′ 45″
28. cot 15° 10′ 3″.
29. sin 32.25°.
30. – cos 52.25°.

Exercise 39. Page 93

1. cos 10°.
2. cos 30°.
3. cos 20°.
4. cos 40°.
5. – sin 5°.
6. – sin 7°.
7. – sin 21°.
8. – sin 37°.
9. – cot 1°.
10. – cot 9°.
11. – cot 29°.
12. – cot 39°.
13. – tan 4° 1′.
14. – tan 7° 2′.
15. – tan 8° 3′.
16. – tan 9° 9′.
17. – sin 3°.
18. – sin 9°.
19. – sin 86°.
20. cos 75°.
21. cos 87°.
22. – sin 5°.
23. tan 80°.
24. tan 30°.
25. – tan 20°.
26. – cot 1.5°.
27. – cot 7.8°.
28. – cot 9.1°.
29. 0.0262.
30. – 0.5483.
31. – 0.7729.
32. 0.5040.
33. – 0.1304.
34. 0.8686.
35. 0.1357.
36. – 0.1354.
37. 9.89947 – 10.
38. – (9.83861 – 10).
39. – (9.79916 – 10).
40. – (10.52286 – 10).
41. – (9.91969 – 10).
42. 9.92401 – 10.
43. 10.14753 – 10.
44. – (9.82489 – 10).
46. 225°; 315°; 585°; 675°

Exercise 40. Page 95

6. $\sin x = \pm \dfrac{1}{\sqrt{\cot^2 x + 1}}$.
7. $\cos x = \pm \dfrac{1}{\sqrt{\tan^2 x + 1}}$.
8. $\sec x = \pm \dfrac{1}{\sqrt{1 - \sin^2 x}}$.
9. $\csc x = \pm \dfrac{1}{\sqrt{1 - \cos^2 x}}$.
19. 45°.
20. 30°.
21. 60°.
22. 45°.
23. 45°.
24. 45°.
25. 60°.
26. 45°.
27. 60°.
28. 60° or 180°.
29. 45°.
30. 30°.
31. 45°.
32. $\frac{1}{5}\sqrt{5}$; $\frac{2}{5}\sqrt{5}$.
33. $\frac{1}{4}\sqrt{15}$; $\sqrt{15}$
34. $\frac{1}{5}$; 5.
35. $\sin x = \frac{2}{5}\sqrt{5}$, $\cos x = \frac{1}{5}\sqrt{5}$, $\tan x = 2$; $\csc x = \frac{1}{2}\sqrt{5}$, $\sec x = \sqrt{5}$, $\cot x = \frac{1}{2}$.
36. $\frac{4}{17}\sqrt{17}$; $\frac{1}{17}\sqrt{17}$.
37. $\frac{9}{41}$; $\frac{40}{41}$.
38. When $x = 0°$.
39. 0° or 180°.
40. 38° 10′.
41. 45° or 225°.
42. 45°, 135°, 225°, or 315°.
43. 45° or 225°.
44. 0° or 60°.
45. 270° or 30°.
46. 30° or 150°.
47. 45°, 135°, 225°, or 315°.
48. 60°.
53. $\cos A = \frac{1}{3}\sqrt{5}$, $\tan A = \frac{2}{5}\sqrt{5}$, $\csc A = \frac{3}{2}$, $\sec A = \frac{3}{5}\sqrt{5}$, $\cot A = \frac{1}{2}\sqrt{5}$.
54. $\sin A = \frac{1}{4}\sqrt{7}$, $\tan A = \frac{1}{3}\sqrt{7}$, $\csc A = \frac{4}{7}\sqrt{7}$, $\sec A = \frac{4}{3}$, $\cot A = \frac{3}{7}\sqrt{7}$.
55. $\sin A = \frac{3}{13}\sqrt{13}$, $\cos A = \frac{2}{13}\sqrt{13}$, $\csc A = \frac{1}{3}\sqrt{13}$, $\sec A = \frac{1}{2}\sqrt{13}$, $\cot A = \frac{2}{3}$.
56. $\sin A = \frac{4}{5}$, $\cos A = \frac{3}{5}$, $\tan A = \frac{4}{3}$, $\csc A = \frac{5}{4}$, $\sec A = \frac{5}{3}$.
57. $\sin A = \frac{1}{3}\sqrt{5}$, $\cos A = \frac{2}{3}$, $\tan A = \frac{1}{2}\sqrt{5}$, $\csc A = \frac{3}{5}\sqrt{5}$, $\cot A = \frac{2}{5}\sqrt{5}$
58. $\cos A = \frac{5}{13}$, $\tan A = \frac{12}{5}$, $\csc A = \frac{13}{12}$, $\sec A = \frac{13}{5}$, $\cot A = \frac{5}{12}$.
59. $\cos A = \frac{3}{5}$, $\tan A = \frac{4}{3}$, $\csc A = \frac{5}{4}$, $\sec A = \frac{5}{3}$, $\cot A = \frac{3}{4}$.
60. $\sin A = \frac{11}{61}$, $\tan A = \frac{11}{60}$, $\csc A = \frac{61}{11}$, $\sec A = \frac{61}{60}$, $\cot A = \frac{60}{11}$.

61. $\sin A = \frac{24}{25}$, $\tan A = \frac{24}{7}$, $\csc A = \frac{25}{24}$, $\sec A = \frac{25}{7}$, $\cot A = \frac{7}{24}$.
62. $\sin A = \frac{4}{5}$, $\cos A = \frac{3}{5}$, $\csc A = \frac{5}{4}$, $\sec A = \frac{5}{3}$, $\cot A = \frac{3}{4}$.
63. $\sin A = \frac{1}{2}\sqrt{2}$, $\cos A = \frac{1}{2}\sqrt{2}$, $\tan A = 1$, $\csc A = \sqrt{2}$, $\sec A = \sqrt{2}$.
64. $\sin A = \frac{2}{5}\sqrt{5}$, $\cos A = \frac{1}{5}\sqrt{5}$, $\tan A = 2$, $\csc A = \frac{1}{2}\sqrt{5}$, $\sec A = \sqrt{5}$.
65. $\sin A = \frac{1}{2}\sqrt{3}$, $\cos A = \frac{1}{2}$, $\tan A = \sqrt{3}$, $\csc A = \frac{2}{3}\sqrt{3}$, $\cot A = \frac{1}{3}\sqrt{3}$.
66. $\sin A = \frac{1}{2}\sqrt{2}$, $\cos A = \frac{1}{2}\sqrt{2}$, $\tan A = 1$, $\sec A = \sqrt{2}$, $\cot A = 1$.
67. $\cos A = \sqrt{1-m^2}$, $\tan A = \dfrac{m}{\sqrt{1-m^2}}$, $\csc A = \dfrac{1}{m}$, $\sec A = \dfrac{1}{\sqrt{1-m^2}}$, $\cot A = \dfrac{\sqrt{1-m^2}}{m}$.
68. $\dfrac{2m}{1-m^2}$.
69. $\dfrac{m^2+n^2}{2mn}$.
70. $\cos 0° = 1$, $\tan 0° = 0$, $\csc 0° = \infty$, $\sec 0° = 1$, $\cot 0° = \infty$.
71. $\cos 90° = 0$, $\tan 90° = \infty$, $\csc 90° = 1$, $\sec 90° = \infty$, $\cot 90° = 0$.
72. $\sin 90° = 1$, $\cos 90° = 0$, $\csc 90° = 1$, $\sec 90° = \infty$, $\cot 90° = 0$.
73. $\sin 22° 30' = \dfrac{1}{\sqrt{4+2\sqrt{2}}}$, $\cos 22° 30' = \dfrac{1}{\sqrt{4-2\sqrt{2}}}$, $\tan 22° 30' = \sqrt{2}-1$,
$\csc 22° 30' = \sqrt{4+2\sqrt{2}}$, $\sec 22° 30' = \sqrt{4-2\sqrt{2}}$.
74. $\dfrac{1-\cos^2 A}{\cos A} + \dfrac{\cos^2 A}{1-\cos^2 A}$.

Exercise 41. Page 98

1. 0.25875.
2. 0.96575.
3. 0.96575.
4. 0.25875.
5. 1.
6. 0.
7. 0.96575.
8. – 0.25875.
9. 0.866.
10. – 0.5.
11. 0.707.
12. – 0.707.
13. 0.5.
14. – 0.866.
15. 0.25875.
16. – 0.96575

Exercise 42. Page 99

1. 0.268.
2. 3.732.
3. 3.732.
4. 0.268.
5. ∞.
6. 0.
7. – 3.732.
8. – 0.268.
9. – 1.732.
10. – 0.577.
11. – 1.
12. – 1.
13. – 0.577.
14. – 1.732.
15. – 0.268.
16. – 3.732.

Exercise 43. Page 102

1. $\frac{56}{65}$.
2. $\frac{16}{65}$.
3. $\frac{33}{65}$.
4. $\frac{63}{65}$.
5. $1\frac{23}{33}$.
6. $\frac{16}{63}$.
7. $\cos y$.
8. $\sin y$.
9. $\cot y$.
10. $\cos y$.
11. $\sin y$.
12. $-\sin y$.
13. $-\cos y$.
14. $-\cos y$.
15. $-\sin y$
16. $\sin y$.
17. $\sin x$.
18. $-\cos x$.
19. $-\sin x$.
20. $-\cot x$.
21. $\tan x$.
22. $-\tan x$.
23. $\cot x$.
24. $-\sin y$.
25. $\frac{1}{2}\sqrt{2}(\cos y - \sin y)$.
26. $\frac{1}{2}\sqrt{2}(\cos y + \sin y)$.
27. $\dfrac{1-\tan y}{1+\tan y}$.
28. $\dfrac{\sqrt{3}\cot y - 1}{\cot y + \sqrt{3}}$.
29. $\dfrac{\frac{1}{3}\sqrt{3}\cot y + 1}{\cot y - \frac{1}{3}\sqrt{3}}$.
30. $\tan y$.
31. 0.8571; 0.2222.
32. 3.732; 0.268.
33. 1; $\frac{49}{71}$; 45°.
34. $x + y = 90°$, 270° in the three cases.
37. 135°, 405°.

Exercise 44. Page 103

5. 1. **7.** $-\frac{1}{2}$. **9.** 0.8492. **11.** -1.1776. **13.** $\frac{120}{169}$. **15.** $3\sin x - 4\sin^3 x$

6. $\frac{1}{2}\sqrt{3}$. **8.** $\frac{7}{25}$. **10.** 0.5827. **12.** 1.7161. **14.** $\frac{120}{169}$. **16.** $4\cos^3 x - 3\cos x$

Exercise 45. Page 104

1. 0.2588. **3.** 0.2679. **5.** 7.5928. **7.** 0.9239. **9.** 2.4142.

2. 0.9659. **4.** 3.7321. **6.** 0.3827. **8.** 0.4142. **10.** 5.0280.

11. 0.10051; 0.99493. **12.** 0.38730; 0.92196; 0.42009; 2.3805.

Exercise 46. Page 105

8. 0.

9. $\frac{1}{2}\sqrt{3}$.

15. $\dfrac{2}{\sin 2x}$.

16. $2\cot 2x$.

17. $\dfrac{\cos(x-y)}{\sin x\cos y}$.

18. $\dfrac{\cos(x+y)}{\sin x\cos y}$.

19. $\tan^2 x$.

20. $\dfrac{\cos(x-y)}{\cos x\cos y}$.

21. $\dfrac{\cos(x+y)}{\cos x\cos y}$.

22. $\dfrac{\cos(x-y)}{\sin x\sin y}$.

23. $\dfrac{\cos(x+y)}{\sin x\sin y}$.

24. $\tan x\tan y$.

27. $\frac{1}{7}$.

Exercise 47. Page 109

1. $a = b\sin A$; $b = a\sin B$; $a = b$; $\sin A = \sin B$.

4. 8 in.

5. 1000 ft.

6. 8.5450 in.; 4.2728 in

7. 27.6498 in.

8. 9.1121 in.

Exercise 48. Page 110

1. $C = 123° 12'$, $b = 2051.5$, $c = 2362.6$.

2. $C = 55° 20'$, $b = 567.69$, $c = 663.99$.

3. $C = 35° 4'$, $b = 577.31$, $c = 468.93$.

4. $C = 25° 12'$, $b = 2276.6$, $c = 1573.9$.

5. $C = 47° 14'$, $a = 1340.6$, $b = 1113.8$.

6. $A = 108° 50'$, $a = 53.276$, $c = 47.324$.

7. $B = 56° 56'$, $b = 5685.9$, $c = 5357.5$.

8. $B = 77°$, $a = 630.77$, $c = 929.48$.

9. $a = 5$; $c = 9.659$.

10. $a = 7$; $b = 8.573$.

11. Sides, 600 ft. and 1039.2 ft. altitude, 519.6 ft.

12. 855 : 1607.

13. 5.438; 6.857.

14. 15.588 in.

15. $AB = 59.564$ mi.; $AC = 54.285$ mi.

16. 4.1365 and 8.6416.

17. 6.1433 mi. and 8.7918 mi.

18. 6.4343 mi. and 5.7673 mi.

19. 8 and 5.4723.

20. 4.6064 mi.; 4.4494 mi.; 3.7733 mi.

21. 5.4709 mi.; 5.8013 mi.; 4.3111 mi.

Exercise 50. Page 115

1. Two. **3.** No solution. **5.** One. **7.** No solution

2. One. **4.** One. **6.** Two. **8.** One.

9. $B = 12° 13' 34''$, $C = 146° 15' 26''$, $c = 1272.1$.

10. $B = 57° 23' 40''$, $C = 2° 1' 20''$, $c = 0.38525$.

11. $B = 41° 12' 56''$, $C = 87° 38' 4''$, $c = 116.83$.

12. $A = 54° 31'$, $C = 47° 45'$. $c = 50.496$.

13. $B = 24° 57' 26''$, $C = 133° 48' 34''$, $c = 615.7$;
$B' = 155° 2' 34''$, $C' = 3° 43' 26''$, $c' = 55.414$.

14. $A = 51°\,18'\,27''$, $C = 98°\,21'\,33''$, $c = 43.098$;
$A' = 128°\,41'\,33''$, $C' = 20°\,58'\,27''$, $c' = 15.593$.

15. $A = 147°\,27'\,47''$, $B = 16°\,43'\,13''$, $a = 35.519$;
$A' = 0°\,54'\,13''$, $B' = 163°\,16'\,47''$, $a' = 1.0415$.

16. $B = 44°\,1'\,28''$, $C = 97°\,44'\,20''$, $c = 13.954$;
$B' = 135°\,58'\,32''$, $C' = 5°\,47'\,16''$, $c' = 1.4202$.

17. $B = 90°$, $C = 32°\,22'\,43''$, $c = 2.7901$.

18. 420. **19.** 124.62. **20.** 3.2096 in.

21. $AB = 3.8771$ in.; $BC = 2.3716$ in.; $CD = 3.7465$ in.; $AD = 6.1817$ in.

22. $C = 125°\,6'$, $D = 93°\,24'$; $AB = 4.3075$ in.; $BC = 3.1288$ in.; $CD = 5.431$ in.; $DE = 4.4186$ in.; $AE = 5.0522$ in.

Exercise 51. Page 117

2. $b = a\cos C + c\cos A$;
$a = b\cos C + c\cos B$;
$c = b\cos A$.

4. Impossible.

5. 5.

6. 7.655.

7. 7.

8. $\cos A = \dfrac{b^2 + c^2 - a^2}{2bc}$; 90°.

14. $AC = 8.499$ in.;
$BD = 3.1254$ in.

15. $BC = 5.9924$ in.;
$BD = 8.3556$ in.

16. $AB = 1.9249$ in.;
$CD = 4.4431$ in.;
$A = 109°\,26'$;
$B = 112°\,13'\,40''$;
$C = 88°\,11'\,40''$;
$D = 50°\,8'\,40''$.

17. 13.3157 in.

Exercise 52. Page 119

1. $\dfrac{a-b}{a+b} = \tan(A - 45°)$.

2. $\tan\frac{1}{2}(A - B) = 0$.

3. $a = b$.

4. $a + b = (a - b)(2 + \sqrt{3})$.

11. $\dfrac{2\sin A}{0} = \dfrac{\tan A}{0}$, or $\infty = \infty$.

12. $\dfrac{\sqrt{3}}{0} = \dfrac{\sqrt{3}}{0}$.

13. $\dfrac{\sqrt{3}}{0} = \infty\sqrt{3}$.

14. $\tan\frac{1}{2}(A - B) = 0$; $A = B$.

17. 5.

18. Sides AB, BC, AE; diagonal AD; angles B, CAD, DAE.

Exercise 53. Page 121

1. $A = 51°\,15'$, $B = 56°\,30'$, $c = 95.24$.

2. $B = 60°\,45'\,2''$, $C = 39°\,14'\,58''$, $a = 984.83$.

3. $A = 77°\,12'\,53''$, $B = 43°\,30'\,7''$, $c = 14.987$.

4. $B = 93°\,28'\,36''$, $C = 50°\,38'\,24''$, $a = 1.3131$.

5. $A = 132°\,18'\,27''$, $B = 14°\,34'\,24''$, $c = 0.6775$.

6. $A = 118°\,55'\,49''$, $C = 45°\,41'\,35''$, $b = 4.1554$.

7. $B = 65°\,13'\,51''$, $C = 28°\,42'\,5''$, $a = 3297.2$.

8. $A = 68°\,29'\,15''$, $B = 45°\,24'\,18''$, $c = 4449$.

9. $A = 117°\,24'\,32''$, $B = 32°\,11'\,28''$, $c = 31.431$.

10. $A = 2°\,46'\,8''$, $B = 1°\,54'\,42''$, $c = 81.066$.

11. $A = 116°\,33'\,54''$, $B = 26°\,33'\,54''$, $c = 140.87$.

12. $A = 6°\,1'\,55''$, $B = 108°\,58'\,5''$, $c = 862.5$.

13. $A = 45°\,14'\,20''$, $B = 17°\,3'\,40''$, $c = 510.02$.

14. $A = 41°\,42'\,33''$, $B = 32°\,31'\,15''$, $c = 9.0398$.

15. $A = 62°\,58'\,26''$, $B = 21°\,9'\,58''$, $c = 4151.7$.

16. $A = 84°\,49'\,58''$, $B = 28°\,48'\,26''$, $c = 42.374$.

17. $B = 24°\,11'\,20''$, $C = 144°\,55'\,52''$, $a = 205$.

18. $B = 20°\,36'\,34''$, $C = 102°\,10'\,14''$, $a = 37.5$.

19. 6.

20. 10.392.

21. $A = B = 90° - \frac{1}{2}C$, $c = \dfrac{a\sin C}{\sin A}$.

22. 8.9212.

23. 25.

24. 3800 yd.

25. 729.67 yd.

26. 430.85 yd.

27. 10.266 mi.

28. 2.3385 and 5.0032.

Exercise 54. Page 125

1. $\frac{1}{2}[\log(s-b)+\log(s-c)+\text{colog}\,s+\text{colog}(s-a)]$.
2. $\frac{1}{2}[\log(s-b)+\log(s-c)+\text{colog}\,b+\text{colog}\,c]$.
3. $\frac{1}{2}[\log(s-a)+\log(s-b)+\log(s-c)+\text{colog}\,s]$.
4. $\log r+\text{colog}(s-a)$.
5. $\log(s-a)+\log\tan\frac{1}{2}A$.
6. The second.
7. $\sqrt{\frac{1}{7}}$, or 0.37796; 41° 24′ 34″.
9. $A=60°$.

Exercise 55. Page 127

1. 38° 52′ 48″; 126° 52′ 12″; 14° 15′.
2. 32° 10′ 55″; 136° 23′ 50″; 11° 25′ 15″.
3. 27° 20′ 32″; 143° 7′ 48″; 9° 31′ 40″.
4. 42° 6′ 13″; 56° 6′ 36″; 81° 47′ 11″.
5. 16° 25′ 36″; 30° 24′; 133° 10′ 24″.
6. 46° 49′ 35″; 57° 59′ 44″; 75° 10′ 41″.
7. 26° 29″; 43° 25′ 20″; 110° 34′ 11″.
8. 49° 34′ 58″; 58° 46′ 58″; 71° 38′ 4″.
9. 51° 53′ 12″; 59° 31′ 48″; 68° 35′.
10. 36° 52′ 12″; 53° 7′ 48″; 90°.
11. 36° 52′ 12″; 53° 7′ 48″; 90°.
12. 33° 33′ 27″; 33° 33′ 27″; 112° 53′ 6″.
13. 60°; 60°; 60°.
14. 28° 57′ 18″; 46° 34′ 6″; 104° 28′ 36″.
15. 36° 52′ 12″; 53° 7′ 48″; 90°.
16. 8° 19′ 9″; 33° 33′ 36″; 138° 7′ 15″.
17. 45°; 120°; 15°.
18. 45°; 60°; 75°.
19. 84° 14′ 34″.
20. 54° 48′ 54″.
21. 105°; 15°; 60°.
22. 54.516.
23. 60°.
24. 12.434 in.
25. 4° 23′ 2″ W. of N. or W. of S.
26. $A=90°\,37'\,3''$;
    $B=104°\,28'\,41''$;
    $C=96°\,55'\,44''$;
    $D=67°\,58'\,32''$.
27. 82° 49′ 10″.
28. 36° 52′ 11″;
    53° 7′ 49″.

Exercise 56. Page 128

1. 277.68.
2. 452.87.
3. 8.0824.
4. 27.891.
5. 139.53.
6. 1380.7.
7. 10,280.9.
8. 82,362.
9. 409.63.
10. 1,067,750.
12. 10.0067 sq. in.
13. 18.064 sq. in.
14. 13.41 sq. in.

Exercise 57. Page 129

1. 85.926.
2. 23,531.
3. 436,540.
4. 157.63.
5. 7,408,200.
6. 398,710.
7. 176,384.
8. 25,848.
9. 92.963.
10. 3176.7.
11. 5.729 sq. in.

Exercise 58. Page 131

1. 6.
2. 150.
3. 43.301.
4. 1.1367.
5. 10.279.
6. 16.307.
7. 1224.8 sq. rd.; 7.655 A.
8. 3.84.
9. 4.8599.
10. 10.14.
11. 62.354.
12. 0.19975.
13. 240.
14. 8160.
15. 26,208.
16. 17.3206.
17. 10.392.
18. 365.68.
19. 29,450; 6982.8.
20. 15,540.
21. 4,333,600.
22. 13,260.
24. 3 A. 0.392 sq. ch.
25. 12 A. 3.45 sq. ch.
26. 4 A. 6.634 sq. ch.
27. 61 A. 4.97 sq. ch.
28. 4 A. 6.633 sq. ch.
29. 13.93 ch., 23.21 ch., 32.50 ch.
30. 14 A. 5.54 sq. ch.
31. 30°; 30°; 120°.
32. 2,421,000 sq. ft.
33. 199 A. 8 sq. ch.
34. 210 A. 9.1 sq. ch.
35. 12 A. 9.78 sq. ch.
37. 876.34 sq. ft.
38. 1229.5 sq. ft.
39. 9 A. 0.055 sq. ch.
41. 1075.3.
42. 2660.4.
43. 16,281.
45. Area $= ab\sin A$.

Exercise 59. Page 133

1. 20 ft.
2. 37° 34′ 5″.
3. 30°.
4. 199.70 ft.
5. 106.69 ft.; 142.85 ft.
6. 43.12 ft.
7. 78.36 ft.
8. 75 ft.
9. 1.4442 mi.
10. 56.649 ft.
11. 2159.5 ft.
12. 7912.8 mi.
13. 260.21 ft.; 3690.3 ft.
14. 2922.4 mi.
15. 60°.
16. 3.2068.
17. 6.6031.
18. 238,410 mi.
19. 1.3438 mi.
20. 861,860 mi.
21. 235.81 yd.
22. 26° 34′.
23. 69.282 ft.
24. 49° 18′ 42″; 40° 41′ 18″.
25. 50° 29′ 35″; 39° 30′ 25″.
26. 74° 44′ 14″.
27. 350.61 in.
28. 115.83 in.
29. 388.62 in.
30. 83° 37′ 40″.
31. 97° 11′.
32. 89° 50′ 18″.
33. 0.2402; 1.9216 in.; 33.306 in.
34. 1.7 in.; 0.588 in.
35. $\frac{a-b}{a+b}$.
36. 30°.
37. 97.86 in.; 153.3 in.; 159.31 in.
38. 1302.5 ft.; 33° 6′ 51″.
39. 0.9428.
41. 45 ft.
43. 0.9524.
44. $\frac{2h\sqrt{l^2+w^2}}{h^2-l^2-w^2}$.

Exercise 60. Page 137

4. 460.46 ft.
5. 88.936 ft.
6. 56.564 ft.
7. 51.595 ft.
8. 422.11 yd.
9. 41.411 ft.
10. 234.51 ft.
11. 12,492.6 ft.
12. 255.78 ft.
13. 529.49 ft.
14. 294.69 ft.
15. 101.892 ft.
16. 210.44 ft.
18. 19.8; 35.7; 44.5.
19. 13.657 mi. per hour.
20. N. 76° 56′ E.; 13.938 mi. per hour.
21. 3121.1 ft.; 3633.5 ft.
22. 25.433 mi.
23. 6.3397 mi.
24. $x = \frac{OB \sin O}{\sin a}$; $\sin a$; 90°; $B = 90°$; $\angle a = 90° - O$.
25. 288.67 ft.
26. 11.314 mi. per hour.
28. 658.36 lb.; 22° 23′ 47″ with first force.
29. 88.326 lb.; 45° 37′ 16″ with known force.
30. 757.50 ft.
31. 520.01 yd.
32. 1366.4 ft.
35. 536.28 ft.; 500.16 ft.
36. 345.46 yd.
37. 61.23 ft.

Exercise 61. Page 141

1. 19,647 sq. ft.
2. 27.527 sq. in.
3. 41.569 sq. in.
4. 6.
6. $\frac{1}{2}$; $\frac{1}{2}\sqrt{2}$.
9. 6.
11. 40,320 sq. ft.

Exercise 62. Page 142

1. 11.124 A.
2. 21.617 A.
3. 15.129 A.
4. 14 A.
5. 13.77 A.
6. 10.026 A.
7. 10 A.
8. 4.5348 A.; 10.4652 A.
9. 36.38 A.
10. 20.07 A.
11. 3.766 A.
12. 2.485 A.

Exercise 63. Page 144

1. 6.5223 sq. in.
2. 66.2343 sq. in.
3. 3.583 sq. in.; 27.6565 sq. in.
4. 8.6965 sq. in.
5. 112.26 sq. in.; 201.9 sq. in.
6. 0.14279.
7. 116.012 sq. in.
8. $\frac{3}{4}$.

Exercise 64. Page 147

1. 18′ 23″; 18.385 mi.
2. 37′ 29″; 37.4775 mi.
3. 51′ 33″; 34.445 mi.
4. 37′ 16″; 7.4135 mi.
5. 13′ 53″; 20.787 mi.
6. 19′ 52″; 12° 57′ 8″ S.
7. 35.207 mi.
8. 16.6296 mi.; 11′ 6.7″.
9. 59.155 mi.
10. 101.44 mi.
11. 11.483 mi.
12. 44.5 mi.
13. S. 75° 31′ 20″ E.; 23.2374 mi.
14. N. 17° 6′ 14″ W.; 32° 50′ 30″ N.
15. 23.854 mi.; S. 56° 58′ 34″ E.
16. 27.803 mi.; N. 52° 18′ 21″ W.

Exercise 65. Page 148

1 42° 16′ N.; 68° 54′ 39″ W.
2. 103.57 mi.
3. 60° 15′ N.; 62° 15′ 55″ W.

Exercise 66. Page 149

1. 31° 26′ 15″ N.; 41° 44′ 23″ W.
2. S. 63° 26′ W.; 42.486 mi.; 16° 14′ 52″ W.
3. 41° 50′ 5″ N.; 58° 15′ 1″ W.
4. 16.727 mi.; 30° 16′ 19″ W.
5. N. 77° 9′ 38″ W.; 33° 11′ W.
6. 40° 4′ 16″ N.; 72° 44′ 56″ W.
7. 42° 47′ 43″ N.; 70° 48′ 25″ W.

Exercise 67. Page 150

1. 35° 49′ 10″ S.; 22° 2′ 44″ W.; N. 61° 42′ W.; 183.16 mi.
2. 42° 15′ 29″ N.; 69° 5′ 11″ W.; 44.939 mi.
3. 32° 53′ 34″ S.; 13° 1′ 53″ E; 287.16 mi.
4. 41° 1′ 40″ N.; 69° 54′ 1″ W.
5. 57′ 19″; 21.4 mi.
6. 1° 37′ 8″; 45.652 mi.

Exercise 68. Page 152

1. $\frac{3}{2}\pi$.
2. $\frac{1}{16}\pi$.
3. $\frac{5}{16}\pi$.
4. $\frac{1}{24}\pi$.
5. $\frac{131}{120}\pi$.
6. 8π.
7. $\frac{10}{9}\pi$.
8. $\frac{50}{3}\pi$.
9. 270°.
10. 240°.
11. 210°.
12. 225°.
13. 7° 30′.
14. 540°.
15. 1080°.
16. 1800°.
17. II.
18. II.
19. III.
20. IV.
21. II.
22. II.
23. I.
24. III.
25. 216°, $\frac{6}{5}\pi$.
26. 300°, $\frac{5}{3}\pi$.
27. 120°, $\frac{2}{3}\pi$.
28. 33° 45′, $\frac{3}{16}\pi$.
29. 0.017453; 0.0002909.
30. 3437.75′; 206,265″.
31. $\frac{1}{3}\pi$ radians.
32. $\frac{1}{2}\pi$ radians.

Exercise 69. Page 154

1. 16°, 164°, 376°, 524°.
2. 30°, 150°, 390°, 510°, 750°, 870°.
3. 30°, 150°, 390°, 510°, 750°, 870°, 1110°, 1230°.
4. 67° 30′, 112° 30′, 427° 30′, 472° 30′.
5. 18°, 162°, 378°, 522°.
6. 0.99999995769.
7. 0.00029088820.
8. 0.00029088821.
9. 0.00058177632.
10. 0.000582.
11. 0.0175.

Exercise 70. Page 155

1. $60°, 300°$.
2. $-60°, -300°$.
3. $25°, 335°, 385°, 695°$.
4. $60°, 300°, 420°, 660°$.
5. $45°, 225°$.
6. $-135°, -315°$.
7. $60°, 240°, 420°, 600°$.
8. $30°, 210°, 390°, 570°$.
9. $26° 34', 206° 34', 386° 34', 566° 34'$.
10. $-116° 34', -296° 34', -476° 34', -656° 34'$.

Exercise 71. Page 156

5. $60°, 120°$.
6. $45°, 135°$.
7. $30°, 210°$.
8. $90°, 270°$.
9. $60°, 300°$.
10. $135°, 225°$.
11. $\frac{1}{2}\sqrt{3}$.
12. $\frac{1}{2}$.
13. $\frac{1}{2}\sqrt{2}$.
14. $\frac{1}{2}\sqrt{2}$.
19. $60°, 240°, 420°, 600°$.
20. $58°, 238°, 418°, 598°$.
21. $74°, 106°, 434°, 466°$.
22. $19°, 161°, 379°, 521°$.
23. $15° 24' 30'', 195° 24' 30'', 375° 24' 30'', 555° 24' 30''$.
24. $19°, 341°, 379°, 701°$.
25. $19° 28' 17'', 160° 31' 43''$.
26. $\pm \frac{1}{2}\sqrt{2}$.
27. $\pm \frac{1}{2}\sqrt{3}$ or 0.

Exercise 74. Page 161

2. $360°$ or 2π.
4. $180°$ or π.
6. $180°$ or π.
8. $360°$ or 2π.
9. $180°$ and $360°$.
10. Complements.

Exercise 75. Page 162

1. 270.63.
2. 416.65.
3. 2695.8.
4. 4.163.
5. Impossible.
6. Impossible.
7. 345.48 ft.
9. $40' 9''$.
10. $-175°, 185°, 535°, 545°$.
11. $-200°, 160°, 560°, 520°$.
12. 2 radians; $114° 35' 30''$.
13. $\frac{1}{3}$ radian; $19° 5' 55''$.
22. $30°, 210°, 390°, 570°$.
23. $60°, 240°, 420°, 600°$.

Exercise 77. Page 166

1. $\frac{1}{2}\pi$ or $\frac{3}{2}\pi$.
2. $90°$ or $270°$.
3. $21° 28'$ or $158° 32'$.
4. $0°$ or $90°$.
5. $30°, 150°, 199° 28'$, or $340° 32'$.
6. $51° 19', 180°$, or $308° 41'$.
7. $30°, 150°$, or $270°$.
8. $35° 16', 144° 44', 215° 16'$, or $324° 44'$.
9. $75° 58'$ or $255° 58'$.
10. $60°, 180°$, or $300°$.
11. $90°$ or $143° 8'$.
12. $30°, 150°, 210°$, or $330°$.
13. $0°, 120°, 180°$, or $240°$.
14. $45°, 161° 34', 225°$, or $341° 34'$.
15. $60°, 120°, 240°$, or $300°$.
16. $26° 34'$ or $206° 34'$.
17. $30°$ or $150°$.
18. $45°$ or $135°$.
19. $60°, 90°, 270°$, or $300°$.
20. $60°, 90°, 120°, 240°, 270°$, or $300°$.
21. $32° 46', 147° 14', 212° 46'$, or $327° 14'$.
22. $\tan^{-1}\frac{a^2-1}{2a}$.
23. $\cos^{-1}\left(\frac{-a \pm \sqrt{a^2+8a+8}}{4}\right)$.
24. 1.
25. 1.
26. $0°, 45°, 90°, 180°, 225°$, or $270°$.
27. $30°, 150°, 210°$, or $330°$.

28. 30°, 60°, 120°, 150°, 210°, 240°, 300°, or 330°.
29. 0°, 65° 42′, 180°, or 204° 18′.
30. 14° 29′, 30°, 150°, or 165° 31′.
31. 0°, 20°, 100°, 140°, 180°, 220°, 260°, or 340°.
32. 45°, 90°, 135°, 225°, 270°, or 315°.
33. 30°, 150°, or 270°.
34. 26° 34′, 90°, 206° 34′, or 270°.
35. 45°, 135°, 225°, or 315°.
36. 45°, 135°, 225°, or 315°.
37. 15°, 75°, 135°, 195°, 255°, or 315°.
38. 45°, 135°, 225°, or 315°.
39. 0°, 45°, 180°, or 225°.
40. 0°, 90°, 120°, 240°, or 270°.
41. 0°, 36°, 72°, 108°, 144°, 180°, 216°, 252°, 288°, or 324°.
42. 120°.
43. 54° 44′, 125° 16′, 234° 44′, 305° 16′.
44. 30°, 60°, 90°, 120°, 150°, 210°, 240°, 270°, 300°, or 330°.
45. $\sin^{-1} \pm \sqrt{\frac{k-1}{2}}$.
46. 90°, 216° 52′, or 323° 8′.
47. 30°, 90°, 150°, 210°, 270°, or 330°.
48. 0°, 45°, 180°, or 225°.
49. 45°, 60°, 120°, 135°, 225°, 240°, 300°, or 315°.
50. 0°, 45°, 135°, 225°, or 315°.
51. 90° or 270°.
52. $\frac{1}{2}\sqrt{3}$.
53. $\frac{1}{2}$.
54. 0°, 45°, 90°, 180°, 225°, or 270°.
55. 30°, 150°, 210°, or 330°.
56. 60°.
57. 105° or 345°.
58. 135°, 315°, or $\frac{1}{2}\sin^{-1}(1-a)$.
59. 30°, 60°, 120°, 150°, 210°, 240°, 300°, or 330°.
60. 60°, 90°, 120°, 240°, 270°, or 300°.
61. 0°, 90°, 180°, or 270°.
62. 0°, 90°, 120°, 180°, 240°, or 270°.
63. 0°, 74° 5′, 127° 25′, 180°, 232° 35′, or 285° 55′.
64. 0°, 180°, 220° 39′, or 319° 21′.
65. 8° or 168°.
66. 40° 12′, 139° 48′, 220° 12′, or 319° 48′
67. 0°, 60°, 120°, 180°, 240°, or 300°.
68. 30° or 3[illegible]°.
69. 60°, 120°, 240°, or 300°.
70. 18°, 90°, 162°, 234°, 270°, or 306°.
71. 30°, 60°, 120°, 150°, 210°, 240°, 300°, or 330°.
72. 53° 8′, 126° 52′, 233° 8′, or 306° 52′.
73. 30°.
74. 22° 37′ or 143° 8′.
75. 0°, 20°, 30°, 40°, 60°, 80°, 90°, 100°, 120°, 140°, 150°, 160°, 180°, 200°, 210°, 220°, 240°, 260°, 270°, 280°, 300°, 320°, 330°, or 340°.
76. $22\frac{1}{2}$°, 45°, $67\frac{1}{2}$°, 90°, $112\frac{1}{2}$°, 135°, $157\frac{1}{2}$°, $202\frac{1}{2}$°, 225°, $247\frac{1}{2}$°, 270°, $292\frac{1}{2}$°, 315°, or $337\frac{1}{2}$°.
77. 45° or 225°.
78. ± 1 or $\pm \frac{1}{7}\sqrt{21}$.
79. $\frac{1}{3}\sqrt{3}$ or $-\frac{1}{2}\sqrt{3}$.
80. 0 or ± 1.
81. 0°, 30°, 90°, 150°, 180°, 210°, 270°, or 330°.
82. 120° or 240°.
83. 60°, 120°, 240°, or 300°.
84. 10° 12′, 34° 48′, 190° 12′, or 214° 48′.
85. 29° 19′, 105° 41′, 209° 19′, or 285° 41′.
86. 0°, 45°, 90°, 180°, 225°, or 270°.
87. 0°, 45°, 135°, 225°, or 315°.
88. 0°, 60°, 120°, 180°, 240°, or 300°.
89. 27° 58′, 135°, 242° 2′, or 315°.

Exercise 78. Page 170

1. $x = a,\ y = 0$; or $x = 0,\ y = a$.

2. $x = \sin^{-1} \pm \sqrt{\frac{a-b}{2}}$,

$y = \sin^{-1} \pm \sqrt{\frac{a+b}{2}}$.

3. $x = 76° 10′,\ y = 15° 30′$.

4. $x = 100,\ y = 200$.

5. $x = \sin^{-1} \pm \sqrt{\frac{m-n+1}{2}}$,

$y = \frac{m+n-1}{2}$.

6. $x = 90°$,

$y = 0°$ or 180°.

7. $x = \cos^{-1}\frac{1}{2}\left(a \pm \sqrt{b - a^2 + 2}\right)$; $y = \cos^{-1}\frac{1}{2}\left(a \pm \sqrt{b - a^2 + 2}\right)$.

8. $x = \tan^{-1}\frac{m}{n}\tan a + \frac{1}{2}\cos^{-1}[2m^2 - (2m^2 - 2n^2)\cos^2 a - 1]$;

$y = \tan^{-1}\frac{m}{n}\tan a - \frac{1}{2}\cos^{-1}[2m^2 - (2m^2 - 2n^2)\cos^2 a - 1]$.

9. $x = \tan^{-1}\frac{a}{b} + \cos^{-1}\frac{1}{2}\sqrt{a^2 + b^2}$; $y = \tan^{-1}\frac{a}{b} - \cos^{-1}\frac{1}{2}\sqrt{a^2 + b^2}$.

10. $x = 24° 13'$, $r = 225.12$; $x = 204° 13'$, $r = -225.12$.

11. $x = 42° 28'$, $r = 151$; $x = 222° 28'$, $r = -151$.

Exercise 79. Page 171

1. $\phi = 30°$ or $150°$; $x = 0.134$ or 1.866.
2. $\theta = \sin^{-1}(a - 1)$; $x = 2 - a$.
3. $\lambda = 45°$, $135°$, $225°$, or $315°$; $\mu = 30°$, $150°$, $210°$, or $330°$.
4. $\theta = \frac{1}{2}\sin^{-1}\left(\frac{a^2 + b^2}{2} - 1\right) + \frac{1}{2}\sin^{-1}\frac{a^2 - b^2}{a^2 + b^2}$;

   $\phi = \frac{1}{2}\sin^{-1}\left(\frac{a^2 + b^2}{2} - 1\right) - \frac{1}{2}\sin^{-1}\frac{a^2 - b^2}{a^2 + b^2}$.
5. $\theta = \cos^{-1}\left[\pm\sqrt[4]{\frac{b^2}{a(b - a)}}\right]$; $\phi = \cos^{-1}\left[\pm\sqrt[4]{\frac{a}{b - a}}\right]$.
6. $\theta = 0°$.

Exercise 80. Page 172

1. $a^2 + b^2 - 2(a - b) = -1$.
2. $ab = 1$.
3. $(n - m)^2 + (q - p)^2 = 1$.
4. $b - a = \frac{1}{p}\sqrt{p^2 + q^2}$.
5. $bc = 1$.
6. $x = \pm\sqrt{2ry - y^2} + r \text{ versin}^{-1}\frac{y}{r}$.
7. $(m^2 + n^2 - 1)^2 = (n + 1)^2 + m^2$.
8. $a^{\frac{4}{3}}b^{\frac{2}{3}} + a^{\frac{2}{3}}b^{\frac{4}{3}} = 1$.
9. $(m + n)\sqrt{4 - (m - n)^2} = 2(m - n)$
10. $p'r = -r'p$.
11. $k^4 + l^4 = 2kl(kl - 2)$.
12. $a^2b^2r^2 + a^2c^2q^2 + b^2c^2p^2 = a^2b^2c^2$.

Exercise 81. Page 176

1. 1; -1.
2. 1; $\sqrt{-1}$; -1; $-\sqrt{-1}$.
3. 1; $0.7660 + 0.6428\,i$; $0.1736 + 0.9848\,i$.
4. 1; $\frac{1}{4}\left(\sqrt{5} - 1 + i\sqrt{10 + 2\sqrt{5}}\right)$; $\frac{1}{4}\left(-\sqrt{5} - 1 + i\sqrt{10 - 2\sqrt{5}}\right)$;

   $\frac{1}{4}\left(-\sqrt{5} - 1 - i\sqrt{10 - 2\sqrt{5}}\right)$; $\frac{1}{4}\left(\sqrt{5} - 1 - i\sqrt{10 + 2\sqrt{5}}\right)$.
5. 1; $\frac{1}{2} + \frac{1}{2}\sqrt{-3}$; $-\frac{1}{2} + \frac{1}{2}\sqrt{-3}$; -1; $-\frac{1}{2} - \frac{1}{2}\sqrt{-3}$; $\frac{1}{2} - \frac{1}{2}\sqrt{-3}$.

   $\frac{1}{2}\sqrt{3} + \frac{1}{2}\sqrt{-1}$; $\sqrt{-1}$; $-\frac{1}{2}\sqrt{3} + \frac{1}{2}\sqrt{-1}$; $-\frac{1}{2}\sqrt{3} - \frac{1}{2}\sqrt{-1}$; $-\sqrt{-1}$;

   $\frac{1}{2}\sqrt{3} - \frac{1}{2}\sqrt{-1}$.
6. $\frac{1}{2}\sqrt{2} + \frac{1}{2}\sqrt{-2}$; $-\frac{1}{2}\sqrt{2} + \frac{1}{2}\sqrt{-2}$; $-\frac{1}{2}\sqrt{2} - \frac{1}{2}\sqrt{-2}$; $\frac{1}{2}\sqrt{2} - \frac{1}{2}\sqrt{-2}$.

Exercise 82. Page 177

1. $-\frac{5}{2}+\frac{5}{2}\sqrt{-3}$; $-\frac{5}{2}-\frac{5}{2}\sqrt{-3}$; 5.
2. $\frac{3}{2}\sqrt{2}+\frac{3}{2}\sqrt{-2}$; $-\frac{3}{2}\sqrt{2}+\frac{3}{2}\sqrt{-2}$; $-\frac{3}{2}\sqrt{2}-\frac{3}{2}\sqrt{-2}$; $\frac{3}{2}\sqrt{2}-\frac{3}{2}\sqrt{-2}$.
3. $\frac{3}{2}+\frac{3}{2}\sqrt{-3}$; $-\frac{3}{2}+\frac{3}{2}\sqrt{-3}$; -3.
4. $2(\cos 36^\circ + i\sin 36^\circ)$; $2(\cos 72^\circ + i\sin 72^\circ)$; $2(\cos 108^\circ + i\sin 108^\circ)$.
5. $0.9980 + 0.0628\,i$; $0.9921 + 0.1253\,i$; $0.9823 + 0.1874\,i$.

Exercise 83. Page 183

7. 120.
8. 5040.
9. 720.
10. 40,320.
11. 3,628,800.
12. 604,800.
13. 90.
14. 42.
15. 15.
16. 6840.
17. 7.38883.
18. 1.64871.
19. $\cos 28^\circ 39'$.
20. $\cos 7^\circ 10'$.
21. $\cos 114^\circ 25' 32''$.
22. $\cos 0^\circ$.
23. $\sin 57^\circ 17' 48''$.
24. $\sin 28^\circ 38' 40''$.
25. $\sin 65^\circ 24' 45''$ or $\sin 114^\circ 35' 15''$.
26. $\sin 0^\circ$ or $\sin 180^\circ$.
27. $\tan 0^\circ$.
28. $\tan 56^\circ 40' 12''$.
29. $\tan 28^\circ 38' 20''$.
30. $\tan 86^\circ 23' 16''$.
35. $0.6931 + 2\pi i$; $0.6931 + 4\pi i$.
36. $1.3862 + 2\pi i$; $1.3862 + 4\pi i$.
37. $0.3465 + 2\pi i$; $0.3465 + 4\pi i$.
38. $0.6931 + \pi i$; $0.6931 + 3\pi i$.
39. $1.609 + 2\pi i$; $1.609 + 4\pi i$; $1.609 + 6\pi i$.
40. $3.218 + 2\pi i$; $3.218 + 4\pi i$; $3.218 + 6\pi i$.
41. $4.827 + 2\pi i$; $4.827 + 4\pi i$; $4.827 + 6\pi i$.
42. $1.609 + \pi i$; $1.609 + 3\pi i$; $1.609 + 5\pi i$.
43. $4.605170 + 2\pi i$; $4.605170 + 4\pi i$.
44. $2.302585 + \pi i$; $2.302585 + 3\pi i$.
45. $6.907755 + 2\pi i$; $6.907755 + 4\pi i$.
46. $1.151292 + 2\pi i$; $1.151292 + 4\pi i$.

Exercise 84. Page 184

1. 362.8 ft.
2. 1445.67 ft.; 1704.7 ft.; 1622.5 ft.
4. $\dfrac{2m(n^2-1)+2n(m^2-1)}{(m^2-1)(n^2-1)-4mn}$.
5. 2.
12. $b\sin C$.
13. 794.73 ft.

TRIGONOMETRIC AND LOGARITHMIC TABLES

BY

GEORGE WENTWORTH

AND

DAVID EUGENE SMITH

GINN AND COMPANY

BOSTON · NEW YORK · CHICAGO · LONDON
ATLANTA · DALLAS · COLUMBUS · SAN FRANCISCO

525.4

The Athenæum Press
GINN AND COMPANY · PRO-
PRIETORS · BOSTON · U.S.A.

PREFACE

In preparing this new set of tables for the use of students of trigonometry care has been taken to meet the modern requirements in every respect, while preserving the best features to be found in those tables that have stood the test of long use. In our country the large majority of teachers prefer five-place logarithmic tables, and for this preference they have cogent reasons. While a five-place table gives the results to a degree of approximation closer than is ordinarily required, nevertheless if a student can use such a table it is a simple matter to use one with four or six places. One who has been brought up to use a table with only four places, however, finds it less easy to adapt himself to a table having a larger number of places. On this account the basal tables of logarithms given in this book have five decimal places. For the natural functions, however, four decimal places are quite sufficient for the kind of applications that the student will meet in his work in trigonometry, and the general custom of using four places has been followed in this respect.

Following the usage found in the best tables, unnecessary figures have been omitted, thus relieving the eye strain. Where, as on page 28, the first two figures of a mantissa are the same for several logarithms, these figures are given only in the line in which they first occur and in the lines corresponding to multiples of five. Where, however, a table is to be read from the foot of the page upwards, as well as from the top downwards, the first two figures are given both at the bottom and at the top of the vacant space, as on page 51, so that the computer may have no difficulty in seeing them in whatever direction the eye is moving over the table.

It will also be seen that great care has been bestowed upon the selection of a type that will relieve the eye from fatigue as far as possible, and upon an arrangement of figures that will assist the computer in every way. It is believed that this care, together with the attention given to spacing and to the general appearance of the page, has resulted in the most usable set of trigonometric and logarithmic tables that has thus far been printed.

In recognition of the tendency at the present time to use four-place tables in certain lines of work, Table I has been prepared. Teachers are advised, however, for the reasons already stated, to use the five-place table first and until it is clearly understood, taking Table I for the work that requires only a low degree of approximation.

The tendency to use decimal parts of a degree instead of minutes and seconds is one that will undoubtedly increase. This tendency is therefore recognized by the introduction of a conversion table. By its use the student can instantly adapt the common tables to the decimal plan. At the same time it is apparent that students will be called upon to use the sexagesimal division of the degree almost exclusively for years to come, and for this reason the emphasis should be placed, as it is in the authors' Plane and Spherical Trigonometry, upon the sexagesimal instead of the decimal division.

It is confidently believed that teachers and students will find in these tables all that they need for the purposes of the computation required in every line of work in trigonometry.

GEORGE WENTWORTH
DAVID EUGENE SMITH

CONTENTS

INTRODUCTION

1. Logarithm. The power to which a given number, called the *base*, must be raised to equal another given number is called the *logarithm* of this second given number.

For example, since $10^3 = 1000$,

therefore, to the base 10, $3 =$ the logarithm of 1000.

In this case 1000 is called the *antilogarithm* of 3, this being the number corresponding to the logarithm.

In this Introduction only the most important facts relating to logarithms are given. For a more complete treatment see the Wentworth-Smith Plane and Spherical Trigonometry, Chapter III.

2. Symbolism. For "logarithm of N" it is customary to write $\log N$. If we wish to specify $\log N$ to the base b we write $\log_b N$, reading this "logarithm of N to the base b."

For example, since $2^3 = 8$, we see that $\log_2 8 = 3$; and since $5^2 = 25$, $\log_5 25 = 2$.

3. Base. We may take various bases for systems of logarithms, but for practical calculation in trigonometry, 10 is taken as the base.

Logarithms are due chiefly to John Napier of Scotland (1614), but the base 10 was suggested by Henry Briggs of Oxford. Hence logarithms to the base 10 are often called Briggs logarithms.

4. Logarithm of a Product. *The logarithm of the product of several numbers is equal to the sum of the logarithms of the numbers.*

For if $A = 10^x$, then $x = \log A$;

and if $B = 10^y$, then $y = \log B$.

Therefore $AB = 10^{x+y}$, and $x + y = \log AB$.

For example, $\log (247 \times 7.21) = \log 247 + \log 7.21$.

5. Logarithm of a Quotient. *The logarithm of the quotient of two numbers is equal to the logarithm of the dividend minus the logarithm of the divisor.*

For if $A = 10^x$, then $x = \log A$;

and if $B = 10^y$, then $y = \log B$.

Therefore $\frac{A}{B} = 10^{x-y}$, and $x - y = \log \frac{A}{B}$.

For example, $\log (9.2 \div 6.7) = \log 9.2 - \log 6.7$.

6. Logarithm of a Power. *The logarithm of a power of a number is equal to the logarithm of the number multiplied by the exponent.*

For if $x = \log A$, then $A = 10^x$.

Raising to the pth power, $A^p = 10^{px}$.

Hence $\log A^p = px = p \log A$.

For example, $\log 7.2^5 = 5 \log 7.2$.

7. Logarithm of a Root. *The logarithm of a root of a number is equal to the logarithm of the number divided by the index of the root.*

For if $x = \log A$, then $A = 10^x$.

Taking the rth root, $A^{\frac{1}{r}} = 10^{\frac{x}{r}}$.

Hence $\log A^{\frac{1}{r}} = \frac{x}{r} = \frac{\log A}{r}$.

For example, $\log \sqrt[3]{9.36} = \frac{1}{3} \log 9.36$.

8. Characteristic and Mantissa. Usually a logarithm consists of an integer plus a decimal fraction.

The integral part of a logarithm is called the *characteristic.*

The decimal part of a logarithm is called the *mantissa.*

Thus, if $\log 2353 = 3.37162$, the characteristic is 3 and the mantissa is 0.37162. This means that $10^{3.37162} = 2353$, or that the 100,000th root of the 337,162d power of 10 is approximately 2353.

The logarithms of integral powers of 10 are, of course, integers, the mantissa in every such case being zero. For example, since $1000 = 10^3$, $\log 1000 = 3$.

9. Finding the Characteristic. The characteristic is not usually given in a table of logarithms, because it is easily found mentally.

The characteristic of the logarithm of a number greater than 1 is positive and is one less than the number of integral places in the number.

The characteristic of the logarithm of a number between 0 and 1 is negative and is one greater than the number of zeros between the decimal point and the first significant figure in the number.

For example, since $10^3 = 1000$ and $10^4 = 10{,}000$, it is evident that $\log 7250$ lies between 3 and 4.

For further explanation see the Wentworth-Smith Plane Trigonometry, § 46.

10. The Negative Characteristic. The mantissa is always considered as positive. If $\log 0.02 = -2 + 0.30103$, we cannot write it -2.30103 because this would mean that both mantissa and characteristic are negative. Hence the form $\overline{2}.30103$ has been chosen, which means that only the characteristic 2 is negative.

In practical computation it is more often written $0.30103 - 2$, or $8.30103 - 10$, but when written by itself the form $\overline{2}.30103$ is convenient.

11. Mantissa independent of Decimal Point. *The mantissa of the logarithm of a number is unchanged by any change in the position of the decimal point of the number.*

For if $10^{3.37107} = 2350$, then $\log 2350 = 3.37107$.

Dividing by 10, $10^{2.37107} = 235$, and $\log 235 = 2.37107$.

That is, the mantissa of log 2350 is the same as that of log 235.0, and so on, wherever the decimal point is placed.

This is of great importance, for if the table gives the mantissa for only 235, we know that this is the mantissa for 0.235, 2.35, 23.5, 235,000, and so on.

12. Logarithms Approximate. Logarithms are, in general, only approximate. Although log 1000 is exactly 3, log 7 is only approximately 0.84510.

To four decimal places, $\log 7 = 0.8451$; to five decimal places, 0.84510; to six decimal places, 0.845098, and so on.

In a four-place table there is a possible error of $\frac{1}{2}$ of 0.0001; in a five-place table, of $\frac{1}{2}$ of 0.00001, and so on, but in each case the probable error is much less.

If several logarithms are added the possible error is correspondingly increased.

In finding antilogarithms the first figure found by interpolation is usually accurate, the second is doubtful, and the third is rarely trustworthy.

13. Cologarithm. The logarithm of the reciprocal of a number is called the *cologarithm* of the number.

The cologarithm of x is expressed thus: $\text{colog}\, x$.

Since $\text{colog}\, x = \log \frac{1}{x} = \log 1 - \log x = 0 - \log x$, we have

$$\text{colog}\, x = -\log x.$$

That is, $\text{colog}\, 2 = -\log 2$.

To avoid a negative mantissa this may be written

$$\text{colog}\, x = 10 - \log x - 10.$$

For example, $\text{colog}\, 2 = -\log 2 = 10 - 0.30103 - 10$

$$= 9.69897 - 10.$$

14. Use of the Cologarithm. Since to divide by a number is the same as to multiply by its reciprocal, *instead of subtracting the logarithm of a divisor we may add its cologarithm.*

The cologarithm of a number is easily written by looking at the logarithm in the table. Thus, since $\log 20 = 1.30103$, we find colog 20 by mentally subtracting this from $10.00000 - 10$. This is done by beginning at the left and subtracting the number represented by each figure from 9, except the right-hand figure, which we subtract from 10.

For example, if we have to simplify

$$\frac{625 \times 7.51}{2.73 \times 14.8},$$

it is easier to add log 625, log 7.51, colog 2.73, and colog 14.8, than to add log 625 and log 7.51, and then to add log 2.73 and log 14.8, and finally to subtract.

15. General Use of the Tables. In writing down a logarithm always write the characteristic before looking for the mantissa. Otherwise the characteristic may be forgotten.

Some computers find it convenient to paste paper tabs so that they project from the side of the first page of each table, thus allowing the book to be opened quickly at the desired table.

Although a table of proportional parts is given, it is best to accustom the eye to interpolate quickly from the regular table.

TABLE I

16. Nature of Table I. This is a table of logarithms of integers from 1 to 1000, and of the sine, cosine, tangent, and cotangent, the mantissas extending to four decimal places and the characteristics being 10 too large, as in Table VI. For the ordinary computations of physics and mensuration this is sufficient, the results in general being correct to four figures.

There is a growing disposition to use the convenient four-place table for ordinary work. Most teachers prefer, however, to use a five-place table, since the student who can use this will have no trouble with the simpler four-place table. For this reason the computations in the Wentworth-Smith Plane and Spherical Trigonometry are based upon the five-place table.

17. Arrangement of the Table. The vertical columns headed **N** contain the numbers, and the other columns the logarithms. On page 17 the characteristics as well as the mantissas are given, but on pages 18 and 19 only the mantissas are given, the characteristics being determined by § 9. To find the mantissa for 16, look on the line to the right of 16 and in the column marked **0**. This mantissa, 0.2041, is the same as that for 1.6, 160, 1600, and so on. To find the mantissa for 167, look on the line to the right of 16 and in the column marked **7**. This mantissa, 0.2227, is the same as that for 0.167, 16.7, 167,000, and so on.

The table of trigonometric functions is arranged for every 10′, this being sufficient for many practical purposes.

18. To find a Logarithm or Antilogarithm. The method of finding the logarithm of a number or the antilogarithm of a logarithm is the same as that employed with a five-place table (§§ 21–24).

TABLE II

19. Nature of Table II. This table (pages 24 and 25) contains the circumferences and areas of circles of given radii, and the diameters of circles of given circumference or given area. It often saves a considerable amount of computation in problems involving circles, cylinders, spheres, and cones.

TABLE III

20. Arrangement of Table III. In this table (pages 27–45) the vertical columns headed **N** contain the numbers, and the other columns the logarithms. On page 27 both the characteristic and the mantissa are printed. On pages 28–45 the mantissa only is printed, and the decimal point and unnecessary figures are omitted so as to relieve the eye from strain.

The fractional part of a logarithm is only approximate, and in a five-place table all figures that follow the fifth are rejected.

Thus, if the mantissa of a logarithm written to seven places is 5326143 it is written in this table (a five-place table) 53261. If it is 5329788 it is written 53298. If it is 5328461 or 5328499 it is written in this table 53285. If the mantissa is 5325506 it is written 53255; and if it is 5324486 it is written $5324\underline{5}$.

21. To find the Logarithm of a Number. If the given number consists of one or two significant figures, the logarithm is given on page 27. If zeros follow the significant figures, or if the number is a proper decimal fraction, the characteristic must be determined.

If the given number has three significant figures, it will be found in the column headed **N** (pages 28–45) and the mantissa of its logarithm will be found in the next column to the right.

For example, on page 28, $\log 145 = 2.16137$, and $\log 14500 = 4.16137$.

If the given number has four significant figures, the first three will be found in the column headed **N**, and the fourth will be found at the top of the page in the line containing the figures 1, 2, 3, etc. The mantissa will be found in the column headed by the fourth figure.

For example, on pages 41 and 44 we find the following:

$$\log 7682 = 3.88547, \qquad \log 76.85 = 1.88564;$$
$$\log 93280 = 4.96979, \qquad \log 0.9468 = 9.97626 - 10.$$

22. Interpolation for Logarithms. If the given number has five or more significant figures, a process called *interpolation* is required.

Interpolation is based on the *assumption* that between two consecutive mantissas of the table the change in the mantissa is directly proportional to the change in the number. This assumption is not exact, but the error does not, in general, affect the first figure found in this manner.

For example, required the logarithm of 34237.

The required mantissa is (§ 11) the same as the mantissa for 3423.7; therefore it will be found by adding to the mantissa of 3423 seven tenths of the difference between the mantissas for 3423 and 3424.

The mantissa for 3423 is 53441, and the mantissa for 3424 is 53453.

The difference between these mantissas (tabular difference) is 12.

Hence the mantissa for 3423.7 is $53441 + (0.7 \text{ of } 12) = 53449$.

Therefore the required logarithm of 34237 is 4.53449.

23. To find the Antilogarithm. If the given mantissa can be found in the table, the first three significant figures of the required number will be found in the column headed **N** in the same line with the mantissa, and the fourth figure at the top of the column containing the mantissa. The position of the decimal point is determined by the characteristic (§ 9).

1. Find the antilogarithm of 0.92002.

The number for the mantissa 92002 is 8318. (Page 42.)
The characteristic is 0 ; therefore the required number is 8.318.

2. Find the antilogarithm of 6.09167.

The number for the mantissa 09167 is 1235. (Page 28.)
The characteristic is 6 ; therefore the required number is 1,235,000.

3. Find the antilogarithm of 7.50325 – 10.

The number for the mantissa 50325 is 3186. (Page 32.)
The characteristic is – 3 ; therefore the required number is 0.003186.

24. Interpolation for Antilogarithms. If the given mantissa cannot be found in the table, find in the table the two adjacent mantissas between which the given mantissa lies, and the four figures corresponding to the smaller of these two mantissas will be the first four significant figures of the required number. If more than four figures are desired, they may be found by interpolation, as in the following examples:

1. Find the antilogarithm of 1.48762.

Here the two adjacent mantissas of the table, between which the given mantissa 48762 lies, are found to be (page 32) 48756 and 48770. The antilogarithms are 3073 and 3074. The smaller of these, 3073, contains the first four significant figures of the required number.

The difference between the two adjacent mantissas is 14, and the difference between the corresponding numbers is 1.

The difference between the smaller of the two adjacent mantissas, 48756, and the given mantissa, 48762, is 6. Therefore the number to be annexed to 3073 is $\frac{6}{14}$ of 1, which is 0.43, and the fifth significant figure of the required antilogarithm is 4.

Hence the required antilogarithm is 30.734.

2. Find the antilogarithm of 7.82326 – 10.

The two adjacent mantissas between which 82326 lies are (page 39) 82321 and 82328. The antilogarithm having the mantissa 82321 is 6656.

The difference between the two adjacent mantissas is 7, and the difference between the corresponding numbers is 1.

The difference between the smaller mantissa, 82321, and the given mantissa, 82326, is 5. Therefore the number to be annexed to 6656 is $\frac{5}{7}$ of 1, which is 0.7, and the fifth significant figure of the required antilogarithm is 7.

Hence the required antilogarithm is 0.0066567.

TABLE IV

25. Proportional Parts. In interpolating (§§ 22, 24) we have to find fractional parts of the difference between two numbers or two logarithms.

For example, in finding log 73.537 we see that

$$\begin{aligned} \log 73.54 &= 1.86652 \\ \log 73.53 &= \underline{1.86646} \\ \text{Tabular difference} &= 6 \\ \tfrac{7}{10}\text{ tabular difference} &= 4 \end{aligned}$$

Adding 1.86646 and 0.00004, we have

$$\log 73.537 = 1.86650$$

These fractional parts of a tabular difference are called *proportional parts.*

26. Nature of Table IV. In Table IV the proportional parts of all differences from 1 to 100 are given, so that by turning to the table we can make any ordinary interpolation at a glance.

For example, if the difference (**D**) is 6, as in the first case considered in § 24, the table shows that $\frac{7}{10}$ of this difference is 4.2, the last figure being rejected because it is less than 5. In such a simple case, however, we would make the interpolation mentally, without reference to the table.

If the difference were 87, and we wished $\frac{9}{10}$ of this difference, the table shows at once that this is 78.3, from which we would reject the last figure as before.

In some sets of tables the proportional parts are printed beside the logarithms themselves, but this necessitates the use of a small type that is trying to the eyes. It is usually easier to make the interpolation mentally than to use the table of proportional parts, but where a large number of interpolations are to be made at the same time the table is helpful.

27. Table IV for Multiplication. By ignoring the decimal points Table IV may be used as a multiplication table, the column marked **D** containing the multiplicands, the multipliers 1–9 appearing at the top, and the products being given below.

For example, $8 \times 79 = 632$, as is seen by looking to the right of 79 and under 8.

TABLE V

28. Logarithms of Constants. There are certain constants, such as π, π^2, 2π, $\sqrt{2}$, and so on, that enter frequently into the computations of trigonometry. To save the trouble of looking for the logarithms of these numbers in the regular table, or of computing their logarithms, Table V has been prepared.

TABLE VI

29. Nature of Table VI. This table (pages 49–77) contains the logarithms of the trigonometric functions of angles. In order to avoid negative characteristics, the characteristic of every logarithm is printed 10 too large. Therefore -10 is to be annexed to each logarithm.

On pages 49–55 the characteristic remains the same throughout each column and is printed at the top and the bottom of the column; but on pages 56–77 when the characteristic changes one unit in value the place of each change is marked with a bar. Above each bar the proper characteristic is printed at the top of the column; below each bar the characteristic is printed at the bottom.

On pages 56–77 the log sin, log cos, log tan, and log cot are given for every minute from 1° to 89°. Conversely, this part of the table gives the value of the angle to the nearest minute when log sin, log cos, log tan, or log cot is known, provided log sin or log cos lies between 8.24186 and 9.99993, and log tan or log cot lies between 8.24192 and 11.75808.

If the exact value of the given logarithm of a function is not found in the table, the value nearest to it is to be taken unless interpolation is employed as explained in § 30.

If the angle is less than 45° the number of degrees is printed at the top of the page, and the number of minutes in the column to the left of the columns containing the logarithms. If the angle is greater than 45° the number of degrees is printed at the bottom of the page, and the number of minutes in the column to the right of the columns containing the logarithms.

If the angle is less than 45° the names of its functions are printed at the top of the page; if greater than 45°, at the bottom of the page. Thus,

$\log \sin 21° 37' = 9.56631 - 10.$	Page 66
$\log \cot 36° 53' = 10.12473 - 10 = 0.12473.$	Page 73
$\log \cos 69° 14' = 9.54969 - 10.$	Page 65
$\log \tan 45° 59' = 10.01491 - 10 = 0.01491.$	Page 77
$\log \tan 75° 12' = 10.57805 - 10.$	Page 62
$\log \cos 82° 17' = 9.12799 - 10.$	Page 59
If $\log \cos x = 9.87468 - 10,\ x = 41° 28'.$	Page 76
If $\log \cot x = 9.39353 - 10,\ x = 76° 6'.$	Page 62
If $\log \sin x = 9.99579 - 10,\ x = 82° 2'.$	Page 59
If $\log \tan x = 9.02162 - 10,\ x = 6°.$	Page 58

If $\log \sin = 9.47760 - 10$, the nearest log sin in the table is $9.47774 - 10$ (page 64), and the angle corresponding to this value is 17° 29′.

If $\log \tan = 0.76520 = 10.76520 - 10$, the nearest log tan in the table is $10.76490 - 10$ (page 60), and the angle corresponding to this value is 80° 15′.

For the method of interpolating, see § 30.

30. Interpolation. If it is desired to obtain the logarithm of the function of an angle that contains seconds, or to obtain the value of an angle in degrees, minutes, and seconds from a logarithm of a function, interpolation must be employed. The theory of interpolation has already been given in §§ 22 and 24.

Here it must be remembered that the difference between two consecutive angles in the table is 1′, and that therefore a proportional part of 60″ must be taken. It must also be remembered that log sin and log tan increase as the angle increases, but log cos and log cot diminish as the angle increases.

1. Find log tan 70° 46′ 8″.

Log tan 70° 46′ = 0.45731. (Page 65.)

The difference between the mantissas of log tan 70° 46′ and log tan 70° 47′ is 41, and $\frac{8}{60}$ of 41 = 5.

As the function is increasing, the 5 must be added to the figure in the fifth place of the mantissa 45731; therefore log tan 70° 46′ 8″ = 0.45736.

2. Find log cos 47° 35′ 4″.

Log cos 47° 35′ = 9.82899 − 10. (Page 76.)

The difference between this mantissa and the mantissa of log cos 47° 36′ is 14, and $\frac{4}{60}$ of 14 = 1.

As the function is decreasing, the 1 must be subtracted from the figure in the fifth place of the mantissa 82899; therefore log cos 47° 35′ 4″ = 9.82898 − 10.

3. Find x when log sin x = 9.45359 − 10.

The mantissa of the nearest smaller log sin in the table is 45334. (Page 63.)

The angle corresponding to this value is 16° 30′.

The difference between 45334 and the given mantissa, 45359, is 25.

The difference between 45334 and the next following mantissa, 45377, is 43 (the tabular difference) and $\frac{25}{43}$ of 60″ = 35″.

As the function is increasing, the 35″ must be added to 16° 30′; therefore the required angle is 16° 30′ 35″.

4. Find x when log cot x = 0.73478.

The mantissa of the nearest smaller log cot in the table is 73415. (Page 60.)

The angle corresponding to this value is 10° 27′.

The difference between 73415 and the given mantissa is 63.

The difference between 73415 and the next larger mantissa is 71 (the tabular difference) and $\frac{63}{71}$ of 60″ = 53″.

As the function is decreasing, the 53″ must be subtracted from 10° 27′; therefore the required angle is 10° 26′ 7″.

5. Find x when log cos x = 0.83584.

The mantissa of the nearest smaller log cos in the table is 83446. (Page 57.)

The angle corresponding to this value is 86° 5′.

The difference between 83446 and the given mantissa is 138.

The tabular difference is 184, and $\frac{138}{184}$ of 60″ is 45″.

As the function is decreasing, 45″ must be subtracted from 86° 5′; therefore x = 86° 5′ − 45″, or 86° 4′ 15″.

31. The Secant and Cosecant. In working with logarithms we very rarely use either the secant or the cosecant; for $\sec x = 1/\cos x$, and $\log \sec x = \text{colog} \cos x$. If, however, log sec or log csc of an angle is desired, it may be found from the table by the formulas,

$$\sec A = \frac{1}{\cos A}, \text{ hence } \log \sec A = \text{colog} \cos A;$$

$$\csc A = \frac{1}{\sin A}, \text{ hence } \log \csc A = \text{colog} \sin A.$$

For example,

log sec 8° 28′	= colog cos 8° 28′	= 0.00476.	Page 59
log csc 18° 36′	= colog sin 18° 36′	= 0.49626.	Page 64
log sec 62° 27′	= colog cos 62° 27′	= 0.33487.	Page 69
log csc 59° 36′ 44″	= colog sin 59° 36′ 44″	= 0.06418.	Page 70

32. Functions of Small Angles. If a given angle is between 0° and 1°, or between 89° and 90°; or, conversely, if a given log sin or log cos does not lie between the limits 8.24186 and 9.99993 in the table; or if a given log tan or log cot does not lie between the limits 8.24192 and 11.75808 in the table,—then pages 49–55 of Table VI must be used.

On page 49, log sin of angles between 0° and 0° 3′, and log cos of the complementary angles between 89° 57′ and 90°, are given to every second; for the angles between 0° and 0° 3′, log tan = log sin, and log cos = 0.00000; for the angles between 89° 57′ and 90°, log cot = log cos, and log sin = 0.00000.

On pages 50–52, log sin, log tan, and log cos of angles between 0° and 1°, or log cos, log cot, and log sin of the complementary angles between 89° and 90°, are given to every 10″.

When log tan and log cot are not given, they may be found by the formulas,

log tan = colog cot.   log cot = colog tan.

Conversely, if a given log tan or log cot is not contained in the table, then the colog must be found; this will be the log cot or log tan, as the case may be, and will be contained in the table.

On pages 53–55 the logarithms of the functions of angles between 1° and 2°, or between 88° and 89°, are given in the manner employed on pages 50–52. These pages should be used if the angle lies between these limits, and if not only degrees and minutes but degrees, minutes, and multiples of 10″ are given or required.

When the angle is between 0° and 2°, or 88° and 90°, and a greater degree of accuracy is desired than that given by the table, interpolation may be employed with some degree of safety; but for these angles interpolation does not always give true results, and it is better to use Table VII.

33. Illustrative Problems. The following problems illustrate the use of Table VI for small angles:

1. Find log tan $0° 2' 47''$, and log cos $89° 37' 20''$.

log tan $0° 2' 47'' =$ log sin $0° 2' 47'' = 6.90829 - 10$. Page 49

log cos $89° 37' 20'' = 7.81911 - 10$. Page 51

2. Find log cot $0° 2' 15''$.

$$\begin{array}{rl} & 10 \qquad\quad -10 \\ \text{log tan } 0° 2' 15'' = & \underline{6.81591 - 10} \\ \text{Therefore log cot } 0° 2' 15'' = & 3.18409 \end{array}$$

Page 49

3. Find log tan $89° 38' 30''$.

$$\begin{array}{rl} & 10 \qquad\quad -10 \\ \text{log cot } 89° 38' 30'' = & \underline{7.79617 - 10} \\ \text{Therefore log tan } 89° 38' 30'' = & 2.20383 \end{array}$$

Page 51

4. Find x when log tan $x = 6.92090 - 10$.

The nearest log tan is $6.92110 - 10$ (page 49), and the angle corresponding to this value of log tan is $0° 2' 52''$.

5. Find x when log cos $x = 7.70240 - 10$.

The nearest log cos is $7.70261 - 10$. Page 50

The corresponding angle for this value is $89° 42' 40''$.

6. Find x when log cot $x = 2.37368$.

This log cot is not contained in the table.

The colog cot $= 7.62632 - 10 =$ log tan.

The log tan in the table nearest to this is (page 50) $7.62510 - 10$, and the angle corresponding to this value of log tan is $0° 14' 30''$.

34. Angles between 90° and 360°. If an angle x is between 90° and 360°, it follows, from formulas established in trigonometry, that,

Between 90° and 180°

$$\log \sin x = \log \sin (180° - x)$$
$$\log \cos x = \log \cos (180° - x)_n$$
$$\log \tan x = \log \tan (180° - x)_n$$
$$\log \cot x = \log \cot (180° - x)_n$$

Between 180° and 270°

$$\log \sin x = \log \sin (x - 180°)_n$$
$$\log \cos x = \log \cos (x - 180°)_n$$
$$\log \tan x = \log \tan (x - 180°)$$
$$\log \cot x = \log \cot (x - 180°)$$

Between 270° and 360°

$$\log \sin x = \log \sin (360° - x)_n$$
$$\log \cos x = \log \cos (360° - x)$$
$$\log \tan x = \log \tan (360° - x)_n$$
$$\log \cot x = \log \cot (360° - x)_n$$

In these formulas the subscript n means that the function is negative. The logarithm of a negative number is imaginary, so we have to take the logarithm of the number as if it were positive; but when we find the function itself we must treat it as negative.

TABLE VII

35. Nature of Table VII. This table (page 78) must be used when great accuracy is desired in working with angles between 0° and 2° or between 88° and 90°.

The values of S and T are such that when the angle a is expressed in seconds,

$$S = \log \sin a - \log a'',$$
$$T = \log \tan a - \log a''.$$

Hence follow the formulas given on page 78.

The values of S and T are printed with the characteristic 10 too large, and in using them -10 must always be annexed.

36. Illustrative Problems. The following problems illustrate the use of Table VII for angles near 0° or 90°:

1. Find log sin 0° 58′ 17″.

$$\begin{aligned} 0° 58' 17'' &= 3497'' \\ \log 3497 &= 3.54370 \\ S &= \underline{4.68555 - 10} \\ \log \sin 0° 58' 17'' &= 8.22925 - 10 \end{aligned}$$

2. Find log cos 88° 26′ 41.2″.

$$\begin{aligned} 90° - 88° 26' 41.2'' &= 1° 33' 18.8'' \\ &= 5598.8'' \\ \log 5598.8 &= 3.74809 \\ S &= \underline{4.68552 - 10} \\ \log \cos 88° 26' 41.2'' &= 8.43361 - 10 \end{aligned}$$

This is nearer than by page 54.

3. Find log tan 0° 52′ 47.5″.

$$\begin{aligned} 0° 52' 47.5'' &= 3167.5'' \\ \log 3167.5 &= 3.50072 \\ T &= \underline{4.68561 - 10} \\ \log \tan 0° 52' 47.5'' &= 8.18633 - 10 \end{aligned}$$

4. Find log tan 89° 54′ 37.362″.

$$\begin{aligned} 90° - 89° 54' 37.362'' &= 0° 5' 22.638'' \\ &= 322.638'' \\ \log 322.638 &= 2.50871 \\ T &= \underline{4.68558 - 10} \\ \log \cot 89° 54' 37.362'' &= 7.19429 - 10 \\ \log \tan 89° 54' 37.362'' &= 2.80571 \end{aligned}$$

5. Find x when $\log \sin x = 6.72306 - 10$.

$$\begin{aligned} & 6.72306 - 10 \\ S = & \underline{4.68557 - 10} \\ \text{Subtracting,} \quad & 2.03749 \quad = \log 109.015 \\ \text{and} \quad & 109.015'' \quad = 0° 1' 49.015'' \end{aligned}$$

6. Find x when $\log \cot x = 1.67604$.

$$\begin{aligned} \text{colog} \cot x = & 8.32396 - 10 \\ T = & \underline{4.68564 - 10} \\ \text{Subtracting,} \quad & 3.63832 \quad = \log 4348.3 \\ \text{and} \quad & 4348.3'' \quad = 1° 12' 28.3'' \end{aligned}$$

7. Find x when $\log \tan x = 1.55407$.

$$\begin{aligned} \text{colog} \tan x = & 8.44593 - 10 \\ T = & \underline{4.68569 - 10} \\ \text{Subtracting,} \quad & 3.76024 \quad = \log 5757.6 \\ & 5757.6'' \quad = 1° 35' 57.6'' \\ \text{and} \quad 90° - & 1° 35' 57.6'' = 88° 24' 2.4'' \end{aligned}$$

Therefore the angle required is 88° 24′ 2.4″.

TABLE VIII

37. Nature of Table VIII. This table (pages 79–101) contains the natural sines, cosines, tangents, and cotangents of angles from 0° to 90°, at intervals of 1′. If greater accuracy is desired, interpolation may be employed.

The table is arranged on a plan similar to that used in Table VI.

Angles from 0° to 44° are listed at the top of the pages, the minutes being read downwards in the left-hand column. Angles from 45° to 89° are listed at the bottom, the minutes being read upwards in the right-hand column.

The names of the functions at the top of the columns are to be used in reading downwards, and those at the bottom are to be used in reading upwards.

38. Illustrative Problems. The following problems illustrate the use of Table VIII:

1. Find sin 5° 29′.

We find directly from the table (page 82) that

$$\sin 5^\circ 29' = 0.0956$$

2. Find cot 78° 18′.

We find directly from the table (page 85) that

$$\cot 78^\circ 18' = 0.2071$$

3. Find cos 42° 7′ 30″.

From the table (page 100), $\cos 42^\circ 7' = 0.7418$
Tabular difference = 0.0002.
$\frac{30}{60}$ of this difference $= \underline{0.0001}$
Since the cosine is decreasing, we subtract.
$\therefore \cos 42^\circ 7' 30'' = 0.7417$

4. Find tan 75° 35′ 25″.

From the table (page 86), $\tan 75^\circ 35' = 3.8900$
Tabular difference = 0.0047.
$\frac{25}{60}$ of this difference = 0.00196 $= \underline{0.0020}$
Since the tangent is increasing, we add.
$\therefore \tan 75^\circ 35' 25'' = 3.8920$

TABLE IX

39. Nature of Table IX. This table converts degrees to radians, and also degrees and parts of a degree indicated by 10′, 20′, 30′, 40′, and 50′.

40. Illustrative Problems. The following problems illustrate the use of Table IX:

1. Express 62° as radians.

From the table, 62° = 1.0821 radians.

2. Express 82° 40′ as radians.

From the table, 82° 40′ = 1.4428 radians.

TABLE X

41. Nature of Table X. This table converts minutes to thousandths of a degree, and seconds to ten-thousandths of a degree, this being accurate enough for all the purposes of elementary trigonometry. It also converts thousandths of a degree, from 0.001° to 0.009°, to seconds; and hundredths of a degree to minutes and seconds, so that a computer who has the decimal divisions of an angle given can easily find the sexagesimal equivalent.

Table X thus provides for using the decimal divisions of the degree instead of the ancient sexagesimal division into minutes and seconds.

There seems to be little doubt that the cumbersome division of the degree into 60 minutes, and the minute into 60 seconds, will disappear in due time, by the introduction either of the *grade* (0.01 of a right angle) divided decimally or of decimal divisions of the degree. At present, however, it must be remembered that our instruments for the measure of angles are generally arranged upon the sexagesimal scale, and that we can serve the new system best by making the change gradually. It is of first importance that the student shall learn how to use the common sexagesimal system.

42. Illustrative Problems. The following problems illustrate the use of the table:

1. Find sin 21.34°.

By Table X, $0.34° = 20' 24''$
Hence we have to find sin 21° 20′ 24″.
By Table VIII, $\sin 21° 20' 24'' = 0.36390$

2. Find log tan 15.963°.

By Table X, $0.96° = 57' 36''$
and $0.003° = 11''$
$\therefore 15.963° = 15° 57' 47''$

By Table V, $\log \tan 15° 57' 47'' = 9.45644 - 10$

3. Find cos 63.72°.

By Table X, $0.72° = 43' 12''$
Hence we have to find cos 63° 43′ 12″.
By Table VIII, $\cos 63° 43' 12'' = 0.4427$

4. Find tan 68.651°.

By Table X, $0.651° = 39' 4''$
Hence we have to find tan 68° 39′ 4″.
By Table VIII, $\tan 68° 39' 4'' = 2.5538$

5. Find log cot 56.388°.

By Table X, $0.388° = 23' 17''$
Hence we have to find log cot 56° 23′ 17″.
By Table VIII, $\log \cot 56° 23' 17'' = 9.82262$

EXERCISE

Using Table I, find the logarithms of the following:

1. 75.
2. 96.
3. 37.
4. 423.
5. 568.
6. 647.
7. 57.8.
8. 42.6.
9. 93.9.
10. 4.27.
11. 6.42.
12. 7.53.
13. 0.725.
14. 7.250.
15. 72.50.
16. 24.3.
17. 2.43.
18. 0.243.
19. 8.
20. 0.8.
21. 0.08.
22. 0.008.
23. 8.08.
24. 8.80.
25. 140.
26. 141.
27. 14.2.
28. 1.43.
29. 0.144.
30. 0.145.

Using Table I, find the antilogarithms of the following:

31. 1.4771.
32. 0.9031.
33. 1.7076.
34. 1.9031.
35. 1.9345.
36. 0.8451.
37. 2.5988.
38. 1.6590.
39. 4.6749.
40. 3.9595.
41. 0.9581.
42. 2.8494.
43. 1.9510.
44. 0.9607.
45. 3.9753.
46. 2.6196.
47. 0.6360.
48. 2.6640.
49. 1.9518.
50. 2.8978.
51. 0.9335.
52. 4.8460.
53. 1.3714.
54. 2.4448.

Using Table I, find the logarithms of the following:

55. log sin 29°.
56. log cos 42°.
57. log tan 51°.
58. log cot 20°.
59. log sin 45°.
60. log cos 45°.
61. log sin 6° 10′.
62. log cos 7° 20′.
63. log tan 5° 30′.
64. log cot 8° 50′.
65. log sin 45° 10′.
66. log cos 44° 80′.
67. log sin 20° 10′.
68. log cos 42° 20′.
69. log tan 37° 50′.
70. log cot 82° 40′.
71. log sin 22° 30′.
72. log tan 81° 10′.

Using Table I, find the value of x in the following:

73. $\log \sin x = 9.7861$.
74. $\log \sin x = 9.9116$.
75. $\log \tan x = 9.9772$.
76. $\log \tan x = 9.8771$.
77. $\log \cos x = 9.9089$.
78. $\log \cot x = 10.0711$.
79. $\log \sin x = 9.8058$.
80. $\log \cos x = 9.9252$.
81. $\log \cos x = 9.9101$.
82. $\log \tan x = 8.9118$.
83. $\log \tan x = 9.0093$.
84. $\log \cot x = 10.1944$.

Using Table III, find the logarithms of the following:

85. 1475.
86. 2836.
87. 4293.
88. 564.8.
89. 392.7.
90. 586.4.
91. 29.37.
92. 42.86.
93. 53.91.
94. 0.4236.
95. 0.09873.
96. 487.48.

Using Table III, find the antilogarithms of the following:

97. 2.02078.
98. 3.55967.
99. 1.75686.
100. 0.82756.
101. $\bar{1}.82988$.
102. $\bar{2}.96052$.
103. 2.95873.
104. 3.81792.
105. 1.82725.
106. 0.70804.
107. $\bar{2}.34404$.
108. $\bar{3}.35054$.

Using Table VI, find the following logarithms:

109. log sin 10°.
110. log sin 30°.
111. log sin 60°.
112. log sin 79°.
113. log cos 87°.
114. log tan 33°.
115. log cot 72°.
116. log sin 1′ 51″.
117. log tan 37′ 50″.
118. log cos 1° 19′.
119. log cot 88° 24′.
120. log sin 19° 37′.
121. log cos 72° 43′.
122. log cot 88° 18′.
123. log sin 10′ 37″.
124. log cot 67° 42′.
125. log cos 32° 36′ 10″.
126. log tan 73° 42′ 15″.
127. log sin 15° 15′ 15″.
128. log cos 29° 32′ 40″.
129. log cot 78° 33′ 25″.

Using Table VI, find the value of x in the following:

130. $\log \sin x = 9.52563$.
131. $\log \cot x = 9.57658$.
132. $\log \cos x = 9.73435$.
133. $\log \sin x = 9.93386$.
134. $\log \cot x = 9.75837$.
135. $\log \cos x = 9.99843$.

Using Table IV, find the following:

136. 0.8 of 37. **137.** 0.6 of 79. **138.** 0.7 of 68. **139.** 0.9 of 29.

Using Table V, find the following:

140. $\log 4\pi$. **141.** $\log \sqrt[3]{\pi}$. **142.** log 57.2958°. **143.** $\log \sqrt[3]{5}$.

Using Table VII, find the following:

144. log sin 57″. **145.** log sin 48″. **146.** log tan 89° 58′ 10″.

Using Table V, find the following:

147. $2\pi \cdot 87$. **148.** $\pi \cdot 75^2$. **149.** $\dfrac{55}{2\pi}$. **150.** $\dfrac{37^2}{4\pi}$.

Using Table VIII, find the following:

151. sin 10° 17′.
152. sin 37° 40′.
153. sin 68° 10′.
154. cos 10° 39′.
155. cos 46° 38′.
156. cos 78° 19′.
157. tan 16° 29′.
158. tan 88° 8′.
159. cot 1° 52′.
160. cot 63° 48′.
161. cot 10° 9′ 10″.
162. cot 5° 17′ 8″.

163. The angles whose sines are 0.5113 and 0.7801.

Using Table IX, express the following:

164. 52° 40′ as radians. **165.** 0.8116 radians as degrees.

Using Table X, express the following:

166. 31′ as a decimal of a degree. **167.** 0.96° as minutes and seconds.

TABLE I

FOUR-PLACE MANTISSAS
OF THE COMMON LOGARITHMS OF
INTEGERS FROM 1 TO 1000
AND OF THE TRIGONOMETRIC FUNCTIONS

On this page the logarithms of integers from 1 to 100 are given in full, with characteristics as well as mantissas. On account of the great differences between the successive mantissas, interpolation cannot safely be employed on this page. On pages 18 and 19 are given the mantissas of numbers from 100 to 1000, and on pages 20–23 the logarithms of trigonometric functions.

1—100

N	log	N	log	N	log	N	log	N	log
1	0. 0000	**21**	1. 3222	**41**	1. 6128	**61**	1. 7853	**81**	1. 9085
2	0. 3010	22	1. 3424	42	1. 6232	62	1. 7924	82	1. 9138
3	0. 4771	23	1. 3617	43	1. 6335	63	1. 7993	83	1. 9191
4	0. 6021	24	1. 3802	44	1. 6435	64	1. 8062	84	1. 9243
5	0. 6990	25	1. 3979	45	1. 6532	65	1. 8129	85	1. 9294
6	0. 7782	**26**	1. 4150	**46**	1. 6628	**66**	1. 8195	**86**	1. 9345
7	0. 8451	27	1. 4314	47	1. 6721	67	1. 8261	87	1. 9395
8	0. 9031	28	1. 4472	48	1. 6812	68	1. 8325	88	1. 9445
9	0. 9542	29	1. 4624	49	1. 6902	69	1. 8388	89	1. 9494
10	1. 0000	30	1. 4771	50	1. 6990	70	1. 8451	90	1. 9542
11	1. 0414	**31**	1. 4914	**51**	1. 7076	**71**	1. 8513	**91**	1. 9590
12	1. 0792	32	1. 5051	52	1. 7160	72	1. 8573	92	1. 9638
13	1. 1139	33	1. 5185	53	1. 7243	73	1. 8633	93	1. 9685
14	1. 1461	34	1. 5315	54	1. 7324	74	1. 8692	94	1. 9731
15	1. 1761	35	1. 5441	55	1. 7404	75	1. 8751	95	1. 9777
16	1. 2041	**36**	1. 5563	**56**	1. 7482	**76**	1. 8808	**96**	1. 9823
17	1. 2304	37	1. 5682	57	1. 7559	77	1. 8865	97	1. 9868
18	1. 2553	38	1. 5798	58	1. 7634	78	1. 8921	98	1. 9912
19	1. 2788	39	1. 5911	59	1. 7709	79	1. 8976	99	1. 9956
20	1. 3010	40	1. 6021	60	1. 7782	80	1. 9031	100	2. 0000
N	log	N	log	N	log	N	log	N	log

Each mantissa should be preceded by a decimal point, and the proper characteristic should be written.

On account of the great differences between the successive mantissas in the first ten rows, interpolation should not be employed in that part of the table. Table III should be used in this case. In general, an error of one unit may appear in the last figure of any interpolated value.

N	0	1	2	3	4	5	6	7	8	9
10	0000	0043	0086	0128	0170	0212	0253	0294	0334	0374
11	0414	0453	0492	0531	0569	0607	0645	0682	0719	0755
12	0792	0828	0864	0899	0934	0969	1004	1038	1072	1106
13	1139	1173	1206	1239	1271	1303	1335	1367	1399	1430
14	1461	1492	1523	1553	1584	1614	1644	1673	1703	1732
15	1761	1790	1818	1847	1875	1903	1931	1959	1987	2014
16	2041	2068	2095	2122	2148	2175	2201	2227	2253	2279
17	2304	2330	2355	2380	2405	2430	2455	2480	2504	2529
18	2553	2577	2601	2625	2648	2672	2695	2718	2742	2765
19	2788	2810	2833	2856	2878	2900	2923	2945	2967	2989
20	3010	3032	3054	3075	3096	3118	3139	3160	3181	3201
21	3222	3243	3263	3284	3304	3324	3345	3365	3385	3404
22	3424	3444	3464	3483	3502	3522	3541	3560	3579	3598
23	3617	3636	3655	3674	3692	3711	3729	3747	3766	3784
24	3802	3820	3838	3856	3874	3892	3909	3927	3945	3962
25	3979	3997	4014	4031	4048	4065	4082	4099	4116	4133
26	4150	4166	4183	4200	4216	4232	4249	4265	4281	4298
27	4314	4330	4346	4362	4378	4393	4409	4425	4440	4456
28	4472	4487	4502	4518	4533	4548	4564	4579	4594	4609
29	4624	4639	4654	4669	4683	4698	4713	4728	4742	4757
30	4771	4786	4800	4814	4829	4843	4857	4871	4886	4900
31	4914	4928	4942	4955	4969	4983	4997	5011	5024	5038
32	5051	5065	5079	5092	5105	5119	5132	5145	5159	5172
33	5185	5198	5211	5224	5237	5250	5263	5276	5289	5302
34	5315	5328	5340	5353	5366	5378	5391	5403	5416	5428
35	5441	5453	5465	5478	5490	5502	5514	5527	5539	5551
36	5563	5575	5587	5599	5611	5623	5635	5647	5658	5670
37	5682	5694	5705	5717	5729	5740	5752	5763	5775	5786
38	5798	5809	5821	5832	5843	5855	5866	5877	5888	5899
39	5911	5922	5933	5944	5955	5966	5977	5988	5999	6010
40	6021	6031	6042	6053	6064	6075	6085	6096	6107	6117
41	6128	6138	6149	6160	6170	6180	6191	6201	6212	6222
42	6232	6243	6253	6263	6274	6284	6294	6304	6314	6325
43	6335	6345	6355	6365	6375	6385	6395	6405	6415	6425
44	6435	6444	6454	6464	6474	6484	6493	6503	6513	6522
45	6532	6542	6551	6561	6571	6580	6590	6599	6609	6618
46	6628	6637	6646	6656	6665	6675	6684	6693	6702	6712
47	6721	6730	6739	6749	6758	6767	6776	6785	6794	6803
48	6812	6821	6830	6839	6848	6857	6866	6875	6884	6893
49	6902	6911	6920	6928	6937	6946	6955	6964	6972	6981
50	6990	6998	7007	7016	7024	7033	7042	7050	7059	7067
N	0	1	2	3	4	5	6	7	8	9

N	0	1	2	3	4	5	6	7	8	9
50	6990	6998	7007	7016	7024	7033	7042	7050	7059	7067
51	7076	7084	7093	7101	7110	7118	7126	7135	7143	7152
52	7160	7168	7177	7185	7193	7202	7210	7218	7226	7235
53	7243	7251	7259	7267	7275	7284	7292	7300	7308	7316
54	7324	7332	7340	7348	7356	7364	7372	7380	7388	7396
55	7404	7412	7419	7427	7435	7443	7451	7459	7466	7474
56	7482	7490	7497	7505	7513	7520	7528	7536	7543	7551
57	7559	7566	7574	7582	7589	7597	7604	7612	7619	7627
58	7634	7642	7649	7657	7664	7672	7679	7686	7694	7701
59	7709	7716	7723	7731	7738	7745	7752	7760	7767	7774
60	7782	7789	7796	7803	7810	7818	7825	7832	7839	7846
61	7853	7860	7868	7875	7882	7889	7896	7903	7910	7917
62	7924	7931	7938	7945	7952	7959	7966	7973	7980	7987
63	7993	8000	8007	8014	8021	8028	8035	8041	8048	8055
64	8062	8069	8075	8082	8089	8096	8102	8109	8116	8122
65	8129	8136	8142	8149	8156	8162	8169	8176	8182	8189
66	8195	8202	8209	8215	8222	8228	8235	8241	8248	8254
67	8261	8267	8274	8280	8287	8293	8299	8306	8312	8319
68	8325	8331	8338	8344	8351	8357	8363	8370	8376	8382
69	8388	8395	8401	8407	8414	8420	8426	8432	8439	8445
70	8451	8457	8463	8470	8476	8482	8488	8494	8500	8506
71	8513	8519	8525	8531	8537	8543	8549	8555	8561	8567
72	8573	8579	8585	8591	8597	8603	8609	8615	8621	8627
73	8633	8639	8645	8651	8657	8663	8669	8675	8681	8686
74	8692	8698	8704	8710	8716	8722	8727	8733	8739	8745
75	8751	8756	8762	8768	8774	8779	8785	8791	8797	8802
76	8808	8814	8820	8825	8831	8837	8842	8848	8854	8859
77	8865	8871	8876	8882	8887	8893	8899	8904	8910	8915
78	8921	8927	8932	8938	8943	8949	8954	8960	8965	8971
79	8976	8982	8987	8993	8998	9004	9009	9015	9020	9025
80	9031	9036	9042	9047	9053	9058	9063	9069	9074	9079
81	9085	9090	9096	9101	9106	9112	9117	9122	9128	9133
82	9138	9143	9149	9154	9159	9165	9170	9175	9180	9186
83	9191	9196	9201	9206	9212	9217	9222	9227	9232	9238
84	9243	9248	9253	9258	9263	9269	9274	9279	9284	9289
85	9294	9299	9304	9309	9315	9320	9325	9330	9335	9340
86	9345	9350	9355	9360	9365	9370	9375	9380	9385	9390
87	9395	9400	9405	9410	9415	9420	9425	9430	9435	9440
88	9445	9450	9455	9460	9465	9469	9474	9479	9484	9489
89	9494	9499	9504	9509	9513	9518	9523	9528	9533	9538
90	9542	9547	9552	9557	9562	9566	9571	9576	9581	9586
91	9590	9595	9600	9605	9609	9614	9619	9624	9628	9633
92	9638	9643	9647	9652	9657	9661	9666	9671	9675	9680
93	9685	9689	9694	9699	9703	9708	9713	9717	9722	9727
94	9731	9736	9741	9745	9750	9754	9759	9763	9768	9773
95	9777	9782	9786	9791	9795	9800	9805	9809	9814	9818
96	9823	9827	9832	9836	9841	9845	9850	9854	9859	9863
97	9868	9872	9877	9881	9886	9890	9894	9899	9903	9908
98	9912	9917	9921	9926	9930	9934	9939	9943	9948	9952
99	9956	9961	9965	9969	9974	9978	9983	9987	9991	9996
100	0000	0004	0009	0013	0017	0022	0026	0030	0035	0039
N	**0**	**1**	**2**	**3**	**4**	**5**	**6**	**7**	**8**	**9**

°	0′	10′	20′	30′	40′	50′	60′	°
0	$-\infty$	7.4637	7.7648	7.9408	8.0658	8.1627	8.2419	89
1	8.2419	8.3088	8.3668	8.4179	4637	5050	5428	88
2	5428	5776	6097	6397	6677	6940	7188	87
3	7188	7423	7645	7857	8059	8251	8436	86
4	8436	8613	8783	8946	9104	8.9256	8.9403	**85**
5	8.9403	8.9545	8.9682	8.9816	8.9945	9.0070	9.0192	84
6	9.0192	9.0311	9.0426	9.0539	9.0648	0755	0859	83
7	0859	0961	1060	1157	1252	1345	1436	82
8	1436	1525	1612	1697	1781	1863	1943	81
9	1943	2022	2100	2176	2251	2324	2397	**80**
10	9.2397	9.2468	9.2538	9.2606	9.2674	9.2740	9.2806	79
11	2806	2870	2934	2997	3058	3119	3179	78
12	3179	3238	3296	3353	3410	3466	3521	77
13	3521	3575	3629	3682	3734	3786	3837	76
14	3837	3887	3937	3986	4035	4083	4130	**75**
15	9.4130	9.4177	9.4223	9.4269	9.4314	9.4359	9.4403	74
16	4403	4447	4491	4533	4576	4618	4659	73
17	4659	4700	4741	4781	4821	4861	4900	72
18	4900	4939	4977	5015	5052	5090	5126	71
19	5126	5163	5199	5235	5270	5306	5341	**70**
20	9.5341	9.5375	9.5409	9.5443	9.5477	9.5510	9.5543	69
21	5543	5576	5609	5641	5673	5704	5736	68
22	5736	5767	5798	5828	5859	5889	5919	67
23	5919	5948	5978	6007	6036	6065	6093	66
24	6093	6121	6149	6177	6205	6232	6259	**65**
25	9.6259	9.6286	9.6313	9.6340	9.6366	9.6392	9.6418	64
26	6418	6444	6470	6495	6521	6546	6570	63
27	6570	6595	6620	6644	6668	6692	6716	62
28	6716	6740	6763	6787	6810	6833	6856	61
29	6856	6878	6901	6923	6946	6968	6990	**60**
30	9.6990	9.7012	9.7033	9.7055	9.7076	9.7097	9.7118	59
31	7118	7139	7160	7181	7201	7222	7242	58
32	7242	7262	7282	7302	7322	7342	7361	57
33	7361	7380	7400	7419	7438	7457	7476	56
34	7476	7494	7513	7531	7550	7568	7586	**55**
35	9.7586	9.7604	9.7622	9.7640	9.7657	9.7675	9.7692	54
36	7692	7710	7727	7744	7761	7778	7795	53
37	7795	7811	7828	7844	7861	7877	7893	52
38	7893	7910	7926	7941	7957	7973	7989	51
39	7989	8004	8020	8035	8050	8066	8081	**50**
40	9.8081	9.8096	9.8111	9.8125	9.8140	9.8155	9.8169	49
41	8169	8184	8198	8213	8227	8241	8255	48
42	8255	8269	8283	8297	8311	8324	8338	47
43	8338	8351	8365	8378	8391	8405	8418	46
44	9.8418	9.8431	9.8444	9.8457	9.8469	9.8482	9.8495	**45**
°	60′	50′	40′	30′	20′	10′	0′	°

LOGARITHMS OF COSINES

°	0′	10′	20′	30′	40′	50′	60′	°
0	10.0000	10.0000	10.0000	10.0000	10.0000	10.0000	9.9999	89
1	9.9999	9.9999	9.9999	9.9999	9.9998	9.9998	9997	88
2	9997	9997	9996	9996	9995	9995	9994	87
3	9994	9993	9993	9992	9991	9990	9989	86
4	9989	9989	9988	9987	9986	9985	9983	**85**
5	9.9983	9.9982	9.9981	9.9980	9.9979	9.9977	9.9976	84
6	9976	9975	9973	9972	9971	9969	9968	83
7	9968	9966	9964	9963	9961	9959	9958	82
8	9958	9956	9954	9952	9950	9948	9946	81
9	9946	9944	9942	9940	9938	9936	9934	**80**
10	9.9934	9.9931	9.9929	9.9927	9.9924	9.9922	9.9919	79
11	9919	9917	9914	9912	9909	9907	9904	78
12	9904	9901	9899	9896	9893	9890	9887	77
13	9887	9884	9881	9878	9875	9872	9869	76
14	9869	9866	9863	9859	9856	9853	9849	**75**
15	9.9849	9.9846	9.9843	9.9839	9.9836	9.9832	9.9828	74
16	9828	9825	9821	9817	9814	9810	9806	73
17	9806	9802	9798	9794	9790	9786	9782	72
18	9782	9778	9774	9770	9765	9761	9757	71
19	9757	9752	9748	9743	9739	9734	9730	**70**
20	9.9730	9.9725	9.9721	9.9716	9.9711	9.9706	9.9702	69
21	9702	9697	9692	9687	9682	9677	9672	68
22	9672	9667	9661	9656	9651	9646	9640	67
23	9640	9635	9629	9624	9618	9613	9607	66
24	9607	9602	9596	9590	9584	9579	9573	**65**
25	9.9573	9.9567	9.9561	9.9555	9.9549	9.9543	9.9537	64
26	9537	9530	9524	9518	9512	9505	9499	63
27	9499	9492	9486	9479	9473	9466	9459	62
28	9459	9453	9446	9439	9432	9425	9418	61
29	9418	9411	9404	9397	9390	9383	9375	**60**
30	9.9375	9.9368	9.9361	9.9353	9.9346	9.9338	9.9331	59
31	9331	9323	9315	9308	9300	9292	9284	58
32	9284	9276	9268	9260	9252	9244	9236	57
33	9236	9228	9219	9211	9203	9194	9186	56
34	9186	9177	9169	9160	9151	9142	9134	**55**
35	9.9134	9.9125	9.9116	9.9107	9.9098	9.9089	9.9080	54
36	9080	9070	9061	9052	9042	9033	9023	53
37	9023	9014	9004	8995	8985	8975	8965	52
38	8965	8955	8945	8935	8925	8915	8905	51
39	8905	8895	8884	8874	8864	8853	8843	**50**
40	9.8843	9.8832	9.8821	9.8810	9.8800	9.8789	9.8778	49
41	8778	8767	8756	8745	8733	8722	8711	48
42	8711	8699	8688	8676	8665	8653	8641	47
43	8641	8629	8618	8606	8594	8582	8569	46
44	9.8569	9.8557	9.8545	9.8532	9.8520	9.8507	9.8495	**45**
°	**60′**	**50′**	**40′**	**30′**	**20′**	**10′**	**0′**	°

LOGARITHMS OF SINES

°	0′	10′	20′	30′	40′	50′	60′	°
0	− ∞	7.4637	7.7648	7.9409	8.0658	8.1627	8.2419	89
1	8.2419	8.3089	8.3669	8.4181	4638	5053	5431	88
2	5431	5779	6101	6401	6682	6945	7194	87
3	7194	7429	7652	7865	8067	8261	8446	86
4	8446	8624	8795	8960	9118	8.9272	8.9420	**85**
5	8.9420	8.9563	8.9701	8.9836	8.9966	9.0093	9.0216	84
6	9.0216	9.0336	9.0453	9.0567	9.0678	0786	0891	83
7	0891	0995	1096	1194	1291	1385	1478	82
8	1478	1569	1658	1745	1831	1915	1997	81
9	1997	2078	2158	2236	2313	2389	2463	**80**
10	9.2463	9.2536	9.2609	9.2680	9.2750	9.2819	9.2887	79
11	2887	2953	3020	3085	3149	3212	3275	78
12	3275	3336	3397	3458	3517	3576	3634	77
13	3634	3691	3748	3804	3859	3914	3968	76
14	3968	4021	4074	4127	4178	4230	4281	**75**
15	9.4281	9.4331	9.4381	9.4430	9.4479	9.4527	9.4575	74
16	4575	4622	4669	4716	4762	4808	4853	73
17	4853	4898	4943	4987	5031	5075	5118	72
18	5118	5161	5203	5245	5287	5329	5370	71
19	5370	5411	5451	5491	5531	5571	5611	**70**
20	9.5611	9.5650	9.5689	9.5727	9.5766	9.5804	9.5842	69
21	5842	5879	5917	5954	5991	6028	6064	68
22	6064	6100	6136	6172	6208	6243	6279	67
23	6279	6314	6348	6383	6417	6452	6486	66
24	6486	6520	6553	6587	6620	6654	6687	**65**
25	9.6687	9.6720	9.6752	9.6785	9.6817	9.6850	9.6882	64
26	6882	6914	6946	6977	7009	7040	7072	63
27	7072	7103	7134	7165	7196	7226	7257	62
28	7257	7287	7317	7348	7378	7408	7438	61
29	7438	7467	7497	7526	7556	7585	7614	**60**
30	9.7614	9.7644	9.7673	9.7701	9.7730	9.7759	9.7788	59
31	7788	7816	7845	7873	7902	7930	7958	58
32	7958	7986	8014	8042	8070	8097	8125	57
33	8125	8153	8180	8208	8235	8263	8290	56
34	8290	8317	8344	8371	8398	8425	8452	**55**
35	9.8452	9.8479	9.8506	9.8533	9.8559	9.8586	9.8613	54
36	8613	8639	8666	8692	8718	8745	8771	53
37	8771	8797	8824	8850	8876	8902	8928	52
38	8928	8954	8980	9006	9032	9058	9084	51
39	9084	9110	9135	9161	9187	9212	9238	**50**
40	9.9238	9.9264	9.9289	9.9315	9.9341	9.9366	9.9392	49
41	9392	9417	9443	9468	9494	9519	9544	48
42	9544	9570	9595	9621	9646	9671	9697	47
43	9697	9722	9747	9772	9798	9823	9.9848	46
44	9.9848	9.9874	9.9899	9.9924	9.9949	9.9975	10.0000	**45**
°	60′	50′	40′	30′	20′	10′	0′	°

LOGARITHMS OF COTANGENTS

°	0′	10′	20′	30′	40′	50′	60′	°
0	∞	12.5363	12.2352	12.0591	11.9342	11.8373	11.7581	89
1	11.7581	11.6911	11.6331	11.5819	5362	4947	4569	88
2	4569	4221	3899	3599	3318	3055	2806	87
3	2806	2571	2348	2135	1933	1739	1554	86
4	1554	1376	1205	1040	0882	11.0728	11.0580	**85**
5	11.0580	11.0437	11.0299	11.0164	11.0034	10.9907	10.9784	84
6	10.9784	10.9664	10.9547	10.9433	10.9322	9214	9109	83
7	9109	9005	8904	8806	8709	8615	8522	82
8	8522	8431	8342	8255	8169	8085	8003	81
9	8003	7922	7842	7764	7687	7611	7537	**80**
10	10.7537	10.7464	10.7391	10.7320	10.7250	10.7181	10.7113	79
11	7113	7047	6980	6915	6851	6788	6725	78
12	6725	6664	6603	6542	6483	5424	6366	77
13	6366	6309	6252	6196	6141	6086	6032	76
14	6032	5979	5926	5873	5822	5770	5719	**75**
15	10.5719	10.5669	10.5619	10.5570	10.5521	10.5473	10.5425	74
16	5425	5378	5331	5284	5238	5192	5147	73
17	5147	5102	5057	5013	4969	4925	4882	72
18	4882	4839	4797	4755	4713	4671	4630	71
19	4630	4589	4549	4509	4469	4429	4389	**70**
20	10.4389	10.4350	10.4311	10.4273	10.4234	10.4196	10.4158	69
21	4158	4121	4083	4046	4009	3972	3936	68
22	3936	3900	3864	3828	3792	3757	3721	67
23	3721	3686	3652	3617	3583	3548	3514	66
24	3514	3480	3447	3413	3380	3346	3313	**65**
25	10.3313	10.3280	10.3248	10.3215	10.3183	10.3150	10.3118	64
26	3118	3086	3054	3023	2991	2960	2928	63
27	2928	2897	2866	2835	2804	2774	2743	62
28	2743	2713	2683	2652	2622	2592	2562	61
29	2562	2533	2503	2474	2444	2415	2386	**60**
30	10.2386	10.2356	10.2327	10.2299	10.2270	10.2241	10.2212	59
31	2212	2184	2155	2127	2098	2070	2042	58
32	2042	2014	1986	1958	1930	1903	1875	57
33	1875	1847	1820	1792	1765	1737	1710	56
34	1710	1683	1656	1629	1602	1575	1548	**55**
35	10.1548	10.1521	10.1494	10.1467	10.1441	10.1414	10.1387	54
36	1387	1361	1334	1308	1282	1255	1229	53
37	1229	1203	1176	1150	1124	1098	1072	52
38	1072	1046	1020	0994	0968	0942	0916	51
39	0916	0890	0865	0839	0813	0788	0762	**50**
40	10.0762	10.0736	10.0711	10.0685	10.0659	10.0634	10.0608	49
41	0608	0583	0557	0532	0506	0481	0456	48
42	0456	0430	0405	0379	0354	0329	0303	47
43	0303	0278	0253	0228	0202	0177	0152	46
44	10.0152	10.0126	10.0101	10.0076	10.0051	10.0025	10.0000	**45**
°	**60′**	**50′**	**40′**	**30′**	**20′**	**10′**	**0′**	°

LOGARITHMS OF TANGENTS

TABLE II

d	πd	$\frac{1}{4}\pi d^2$	d^2	d^3	$\sqrt{d}$	$\sqrt[3]{d}$
0	0.0000	0.0000	0	0	0.0000	0.0000
1	3.1416	0.7854	1	1	1.0000	1.0000
2	6.2832	3.1416	4	8	4142	2599
3	9.4248	7.0686	9	27	1.7321	4422
4	12.5664	12.5664	16	64	2.0000	5874
5	15.7080	19.6350	25	125	2.2361	1.7100
6	18.8496	28.2743	36	216	4495	8171
7	21.9911	38.4845	49	343	6458	1.9129
8	25.1327	50.2655	64	512	2.8284	2.0000
9	28.2743	63.6173	81	729	3.0000	0801
10	31.4159	78.5398	100	1,000	3.1623	2.1544
11	34.5575	95.0332	121	1,331	3166	2240
12	37.6991	113.0973	144	1,728	4641	2894
13	40.8407	132.7323	169	2,197	6056	3513
14	43.9823	153.9380	196	2,744	7417	4101
15	47.1239	176.7146	225	3,375	3.8730	2.4662
16	50.2655	201.0619	256	4,096	4.0000	5198
17	53.4071	226.9801	289	4,913	1231	5713
18	56.5487	254.4690	324	5,832	2426	6207
19	59.6903	283.5287	361	6,859	3589	6684
20	62.8319	314.1593	400	8,000	4.4721	2.7144
21	65.9734	346.3606	441	9,261	5826	7589
22	69.1150	380.1327	484	10,648	6904	8020
23	72.2566	415.4756	529	12,167	7958	8439
24	75.3982	452.3893	576	13,824	4.8990	8845
25	78.5398	490.8739	625	15,625	5.0000	2.9240
26	81.6814	530.9292	676	17,576	0990	2.9625
27	84.8230	572.5553	729	19,683	1962	3.0000
28	87.9646	615.7522	784	21,952	2915	0366
29	91.1062	660.5199	841	24,389	3852	0723
30	94.2478	706.8583	900	27,000	5.4772	3.1072
31	97.3894	754.7676	961	29,791	5678	1414
32	100.5310	804.2477	1024	32,768	6569	1748
33	103.6726	855.2986	1089	35,937	7446	2075
34	106.8142	907.9203	1156	39,304	8310	2396
35	109.9557	962.1128	1225	42,875	5.9161	3.2711
36	113.0973	1017.8760	1296	46,656	6.0000	3019
37	116.2389	1075.2101	1369	50,653	0828	3322
38	119.3805	1134.1149	1444	54,872	1644	3620
39	122.5221	1194.5906	1521	59,319	2450	3912
40	125.6637	1256.6371	1600	64,000	6.3246	3.4200
41	128.8053	1320.2543	1681	68,921	4031	4482
42	131.9469	1385.4424	1764	74,088	4807	4760
43	135.0885	1452.2012	1849	79,507	5574	5034
44	138.2301	1520.5308	1936	85,184	6332	5303
45	141.3717	1590.4313	2025	91,125	6.7082	3.5569
46	144.5133	1661.9025	2116	97,336	7823	5830
47	147.6549	1734.9445	2209	103,823	8557	6088
48	150.7964	1809.5574	2304	110,592	6.9282	6342
49	153.9380	1885.7410	2401	117,649	7.0000	6593
50	157.0796	1963.4954	2500	125,000	7.0711	3.6840

CIRCUMFERENCES AND AREAS OF CIRCLES
SQUARES, CUBES, SQUARE ROOTS, CUBE ROOTS

d	πd	$\frac{1}{4}\pi d^2$	d^2	d^3	$\sqrt{d}$	$\sqrt[3]{d}$
50	157.0796	1963.4954	2500	125,000	7.0711	3.6840
51	160.2212	2042.8206	2601	132,651	1414	7084
52	163.3628	2123.7166	2704	140,608	2111	7325
53	166.5044	2206.1834	2809	148,877	2801	7563
54	169.6460	2290.2210	2916	157,464	3485	7798
55	172.7876	2375.8294	3025	166,375	7.4162	3.8030
56	175.9292	2463.0086	3136	175,616	4833	8259
57	179.0708	2551.7586	3249	185,193	5498	8485
58	182.2124	2642.0794	3364	195,112	6158	8709
59	185.3540	2733.9710	3481	205,379	6811	8930
60	188.4956	2827.4334	3600	216,000	7.7460	3.9149
61	191.6372	2922.4666	3721	226,981	8102	9365
62	194.7787	3019.0705	3844	238,328	8740	9579
63	197.9203	3117.2453	3969	250,047	7.9373	3.9791
64	201.0619	3216.9909	4096	262,144	8.0000	4.0000
65	204.2035	3318.3072	4225	274,625	8.0623	4.0207
66	207.3451	3421.1944	4356	287,496	1240	0412
67	210.4867	3525.6524	4489	300,763	1854	0615
68	213.6283	3631.6811	4624	314,432	2462	0817
69	216.7699	3739.2807	4761	328,509	3066	1016
70	219.9115	3848.4510	4900	343,000	8.3666	4.1213
71	223.0531	3959.1921	5041	357,911	4261	1408
72	226.1947	4071.5041	5184	373,248	4853	1602
73	229.3363	4185.3868	5329	389,017	5440	1793
74	232.4779	4300.8403	5476	405,224	6023	1983
75	235.6194	4417.8647	5625	421,875	8.6603	4.2172
76	238.7610	4536.4598	5776	438,976	7178	2358
77	241.9026	4656.6257	5929	456,533	7750	2543
78	245.0442	4778.3624	6084	474,552	8318	2727
79	248.1858	4901.6699	6241	493,039	8882	2908
80	251.3274	5026.5482	6400	512,000	8.9443	4.3089
81	254.4690	5152.9974	6561	531,441	9.0000	3267
82	257.6106	5281.0173	6724	551,368	0554	3445
83	260.7522	5410.6079	6889	571,787	1104	3621
84	263.8938	5541.7694	7056	592,704	1652	3795
85	267.0354	5674.5017	7225	614,125	9.2195	4.3968
86	270.1770	5808.8048	7396	636,056	2736	4140
87	273.3186	5944.6787	7569	658,503	3274	4310
88	276.4602	6082.1234	7744	681,472	3808	4480
89	279.6017	6221.1389	7921	704,969	4340	4647
90	282.7433	6361.7251	8100	729,000	9.4868	4.4814
91	285.8849	6503.8822	8281	753,571	5394	4979
92	289.0265	6647.6101	8464	778,688	5917	5144
93	292.1681	6792.9087	8649	804,357	6437	5307
94	295.3097	6939.7782	8836	830,584	6954	5468
95	298.4513	7088.2184	9025	857,375	9.7468	4.5629
96	301.5929	7238.2295	9216	884,736	7980	5789
97	304.7345	7389.8113	9409	912,673	8489	5947
98	307.8761	7542.9640	9604	941,192	8995	6104
99	311.0177	7697.6874	9801	970,299	9.9499	6261
100	314.1593	7853.9816	10000	1,000,000	10.0000	4.6416

If n = the radius of the circle, the circumference $= 2\pi n$.

If n = the radius of the circle, the area $= \pi n^2$.

If n = the circumference of the circle, the radius $= \frac{1}{2\pi} n$.

If n = the circumference of the circle, the area $= \frac{1}{4\pi} n^2$.

n	$2\pi n$	πn^2	$\frac{1}{2\pi} n$	$\frac{1}{4\pi} n^2$	n	$2\pi n$	πn^2	$\frac{1}{2\pi} n$	$\frac{1}{4\pi} n^2$
0	0.00	0.0	0.000	0.00	**50**	314.16	7 854	7.96	198.94
1	6.28	3.1	0.159	0.08	51	320.44	8 171	8.12	206.98
2	12.57	12.6	0.318	0.32	52	326.73	8 495	8.28	215.18
3	18.85	28.3	0.477	0.72	53	333.01	8 825	8.44	223.53
4	25.13	50.3	0.637	1.27	54	339.29	9 161	8.59	232.05
5	31.42	78.5	0.796	1.99	**55**	345.58	9 503	8.75	240.72
6	37.70	113.1	0.955	2.86	56	351.86	9 852	8.91	249.55
7	43.98	153.9	1.114	3.90	57	358.14	10 207	9.07	258.55
8	50.27	201.1	1.273	5.09	58	364.42	10 568	9.23	267.70
9	56.55	254.5	1.432	6.45	59	370.71	10 936	9.39	277.01
10	62.83	314.2	1.592	7.96	**60**	376.99	11 310	9.55	286.48
11	69.12	380.1	1.751	9.63	61	383.27	11 690	9.71	296.11
12	75.40	452.4	1.910	11.46	62	389.56	12 076	9.87	305.90
13	81.68	530.9	2.069	13.45	63	395.84	12 469	10.03	315.84
14	87.96	615.8	2.228	15.60	64	402.12	12 868	10.19	325.95
15	94.25	706.9	2.387	17.90	**65**	408.41	13 273	10.35	336.21
16	100.53	804.2	2.546	20.37	66	414.69	13 685	10.50	346.64
17	106.81	907.9	2.706	23.00	67	420.97	14 103	10.66	357.22
18	113.10	1 017.9	2.865	25.78	68	427.26	14 527	10.82	367.97
19	119.38	1 134.1	3.024	28.73	69	433.54	14 957	10.98	378.87
20	125.66	1 256.6	3.183	31.83	**70**	439.82	15 394	11.14	389.93
21	131.95	1 385.4	3.342	35.09	71	446.11	15 837	11.30	401.15
22	138.23	1 520.5	3.501	38.52	72	452.39	16 286	11.46	412.53
23	144.51	1 661.9	3.661	42.10	73	458.67	16 742	11.62	424.07
24	150.80	1 809.6	3.820	45.84	74	464.96	17 203	11.78	435.77
25	157.08	1 963.5	3.979	49.74	**75**	471.24	17 671	11.94	447.62
26	163.36	2 123.7	4.138	53.79	76	477.52	18 146	12.10	459.64
27	169.65	2 290.2	4.297	58.01	77	483.81	18 627	12.25	471.81
28	175.93	2 463.0	4.456	62.39	78	490.09	19 113	12.41	484.15
29	182.21	2 642.1	4.615	66.92	79	496.37	19 607	12.57	496.64
30	188.50	2 827.4	4.775	71.62	**80**	502.65	20 106	12.73	509.30
31	194.78	3 019.1	4.934	76.47	81	508.94	20 612	12.89	522.11
32	201.06	3 217.0	5.093	81.49	82	515.22	21 124	13.05	535.08
33	207.35	3 421.2	5.252	86.66	83	521.50	21 642	13.21	548.21
34	213.63	3 631.7	5.411	91.99	84	527.79	22 167	13.37	561.50
35	219.91	3 848.5	5.570	97.48	**85**	534.07	22 698	13.53	574.95
36	226.19	4 071.5	5.730	103.13	86	540.35	23 235	13.69	588.55
37	232.48	4 300.8	5.889	108.94	87	546.64	23 779	13.85	602.32
38	238.76	4 536.5	6.048	114.91	88	552.92	24 328	14.01	616.25
39	245.04	4 778.4	6.207	121.04	89	559.20	24 885	14.16	630.33
40	251.33	5 026.5	6.366	127.32	**90**	565.49	25 447	14.32	644.58
41	257.61	5 281.0	6.525	133.77	91	571.77	26 016	14.48	658.98
42	263.89	5 541.8	6.685	140.37	92	578.05	26 590	14.64	673.54
43	270.18	5 808.8	6.844	147.14	93	584.34	27 172	14.80	688.27
44	276.46	6 082.1	7.003	154.06	94	590.62	27 759	14.96	703.15
45	282.74	6 361.7	7.162	161.14	**95**	596.90	28 353	15.12	718.19
46	289.03	6 647.6	7.321	168.39	96	603.19	28 953	15.28	733.39
47	295.31	6 939.8	7.480	175.79	97	609.47	29 559	15.44	748.74
48	301.59	7 238.2	7.639	183.35	98	615.75	30 172	15.60	764.26
49	307.88	7 543.0	7.799	191.07	99	622.04	30 791	15.76	779.94
50	314.16	7 854.0	7.958	198.94	**100**	628.32	31 416	15.92	795.77
n	$2\pi n$	πn^2	$\frac{1}{2\pi} n$	$\frac{1}{4\pi} n^2$	n	$2\pi n$	πn^2	$\frac{1}{2\pi} n$	$\frac{1}{4\pi} n^2$

TABLE III

FIVE-PLACE MANTISSAS

OF THE COMMON LOGARITHMS OF

INTEGERS FROM 1 TO 10,000

On this page the logarithms of integers from 1 to 100 are given in full, with characteristics as well as mantissas. On account of the great differences between the successive mantissas, interpolation cannot safely be employed on this page.

In the remainder of the table only the mantissas are given.

In general, an error of one unit may appear in the last figure of any interpolated value.

Table III is to be used when accuracy is required to more than four figures in the results. In general, the results will be accurate to five figures.

1—100

N	log	N	log	N	log	N	log	N	log
1	0. 00 000	**21**	1. 32 222	**41**	1. 61 278	**61**	1. 78 533	**81**	1. 90 849
2	0. 30 103	22	1. 34 242	42	1. 62 325	62	1. 79 239	82	1. 91 381
3	0. 47 712	23	1. 36 173	43	1. 63 347	63	1. 79 934	83	1. 91 908
4	0. 60 206	24	1. 38 021	44	1. 64 345	64	1. 80 618	84	1. 92 428
5	0. 69 897	25	1. 39 794	45	1. 65 321	65	1. 81 291	85	1. 92 942
6	0. 77 815	**26**	1. 41 497	**46**	1. 66 276	**66**	1. 81 954	**86**	1. 93 450
7	0. 84 510	27	1. 43 136	47	1. 67 210	67	1. 82 607	87	1. 93 952
8	0. 90 309	28	1. 44 716	48	1. 68 124	68	1. 83 251	88	1. 94 448
9	0. 95 424	29	1. 46 240	49	1. 69 020	69	1. 83 885	89	1. 94 939
10	1. 00 000	30	1. 47 712	50	1. 69 897	70	1. 84 510	90	1. 95 424
11	1. 04 139	**31**	1. 49 136	**51**	1. 70 757	**71**	1. 85 126	**91**	1. 95 904
12	1. 07 918	32	1. 50 515	52	1. 71 600	72	1. 85 733	92	1. 96 379
13	1. 11 394	33	1. 51 851	53	1. 72 428	73	1. 86 332	93	1. 96 848
14	1. 14 613	34	1. 53 148	54	1. 73 239	74	1. 86 923	94	1. 97 313
15	1. 17 609	35	1. 54 407	55	1. 74 036	75	1. 87 506	95	1. 97 772
16	1. 20 412	**36**	1. 55 630	**56**	1. 74 819	**76**	1. 88 081	**96**	1. 98 227
17	1. 23 045	37	1. 56 820	57	1. 75 587	77	1. 88 649	97	1. 98 677
18	1. 25 527	38	1. 57 978	58	1. 76 343	78	1. 89 209	98	1. 99 123
19	1. 27 875	39	1. 59 106	59	1. 77 085	79	1. 89 763	99	1. 99 564
20	1. 30 103	40	1. 60 206	60	1. 77 815	80	1. 90 309	100	2. 00 000
N	**log**	**N**	**log**	**N**	**log**	**N**	**log**	**N**	**log**

N	0	1	2	3	4	5	6	7	8	9
100	00 000	00 043	00 087	00 130	00 173	00 217	00 260	00 303	00 346	00 389
101	432	475	518	561	604	647	689	732	775	817
102	860	903	945	988	01 030	01 072	01 115	01 157	01 199	01 242
103	01 284	01 326	01 368	01 410	452	494	536	578	620	662
104	703	745	787	828	870	912	953	995	02 036	02 078
105	02 119	02 160	02 202	02 243	02 284	02 325	02 366	02 407	02 449	02 490
106	531	572	612	653	694	735	776	816	857	898
107	938	979	03 019	03 060	03 100	03 141	03 181	03 222	03 262	03 302
108	03 342	03 383	423	463	503	543	583	623	663	703
109	743	782	822	862	902	941	981	04 021	04 060	04 100
110	04 139	04 179	04 218	04 258	04 297	04 336	04 376	04 415	04 454	04 493
111	532	571	610	650	689	727	766	805	844	883
112	922	961	999	05 038	05 077	05 115	05 154	05 192	05 231	05 269
113	05 308	05 346	05 385	423	461	500	538	576	614	652
114	690	729	767	805	843	881	918	956	994	06 032
115	06 070	06 108	06 145	06 183	06 221	06 258	06 296	06 333	06 371	06 408
116	446	483	521	558	595	633	670	707	744	781
117	819	856	893	930	967	07 004	07 041	07 078	07 115	07 151
118	07 188	07 225	07 262	07 298	07 335	372	408	445	482	518
119	555	591	628	664	700	737	773	809	846	882
120	07 918	07 954	07 990	08 027	08 063	08 099	08 135	08 171	08 207	08 243
121	08 279	08 314	08 350	386	422	458	493	529	565	600
122	636	672	707	743	778	814	849	884	920	955
123	991	09 026	09 061	09 096	09 132	09 167	09 202	09 237	09 272	09 307
124	09 342	377	412	447	482	517	552	587	621	656
125	09 691	09 726	09 760	09 795	09 830	09 864	09 899	09 934	09 968	10 003
126	10 037	10 072	10 106	10 140	10 175	10 209	10 243	10 278	10 312	346
127	380	415	449	483	517	551	585	619	653	687
128	721	755	789	823	857	890	924	958	992	11 025
129	11 059	11 093	11 126	11 160	11 193	11 227	11 261	11 294	11 327	361
130	11 394	11 428	11 461	11 494	11 528	11 561	11 594	11 628	11 661	11 694
131	727	760	793	826	860	893	926	959	992	12 024
132	12 057	12 090	12 123	12 156	12 189	12 222	12 254	12 287	12 320	352
133	385	418	450	483	516	548	581	613	646	678
134	710	743	775	808	840	872	905	937	969	13 001
135	13 033	13 066	13 098	13 130	13 162	13 194	13 226	13 258	13 290	13 322
136	354	386	418	450	481	513	545	577	609	640
137	672	704	735	767	799	830	862	893	925	956
138	988	14 019	14 051	14 082	14 114	14 145	14 176	14 208	14 239	14 270
139	14 301	333	364	395	426	457	489	520	551	582
140	14 613	14 644	14 675	14 706	14 737	14 768	14 799	14 829	14 860	14 891
141	922	953	983	15 014	15 045	15 076	15 106	15 137	15 168	15 198
142	15 229	15 259	15 290	320	351	381	412	442	473	503
143	534	564	594	625	655	685	715	746	776	806
144	836	866	897	927	957	987	16 017	16 047	16 077	16 107
145	16 137	16 167	16 197	16 227	16 256	16 286	16 316	16 346	16 376	16 406
146	435	465	495	524	554	584	613	643	673	702
147	732	761	791	820	850	879	909	938	967	997
148	17 026	17 056	17 085	17 114	17 143	17 173	17 202	17 231	17 260	17 289
149	319	348	377	406	435	464	493	522	551	580
150	17 609	17 638	17 667	17 696	17 725	17 754	17 782	17 811	17 840	17 869
N	0	1	2	3	4	5	6	7	8	9

N	0	1	2	3	4	5	6	7	8	9
150	17 609	17 638	17 667	17 696	17 725	17 754	17 782	17 811	17 840	17 869
151	898	926	955	984	18 013	18 041	18 070	18 099	18 127	18 156
152	18 184	18 213	18 241	18 270	298	327	355	384	412	441
153	469	498	526	554	583	611	639	667	696	724
154	752	780	808	837	865	893	921	949	977	19 005
155	19 033	19 061	19 089	19 117	19 145	19 173	19 201	19 229	19 257	19 285
156	312	340	368	396	424	451	479	507	535	562
157	590	618	645	673	700	728	756	783	811	838
158	866	893	921	948	976	20 003	20 030	20 058	20 085	20 112
159	20 140	20 167	20 194	20 222	20 249	276	303	330	358	385
160	20 412	20 439	20 466	20 493	20 520	20 548	20 575	20 602	20 629	20 656
161	683	710	737	763	790	817	844	871	898	925
162	952	978	21 005	21 032	21 059	21 085	21 112	21 139	21 165	21 192
163	21 219	21 245	272	299	325	352	378	405	431	458
164	484	511	537	564	590	617	643	669	696	722
165	21 748	21 775	21 801	21 827	21 854	21 880	21 906	21 932	21 958	21 985
166	22 011	22 037	22 063	22 089	22 115	22 141	22 167	22 194	22 220	22 246
167	272	298	324	350	376	401	427	453	479	505
168	531	557	583	608	634	660	686	712	737	763
169	789	814	840	866	891	917	943	968	994	23 019
170	23 045	23 070	23 096	23 121	23 147	23 172	23 198	23 223	23 249	23 274
171	300	325	350	376	401	426	452	477	502	528
172	553	578	603	629	654	679	704	729	754	779
173	805	830	855	880	905	930	955	980	24 005	24 030
174	24 055	24 080	24 105	24 130	24 155	24 180	24 204	24 229	254	279
175	24 304	24 329	24 353	24 378	24 403	24 428	24 452	24 477	24 502	24 527
176	551	576	601	625	650	674	699	724	748	773
177	797	822	846	871	895	920	944	969	993	25 018
178	25 042	25 066	25 091	25 115	25 139	25 164	25 188	25 212	25 237	261
179	285	310	334	358	382	406	431	455	479	503
180	25 527	25 551	25 575	25 600	25 624	25 648	25 672	25 696	25 720	25 744
181	768	792	816	840	864	888	912	935	959	983
182	26 007	26 031	26 055	26 079	26 102	26 126	26 150	26 174	26 198	26 221
183	245	269	293	316	340	364	387	411	435	458
184	482	505	529	553	576	600	623	647	670	694
185	26 717	26 741	26 764	26 788	26 811	26 834	26 858	26 881	26 905	26 928
186	951	975	998	27 021	27 045	27 068	27 091	27 114	27 138	27 161
187	27 184	27 207	27 231	254	277	300	323	346	370	393
188	416	439	462	485	508	531	554	577	600	623
189	646	669	692	715	738	761	784	807	830	852
190	27 875	27 898	27 921	27 944	27 967	27 989	28 012	28 035	28 058	28 081
191	28 103	28 126	28 149	28 171	28 194	28 217	240	262	285	307
192	330	353	375	398	421	443	466	488	511	533
193	556	578	601	623	646	668	691	713	735	758
194	780	803	825	847	870	892	914	937	959	981
195	29 003	29 026	29 048	29 070	29 092	29 115	29 137	29 159	29 181	29 203
196	226	248	270	292	314	336	358	380	403	425
197	447	469	491	513	535	557	579	601	623	645
198	667	688	710	732	754	776	798	820	842	863
199	885	907	929	951	973	994	30 016	30 038	30 060	30 081
200	30 103	30 125	30 146	30 168	30 190	30 211	30 233	30 255	30 276	30 298
N	0	1	2	3	4	5	6	7	8	9

N	0	1	2	3	4	5	6	7	8	9
200	30 103	30 125	30 146	30 168	30 190	30 211	30 233	30 255	30 276	30 298
201	320	341	363	384	406	428	449	471	492	514
202	535	557	578	600	621	643	664	685	707	728
203	750	771	792	814	835	856	878	899	920	942
204	963	984	31 006	31 027	31 048	31 069	31 091	31 112	31 133	31 154
205	31 175	31 197	31 218	31 239	31 260	31 281	31 302	31 323	31 345	31 366
206	387	408	429	450	471	492	513	534	555	576
207	597	618	639	660	681	702	723	744	765	785
208	806	827	848	869	890	911	931	952	973	994
209	32 015	32 035	32 056	32 077	32 098	32 118	32 139	32 160	32 181	32 201
210	32 222	32 243	32 263	32 284	32 305	32 325	32 346	32 366	32 387	32 408
211	428	449	469	490	510	531	552	572	593	613
212	634	654	675	695	715	736	756	777	797	818
213	838	858	879	899	919	940	960	980	33 001	33 021
214	33 041	33 062	33 082	33 102	33 122	33 143	33 163	33 183	203	224
215	33 244	33 264	33 284	33 304	33 325	33 345	33 365	33 385	33 405	33 425
216	445	465	486	506	526	546	566	586	606	626
217	646	666	686	706	726	746	766	786	806	826
218	846	866	885	905	925	945	965	985	34 005	34 025
219	34 044	34 064	34 084	34 104	34 124	34 143	34 163	34 183	203	223
220	34 242	34 262	34 282	34 301	34 321	34 341	34 361	34 380	34 400	34 420
221	439	459	479	498	518	537	557	577	596	616
222	635	655	674	694	713	733	753	772	792	811
223	830	850	869	889	908	928	947	967	986	35 005
224	35 025	35 044	35 064	35 083	35 102	35 122	35 141	35 160	35 180	199
225	35 218	35 238	35 257	35 276	35 295	35 315	35 334	35 353	35 372	35 392
226	411	430	449	468	488	507	526	545	564	583
227	603	622	641	660	679	698	717	736	755	774
228	793	813	832	851	870	889	908	927	946	965
229	984	36 003	36 021	36 040	36 059	36 078	36 097	36 116	36 135	36 154
230	36 173	36 192	36 211	36 229	36 248	36 267	36 286	36 305	36 324	36 342
231	361	380	399	418	436	455	474	493	511	530
232	549	568	586	605	624	642	661	680	698	717
233	736	754	773	791	810	829	847	866	884	903
234	922	940	959	977	996	37 014	37 033	37 051	37 070	37 088
235	37 107	37 125	37 144	37 162	37 181	37 199	37 218	37 236	37 254	37 273
236	291	310	328	346	365	383	401	420	438	457
237	475	493	511	530	548	566	585	603	621	639
238	658	676	694	712	731	749	767	785	803	822
239	840	858	876	894	912	931	949	967	985	38 003
240	38 021	38 039	38 057	38 075	38 093	38 112	38 130	38 148	38 166	38 184
241	202	220	238	256	274	292	310	328	346	364
242	382	399	417	435	453	471	489	507	525	543
243	561	578	596	614	632	650	668	686	703	721
244	739	757	775	792	810	828	846	863	881	899
245	38 917	38 934	38 952	38 970	38 987	39 005	39 023	39 041	39 058	39 076
246	39 094	39 111	39 129	39 146	39 164	182	199	217	235	252
247	270	287	305	322	340	358	375	393	410	428
248	445	463	480	498	515	533	550	568	585	602
249	620	637	655	672	690	707	724	742	759	777
250	39 794	39 811	39 829	39 846	39 863	39 881	39 898	39 915	39 933	39 950
N	**0**	**1**	**2**	**3**	**4**	**5**	**6**	**7**	**8**	**9**

N	0	1	2	3	4	5	6	7	8	9
250	39 794	39 811	39 829	39 846	39 863	39 881	39 898	39 915	39 933	39 950
251	967	985	40 002	40 019	40 037	40 054	40 071	40 088	40 106	40 123
252	40 140	40 157	175	192	209	226	243	261	278	295
253	312	329	346	364	381	398	415	432	449	466
254	483	500	518	535	552	569	586	603	620	637
255	40 654	40 671	40 688	40 705	40 722	40 739	40 756	40 773	40 790	40 807
256	824	841	858	875	892	909	926	943	960	976
257	993	41 010	41 027	41 044	41 061	41 078	41 095	41 111	41 128	41 145
258	41 162	179	196	212	229	246	263	280	296	313
259	330	347	363	380	397	414	430	447	464	481
260	41 497	41 514	41 531	41 547	41 564	41 581	41 597	41 614	41 631	41 647
261	664	681	697	714	731	747	764	780	797	814
262	830	847	863	880	896	913	929	946	963	979
263	996	42 012	42 029	42 045	42 062	42 078	42 095	42 111	42 127	42 144
264	42 160	177	193	210	226	243	259	275	292	308
265	42 325	42 341	42 357	42 374	42 390	42 406	42 423	42 439	42 455	42 472
266	488	504	521	537	553	570	586	602	619	635
267	651	667	684	700	716	732	749	765	781	797
268	813	830	846	862	878	894	911	927	943	959
269	975	991	43 008	43 024	43 040	43 056	43 072	43 088	43 104	43 120
270	43 136	43 152	43 169	43 185	43 201	43 217	43 233	43 249	43 265	43 281
271	297	313	329	345	361	377	393	409	425	441
272	457	473	489	505	521	537	553	569	584	600
273	616	632	648	664	680	696	712	727	743	759
274	775	791	807	823	838	854	870	886	902	917
275	43 933	43 949	43 965	43 981	43 996	44 012	44 028	44 044	44 059	44 075
276	44 091	44 107	44 122	44 138	44 154	170	185	201	217	232
277	248	264	279	295	311	326	342	358	373	389
278	404	420	436	451	467	483	498	514	529	545
279	560	576	592	607	623	638	654	669	685	700
280	44 716	44 731	44 747	44 762	44 778	44 793	44 809	44 824	44 840	44 855
281	871	886	902	917	932	948	963	979	994	45 010
282	45 025	45 040	45 056	45 071	45 086	45 102	45 117	45 133	45 148	163
283	179	194	209	225	240	255	271	286	301	317
284	332	347	362	378	393	408	423	439	454	469
285	45 484	45 500	45 515	45 530	45 545	45 561	45 576	45 591	45 606	45 621
286	637	652	667	682	697	712	728	743	758	773
287	788	803	818	834	849	864	879	894	909	924
288	939	954	969	984	46 000	46 015	46 030	46 045	46 060	46 075
289	46 090	46 105	46 120	46 135	150	165	180	195	210	225
290	46 240	46 255	46 270	46 285	46 300	46 315	46 330	46 345	46 359	46 374
291	389	404	419	434	449	464	479	494	509	523
292	538	553	568	583	598	613	627	642	657	672
293	687	702	716	731	746	761	776	790	805	820
294	835	850	864	879	894	909	923	938	953	967
295	46 982	46 997	47 012	47 026	47 041	47 056	47 070	47 085	47 100	47 114
296	47 129	47 144	159	173	188	202	217	232	246	261
297	276	290	305	319	334	349	363	378	392	407
298	422	436	451	465	480	494	509	524	538	553
299	567	582	596	611	625	640	654	669	683	698
300	47 712	47 727	47 741	47 756	47 770	47 784	47 799	47 813	47 828	47 842
N	0	1	2	3	4	5	6	7	8	9

N	0	1	2	3	4	5	6	7	8	9
300	47 712	47 727	47 741	47 756	47 770	47 784	47 799	47 813	47 828	47 842
301	857	871	885	900	914	929	943	958	972	986
302	48 001	48 015	48 029	48 044	48 058	48 073	48 087	48 101	48 116	48 130
303	144	159	173	187	202	216	230	244	259	273
304	287	302	316	330	344	359	373	387	401	416
305	48 430	48 444	48 458	48 473	48 487	48 501	48 515	48 530	48 544	48 558
306	572	586	601	615	629	643	657	671	686	700
307	714	728	742	756	770	785	799	813	827	841
308	855	869	883	897	911	926	940	954	968	982
309	996	49 010	49 024	49 038	49 052	49 066	49 080	49 094	49 108	49 122
310	49 136	49 150	49 164	49 178	49 192	49 206	49 220	49 234	49 248	49 262
311	276	290	304	318	332	346	360	374	388	402
312	415	429	443	457	471	485	499	513	527	541
313	554	568	582	596	610	624	638	651	665	679
314	693	707	721	734	748	762	776	790	803	817
315	49 831	49 845	49 859	49 872	49 886	49 900	49 914	49 927	49 941	49 955
316	969	982	996	50 010	50 024	50 037	50 051	50 065	50 079	50 092
317	50 106	50 120	50 133	147	161	174	188	202	215	229
318	243	256	270	284	297	311	325	338	352	365
319	379	393	406	420	433	447	461	474	488	501
320	50 515	50 529	50 542	50 556	50 569	50 583	50 596	50 610	50 623	50 637
321	651	664	678	691	705	718	732	745	759	772
322	786	799	813	826	840	853	866	880	893	907
323	920	934	947	961	974	987	51 001	51 014	51 028	51 041
324	51 055	51 068	51 081	51 095	51 108	51 121	135	148	162	175
325	51 188	51 202	51 215	51 228	51 242	51 255	51 268	51 282	51 295	51 308
326	322	335	348	362	375	388	402	415	428	441
327	455	468	481	495	508	521	534	548	561	574
328	587	601	614	627	640	654	667	680	693	706
329	720	733	746	759	772	786	799	812	825	838
330	51 851	51 865	51 878	51 891	51 904	51 917	51 930	51 943	51 957	51 970
331	983	996	52 009	52 022	52 035	52 048	52 061	52 075	52 088	52 101
332	52 114	52 127	140	153	166	179	192	205	218	231
333	244	257	270	284	297	310	323	336	349	362
334	375	388	401	414	427	440	453	466	479	492
335	52 504	52 517	52 530	52 543	52 556	52 569	52 582	52 595	52 608	52 621
336	634	647	660	673	686	699	711	724	737	750
337	763	776	789	802	815	827	840	853	866	879
338	892	905	917	930	943	956	969	982	994	53 007
339	53 020	53 033	53 046	53 058	53 071	53 084	53 097	53 110	53 122	135
340	53 148	53 161	53 173	53 186	53 199	53 212	53 224	53 237	53 250	53 263
341	275	288	301	314	326	339	352	364	377	390
342	403	415	428	441	453	466	479	491	504	517
343	529	542	555	567	580	593	605	618	631	643
344	656	668	681	694	706	719	732	744	757	769
345	53 782	53 794	53 807	53 820	53 832	53 845	53 857	53 870	53 882	53 895
346	908	920	933	945	958	970	983	995	54 008	54 020
347	54 033	54 045	54 058	54 070	54 083	54 095	54 108	54 120	133	145
348	158	170	183	195	208	220	233	245	258	270
349	283	295	307	320	332	345	357	370	382	394
350	54 407	54 419	54 432	54 444	54 456	54 469	54 481	54 494	54 506	54 518
N	0	1	2	3	4	5	6	7	8	9

N	0	1	2	3	4	5	6	7	8	9
350	54 407	54 419	54 432	54 444	54 456	54 469	54 481	54 494	54 506	54 518
351	531	543	555	568	580	593	605	617	630	642
352	654	667	679	691	704	716	728	741	753	765
353	777	790	802	814	827	839	851	864	876	888
354	900	913	925	937	949	962	974	986	998	55 011
355	55 023	55 035	55 047	55 060	55 072	55 084	55 096	55 108	55 121	55 133
356	145	157	169	182	194	206	218	230	242	255
357	267	279	291	303	315	328	340	352	364	376
358	388	400	413	425	437	449	461	473	485	497
359	509	522	534	546	558	570	582	594	606	618
360	55 630	55 642	55 654	55 666	55 678	55 691	55 703	55 715	55 727	55 739
361	751	763	775	787	799	811	823	835	847	859
362	871	883	895	907	919	931	943	955	967	979
363	991	56 003	56 015	56 027	56 038	56 050	56 062	56 074	56 086	56 098
364	56 110	122	134	146	158	170	182	194	205	217
365	56 229	56 241	56 253	56 265	56 277	56 289	56 301	56 312	56 324	56 336
366	348	360	372	384	396	407	419	431	443	455
367	467	478	490	502	514	526	538	549	561	573
368	585	597	608	620	632	644	656	667	679	691
369	703	714	726	738	750	761	773	785	797	808
370	56 820	56 832	56 844	56 855	56 867	56 879	56 891	56 902	56 914	56 926
371	937	949	961	972	984	996	57 008	57 019	57 031	57 043
372	57 054	57 066	57 078	57 089	57 101	57 113	124	136	148	159
373	171	183	194	206	217	229	241	252	264	276
374	287	299	310	322	334	345	357	368	380	392
375	57 403	57 415	57 426	57 438	57 449	57 461	57 473	57 484	57 496	57 507
376	519	530	542	553	565	576	588	600	611	623
377	634	646	657	669	680	692	703	715	726	738
378	749	761	772	784	795	807	818	830	841	852
379	864	875	887	898	910	921	933	944	955	967
380	57 978	57 990	58 001	58 013	58 024	58 035	58 047	58 058	58 070	58 081
381	58 092	58 104	115	127	138	149	161	172	184	195
382	206	218	229	240	252	263	274	286	297	309
383	320	331	343	354	365	377	388	399	410	422
384	433	444	456	467	478	490	501	512	524	535
385	58 546	58 557	58 569	58 580	58 591	58 602	58 614	58 625	58 636	58 647
386	659	670	681	692	704	715	726	737	749	760
387	771	782	794	805	816	827	838	850	861	872
388	883	894	906	917	928	939	950	961	973	984
389	995	59 006	59 017	59 028	59 040	59 051	59 062	59 073	59 084	59 095
390	59 106	59 118	59 129	59 140	59 151	59 162	59 173	59 184	59 195	59 207
391	218	229	240	251	262	273	284	295	306	318
392	329	340	351	362	373	384	395	406	417	428
393	439	450	461	472	483	494	506	517	528	539
394	550	561	572	583	594	605	616	627	638	649
395	59 660	59 671	59 682	59 693	59 704	59 715	59 726	59 737	59 748	59 759
396	770	780	791	802	813	824	835	846	857	868
397	879	890	901	912	923	934	945	956	966	977
398	988	999	60 010	60 021	60 032	60 043	60 054	60 065	60 076	60 086
399	60 097	60 108	119	130	141	152	163	173	184	195
400	60 206	60 217	60 228	60 239	60 249	60 260	60 271	60 282	60 293	60 304
N	**0**	**1**	**2**	**3**	**4**	**5**	**6**	**7**	**8**	**9**

N	0	1	2	3	4	5	6	7	8	9
400	60 206	60 217	60 228	60 239	60 249	60 260	60 271	60 282	60 293	60 304
401	314	325	336	347	358	369	379	390	401	412
402	423	433	444	455	466	477	487	498	509	520
403	531	541	552	563	574	584	595	606	617	627
404	638	649	660	670	681	692	703	713	724	735
405	60 746	60 756	60 767	60 778	60 788	60 799	60 810	60 821	60 831	60 842
406	853	863	874	885	895	906	917	927	938	949
407	959	970	981	991	61 002	61 013	61 023	61 034	61 045	61 055
408	61 066	61 077	61 087	61 098	109	119	130	140	151	162
409	172	183	194	204	215	225	236	247	257	268
410	61 278	61 289	61 300	61 310	61 321	61 331	61 342	61 352	61 363	61 374
411	384	395	405	416	426	437	448	458	469	479
412	490	500	511	521	532	542	553	563	574	584
413	595	606	616	627	637	648	658	669	679	690
414	700	711	721	731	742	752	763	773	784	794
415	61 805	61 815	61 826	61 836	61 847	61 857	61 868	61 878	61 888	61 899
416	909	920	930	941	951	962	972	982	993	62 003
417	62 014	62 024	62 034	62 045	62 055	62 066	62 076	62 086	62 097	107
418	118	128	138	149	159	170	180	190	201	211
419	221	232	242	252	263	273	284	294	304	315
420	62 325	62 335	62 346	62 356	62 366	62 377	62 387	62 397	62 408	62 418
421	428	439	449	459	469	480	490	500	511	521
422	531	542	552	562	572	583	593	603	613	624
423	634	644	655	665	675	685	696	706	716	726
424	737	747	757	767	778	788	798	808	818	829
425	62 839	62 849	62 859	62 870	62 880	62 890	62 900	62 910	62 921	62 931
426	941	951	961	972	982	992	63 002	63 012	63 022	63 033
427	63 043	63 053	63 063	63 073	63 083	63 094	104	114	124	134
428	144	155	165	175	185	195	205	215	225	236
429	246	256	266	276	286	296	306	317	327	337
430	63 347	63 357	63 367	63 377	63 387	63 397	63 407	63 417	63 428	63 438
431	448	458	468	478	488	498	508	518	528	538
432	548	558	568	579	589	599	609	619	629	639
433	649	659	669	679	689	699	709	719	729	739
434	749	759	769	779	789	799	809	819	829	839
435	63 849	63 859	63 869	63 879	63 889	63 899	63 909	63 919	63 929	63 939
436	949	959	969	979	988	998	64 008	64 018	64 028	64 038
437	64 048	64 058	64 068	64 078	64 088	64 098	108	118	128	137
438	147	157	167	177	187	197	207	217	227	237
439	246	256	266	276	286	296	306	316	326	335
440	64 345	64 355	64 365	64 375	64 385	64 395	64 404	64 414	64 424	64 434
441	444	454	464	473	483	493	503	513	523	532
442	542	552	562	572	582	591	601	611	621	631
443	640	650	660	670	680	689	699	709	719	729
444	738	748	758	768	777	787	797	807	816	826
445	64 836	64 846	64 856	64 865	64 875	64 885	64 895	64 904	64 914	64 924
446	933	943	953	963	972	982	992	65 002	65 011	65 021
447	65 031	65 040	65 050	65 060	65 070	65 079	65 089	099	108	118
448	128	137	147	157	167	176	186	196	205	215
449	225	234	244	254	263	273	283	292	302	312
450	65 321	65 331	65 341	65 350	65 360	65 369	65 379	65 389	65 398	65 408
N	0	1	2	3	4	5	6	7	8	9

N	0	1	2	3	4	5	6	7	8	9
450	65 321	65 331	65 341	65 350	65 360	65 369	65 379	65 389	65 398	65 408
451	418	427	437	447	456	466	475	485	495	504
452	514	523	533	543	552	562	571	581	591	600
453	610	619	629	639	648	658	667	677	686	696
454	706	715	725	734	744	753	763	772	782	792
455	65 801	65 811	65 820	65 830	65 839	65 849	65 858	65 868	65 877	65 887
456	896	906	916	25	935	944	954	963	973	982
457	992	66 001	66 011	66 020	66 030	66 039	66 049	66 058	66 068	66 077
458	66 087	096	106	115	124	134	143	153	162	172
459	181	191	200	210	219	229	238	247	257	266
460	66 276	66 285	66 295	66 304	66 314	66 323	66 332	66 342	66 351	66 361
461	370	380	389	398	408	417	427	436	445	455
462	464	474	483	492	502	511	521	530	539	549
463	558	567	577	586	596	605	614	624	633	642
464	652	661	671	680	689	699	708	717	727	736
465	66 745	66 755	66 764	66 773	66 783	66 792	66 801	66 811	66 820	66 829
466	839	848	857	867	876	885	894	904	913	922
467	932	941	950	960	969	978	987	997	67 006	67 015
468	67 025	67 034	67 043	67 052	67 062	67 071	67 080	67 089	099	108
469	117	127	136	145	154	164	173	182	191	201
470	67 210	67 219	67 228	67 237	67 247	67 256	67 265	67 274	67 284	67 293
471	302	311	321	330	339	348	357	367	376	385
472	394	403	413	422	431	440	449	459	468	477
473	486	495	504	514	523	532	541	550	560	569
474	578	587	596	605	614	624	633	642	651	660
475	67 669	67 679	67 688	67 697	67 706	67 715	67 724	67 733	67 742	67 752
476	761	770	779	788	797	806	815	825	834	843
477	852	861	870	879	888	897	906	916	925	934
478	943	952	961	970	979	988	997	68 006	68 015	68 024
479	68 034	68 043	68 052	68 061	68 070	68 079	68 088	097	106	115
480	68 124	68 133	68 142	68 151	68 160	68 169	68 178	68 187	68 196	68 205
481	215	224	233	242	251	260	269	278	287	296
482	305	314	323	332	341	350	359	368	377	386
483	395	404	413	422	431	440	449	458	467	476
484	485	494	502	511	520	529	538	547	556	565
485	68 574	68 583	68 592	68 601	68 610	68 619	68 628	68 637	68 646	68 655
486	664	673	681	690	699	708	717	726	735	744
487	753	762	771	780	789	797	806	815	824	833
488	842	851	860	869	878	886	895	904	913	922
489	931	940	949	958	966	975	984	993	69 002	69 011
490	69 020	69 028	69 037	69 046	69 055	69 064	69 073	69 082	69 090	69 099
491	108	117	126	135	144	152	161	170	179	188
492	197	205	214	223	232	241	249	258	267	276
493	285	294	302	311	320	329	338	346	355	364
494	373	381	390	399	408	417	425	434	443	452
495	69 461	69 469	69 478	69 487	69 496	69 504	69 513	69 522	69 531	69 539
496	548	557	566	574	583	592	601	609	618	627
497	636	644	653	662	671	679	688	697	705	714
498	723	732	740	749	758	767	775	784	793	801
499	810	819	827	836	845	854	862	871	880	888
500	69 897	69 906	69 914	69 923	69 932	69 940	69 949	69 958	69 966	69 975
N	0	1	2	3	4	5	6	7	8	9

N	0	1	2	3	4	5	6	7	8	9
500	69 897	69 906	69 914	69 923	69 932	69 940	69 949	69 958	69 966	69 975
501	984	992	70 001	70 010	70 018	70 027	70 036	70 044	70 053	70 062
502	70 070	70 079	088	096	105	114	122	131	140	148
503	157	165	174	183	191	200	209	217	226	234
504	243	252	260	269	278	286	295	303	312	321
505	70 329	70 338	70 346	70 355	70 364	70 372	70 381	70 389	70 398	70 406
506	415	424	432	441	449	458	467	475	484	492
507	501	509	518	526	535	544	552	561	569	578
508	586	595	603	612	621	629	638	646	655	663
509	672	680	689	697	706	714	723	731	740	749
510	70 757	70 766	70 774	70 783	70 791	70 800	70 808	70 817	70 825	70 834
511	842	851	859	868	876	885	893	902	910	919
512	927	935	944	952	961	969	978	986	995	71 003
513	71 012	71 020	71 029	71 037	71 046	71 054	71 063	71 071	71 079	088
514	096	105	113	122	130	139	147	155	164	172
515	71 181	71 189	71 198	71 206	71 214	71 223	71 231	71 240	71 248	71 257
516	265	273	282	290	299	307	315	324	332	341
517	349	357	366	374	383	391	399	408	416	425
518	433	441	450	458	466	475	483	492	500	508
519	517	525	533	542	550	559	567	575	584	592
520	71 600	71 609	71 617	71 625	71 634	71 642	71 650	71 659	71 667	71 675
521	684	692	700	709	717	725	734	742	750	759
522	767	775	784	792	800	809	817	825	834	842
523	850	858	867	875	883	892	900	908	917	925
524	933	941	950	958	966	975	983	991	999	72 008
525	72 016	72 024	72 032	72 041	72 049	72 057	72 066	72 074	72 082	72 090
526	099	107	115	123	132	140	148	156	165	173
527	181	189	198	206	214	222	230	239	247	255
528	263	272	280	288	296	304	313	321	329	337
529	346	354	362	370	378	387	395	403	411	419
530	72 428	72 436	72 444	72 452	72 460	72 469	72 477	72 485	72 493	72 501
531	509	518	526	534	542	550	558	567	575	583
532	591	599	607	616	624	632	640	648	656	665
533	673	681	689	697	705	713	722	730	738	746
534	754	762	770	779	787	795	803	811	819	827
535	72 835	72 843	72 852	72 860	72 868	72 876	72 884	72 892	72 900	72 908
536	916	925	933	941	949	957	965	973	981	989
537	997	73 006	73 014	73 022	73 030	73 038	73 046	73 054	73 062	73 070
538	73 078	086	094	102	111	119	127	135	143	151
539	159	167	175	183	191	199	207	215	223	231
540	73 239	73 247	73 255	73 263	73 272	73 280	73 288	73 296	73 304	73 312
541	320	328	336	344	352	360	368	376	384	392
542	400	408	416	424	432	440	448	456	464	472
543	480	488	496	504	512	520	528	536	544	552
544	560	568	576	584	592	600	608	616	624	632
545	73 640	73 648	73 656	73 664	73 672	73 679	73 687	73 695	73 703	73 711
546	719	727	735	743	751	759	767	775	783	791
547	799	807	815	823	830	838	846	854	862	870
548	878	886	894	902	910	918	926	933	941	949
549	957	965	973	981	989	997	74 005	74 013	74 020	74 028
550	74 036	74 044	74 052	74 060	74 068	74 076	74 084	74 092	74 099	74 107
N	0	1	2	3	4	5	6	7	8	9

N	0	1	2	3	4	5	6	7	8	9
550	74 036	74 044	74 052	74 060	74 068	74 076	74 084	74 092	74 099	74 107
551	115	123	131	139	147	155	162	170	178	186
552	194	202	210	218	225	233	241	249	257	265
553	273	280	288	296	304	312	320	327	335	343
554	351	359	367	374	382	390	398	406	414	421
555	74 429	74 437	74 445	74 453	74 461	74 468	74 476	74 484	74 492	74 500
556	507	515	523	531	539	547	554	562	570	578
557	586	593	601	609	617	624	632	640	648	656
558	663	671	679	687	695	702	710	718	726	733
559	741	749	757	764	772	780	788	796	803	811
560	74 819	74 827	74 834	74 842	74 850	74 858	74 865	74 873	74 881	74 889
561	896	904	912	920	927	935	943	950	958	966
562	974	981	989	997	75 005	75 012	75 020	75 028	75 035	75 043
563	75 051	75 059	75 066	75 074	082	089	097	105	113	120
564	128	136	143	151	159	166	174	182	189	197
565	75 205	75 213	75 220	75 228	75 236	75 243	75 251	75 259	75 266	75 274
566	282	289	297	305	312	320	328	335	343	351
567	358	366	374	381	389	397	404	412	420	427
568	435	442	450	458	465	473	481	488	496	504
569	511	519	526	534	542	549	557	565	572	580
570	75 587	75 595	75 603	75 610	75 618	75 626	75 633	75 641	75 648	75 656
571	664	671	679	686	694	702	709	717	724	732
572	740	747	755	762	770	778	785	793	800	808
573	815	823	831	838	846	853	861	868	876	884
574	891	899	906	914	921	929	937	944	952	959
575	75 967	75 974	75 982	75 989	75 997	76 005	76 012	76 020	76 027	76 035
576	76 042	76 050	76 057	76 065	76 072	080	087	095	103	110
577	118	125	133	140	148	155	163	170	178	185
578	193	200	208	215	223	230	238	245	253	260
579	268	275	283	290	298	305	313	320	328	335
580	76 343	76 350	76 358	76 365	76 373	76 380	76 388	76 395	76 403	76 410
581	418	425	433	440	448	455	462	470	477	485
582	492	500	507	515	522	530	537	545	552	559
583	567	574	582	589	597	604	612	619	626	634
584	641	649	656	664	671	678	686	693	701	708
585	76 716	76 723	76 730	76 738	76 745	76 753	76 760	76 768	76 775	76 782
586	790	797	805	812	819	827	834	842	849	856
587	864	871	879	886	893	901	908	916	923	930
588	938	945	953	960	967	975	982	989	997	77 004
589	77 012	77 019	77 026	77 034	77 041	77 048	77 056	77 063	77 070	078
590	77 085	77 093	77 100	77 107	77 115	77 122	77 129	77 137	77 144	77 151
591	159	166	173	181	188	195	203	210	217	225
592	232	240	247	254	262	269	276	283	291	298
593	305	313	320	327	335	342	349	357	364	371
594	379	386	393	401	408	415	422	430	437	444
595	77 452	77 459	77 466	77 474	77 481	77 488	77 495	77 503	77 510	77 517
596	525	532	539	546	554	561	568	576	583	590
597	597	605	612	619	627	634	641	648	656	663
598	670	677	685	692	699	706	714	721	728	735
599	743	750	757	764	772	779	786	793	801	808
600	77 815	77 822	77 830	77 837	77 844	77 851	77 859	77 866	77 873	77 880
N	0	1	2	3	4	5	6	7	8	9

N	0	1	2	3	4	5	6	7	8	9
600	77 815	77 822	77 830	77 837	77 844	77 851	77 859	77 866	77 873	77 880
601	887	895	902	909	916	924	931	938	945	952
602	960	967	974	981	988	996	78 003	78 010	78 017	78 025
603	78 032	78 039	78 046	78 053	78 061	78 068	075	082	089	097
604	104	111	118	125	132	140	147	154	161	168
605	78 176	78 183	78 190	78 197	78 204	78 211	78 219	78 226	78 233	78 240
606	247	254	262	269	276	283	290	297	305	312
607	319	326	333	340	347	355	362	369	376	383
608	390	398	405	412	419	426	433	440	447	455
609	462	469	476	483	490	497	504	512	519	526
610	78 533	78 540	78 547	78 554	78 561	78 569	78 576	78 583	78 590	78 597
611	604	611	618	625	633	640	647	654	661	668
612	675	682	689	696	704	711	718	725	732	739
613	746	753	760	767	774	781	789	796	803	810
614	817	824	831	838	845	852	859	866	873	880
615	78 888	78 895	78 902	78 909	78 916	78 923	78 930	78 937	78 944	78 951
616	958	965	972	979	986	993	79 000	79 007	79 014	79 021
617	79 029	79 036	79 043	79 050	79 057	79 064	071	078	085	092
618	099	106	113	120	127	134	141	148	155	162
619	169	176	183	190	197	204	211	218	225	232
620	79 239	79 246	79 253	79 260	79 267	79 274	79 281	79 288	79 295	79 302
621	309	316	323	330	337	344	351	358	365	372
622	379	386	393	400	407	414	421	428	435	442
623	449	456	463	470	477	484	491	498	505	511
624	518	525	532	539	546	553	560	567	574	581
625	79 588	79 595	79 602	79 609	79 616	79 623	79 630	79 637	79 644	79 650
626	657	664	671	678	685	692	699	706	713	720
627	727	734	741	748	754	761	768	775	782	789
628	796	803	810	817	824	831	837	844	851	858
629	865	872	879	886	893	900	906	913	920	927
630	79 934	79 941	79 948	79 955	79 962	79 969	79 975	79 982	79 989	79 996
631	80 003	80 010	80 017	80 024	80 030	80 037	80 044	80 051	80 058	80 065
632	072	079	085	092	099	106	113	120	127	134
633	140	147	154	161	168	175	182	188	195	202
634	209	216	223	229	236	243	250	257	264	271
635	80 277	80 284	80 291	80 298	80 305	80 312	80 318	80 325	80 332	80 339
636	346	353	359	366	373	380	387	393	400	407
637	414	421	428	434	441	448	455	462	468	475
638	482	489	496	502	509	516	523	530	536	543
639	550	557	564	570	577	584	591	598	604	611
640	80 618	80 625	80 632	80 638	80 645	80 652	80 659	80 665	80 672	80 679
641	686	693	699	706	713	720	726	733	740	747
642	754	760	767	774	781	787	794	801	808	814
643	821	828	835	841	848	855	862	868	875	882
644	889	895	902	909	916	922	929	936	943	949
645	80 956	80 963	80 969	80 976	80 983	80 990	80 996	81 003	81 010	81 017
646	81 023	81 030	81 037	81 043	81 050	81 057	81 064	070	077	084
647	090	097	104	111	117	124	131	137	144	151
648	158	164	171	178	184	191	198	204	211	218
649	224	231	238	245	251	258	265	271	278	285
650	81 291	81 298	81 305	81 311	81 318	81 325	81 331	81 338	81 345	81 351
N	0	1	2	3	4	5	6	7	8	9

N	0	1	2	3	4	5	6	7	8	9
650	81 291	81 298	81 305	81 311	81 318	81 325	81 331	81 338	81 345	81 351
651	358	365	371	378	385	391	398	405	411	418
652	425	431	438	445	451	458	465	471	478	485
653	491	498	505	511	518	525	531	538	544	551
654	558	564	571	578	584	591	598	604	611	617
655	81 624	81 631	81 637	81 644	81 651	81 657	81 664	81 671	81 677	81 684
656	690	697	704	710	717	723	730	737	743	750
657	757	763	770	776	783	790	796	803	809	816
658	823	829	836	842	849	856	862	869	875	882
659	889	895	902	908	915	921	928	935	941	948
660	81 954	81 961	81 968	81 974	81 981	81 987	81 994	82 000	82 007	82 014
661	82 020	82 027	82 033	82 040	82 046	82 053	82 060	066	073	079
662	086	092	099	105	112	119	125	132	138	145
663	151	158	164	171	178	184	191	197	204	210
664	217	223	230	236	243	249	256	263	269	276
665	82 282	82 289	82 295	82 302	82 308	82 315	82 321	82 328	82 334	82 341
666	347	354	360	367	373	380	387	393	400	406
667	413	419	426	432	439	445	452	458	465	471
668	478	484	491	497	504	510	517	523	530	536
669	543	549	556	562	569	575	582	588	595	601
670	82 607	82 614	82 620	82 627	82 633	82 640	82 646	82 653	82 659	82 666
671	672	679	685	692	698	705	711	718	724	730
672	737	743	750	756	763	769	776	782	789	795
673	802	808	814	821	827	834	840	847	853	860
674	866	872	879	885	892	898	905	911	918	924
675	82 930	82 937	82 943	82 950	82 956	82 963	82 969	82 975	82 982	82 988
676	995	83 001	83 008	83 014	83 020	83 027	83 033	83 040	83 046	83 052
677	83 059	065	072	078	085	091	097	104	110	117
678	123	129	136	142	149	155	161	168	174	181
679	187	193	200	206	213	219	225	232	238	245
680	83 251	83 257	83 264	83 270	83 276	83 283	83 289	83 296	83 302	83 308
681	315	321	327	334	340	347	353	359	366	372
682	378	385	391	398	404	410	417	423	429	436
683	442	448	455	461	467	474	480	487	493	499
684	506	512	518	525	531	537	544	550	556	563
685	83 569	83 575	83 582	83 588	83 594	83 601	83 607	83 613	83 620	83 626
686	632	639	645	651	658	664	670	677	683	689
687	696	702	708	715	721	727	734	740	746	753
688	759	765	771	778	784	790	797	803	809	816
689	822	828	835	841	847	853	860	866	872	879
690	83 885	83 891	83 897	83 904	83 910	83 916	83 923	83 929	83 935	83 942
691	948	954	960	967	973	979	985	992	998	84 004
692	84 011	84 017	84 023	84 029	84 036	84 042	84 048	84 055	84 061	067
693	073	080	086	092	098	105	111	117	123	130
694	136	142	148	155	161	167	173	180	186	192
695	84 198	84 205	84 211	84 217	84 223	84 230	84 236	84 242	84 248	84 255
696	261	267	273	280	286	292	298	305	311	317
697	323	330	336	342	348	354	361	367	373	379
698	386	392	398	404	410	417	423	429	435	442
699	448	454	460	466	473	479	485	491	497	504
700	84 510	84 516	84 522	84 528	84 535	84 541	84 547	84 553	84 559	84 566
N	0	1	2	3	4	5	6	7	8	9

N	0	1	2	3	4	5	6	7	8	9
700	84 510	84 516	84 522	84 528	84 535	84 541	84 547	84 553	84 559	84 566
701	572	578	584	590	597	603	609	615	621	628
702	634	640	646	652	658	665	671	677	683	689
703	696	702	708	714	720	726	733	739	745	751
704	757	763	770	776	782	788	794	800	807	813
705	84 819	84 825	84 831	84 837	84 844	84 850	84 856	84 862	84 868	84 874
706	880	887	893	899	905	911	917	924	930	936
707	942	948	954	960	967	973	979	985	991	997
708	85 003	85 009	85 016	85 022	85 028	85 034	85 040	85 046	85 052	85 058
709	065	071	077	083	089	095	101	107	114	120
710	85 126	85 132	85 138	85 144	85 150	85 156	85 163	85 169	85 175	85 181
711	187	193	199	205	211	217	224	230	236	242
712	248	254	260	266	272	278	285	291	297	303
713	309	315	321	327	333	339	345	352	358	364
714	370	376	382	388	394	400	406	412	418	425
715	85 431	85 437	85 443	85 449	85 455	85 461	85 467	85 473	85 479	85 485
716	491	497	503	509	516	522	528	534	540	546
717	552	558	564	570	576	582	588	594	600	606
718	612	618	625	631	637	643	649	655	661	667
719	673	679	685	691	697	703	709	715	721	727
720	85 733	85 739	85 745	85 751	85 757	85 763	85 769	85 775	85 781	85 788
721	794	800	806	812	818	824	830	836	842	848
722	854	860	866	872	878	884	890	896	902	908
723	914	920	926	932	938	944	950	956	962	968
724	974	980	986	992	998	86 004	86 010	86 016	86 022	86 028
725	86 034	86 040	86 046	86 052	86 058	86 064	86 070	86 076	86 082	86 088
726	094	100	106	112	118	124	130	136	141	147
727	153	159	165	171	177	183	189	195	201	207
728	213	219	225	231	237	243	249	255	261	267
729	273	279	285	291	297	303	308	314	320	326
730	86 332	86 338	86 344	86 350	86 356	86 362	86 368	86 374	86 380	86 386
731	392	398	404	410	415	421	427	433	439	445
732	451	457	463	469	475	481	487	493	499	504
733	510	516	522	528	534	540	546	552	558	564
734	570	576	581	587	593	599	605	611	617	623
735	86 629	86 635	86 641	86 646	86 652	86 658	86 664	86 670	86 676	86 682
736	688	694	700	705	711	717	723	729	735	741
737	747	753	759	764	770	776	782	788	794	800
738	806	812	817	823	829	835	841	847	853	859
739	864	870	876	882	888	894	900	906	911	917
740	86 923	86 929	86 935	86 941	86 947	86 953	86 958	86 964	86 970	86 976
741	982	988	994	999	87 005	87 011	87 017	87 023	87 029	87 035
742	87 040	87 046	87 052	87 058	064	070	075	081	087	093
743	099	105	111	116	122	128	134	140	146	151
744	157	163	169	175	181	186	192	198	204	210
745	87 216	87 221	87 227	87 233	87 239	87 245	87 251	87 256	87 262	87 268
746	274	280	286	291	297	303	309	315	320	326
747	332	338	344	349	355	361	367	373	379	384
748	390	396	402	408	413	419	425	431	437	442
749	448	454	460	466	471	477	483	489	495	500
750	87 506	87 512	87 518	87 523	87 529	87 535	87 541	87 547	87 552	87 558
N	0	1	2	3	4	5	6	7	8	9

N	0	1	2	3	4	5	6	7	8	9
750	87 506	87 512	87 518	87 523	87 529	87 535	87 541	87 547	87 552	87 558
751	564	570	576	581	587	593	599	604	610	616
752	622	628	633	639	645	651	656	662	668	674
753	679	685	691	697	703	708	714	720	726	731
754	737	743	749	754	760	766	772	777	783	789
755	87 795	87 800	87 806	87 812	87 818	87 823	87 829	87 835	87 841	87 846
756	852	858	864	869	875	881	887	892	898	904
757	910	915	921	927	933	938	944	950	955	961
758	967	973	978	984	990	996	88 001	88 007	88 013	88 018
759	88 024	88 030	88 036	88 041	88 047	88 053	058	064	070	076
760	88 081	88 087	88 093	88 098	88 104	88 110	88 116	88 121	88 127	88 133
761	138	144	150	156	161	167	173	178	184	190
762	195	201	207	213	218	224	230	235	241	247
763	252	258	264	270	275	281	287	292	298	304
764	309	315	321	326	332	338	343	349	355	360
765	88 366	88 372	88 377	88 383	88 389	88 395	88 400	88 406	88 412	88 417
766	423	429	434	440	446	451	457	463	468	474
767	480	485	491	497	502	508	513	519	525	530
768	536	542	547	553	559	564	570	576	581	587
769	593	598	604	610	615	621	627	632	638	643
770	88 649	88 655	88 660	88 666	88 672	88 677	88 683	88 689	88 694	88 700
771	705	711	717	722	728	734	739	745	750	756
772	762	767	773	779	784	790	795	801	807	812
773	818	824	829	835	840	846	852	857	863	868
774	874	880	885	891	897	902	908	913	919	925
775	88 930	88 936	88 941	88 947	88 953	88 958	88 964	88 969	88 975	88 981
776	986	992	997	89 003	89 009	89 014	89 020	89 025	89 031	89 037
777	89 042	89 048	89 053	059	064	070	076	081	087	092
778	098	104	109	115	120	126	131	137	143	148
779	154	159	165	170	176	182	187	193	198	204
780	89 209	89 215	89 221	89 226	89 232	89 237	89 243	89 248	89 254	89 260
781	265	271	276	282	287	293	298	304	310	315
782	321	326	332	337	343	348	354	360	365	371
783	376	382	387	393	398	404	409	415	421	426
784	432	437	443	448	454	459	465	470	476	481
785	89 487	89 492	89 498	89 504	89 509	89 515	89 520	89 526	89 531	89 537
786	542	548	553	559	564	570	575	581	586	592
787	597	603	609	614	620	625	631	636	642	647
788	653	658	664	669	675	680	686	691	697	702
789	708	713	719	724	730	735	741	746	752	757
790	89 763	89 768	89 774	89 779	89 785	89 790	89 796	89 801	89 807	89 812
791	818	823	829	834	840	845	851	856	862	867
792	873	878	883	889	894	900	905	911	916	922
793	927	933	938	944	949	955	960	966	971	977
794	982	988	993	998	90 004	90 009	90 015	90 020	90 026	90 031
795	90 037	90 042	90 048	90 053	90 059	90 064	90 069	90 075	90 080	90 086
796	091	097	102	108	113	119	124	129	135	140
797	146	151	157	162	168	173	179	184	189	195
798	200	206	211	217	222	227	233	238	244	249
799	255	260	266	271	276	282	287	293	298	304
800	90 309	90 314	90 320	90 325	90 331	90 336	90 342	90 347	90 352	90 358
N	**0**	**1**	**2**	**3**	**4**	**5**	**6**	**7**	**8**	**9**

N	0	1	2	3	4	5	6	7	8	9
800	90 309	90 314	90 320	90 325	90 331	90 336	90 342	90 347	90 352	90 358
801	363	369	374	380	385	390	396	401	407	412
802	417	423	428	434	439	445	450	455	461	466
803	472	477	482	488	493	499	504	509	515	520
804	526	531	536	542	547	553	558	563	569	574
805	90 580	90 585	90 590	90 596	90 601	90 607	90 612	90 617	90 623	90 628
806	634	639	644	650	655	660	666	671	677	682
807	687	693	698	703	709	714	720	725	730	736
808	741	747	752	757	763	768	773	779	784	789
809	795	800	806	811	816	822	827	832	838	843
810	90 849	90 854	90 859	90 865	90 870	90 875	90 881	90 886	90 891	90 897
811	902	907	913	918	924	929	934	940	945	950
812	956	961	966	972	977	982	988	993	998	91 004
813	91 009	91 014	91 020	91 025	91 030	91 036	91 041	91 046	91 052	057
814	062	068	073	078	084	089	094	100	105	110
815	91 116	91 121	91 126	91 132	91 137	91 142	91 148	91 153	91 158	91 164
816	169	174	180	185	190	196	201	206	212	217
817	222	228	233	238	243	249	254	259	265	270
818	275	281	286	291	297	302	307	312	318	323
819	328	334	339	344	350	355	360	365	371	376
820	91 381	91 387	91 392	91 397	91 403	91 408	91 413	91 418	91 424	91 429
821	434	440	445	450	455	461	466	471	477	482
822	487	492	498	503	508	514	519	524	529	535
823	540	545	551	556	561	566	572	577	582	587
824	593	598	603	609	614	619	624	630	635	640
825	91 645	91 651	91 656	91 661	91 666	91 672	91 677	91 682	91 687	91 693
826	698	703	709	714	719	724	730	735	740	745
827	751	756	761	766	772	777	782	787	793	798
828	803	808	814	819	824	829	834	840	845	850
829	855	861	866	871	876	882	887	892	897	903
830	91 908	91 913	91 918	91 924	91 929	91 934	91 939	91 944	91 950	91 955
831	960	965	971	976	981	986	991	997	92 002	92 007
832	92 012	92 018	92 023	92 028	92 033	92 038	92 044	92 049	054	059
833	065	070	075	080	085	091	096	101	106	111
834	117	122	127	132	137	143	148	153	158	163
835	92 169	92 174	92 179	92 184	92 189	92 195	92 200	92 205	92 210	92 215
836	221	226	231	236	241	247	252	257	262	267
837	273	278	283	288	293	298	304	309	314	319
838	324	330	335	340	345	350	355	361	366	371
839	376	381	387	392	397	402	407	412	418	423
840	92 428	92 433	92 438	92 443	92 449	92 454	92 459	92 464	92 469	92 474
841	480	485	490	495	500	505	511	516	521	526
842	531	536	542	547	552	557	562	567	572	578
843	583	588	593	598	603	609	614	619	624	629
844	634	639	645	650	655	660	665	670	675	681
845	92 686	92 691	92 696	92 701	92 706	92 711	92 716	92 722	92 727	92 732
846	737	742	747	752	758	763	768	773	778	783
847	788	793	799	804	809	814	819	824	829	834
848	840	845	850	855	860	865	870	875	881	886
849	891	896	901	906	911	916	921	927	932	937
850	92 942	92 947	92 952	92 957	92 962	92 967	92 973	92 978	92 983	92 988
N	0	1	2	3	4	5	6	7	8	9

N	0	1	2	3	4	5	6	7	8	9
850	92 942	92 947	92 952	92 957	92 962	92 967	92 973	92 978	92 983	92 988
851	993	998	93 003	93 008	93 013	93 018	93 024	93 029	93 034	93 039
852	93 044	93 049	054	059	064	069	075	080	085	090
853	095	100	105	110	115	120	125	131	136	141
854	146	151	156	161	166	171	176	181	186	192
855	93 197	93 202	93 207	93 212	93 217	93 222	93 227	93 232	93 237	93 242
856	247	252	258	263	268	273	278	283	288	293
857	298	303	308	313	318	323	328	334	339	344
858	349	354	359	364	369	374	379	384	389	394
859	399	404	409	414	420	425	430	435	440	445
860	93 450	93 455	93 460	93 465	93 470	93 475	93 480	93 485	93 490	93 495
861	500	505	510	515	520	526	531	536	541	546
862	551	556	561	566	571	576	581	586	591	596
863	601	606	611	616	621	626	631	636	641	646
864	651	656	661	666	671	676	682	687	692	697
865	93 702	93 707	93 712	93 717	93 722	93 727	93 732	93 737	93 742	93 747
866	752	757	762	767	772	777	782	787	792	797
867	802	807	812	817	822	827	832	837	842	847
868	852	857	862	867	872	877	882	887	892	897
869	902	907	912	917	922	927	932	937	942	947
870	93 952	93 957	93 962	93 967	93 972	93 977	93 982	93 987	93 992	93 997
871	94 002	94 007	94 012	94 017	94 022	94 027	94 032	94 037	94 042	94 047
872	052	057	062	067	072	077	082	086	091	096
873	101	106	111	116	121	126	131	136	141	146
874	151	156	161	166	171	176	181	186	191	196
875	94 201	94 206	94 211	94 216	94 221	94 226	94 231	94 236	94 240	94 245
876	250	255	260	265	270	275	280	285	290	295
877	300	305	310	315	320	325	330	335	340	345
878	349	354	359	364	369	374	379	384	389	394
879	399	404	409	414	419	424	429	433	438	443
880	94 448	94 453	94 458	94 463	94 468	94 473	94 478	94 483	94 488	94 493
881	498	503	507	512	517	522	527	532	537	542
882	547	552	557	562	567	571	576	581	586	591
883	596	601	606	611	616	621	626	630	635	640
884	645	650	655	660	665	670	675	680	685	689
885	94 694	94 699	94 704	94 709	94 714	94 719	94 724	94 729	94 734	94 738
886	743	748	753	758	763	768	773	778	783	787
887	792	797	802	807	812	817	822	827	832	836
888	841	846	851	856	861	866	871	876	880	885
889	890	895	900	905	910	915	919	924	929	934
890	94 939	94 944	94 949	94 954	94 959	94 963	94 968	94 973	94 978	94 983
891	988	993	998	95 002	95 007	95 012	95 017	95 022	95 027	95 032
892	95 036	95 041	95 046	051	056	061	066	071	075	080
893	085	090	095	100	105	109	114	119	124	129
894	134	139	143	148	153	158	163	168	173	177
895	95 182	95 187	95 192	95 197	95 202	95 207	95 211	95 216	95 221	95 226
896	231	236	240	245	250	255	260	265	270	274
897	279	284	289	294	299	303	308	313	318	323
898	328	332	337	342	347	352	357	361	366	371
899	376	381	386	390	395	400	405	410	415	419
900	95 424	95 429	95 434	95 439	95 444	95 448	95 453	95 458	95 463	95 468
N	0	1	2	3	4	5	6	7	8	9

N	0	1	2	3	4	5	6	7	8	9
900	95 424	95 429	95 434	95 439	95 444	95 448	95 453	95 458	95 463	95 468
901	472	477	482	487	492	497	501	506	511	516
902	521	525	530	535	540	545	550	554	559	564
903	569	574	578	583	588	593	598	602	607	612
904	617	622	626	631	636	641	646	650	655	660
905	95 665	95 670	95 674	95 679	95 684	95 689	95 694	95 698	95 703	95 708
906	713	718	722	727	732	737	742	746	751	756
907	761	766	770	775	780	785	789	794	799	804
908	809	813	818	823	828	832	837	842	847	852
909	856	861	866	871	875	880	885	890	895	899
910	95 904	95 909	95 914	95 918	95 923	95 928	95 933	95 938	95 942	95 947
911	952	957	961	966	971	976	980	985	990	995
912	999	96 004	96 009	96 014	96 019	96 023	96 028	96 033	96 038	96 042
913	96 047	052	057	061	066	071	076	080	085	090
914	095	099	104	109	114	118	123	128	133	137
915	96 142	96 147	96 152	96 156	96 161	96 166	96 171	96 175	96 180	96 185
916	190	194	199	204	209	213	218	223	227	232
917	237	242	246	251	256	261	265	270	275	280
918	284	289	294	298	303	308	313	317	322	327
919	332	336	341	346	350	355	360	365	369	374
920	96 379	96 384	96 388	96 393	96 398	96 402	96 407	96 412	96 417	96 421
921	426	431	435	440	445	450	454	459	464	468
922	473	478	483	487	492	497	501	506	511	515
923	520	525	530	534	539	544	548	553	558	562
924	567	572	577	581	586	591	595	600	605	609
925	96 614	96 619	96 624	96 628	96 633	96 638	96 642	96 647	96 652	96 656
926	661	666	670	675	680	685	689	694	699	703
927	708	713	717	722	727	731	736	741	745	750
928	755	759	764	769	774	778	783	788	792	797
929	802	806	811	816	820	825	830	834	839	844
930	96 848	96 853	96 858	96 862	96 867	96 872	96 876	96 881	96 886	96 890
931	895	900	904	909	914	918	923	928	932	937
932	942	946	951	956	960	965	970	974	979	984
933	988	993	997	97 002	97 007	97 011	97 016	97 021	97 025	97 030
934	97 035	97 039	97 044	049	053	058	063	067	072	077
935	97 081	97 086	97 090	97 095	97 100	97 104	97 109	97 114	97 118	97 123
936	128	132	137	142	146	151	155	160	165	169
937	174	179	183	188	192	197	202	206	211	216
938	220	225	230	234	239	243	248	253	257	262
939	267	271	276	280	285	290	294	299	304	308
940	97 313	97 317	97 322	97 327	97 331	97 336	97 340	97 345	97 350	97 354
941	359	364	368	373	377	382	387	391	396	400
942	405	410	414	419	424	428	433	437	442	447
943	451	456	460	465	470	474	479	483	488	493
944	497	502	506	511	516	520	525	529	534	539
945	97 543	97 548	97 552	97 557	97 562	97 566	97 571	97 575	97 580	97 585
946	589	594	598	603	607	612	617	621	626	630
947	635	640	644	649	653	658	663	667	672	676
948	681	685	690	695	699	704	708	713	717	722
949	727	731	736	740	745	749	754	759	763	768
950	97 772	97 777	97 782	97 786	97 791	97 795	97 800	97 804	97 809	97 813
N	0	1	2	3	4	5	6	7	8	9

N	0	1	2	3	4	5	6	7	8	9
950	97 772	97 777	97 782	97 786	97 791	97 795	97 800	97 804	97 809	97 813
951	818	823	827	832	836	841	845	850	855	859
952	864	868	873	877	882	886	891	896	900	905
953	909	914	918	923	928	932	937	941	946	950
954	955	959	964	968	973	978	982	987	991	996
955	98 000	98 005	98 009	98 014	98 019	98 023	98 028	98 032	98 037	98 041
956	046	050	055	059	064	068	073	078	082	087
957	091	096	100	105	109	114	118	123	127	132
958	137	141	146	150	155	159	164	168	173	177
959	182	186	191	195	200	204	209	214	218	223
960	98 227	98 232	98 236	98 241	98 245	98 250	98 254	98 259	98 263	98 268
961	272	277	281	286	290	295	299	304	308	313
962	318	322	327	331	336	340	345	349	354	358
963	363	367	372	376	381	385	390	394	399	403
964	408	412	417	421	426	430	435	439	444	448
965	98 453	98 457	98 462	98 466	98 471	98 475	98 480	98 484	98 489	98 493
966	498	502	507	511	516	520	525	529	534	538
967	543	547	552	556	561	565	570	574	579	583
968	588	592	597	601	605	610	614	619	623	628
969	632	637	641	646	650	655	659	664	668	673
970	98 677	98 682	98 686	98 691	98 695	98 700	98 704	98 709	98 713	98 717
971	722	726	731	735	740	744	749	753	758	762
972	767	771	776	780	784	789	793	798	802	807
973	811	816	820	825	829	834	838	843	847	851
974	856	860	865	869	874	878	883	887	892	896
975	98 900	98 905	98 909	98 914	98 918	98 923	98 927	98 932	98 936	98 941
976	945	949	954	958	963	967	972	976	981	985
977	989	994	998	99 003	99 007	99 012	99 016	99 021	99 025	99 029
978	99 034	99 038	99 043	047	052	056	061	065	069	074
979	078	083	087	092	096	100	105	109	114	118
980	99 123	99 127	99 131	99 136	99 140	99 145	99 149	99 154	99 158	99 162
981	167	171	176	180	185	189	193	198	202	207
982	211	216	220	224	229	233	238	242	247	251
983	255	260	264	269	273	277	282	286	291	295
984	300	304	308	313	317	322	326	330	335	339
985	99 344	99 348	99 352	99 357	99 361	99 366	99 370	99 374	99 379	99 383
986	388	392	396	401	405	410	414	419	423	427
987	432	436	441	445	449	454	458	463	467	471
988	476	480	484	489	493	498	502	506	511	515
989	520	524	528	533	537	542	546	550	555	559
990	99 564	99 568	99 572	99 577	99 581	99 585	99 590	99 594	99 599	99 603
991	607	612	616	621	625	629	634	638	642	647
992	651	656	660	664	669	673	677	682	686	691
993	695	699	704	708	712	717	721	726	730	734
994	739	743	747	752	756	760	765	769	774	778
995	99 782	99 787	99 791	99 795	99 800	99 804	99 808	99 813	99 817	99 822
996	826	830	835	839	843	848	852	856	861	865
997	870	874	878	883	887	891	896	900	904	909
998	913	917	922	926	930	935	939	944	948	952
999	957	961	965	970	974	978	983	987	991	996
1000	00 000	00 004	00 009	00 013	00 017	00 022	00 026	00 030	00 035	00 039
N	0	1	2	3	4	5	6	7	8	9

TABLE IV

PROPORTIONAL PARTS OF DIFFERENCES

D	1	2	3	4	5	6	7	8	9
1	0.1	0.2	0.3	0.4	0.5	0.6	0.7	0.8	0.9
2	0.2	0.4	0.6	0.8	1.0	1.2	1.4	1.6	1.8
3	0.3	0.6	0.9	1.2	1.5	1.8	2.1	2.4	2.7
4	0.4	0.8	1.2	1.6	2.0	2.4	2.8	3.2	3.6
5	0.5	1.0	1.5	2.0	2.5	3.0	3.5	4.0	4.5
6	0.6	1.2	1.8	2.4	3.0	3.6	4.2	4.8	5.4
7	0.7	1.4	2.1	2.8	3.5	4.2	4.9	5.6	6.3
8	0.8	1.6	2.4	3.2	4.0	4.8	5.6	6.4	7.2
9	0.9	1.8	2.7	3.6	4.5	5.4	6.3	7.2	8.1
10	1.0	2.0	3.0	4.0	5.0	6.0	7.0	8.0	9.0
11	1.1	2.2	3.3	4.4	5.5	6.6	7.7	8.8	9.9
12	1.2	2.4	3.6	4.8	6.0	7.2	8.4	9.6	10.8
13	1.3	2.6	3.9	5.2	6.5	7.8	9.1	10.4	11.7
14	1.4	2.8	4.2	5.6	7.0	8.4	9.8	11.2	12.6
15	1.5	3.0	4.5	6.0	7.5	9.0	10.5	12.0	13.5
16	1.6	3.2	4.8	6.4	8.0	9.6	11.2	12.8	14.4
17	1.7	3.4	5.1	6.8	8.5	10.2	11.9	13.6	15.3
18	1.8	3.6	5.4	7.2	9.0	10.8	12.6	14.4	16.2
19	1.9	3.8	5.7	7.6	9.5	11.4	13.3	15.2	17.1
20	2.0	4.0	6.0	8.0	10.0	12.0	14.0	16.0	18.0
21	2.1	4.2	6.3	8.4	10.5	12.6	14.7	16.8	18.9
22	2.2	4.4	6.6	8.8	11.0	13.2	15.4	17.6	19.8
23	2.3	4.6	6.9	9.2	11.5	13.8	16.1	18.4	20.7
24	2.4	4.8	7.2	9.6	12.0	14.4	16.8	19.2	21.6
25	2.5	5.0	7.5	10.0	12.5	15.0	17.5	20.0	22.5
26	2.6	5.2	7.8	10.4	13.0	15.6	18.2	20.8	23.4
27	2.7	5.4	8.1	10.8	13.5	16.2	18.9	21.6	24.3
28	2.8	5.6	8.4	11.2	14.0	16.8	19.6	22.4	25.2
29	2.9	5.8	8.7	11.6	14.5	17.4	20.3	23.2	26.1
30	3.0	6.0	9.0	12.0	15.0	18.0	21.0	24.0	27.0
31	3.1	6.2	9.3	12.4	15.5	18.6	21.7	24.8	27.9
32	3.2	6.4	9.6	12.8	16.0	19.2	22.4	25.6	28.8
33	3.3	6.6	9.9	13.2	16.5	19.8	23.1	26.4	29.7
34	3.4	6.8	10.2	13.6	17.0	20.4	23.8	27.2	30.6
35	3.5	7.0	10.5	14.0	17.5	21.0	24.5	28.0	31.5
36	3.6	7.2	10.8	14.4	18.0	21.6	25.2	28.8	32.4
37	3.7	7.4	11.1	14.8	18.5	22.2	25.9	29.6	33.3
38	3.8	7.6	11.4	15.2	19.0	22.8	26.6	30.4	34.2
39	3.9	7.8	11.7	15.6	19.5	23.4	27.3	31.2	35.1
40	4.0	8.0	12.0	16.0	20.0	24.0	28.0	32.0	36.0
41	4.1	8.2	12.3	16.4	20.5	24.6	28.7	32.8	36.9
42	4.2	8.4	12.6	16.8	21.0	25.2	29.4	33.6	37.8
43	4.3	8.6	12.9	17.2	21.5	25.8	30.1	34.4	38.7
44	4.4	8.8	13.2	17.6	22.0	26.4	30.8	35.2	39.6
45	4.5	9.0	13.5	18.0	22.5	27.0	31.5	36.0	40.5
46	4.6	9.2	13.8	18.4	23.0	27.6	32.2	36.8	41.4
47	4.7	9.4	14.1	18.8	23.5	28.2	32.9	37.6	42.3
48	4.8	9.6	14.4	19.2	24.0	28.8	33.6	38.4	43.2
49	4.9	9.8	14.7	19.6	24.5	29.4	34.3	39.2	44.1
50	5.0	10.0	15.0	20.0	25.0	30.0	35.0	40.0	45.0
	1	2	3	4	5	6	7	8	9

This table contains the proportional parts of differences from 1 to 100. For example, if the difference between two numbers is 73, 0.7 of this difference is 51.1.

D	1	2	3	4	5	6	7	8	9
51	5.1	10.2	15.3	20.4	25.5	30.6	35.7	40.8	45.9
52	5.2	10.4	15.6	20.8	26.0	31.2	36.4	41.6	46.8
53	5.3	10.6	15.9	21.2	26.5	31.8	37.1	42.4	47.7
54	5.4	10.8	16.2	21.6	27.0	32.4	37.8	43.2	48.6
55	5.5	11.0	16.5	22.0	27.5	33.0	38.5	44.0	49.5
56	5.6	11.2	16.8	22.4	28.0	33.6	39.2	44.8	50.4
57	5.7	11.4	17.1	22.8	28.5	34.2	39.9	45.6	51.3
58	5.8	11.6	17.4	23.2	29.0	34.8	40.6	46.4	52.2
59	5.9	11.8	17.7	23.6	29.5	35.4	41.3	47.2	53.1
60	6.0	12.0	18.0	24.0	30.0	36.0	42.0	48.0	54.0
61	6.1	12.2	18.3	24.4	30.5	36.6	42.7	48.8	54.9
62	6.2	12.4	18.6	24.8	31.0	37.2	43.4	49.6	55.8
63	6.3	12.6	18.9	25.2	31.5	37.8	44.1	50.4	56.7
64	6.4	12.8	19.2	25.6	32.0	38.4	44.8	51.2	57.6
65	6.5	13.0	19.5	26.0	32.5	39.0	45.5	52.0	58.5
66	6.6	13.2	19.8	26.4	33.0	39.6	46.2	52.8	59.4
67	6.7	13.4	20.1	26.8	33.5	40.2	46.9	53.6	60.3
68	6.8	13.6	20.4	27.2	34.0	40.8	47.6	54.4	61.2
69	6.9	13.8	20.7	27.6	34.5	41.4	48.3	55.2	62.1
70	7.0	14.0	21.0	28.0	35.0	42.0	49.0	56.0	63.0
71	7.1	14.2	21.3	28.4	35.5	42.6	49.7	56.8	63.9
72	7.2	14.4	21.6	28.8	36.0	43.2	50.4	57.6	64.8
73	7.3	14.6	21.9	29.2	36.5	43.8	51.1	58.4	65.7
74	7.4	14.8	22.2	29.6	37.0	44.4	51.8	59.2	66.6
75	7.5	15.0	22.5	30.0	37.5	45.0	52.5	60.0	67.5
76	7.6	15.2	22.8	30.4	38.0	45.6	53.2	60.8	68.4
77	7.7	15.4	23.1	30.8	38.5	46.2	53.9	61.6	69.3
78	7.8	15.6	23.4	31.2	39.0	46.8	54.6	62.4	70.2
79	7.9	15.8	23.7	31.6	39.5	47.4	55.3	63.2	71.1
80	8.0	16.0	24.0	32.0	40.0	48.0	56.0	64.0	72.0
81	8.1	16.2	24.3	32.4	40.5	48.6	56.7	64.8	72.9
82	8.2	16.4	24.6	32.8	41.0	49.2	57.4	65.6	73.8
83	8.3	16.6	24.9	33.2	41.5	49.8	58.1	66.4	74.7
84	8.4	16.8	25.2	33.6	42.0	50.4	58.8	67.2	75.6
85	8.5	17.0	25.5	34.0	42.5	51.0	59.5	68.0	76.5
86	8.6	17.2	25.8	34.4	43.0	51.6	60.2	68.8	77.4
87	8.7	17.4	26.1	34.8	43.5	52.2	60.9	69.6	78.3
88	8.8	17.6	26.4	35.2	44.0	52.8	61.6	70.4	79.2
89	8.9	17.8	26.7	35.6	44.5	53.4	62.3	71.2	80.1
90	9.0	18.0	27.0	36.0	45.0	54.0	63.0	72.0	81.0
91	9.1	18.2	27.3	36.4	45.5	54.6	63.7	72.8	81.9
92	9.2	18.4	27.6	36.8	46.0	55.2	64.4	73.6	82.8
93	9.3	18.6	27.9	37.2	46.5	55.8	65.1	74.4	83.7
94	9.4	18.8	28.2	37.6	47.0	56.4	65.8	75.2	84.6
95	9.5	19.0	28.5	38.0	47.5	57.0	66.5	76.0	85.5
96	9.6	19.2	28.8	38.4	48.0	57.6	67.2	76.8	86.4
97	9.7	19.4	29.1	38.8	48.5	58.2	67.9	77.6	87.3
98	9.8	19.6	29.4	39.2	49.0	58.8	68.6	78.4	88.2
99	9.9	19.8	29.7	39.6	49.5	59.4	69.3	79.2	89.1
100	10.0	20.0	30.0	40.0	50.0	60.0	70.0	80.0	90.0
	1	2	3	4	5	6	7	8	9

NUMBER	LOG	NUMBER	LOG
Circle = 360°	2.55630	$\pi^2 = 9.86960$	0.99430
= 21,600′	4.33445	$\frac{1}{\pi^2} = 0.10132$	9.00570 – 10
= 1,296,000″	6.11261		
$\pi = 3.14159$	0.49715	$\sqrt{\pi} = 1.77245$	0.24857
$2\pi = 6.28319$	0.79818	$\frac{1}{\sqrt{\pi}} = 0.56419$	9.75143 – 10
$4\pi = 12.56637$	1.09921		
$\frac{4\pi}{3} = 4.18879$	0.62209	$\sqrt{\frac{4}{\pi}} = 1.12838$	0.05246
$\frac{\pi}{4} = 0.78540$	9.89509 – 10	$\sqrt[3]{\pi} = 1.46459$	0.16572
$\frac{\pi}{6} = 0.52360$	9.71900 – 10	$\frac{1}{\sqrt[3]{\pi}} = 0.68278$	9.83428 – 10
$\frac{1}{\pi} = 0.31831$	9.50285 – 10	$\sqrt[3]{\frac{3}{4\pi}} = 0.62035$	9.79264 – 10
$\frac{1}{2\pi} = 0.15915$	9.20182 – 10	$\sqrt[3]{\frac{\pi}{6}} = 0.80600$	9.90633 – 10
$\sqrt{2} = 1.41421$	0.15052	$\sqrt[3]{2} = 1.25992$	0.10034
$\sqrt{3} = 1.73205$	0.23856	$\sqrt[3]{3} = 1.44225$	0.15904
$\sqrt{5} = 2.23606$	0.34949	$\sqrt[3]{5} = 1.70997$	0.23299
$\sqrt{6} = 2.44948$	0.38908	$\sqrt[3]{6} = 1.81712$	0.25938
1 radian = $\frac{180°}{\pi}$		$1° = \frac{\pi}{180}$ radians	
= 57.2958°	1.75812	1° = 0.01745 radians	8.24188 – 10
= 3437.75′	3.53627	1′ = 0.00029 radians	6.46373 – 10
= 206,264.81″	5.31443	1″ = 0.000005 radians	4.68557 – 10
Base of natural logs., ϵ		$\log_{10}\epsilon = \log_{10} 2.71828$	0.43429
$\epsilon = 2.71828$	0.43429	$1 : \log_{10}\epsilon = 2.302585$	0.36222
1 m. = 39.3708 in.	1.59517	1 knot = 6080.27 ft.	3.78392
= 1.0936 yd.	0.03886	= 1.1516 mi.	0.06130
= 3.2809 ft.	0.51599	1 lb. Av. = 7000 gr.	3.84510
1 km. = 0.6214 mi.	9.79336 – 10	1 bu. = 2150.42 cu. in.	3.33252
1 mi. = 1.6093 km.	0.20664	1 U.S. gal. = 231 cu. in.	2.36361
1 oz. Av. = 28.3495 g.	1.45254	1 Brit. gal. = 277.463 cu. in.	2.44320
1 lb. Av. = 453.5927 g.	2.65666	Earth's radii	
1 kg. = 2.2046 lb.	0.34333	= 3963 mi.	3.59802
1 l. = 1.0567 liq. qt.	0.02396	and 3950 mi.	3.59660
1 liq. qt. = 0.9463 l.	9.97603 – 10	1 ft./lb. = 0.1383 kg./m.	9.14082 – 10

TABLE VI

THE LOGARITHMS OF THE TRIGONOMETRIC FUNCTIONS

From 0° to 0° 3′, and from 89° 57′ to 90°, for every second
From 0° to 2°, and from 88° to 90°, for every ten seconds
From 1° to 89°, for every minute

To each logarithm – 10 is to be appended

log sin **0°** log tan = log sin; log cos = 10.00 000

″	0′	1′	2′	″	″	0′	1′	2′	″
0	—	6.46 373	6.76 476	**60**	**30**	6.16 270	6.63 982	6.86 167	**30**
1	4.68 557	6.47 090	6.76 836	59	31	6.17 694	6.64 462	6.86 455	29
2	4.98 660	6.47 797	6.77 193	58	32	6.19 072	6.64 936	6.86 742	28
3	5.16 270	6.48 492	6.77 548	57	33	6.20 409	6.65 406	6.87 027	27
4	5.28 763	6.49 175	6.77 900	56	34	6.21 705	6.65 870	6.87 310	26
5	5.38 454	6.49 849	6.78 248	**55**	**35**	6.22 964	6.66 330	6.87 591	**25**
6	5.46 373	6.50 512	6.78 595	54	36	6.24 188	6.66 785	6.87 870	24
7	5.53 067	6.51 165	6.78 938	53	37	6.25 378	6.67 235	6.88 147	23
8	5.58 866	6.51 808	6.79 278	52	38	6.26 536	6.67 680	6.88 423	22
9	5.63 982	6.52 442	6.79 616	51	39	6.27 664	6.68 121	6.88 697	21
10	5.68 557	6.53 067	6.79 952	**50**	**40**	6.28 763	6.68 557	6.88 969	**20**
11	5.72 697	6.53 683	6.80 285	49	41	6.29 836	6.68 990	6.89 240	19
12	5.76 476	6.54 291	6.80 615	48	42	6.30 882	6.69 418	6.89 509	18
13	5.79 952	6.54 890	6.80 943	47	43	6.31 904	6.69 841	6.89 776	17
14	5.83 170	6.55 481	6.81 268	46	44	6.32 903	6.70 261	6.90 042	16
15	5.86 167	6.56 064	6.81 591	**45**	**45**	6.33 879	6.70 676	6.90 306	**15**
16	5.88 969	6.56 639	6.81 911	44	46	6.34 833	6.71 088	6.90 568	14
17	5.91 602	6.57 207	6.82 230	43	47	6.35 767	6.71 496	6.90 829	13
18	5.94 085	6.57 767	6.82 545	42	48	6.36 682	6.71 900	6.91 088	12
19	5.96 433	6.58 320	6.82 859	41	49	6.37 577	6.72 300	6.91 346	11
20	5.98 660	6.58 866	6.83 170	**40**	**50**	6.38 454	6.72 697	6.91 602	**10**
21	6.00 779	6.59 406	6.83 479	39	51	6.39 315	6.73 090	6.91 857	9
22	6.02 800	6.59 939	6.83 786	38	52	6.40 158	6.73 479	6.92 110	8
23	6.04 730	6.60 465	6.84 091	37	53	6.40 985	6.73 865	6.92 362	7
24	6.06 579	6.60 985	6.84 394	36	54	6.41 797	6.74 248	6.92 612	6
25	6.08 351	6.61 499	6.84 694	**35**	**55**	6.42 594	6.74 627	6.92 861	**5**
26	6.10 055	6.62 007	6.84 993	34	56	6.43 376	6.75 003	6.93 109	4
27	6.11 694	6.62 509	6.85 289	33	57	6.44 145	6.75 376	6.93 355	3
28	6.13 273	6.63 006	6.85 584	32	58	6.44 900	6.75 746	6.93 599	2
29	6.14 797	6.63 496	6.85 876	31	59	6.45 643	6.76 112	6.93 843	1
30	6.16 270	6.63 982	6.86 167	**30**	**60**	6.46 373	6.76 476	6.94 085	**0**
″	59′	58′	57′	″	″	59′	58′	57′	″

log cot = log cos; log sin = 10.00 000 **89°** **log cos**

0°

′ ″	log sin	log cos	log tan	′ ″	′ ″	log sin	log cos	log tan	′ ″
0 0	—	10.00000	—	**60** 0	**10** 0	7.46 373	10.00000	7.46 373	**50** 0
10	5.68 557	10.00000	5.68 557	50	10	7.47 090	10.00000	7.47 091	50
20	5.98 660	10.00000	5.98 660	40	20	7.47 797	10.00000	7.47 797	40
30	6.16 270	10.00000	6.16 270	30	30	7.48 491	10.00000	7.48 492	30
40	6.28 763	10.00000	6.28 763	20	40	7.49 175	10.00000	7.49 176	20
50	6.38 454	10.00000	6.38 454	10	50	7.49 849	10.00000	7.49 849	10
1 0	6.46 373	10.00000	6.46 373	**59** 0	**11** 0	7.50 512	10.00000	7.50 512	**49** 0
10	6.53 067	10.00000	6.53 067	50	10	7.51 165	10.00000	7.51 165	50
20	6.58 866	10.00000	6.58 866	40	20	7.51 808	10.00000	7.51 809	40
30	6.63 982	10.00000	6.63 982	30	30	7.52 442	10.00000	7.52 443	30
40	6.68 557	10.00000	6.68 557	20	40	7.53 067	10.00000	7.53 067	20
50	6.72 697	10.00000	6.72 697	10	50	7.53 683	10.00000	7.53 683	10
2 0	6.76 476	10.00000	6.76 476	**58** 0	**12** 0	7.54 291	10.00000	7.54 291	**48** 0
10	6.79 952	10.00000	6.79 952	50	10	7.54 890	10.00000	7.54 890	50
20	6.83 170	10.00000	6.83 170	40	20	7.55 481	10.00000	7.55 481	40
30	6.86 167	10.00000	6.86 167	30	30	7.56 064	10.00000	7.56 064	30
40	6.88 969	10.00000	6.88 969	20	40	7.56 639	10.00000	7.56 639	20
50	6.91 602	10.00000	6.91 602	10	50	7.57 206	10.00000	7.57 207	10
3 0	6.94 085	10.00000	6.94 085	**57** 0	**13** 0	7.57 767	10.00000	7.57 767	**47** 0
10	6.96 433	10.00000	6.96 433	50	10	7.58 320	10.00000	7.58 320	50
20	6.98 660	10.00000	6.98 661	40	20	7.58 866	10.00000	7.58 867	40
30	7.00 779	10.00000	7.00 779	30	30	7.59 406	10.00000	7.59 406	30
40	7.02 800	10.00000	7.02 800	20	40	7.59 939	10.00000	7.59 939	20
50	7.04 730	10.00000	7.04 730	10	50	7.60 465	10.00000	7.60 466	10
4 0	7.06 579	10.00000	7.06 579	**56** 0	**14** 0	7.60 985	10.00000	7.60 986	**46** 0
10	7.08 351	10.00000	7.08 352	50	10	7.61 499	10.00000	7.61 500	50
20	7.10 055	10.00000	7.10 055	40	20	7.62 007	10.00000	7.62 008	40
30	7.11 694	10.00000	7.11 694	30	30	7.62 509	10.00000	7.62 510	30
40	7.13 273	10.00000	7.13 273	20	40	7.63 006	10.00000	7.63 006	20
50	7.14 797	10.00000	7.14 797	10	50	7.63 496	10.00000	7.63 497	10
5 0	7.16 270	10.00000	7.16 270	**55** 0	**15** 0	7.63 982	10.00000	7.63 982	**45** 0
10	7.17 694	10.00000	7.17 694	50	10	7.64 461	10.00000	7.64 462	50
20	7.19 072	10.00000	7.19 073	40	20	7.64 936	10.00000	7.64 937	40
30	7.20 409	10.00000	7.20 409	30	30	7.65 406	10.00000	7.65 406	30
40	7.21 705	10.00000	7.21 705	20	40	7.65 870	10.00000	7.65 871	20
50	7.22 964	10.00000	7.22 964	10	50	7.66 330	10.00000	7.66 330	10
6 0	7.24 188	10.00000	7.24 188	**54** 0	**16** 0	7.66 784	10.00000	7.66 785	**44** 0
10	7.25 378	10.00000	7.25 378	50	10	7.67 235	10.00000	7.67 235	50
20	7.26 536	10.00000	7.26 536	40	20	7.67 680	10.00000	7.67 680	40
30	7.27 664	10.00000	7.27 664	30	30	7.68 121	10.00000	7.68 121	30
40	7.28 763	10.00000	7.28 764	20	40	7.68 557	9.99999	7.68 558	20
50	7.29 836	10.00000	7.29 836	10	50	7.68 989	9.99999	7.68 990	10
7 0	7.30 882	10.00000	7.30 882	**53** 0	**17** 0	7.69 417	9.99 999	7.69 418	**43** 0
10	7.31 904	10.00000	7.31 904	50	10	7.69 841	9.99 999	7.69 842	50
20	7.32 903	10.00000	7.32 903	40	20	7.70 261	9.99 999	7.70 261	40
30	7.33 879	10.00000	7.33 879	30	30	7.70 676	9.99 999	7.70 677	30
40	7.34 833	10.00000	7.34 833	20	40	7.71 088	9.99 999	7.71 088	20
50	7.35 767	10.00000	7.35 767	10	50	7.71 496	9.99 999	7.71 496	10
8 0	7.36 682	10.00000	7.36 682	**52** 0	**18** 0	7.71 900	9.99 999	7.71 900	**42** 0
10	7.37 577	10.00000	7.37 577	50	10	7.72 300	9.99 999	7.72 301	50
20	7.38 454	10.00000	7.38 455	40	20	7.72 697	9.99 999	7.72 697	40
30	7.39 314	10.00000	7.39 315	30	30	7.73 090	9.99 999	7.73 090	30
40	7.40 158	10.00000	7.40 158	20	40	7.73 479	9.99 999	7.73 480	20
50	7.40 985	10.00000	7.40 985	10	50	7.73 865	9.99 999	7.73 866	10
9 0	7.41 797	10.00000	7.41 797	**51** 0	**19** 0	7.74 248	9.99 999	7.74 248	**41** 0
10	7.42 594	10.00000	7.42 594	50	10	7.74 627	9.99 999	7.74 628	50
20	7.43 376	10.00000	7.43 376	40	20	7.75 003	9.99 999	7.75 004	40
30	7.44 145	10.00000	7.44 145	30	30	7.75 376	9.99 999	7.75 377	30
40	7.44 900	10.00000	7.44 900	20	40	7.75 745	9.99 999	7.75 746	20
50	7.45 643	10.00000	7.45 643	10	50	7.76 112	9.99 999	7.76 113	10
10 0	7.46 373	10.00000	7.46 373	**50** 0	**20** 0	7.76 475	9.99 999	7.76 476	**40** 0
′ ″	log cos	log sin	log cot	′ ″	′ ″	log cos	log sin	log cot	′ ″

89°

′ ″	log sin	log cos	log tan	′ ″	′ ″	log sin	log cos	log tan	′ ″
20 0	7.76 475	9.99 999	7.76 476	**40** 0	**30** 0	7.94 084	9.99 998	7.94 086	**30** 0
10	7.76 836	9.99 999	7.76 837	50	10	7.94 325	9.99 998	7.94 326	50
20	7.77 193	9.99 999	7.77 194	40	20	7.94 564	9.99 998	7.94 566	40
30	7.77 548	9.99 999	7.77 549	30	30	7.94 802	9.99 998	7.94 804	30
40	7.77 899	9.99 999	7.77 900	20	40	7.95 039	9.99 998	7.95 040	20
50	7.78 248	9.99 999	7.78 249	10	50	7.95 274	9.99 998	7.95 276	10
21 0	7.78 594	9.99 999	7.78 595	**39** 0	**31** 0	7.95 508	9.99 998	7.95 510	**29** 0
10	7.78 938	9.99 999	7.78 938	50	10	7.95 741	9.99 998	7.95 743	50
20	7.79 278	9.99 999	7.79 279	40	20	7.95 973	9.99 998	7.95 974	40
30	7.79 616	9.99 999	7.79 617	30	30	7.96 203	9.99 998	7.96 205	30
40	7.79 952	9.99 999	7.79 952	20	40	7.96 432	9.99 998	7.96 434	20
50	7.80 284	9.99 999	7.80 285	10	50	7.96 660	9.99 998	7.96 662	10
22 0	7.80 615	9.99 999	7.80 615	**38** 0	**32** 0	7.96 887	9.99 998	7.96 889	**28** 0
10	7.80 942	9.99 999	7.80 943	50	10	7.97 113	9.99 998	7.97 114	50
20	7.81 268	9.99 999	7.81 269	40	20	7.97 337	9.99 998	7.97 339	40
30	7.81 591	9.99 999	7.81 591	30	30	7.97 560	9.99 998	7.97 562	30
40	7.81 911	9.99 999	7.81 912	20	40	7.97 782	9.99 998	7.97 784	20
50	7.82 229	9.99 999	7.82 230	10	50	7.98 003	9.99 998	7.98 005	10
23 0	7.82 545	9.99 999	7.82 546	**37** 0	**33** 0	7.98 223	9.99 998	7.98 225	**27** 0
10	7.82 859	9.99 999	7.82 860	50	10	7.98 442	9.99 998	7.98 444	50
20	7.83 170	9.99 999	7.83 171	40	20	7.98 660	9.99 998	7.98 662	40
30	7.83 479	9.99 999	7.83 480	30	30	7.98 876	9.99 998	7.98 878	30
40	7.83 786	9.99 999	7.83 787	20	40	7.99 092	9.99 998	7.99 094	20
50	7.84 091	9.99 999	7.84 092	10	50	7.99 306	9.99 998	7.99 308	10
24 0	7.84 393	9.99 999	7.84 394	**36** 0	**34** 0	7.99 520	9.99 998	7.99 522	**26** 0
10	7.84 694	9.99 999	7.84 695	50	10	7.99 732	9.99 998	7.99 734	50
20	7.84 992	9.99 999	7.84 994	40	20	7.99 943	9.99 998	7.99 946	40
30	7.85 289	9.99 999	7.85 290	30	30	8.00 154	9.99 998	8.00 156	30
40	7.85 583	9.99 999	7.85 584	20	40	8.00 363	9.99 998	8.00 365	20
50	7.85 876	9.99 999	7.85 877	10	50	8.00 571	9.99 998	8.00 574	10
25 0	7.86 166	9.99 999	7.86 167	**35** 0	**35** 0	8.00 779	9.99 998	8.00 781	**25** 0
10	7.86 455	9.99 999	7.86 456	50	10	8.00 985	9.99 998	8.00 987	50
20	7.86 741	9.99 999	7.86 743	40	20	8.01 190	9.99 998	8.01 193	40
30	7.87 026	9.99 999	7.87 027	30	30	8.01 395	9.99 998	8.01 397	30
40	7.87 309	9.99 999	7.87 310	20	40	8.01 598	9.99 998	8.01 600	20
50	7.87 590	9.99 999	7.87 591	10	50	8.01 801	9.99 998	8.01 803	10
26 0	7.87 870	9.99 999	7.87 871	**34** 0	**36** 0	8.02 002	9.99 998	8.02 004	**24** 0
10	7.88 147	9.99 999	7.88 148	50	10	8.02 203	9.99 998	8.02 205	50
20	7.88 423	9.99 999	7.88 424	40	20	8.02 402	9.99 998	8.02 405	40
30	7.88 697	9.99 999	7.88 698	30	30	8.02 601	9.99 998	8.02 604	30
40	7.88 969	9.99 999	7.88 970	20	40	8.02 799	9.99 998	8.02 801	20
50	7.89 240	9.99 999	7.89 241	10	50	8.02 996	9.99 998	8.02 998	10
27 0	7.89 509	9.99 999	7.89 510	**33** 0	**37** 0	8.03 192	9.99 997	8.03 194	**23** 0
10	7.89 776	9.99 999	7.89 777	50	10	8.03 387	9.99 997	8.03 390	50
20	7.90 041	9.99 999	7.90 043	40	20	8.03 581	9.99 997	8.03 584	40
30	7.90 305	9.99 999	7.90 307	30	30	8.03 775	9.99 997	8.03 777	30
40	7.90 568	9.99 999	7.90 569	20	40	8.03 967	9.99 997	8.03 970	20
50	7.90 829	9.99 999	7.90 830	10	50	8.04 159	9.99 997	8.04 162	10
28 0	7.91 088	9.99 999	7.91 089	**32** 0	**38** 0	8.04 350	9.99 997	8.04 353	**22** 0
10	7.91 346	9.99 999	7.91 347	50	10	8.04 540	9.99 997	8.04 543	50
20	7.91 602	9.99 999	7.91 603	40	20	8.04 729	9.99 997	8.04 732	40
30	7.91 857	9.99 999	7.91 858	30	30	8.04 918	9.99 997	8.04 921	30
40	7.92 110	9.99 998	7.92 111	20	40	8.05 105	9.99 997	8.05 108	20
50	7.92 362	9.99 998	7.92 363	10	50	8.05 292	9.99 997	8.05 295	10
29 0	7.92 612	9.99 998	7.92 613	**31** 0	**39** 0	8.05 478	9.99 997	8.05 481	**21** 0
10	7.92 861	9.99 998	7.92 862	50	10	8.05 663	9.99 997	8.05 666	50
20	7.93 108	9.99 998	7.93 110	40	20	8.05 848	9.99 997	8.05 851	40
30	7.93 354	9.99 998	7.93 356	30	30	8.06 031	9.99 997	8.06 034	30
40	7.93 599	9.99 998	7.93 601	20	40	8.06 214	9.99 997	8.06 217	20
50	7.93 842	9.99 998	7.93 844	10	50	8.06 396	9.99 997	8.06 399	10
30 0	7.94 084	9.99 998	7.94 086	**30** 0	**40** 0	8.06 578	9.99 997	8.06 581	**20** 0
′ ″	log cos	log sin	log cot	′ ″	′ ″	log cos	log sin	log cot	′ ″

0°

′ ″	log sin	log cos	log tan	′ ″	′ ″	log sin	log cos	log tan	′ ″
40 0	8.06 578	9.99 997	8.06 581	**20** 0	**50** 0	8.16 268	9.99 995	8.16 273	**10** 0
10	8.06 758	9.99 997	8.06 761	50	10	8.16 413	9.99 995	8.16 417	50
20	8.06 938	9.99 997	8.06 941	40	20	8.16 557	9.99 995	8.16 561	40
30	8.07 117	9.99 997	8.07 120	30	30	8.16 700	9.99 995	8.16 705	30
40	8.07 295	9.99 997	8.07 299	20	40	8.16 843	9.99 995	8.16 848	20
50	8.07 473	9.99 997	8.07 476	10	50	8.16 986	9.99 995	8.16 991	10
41 0	8.07 650	9.99 997	8.07 653	**19** 0	**51** 0	8.17 128	9.99 995	8.17 133	**9** 0
10	8.07 826	9.99 997	8.07 829	50	10	8.17 270	9.99 995	8.17 275	50
20	8.08 002	9.99 997	8.08 005	40	20	8.17 411	9.99 995	8.17 416	40
30	8.08 176	9.99 997	8.08 180	30	30	8.17 552	9.99 995	8.17 557	30
40	8.08 350	9.99 997	8.08 354	20	40	8.17 692	9.99 995	8.17 697	20
50	8.08 524	9.99 997	8.08 527	10	50	8.17 832	9.99 995	8.17 837	10
42 0	8.08 696	9.99 997	8.08 700	**18** 0	**52** 0	8.17 971	9.99 995	8.17 976	**8** 0
10	8.08 868	9.99 997	8.08 872	50	10	8.18 110	9.99 995	8.18 115	50
20	8.09 040	9.99 997	8.09 043	40	20	8.18 249	9.99 995	8.18 254	40
30	8.09 210	9.99 997	8.09 214	30	30	8.18 387	9.99 995	8.18 392	30
40	8.09 380	9.99 997	8.09 384	20	40	8.18 524	9.99 995	8.18 530	20
50	8.09 550	9.99 997	8.09 553	10	50	8.18 662	9.99 995	8.18 667	10
43 0	8.09 718	9.99 997	8.09 722	**17** 0	**53** 0	8.18 798	9.99 995	8.18 804	**7** 0
10	8.09 886	9.99 997	8.09 890	50	10	8.18 935	9.99 995	8.18 940	50
20	8.10 054	9.99 997	8.10 057	40	20	8.19 071	9.99 995	8.19 076	40
30	8.10 220	9.99 997	8.10 224	30	30	8.19 206	9.99 995	8.19 212	30
40	8.10 386	9.99 997	8.10 390	20	40	8.19 341	9.99 995	8.19 347	20
50	8.10 552	9.99 996	8.10 555	10	50	8.19 476	9.99 995	8.19 481	10
44 0	8.10 717	9.99 996	8.10 720	**16** 0	**54** 0	8.19 610	9.99 995	8.19 616	**6** 0
10	8.10 881	9.99 996	8.10 884	50	10	8.19 744	9.99 995	8.19 749	50
20	8.11 044	9.99 996	8.11 048	40	20	8.19 877	9.99 995	8.19 883	40
30	8.11 207	9.99 996	8.11 211	30	30	8.20 010	9.99 995	8.20 016	30
40	8.11 370	9.99 996	8.11 373	20	40	8.20 143	9.99 995	8.20 149	20
50	8.11 531	9.99 996	8.11 535	10	50	8.20 275	9.99 994	8.20 281	10
45 0	8.11 693	9.99 996	8.11 696	**15** 0	**55** 0	8.20 407	9.99 994	8.20 413	**5** 0
10	8.11 853	9.99 996	8.11 857	50	10	8.20 538	9.99 994	8.20 544	50
20	8.12 013	9.99 996	8.12 017	40	20	8.20 669	9.99 994	8.20 675	40
30	8.12 172	9.99 996	8.12 176	30	30	8.20 800	9.99 994	8.20 806	30
40	8.12 331	9.99 996	8.12 335	20	40	8.20 930	9.99 994	8.20 936	20
50	8.12 489	9.99 996	8.12 493	10	50	8.21 060	9.99 994	8.21 066	10
46 0	8.12 647	9.99 996	8.12 651	**14** 0	**56** 0	8.21 189	9.99 994	8.21 195	**4** 0
10	8.12 804	9.99 996	8.12 808	50	10	8.21 319	9.99 994	8.21 324	50
20	8.12 961	9.99 996	8.12 965	40	20	8.21 447	9.99 994	8.21 453	40
30	8.13 117	9.99 996	8.13 121	30	30	8.21 576	9.99 994	8.21 581	30
40	8.13 272	9.99 996	8.13 276	20	40	8.21 703	9.99 994	8.21 709	20
50	8.13 427	9.99 996	8.13 431	10	50	8.21 831	9.99 994	8.21 837	10
47 0	8.13 581	9.99 996	8.13 585	**13** 0	**57** 0	8.21 958	9.99 994	8.21 964	**3** 0
10	8.13 735	9.99 996	8.13 739	50	10	8.22 085	9.99 994	8.22 091	50
20	8.13 888	9.99 996	8.13 892	40	20	8.22 211	9.99 994	8.22 217	40
30	8.14 041	9.99 996	8.14 045	30	30	8.22 337	9.99 994	8.22 343	30
40	8.14 193	9.99 996	8.14 197	20	40	8.22 463	9.99 994	8.22 469	20
50	8.14 344	9.99 996	8.14 348	10	50	8.22 588	9.99 994	8.22 595	10
48 0	8.14 495	9.99 996	8.14 500	**12** 0	**58** 0	8.22 713	9.99 994	8.22 720	**2** 0
10	8.14 646	9.99 996	8.14 650	50	10	8.22 838	9.99 994	8.22 844	50
20	8.14 796	9.99 996	8.14 800	40	20	8.22 962	9.99 994	8.22 968	40
30	8.14 945	9.99 996	8.14 950	30	30	8.23 086	9.99 994	8.23 092	30
40	8.15 094	9.99 996	8.15 099	20	40	8.23 210	9.99 994	8.23 216	20
50	8.15 243	9.99 996	8.15 247	10	50	8.23 333	9.99 994	8.23 339	10
49 0	8.15 391	9.99 996	8.15 395	**11** 0	**59** 0	8.23 456	9.99 994	8.23 462	**1** 0
10	8.15 538	9.99 996	8.15 543	50	10	8.23 578	9.99 994	8.23 585	50
20	8.15 685	9.99 996	8.15 690	40	20	8.23 700	9.99 994	8.23 707	40
30	8.15 832	9.99 996	8.15 836	30	30	8.23 822	9.99 993	8.23 829	30
40	8.15 978	9.99 995	8.15 982	20	40	8.23 944	9.99 993	8.23 950	20
50	8.16 123	9.99 995	8.16 128	10	50	8.24 065	9.99 993	8.24 071	10
50 0	8.16 268	9.99 995	8.16 273	**10** 0	**60** 0	8.24 186	9.99 993	8.24 192	**0** 0
′ ″	log cos	log sin	log cot	′ ″	′ ″	log cos	log sin	log cot	′ ″

89°

′ ″	log sin	log cos	log tan	′ ″
0 0	8.24 186	9.99 993	8.24 192	**60** 0
10	8.24 306	9.99 993	8.24 313	50
20	8.24 426	9.99 993	8.24 433	40
30	8.24 546	9.99 993	8.24 553	30
40	8.24 665	9.99 993	8.24 672	20
50	8.24 785	9.99 993	8.24 791	10
1 0	8.24 903	9.99 993	8.24 910	**59** 0
10	8.25 022	9.99 993	8.25 029	50
20	8.25 140	9.99 993	8.25 147	40
30	8.25 258	9.99 993	8.25 265	30
40	8.25 375	9.99 993	8.25 382	20
50	8.25 493	9.99 993	8.25 500	10
2 0	8.25 609	9.99 993	8.25 616	**58** 0
10	8.25 726	9.99 993	8.25 733	50
20	8.25 842	9.99 993	8.25 849	40
30	8.25 958	9.99 993	8.25 965	30
40	8.26 074	9.99 993	8.26 081	20
50	8.26 189	9.99 993	8.26 196	10
3 0	8.26 304	9.99 993	8.26 312	**57** 0
10	8.26 419	9.99 993	8.26 426	50
20	8.26 533	9.99 993	8.26 541	40
30	8.26 648	9.99 993	8.26 655	30
40	8.26 761	9.99 993	8.26 769	20
50	8.26 875	9.99 993	8.26 882	10
4 0	8.26 988	9.99 992	8.26 996	**56** 0
10	8.27 101	9.99 992	8.27 109	50
20	8.27 214	9.99 992	8.27 221	40
30	8.27 326	9.99 992	8.27 334	30
40	8.27 438	9.99 992	8.27 446	20
50	8.27 550	9.99 992	8.27 558	10
5 0	8.27 661	9.99 992	8.27 669	**55** 0
10	8.27 773	9.99 992	8.27 780	50
20	8.27 883	9.99 992	8.27 891	40
30	8.27 994	9.99 992	8.28 002	30
40	8.28 104	9.99 992	8.28 112	20
50	8.28 215	9.99 992	8.28 223	10
6 0	8.28 324	9.99 992	8.28 332	**54** 0
10	8.28 434	9.99 992	8.28 442	50
20	8.28 543	9.99 992	8.28 551	40
30	8.28 652	9.99 992	8.28 660	30
40	8.28 761	9.99 992	8.28 769	20
50	8.28 869	9.99 992	8.28 877	10
7 0	8.28 977	9.99 992	8.28 986	**53** 0
10	8.29 085	9.99 992	8.29 094	50
20	8.29 193	9.99 992	8.29 201	40
30	8.29 300	9.99 992	8.29 309	30
40	8.29 407	9.99 992	8.29 416	20
50	8.29 514	9.99 992	8.29 523	10
8 0	8.29 621	9.99 992	8.29 629	**52** 0
10	8.29 727	9.99 991	8.29 736	50
20	8.29 833	9.99 991	8.29 842	40
30	8.29 939	9.99 991	8.29 947	30
40	8.30 044	9.99 991	8.30 053	20
50	8.30 150	9.99 991	8.30 158	10
9 0	8.30 255	9.99 991	8.30 263	**51** 0
10	8.30 359	9.99 991	8.30 368	50
20	8.30 464	9.99 991	8.30 473	40
30	8.30 568	9.99 991	8.30 577	30
40	8.30 672	9.99 991	8.30 681	20
50	8.30 776	9.99 991	8.30 785	10
10 0	8.30 879	9.99 991	8.30 888	**50** 0
′ ″	log cos	log sin	log cot	′ ″

′ ″	log sin	log cos	log tan	′ ″
10 0	8.30 879	9.99 991	8.30 888	**50** 0
10	8.30 983	9.99 991	8.30 992	50
20	8.31 086	9.99 991	8.31 095	40
30	8.31 188	9.99 991	8.31 198	30
40	8.31 291	9.99 991	8.31 300	20
50	8.31 393	9.99 991	8.31 403	10
11 0	8.31 495	9.99 991	8.31 505	**49** 0
10	8.31 597	9.99 991	8.31 606	50
20	8.31 699	9.99 991	8.31 708	40
30	8.31 800	9.99 991	8.31 809	30
40	8.31 901	9.99 991	8.31 911	20
50	8.32 002	9.99 991	8.32 012	10
12 0	8.32 103	9.99 990	8.32 112	**48** 0
10	8.32 203	9.99 990	8.32 213	50
20	8.32 303	9.99 990	8.32 313	40
30	8.32 403	9.99 990	8.32 413	30
40	8.32 503	9.99 990	8.32 513	20
50	8.32 602	9.99 990	8.32 612	10
13 0	8.32 702	9.99 990	8.32 711	**47** 0
10	8.32 801	9.99 990	8.32 811	50
20	8.32 899	9.99 990	8.32 909	40
30	8.32 998	9.99 990	8.33 008	30
40	8.33 096	9.99 990	8.33 106	20
50	8.33 195	9.99 990	8.33 205	10
14 0	8.33 292	9.99 990	8.33 302	**46** 0
10	8.33 390	9.99 990	8.33 400	50
20	8.33 488	9.99 990	8.33 498	40
30	8.33 585	9.99 990	8.33 595	30
40	8.33 682	9.99 990	8.33 692	20
50	8.33 779	9.99 990	8.33 789	10
15 0	8.33 875	9.99 990	8.33 886	**45** 0
10	8.33 972	9.99 990	8.33 982	50
20	8.34 068	9.99 990	8.34 078	40
30	8.34 164	9.99 990	8.34 174	30
40	8.34 260	9.99 989	8.34 270	20
50	8.34 355	9.99 989	8.34 366	10
16 0	8.34 450	9.99 989	8.34 461	**44** 0
10	8.34 546	9.99 989	8.34 556	50
20	8.34 640	9.99 989	8.34 651	40
30	8.34 735	9.99 989	8.34 746	30
40	8.34 830	9.99 989	8.34 840	20
50	8.34 924	9.99 989	8.34 935	10
17 0	8.35 018	9.99 989	8.35 029	**43** 0
10	8.35 112	9.99 989	8.35 123	50
20	8.35 206	9.99 989	8.35 217	40
30	8.35 299	9.99 989	8.35 310	30
40	8.35 392	9.99 989	8.35 403	20
50	8.35 485	9.99 989	8.35 497	10
18 0	8.35 578	9.99 989	8.35 590	**42** 0
10	8.35 671	9.99 989	8.35 682	50
20	8.35 764	9.99 989	8.35 775	40
30	8.35 856	9.99 989	8.35 867	30
40	8.35 948	9.99 989	8.35 959	20
50	8.36 040	9.99 989	8.36 051	10
19 0	8.36 131	9.99 989	8.36 143	**41** 0
10	8.36 223	9.99 988	8.36 235	50
20	8.36 314	9.99 988	8.36 326	40
30	8.36 405	9.99 988	8.36 417	30
40	8.36 496	9.99 988	8.36 508	20
50	8.36 587	9.99 988	8.36 599	10
20 0	8.36 678	9.99 988	8.36 689	**40** 0
′ ″	log cos	log sin	log cot	′ ″

1°

′ ″	log sin	log cos	log tan	′ ″	′ ″	log sin	log cos	log tan	′ ″
20 0	8.36 678	9.99 988	8.36 689	**40** 0	**30** 0	8.41 792	9.99 985	8.41 807	**30** 0
10	8.36 768	9.99 988	8.36 780	50	10	8.41 872	9.99 985	8.41 887	50
20	8.36 858	9.99 988	8.36 870	40	20	8.41 952	9.99 985	8.41 967	40
30	8.36 948	9.99 988	8.36 960	30	30	8.42 032	9.99 985	8.42 048	30
40	8.37 038	9.99 988	8.37 050	20	40	8.42 112	9.99 985	8.42 127	20
50	8.37 128	9.99 988	8.37 140	10	50	8.42 192	9.99 985	8.42 207	10
21 0	8.37 217	9.99 988	8.37 229	**39** 0	**31** 0	8.42 272	9.99 985	8.42 287	**29** 0
10	8.37 306	9.99 988	8.37 318	50	10	8.42 351	9.99 985	8.42 366	50
20	8.37 395	9.99 988	8.37 408	40	20	8.42 430	9.99 985	8.42 446	40
30	8.37 484	9.99 988	8.37 497	30	30	8.42 510	9.99 985	8.42 525	30
40	8.37 573	9.99 988	8.37 585	20	40	8.42 589	9.99 985	8.42 604	20
50	8.37 662	9.99 988	8.37 674	10	50	8.42 667	9.99 985	8.42 683	10
22 0	8.37 750	9.99 988	8.37 762	**38** 0	**32** 0	8.42 746	9.99 984	8.42 762	**28** 0
10	8.37 838	9.99 988	8.37 850	50	10	8.42 825	9.99 984	8.42 840	50
20	8.37 926	9.99 988	8.37 938	40	20	8.42 903	9.99 984	8.42 919	40
30	8.38 014	9.99 987	8.38 026	30	30	8.42 982	9.99 984	8.42 997	30
40	8.38 101	9.99 987	8.38 114	20	40	8.43 060	9.99 984	8.43 075	20
50	8.38 189	9.99 987	8.38 202	10	50	8.43 138	9.99 984	8.43 154	10
23 0	8.38 276	9.99 987	8.38 289	**37** 0	**33** 0	8.43 216	9.99 984	8.43 232	**27** 0
10	8.38 363	9.99 987	8.38 376	50	10	8.43 293	9.99 984	8.43 309	50
20	8.38 450	9.99 987	8.38 463	40	20	8.43 371	9.99 984	8.43 387	40
30	8.38 537	9.99 987	8.38 550	30	30	8.43 448	9.99 984	8.43 464	30
40	8.38 624	9.99 987	8.38 636	20	40	8.43 526	9.99 984	8.43 542	20
50	8.38 710	9.99 987	8.38 723	10	50	8.43 603	9.99 984	8.43 619	10
24 0	8.38 796	9.99 987	8.38 809	**36** 0	**34** 0	8.43 680	9.99 984	8.43 696	**26** 0
10	8.38 882	9.99 987	8.38 895	50	10	8.43 757	9.99 984	8.43 773	50
20	8.38 968	9.99 987	8.38 981	40	20	8.43 834	9.99 984	8.43 850	40
30	8.39 054	9.99 987	8.39 067	30	30	8.43 910	9.99 984	8.43 927	30
40	8.39 139	9.99 987	8.39 153	20	40	8.43 987	9.99 984	8.44 003	20
50	8.39 225	9.99 987	8.39 238	10	50	8.44 063	9.99 983	8.44 080	10
25 0	8.39 310	9.99 987	8.39 323	**35** 0	**35** 0	8.44 139	9.99 983	8.44 156	**25** 0
10	8.39 395	9.99 987	8.39 408	50	10	8.44 216	9.99 983	8.44 232	50
20	8.39 480	9.99 987	8.39 493	40	20	8.44 292	9.99 983	8.44 308	40
30	8.39 565	9.99 987	8.39 578	30	30	8.44 367	9.99 983	8.44 384	30
40	8.39 649	9.99 987	8.39 663	20	40	8.44 443	9.99 983	8.44 460	20
50	8.39 734	9.99 986	8.39 747	10	50	8.44 519	9.99 983	8.44 536	10
26 0	8.39 818	9.99 986	8.39 832	**34** 0	**36** 0	8.44 594	9.99 983	8.44 611	**24** 0
10	8.39 902	9.99 986	8.39 916	50	10	8.44 669	9.99 983	8.44 686	50
20	8.39 986	9.99 986	8.40 000	40	20	8.44 745	9.99 983	8.44 762	40
30	8.40 070	9.99 986	8.40 083	30	30	8.44 820	9.99 983	8.44 837	30
40	8.40 153	9.99 986	8.40 167	20	40	8.44 895	9.99 983	8.44 912	20
50	8.40 237	9.99 986	8.40 251	10	50	8.44 969	9.99 983	8.44 987	10
27 0	8.40 320	9.99 986	8.40 334	**33** 0	**37** 0	8.45 044	9.99 983	8.45 061	**23** 0
10	8.40 403	9.99 986	8.40 417	50	10	8.45 119	9.99 983	8.45 136	50
20	8.40 486	9.99 986	8.40 500	40	20	8.45 193	9.99 983	8.45 210	40
30	8.40 569	9.99 986	8.40 583	30	30	8.45 267	9.99 983	8.45 285	30
40	8.40 651	9.99 986	8.40 665	20	40	8.45 341	9.99 982	8.45 359	20
50	8.40 734	9.99 986	8.40 748	10	50	8.45 415	9.99 982	8.45 433	10
28 0	8.40 816	9.99 986	8.40 830	**32** 0	**38** 0	8.45 489	9.99 982	8.45 507	**22** 0
10	8.40 898	9.99 986	8.40 913	50	10	8.45 563	9.99 982	8.45 581	50
20	8.40 980	9.99 986	8.40 995	40	20	8.45 637	9.99 982	8.45 655	40
30	8.41 062	9.99 986	8.41 077	30	30	8.45 710	9.99 982	8.45 728	30
40	8.41 144	9.99 986	8.41 158	20	40	8.45 784	9.99 982	8.45 802	20
50	8.41 225	9.99 986	8.41 240	10	50	8.45 857	9.99 982	8.45 875	10
29 0	8.41 307	9.99 985	8.41 321	**31** 0	**39** 0	8.45 930	9.99 982	8.45 948	**21** 0
10	8.41 388	9.99 985	8.41 403	50	10	8.46 003	9.99 982	8.46 021	50
20	8.41 469	9.99 985	8.41 484	40	20	8.46 076	9.99 982	8.46 094	40
30	8.41 550	9.99 985	8.41 565	30	30	8.46 149	9.99 982	8.46 167	30
40	8.41 631	9.99 985	8.41 646	20	40	8.46 222	9.99 982	8.46 240	20
50	8.41 711	9.99 985	8.41 726	10	50	8.46 294	9.99 982	8.46 312	10
30 0	8.41 792	9.99 985	8.41 807	**30** 0	**40** 0	8.46 366	9.99 982	8.46 385	**20** 0
′ ″	log cos	log sin	log cot	′ ″	′ ″	log cos	log sin	log cot	′ ″

88°

′ ″	log sin	log cos	log tan	′ ″	′ ″	log sin	log cos	log tan	′ ″
40 0	8.46 366	9.99 982	8.46 385	**20** 0	**50** 0	8.50 504	9.99 978	8.50 527	**10** 0
10	8.46 439	9.99 982	8.46 457	50	10	8.50 570	9.99 978	8.50 593	50
20	8.46 511	9.99 982	8.46 529	40	20	8.50 636	9.99 978	8.50 658	40
30	8.46 583	9.99 981	8.46 602	30	30	8.50 701	9.99 978	8.50 724	30
40	8.46 655	9.99 981	8.46 674	20	40	8.50 767	9.99 977	8.50 789	20
50	8.46 727	9.99 981	8.46 745	10	50	8.50 832	9.99 977	8.50 855	10
41 0	8.46 799	9.99 981	8.46 817	**19** 0	**51** 0	8.50 897	9.99 977	8.50 920	**9** 0
10	8.46 870	9.99 981	8.46 889	50	10	8.50 963	9.99 977	8.50 985	50
20	8.46 942	9.99 981	8.46 960	40	20	8.51 028	9.99 977	8.51 050	40
30	8.47 013	9.99 981	8.47 032	30	30	8.51 092	9.99 977	8.51 115	30
40	8.47 084	9.99 981	8.47 103	20	40	8.51 157	9.99 977	8.51 180	20
50	8.47 155	9.99 981	8.47 174	10	50	8.51 222	9.99 977	8.51 245	10
42 0	8.47 226	9.99 981	8.47 245	**18** 0	**52** 0	8.51 287	9.99 977	8.51 310	**8** 0
10	8.47 297	9.99 981	8.47 316	50	10	8.51 351	9.99 977	8.51 374	50
20	8.47 368	9.99 981	8.47 387	40	20	8.51 416	9.99 977	8.51 439	40
30	8.47 439	9.99 981	8.47 458	30	30	8.51 480	9.99 977	8.51 503	30
40	8.47 509	9.99 981	8.47 528	20	40	8.51 544	9.99 977	8.51 568	20
50	8.47 580	9.99 981	8.47 599	10	50	8.51 609	9.99 977	8.51 632	10
43 0	8.47 650	9.99 981	8.47 669	**17** 0	**53** 0	8.51 673	9.99 977	8.51 696	**7** 0
10	8.47 720	9.99 980	8.47 740	50	10	8.51 737	9.99 976	8.51 760	50
20	8.47 790	9.99 980	8.47 810	40	20	8.51 801	9.99 976	8.51 824	40
30	8.47 860	9.99 980	8.47 880	30	30	8.51 864	9.99 976	8.51 888	30
40	8.47 930	9.99 980	8.47 950	20	40	8.51 928	9.99 976	8.51 952	20
50	8.48 000	9.99 980	8.48 020	10	50	8.51 992	9.99 976	8.52 015	10
44 0	8.48 069	9.99 980	8.48 089	**16** 0	**54** 0	8.52 055	9.99 976	8.52 079	**6** 0
10	8.48 139	9.99 980	8.48 159	50	10	8.52 119	9.99 976	8.52 143	50
20	8.48 208	9.99 980	8.48 228	40	20	8.52 182	9.99 976	8.52 206	40
30	8.48 278	9.99 980	8.48 298	30	30	8.52 245	9.99 976	8.52 269	30
40	8.48 347	9.99 980	8.48 367	20	40	8.52 308	9.99 976	8.52 332	20
50	8.48 416	9.99 980	8.48 436	10	50	8.52 371	9.99 976	8.52 396	10
45 0	8.48 485	9.99 980	8.48 505	**15** 0	**55** 0	8.52 434	9.99 976	8.52 459	**5** 0
10	8.48 554	9.99 980	8.48 574	50	10	8.52 497	9.99 976	8.52 522	50
20	8.48 622	9.99 980	8.48 643	40	20	8.52 560	9.99 976	8.52 584	40
30	8.48 691	9.99 980	8.48 711	30	30	8.52 623	9.99 975	8.52 647	30
40	8.48 760	9.99 979	8.48 780	20	40	8.52 685	9.99 975	8.52 710	20
50	8.48 828	9.99 979	8.48 849	10	50	8.52 748	9.99 975	8.52 772	10
46 0	8.48 896	9.99 979	8.48 917	**14** 0	**56** 0	8.52 810	9.99 975	8.52 835	**4** 0
10	8.48 965	9.99 979	8.48 985	50	10	8.52 872	9.99 975	8.52 897	50
20	8.49 033	9.99 979	8.49 053	40	20	8.52 935	9.99 975	8.52 960	40
30	8.49 101	9.99 979	8.49 121	30	30	8.52 997	9.99 975	8.53 022	30
40	8.49 169	9.99 979	8.49 189	20	40	8.53 059	9.99 975	8.53 084	20
50	8.49 236	9.99 979	8.49 257	10	50	8.53 121	9.99 975	8.53 146	10
47 0	8.49 304	9.99 979	8.49 325	**13** 0	**57** 0	8.53 183	9.99 975	8.53 208	**3** 0
10	8.49 372	9.99 979	8.49 393	50	10	8.53 245	9.99 975	8.53 270	50
20	8.49 439	9.99 979	8.49 460	40	20	8.53 306	9.99 975	8.53 332	40
30	8.49 506	9.99 979	8.49 528	30	30	8.53 368	9.99 975	8.53 393	30
40	8.49 574	9.99 979	8.49 595	20	40	8.53 429	9.99 975	8.53 455	20
50	8.49 641	9.99 979	8.49 662	10	50	8.53 491	9.99 974	8.53 516	10
48 0	8.49 708	9.99 979	8.49 729	**12** 0	**58** 0	8.53 552	9.99 974	8.53 578	**2** 0
10	8.49 775	9.99 979	8.49 796	50	10	8.53 614	9.99 974	8.53 639	50
20	8.49 842	9.99 978	8.49 863	40	20	8.53 675	9.99 974	8.53 700	40
30	8.49 908	9.99 978	8.49 930	30	30	8.53 736	9.99 974	8.53 762	30
40	8.49 975	9.99 978	8.49 997	20	40	8.53 797	9.99 974	8.53 823	20
50	8.50 042	9.99 978	8.50 063	10	50	8.53 858	9.99 974	8.53 884	10
49 0	8.50 108	9.99 978	8.50 130	**11** 0	**59** 0	8.53 919	9.99 974	8.53 945	**1** 0
10	8.50 174	9.99 978	8.50 196	50	10	8.53 979	9.99 974	8.54 005	50
20	8.50 241	9.99 978	8.50 263	40	20	8.54 040	9.99 974	8.54 066	40
30	8.50 307	9.99 978	8.50 329	30	30	8.54 101	9.99 974	8.54 127	30
40	8.50 373	9.99 978	8.50 395	20	40	8.54 161	9.99 974	8.54 187	20
50	8.50 439	9.99 978	8.50 461	10	50	8.54 222	9.99 974	8.54 248	10
50 0	8.50 504	9.99 978	8.50 527	**10** 0	**60** 0	8.54 282	9.99 974	8.54 308	**0** 0
′ ″	log cos	log sin	log cot	′ ″	′ ″	log cos	log sin	log cot	′ ″

1°

′	log sin	log cos	log tan	log cot	′
	8	9	8	11	
0	24 186	99 993	24 192	75 808	**60**
1	24 903	99 993	24 910	75 090	59
2	25 609	99 993	25 616	74 384	58
3	26 304	99 993	26 312	73 688	57
4	26 988	99 992	26 996	73 004	56
5	27 661	99 992	27 669	72 331	**55**
6	28 324	99 992	28 332	71 668	54
7	28 977	99 992	28 986	71 014	53
8	29 621	99 992	29 629	70 371	52
9	30 255	99 991	30 263	69 737	51
10	30 879	99 991	30 888	69 112	**50**
11	31 495	99 991	31 505	68 495	49
12	32 103	99 990	32 112	67 888	48
13	32 702	99 990	32 711	67 289	47
14	33 292	99 990	33 302	66 698	46
15	33 875	99 990	33 886	66 114	**45**
16	34 450	99 989	34 461	65 539	44
17	35 018	99 989	35 029	64 971	43
18	35 578	99 989	35 590	64 410	42
19	36 131	99 989	36 143	63 857	41
20	36 678	99 988	36 689	63 311	**40**
21	37 217	99 988	37 229	62 771	39
22	37 750	99 988	37 762	62 238	38
23	38 276	99 987	38 289	61 711	37
24	38 796	99 987	38 809	61 191	36
25	39 310	99 987	39 323	60 677	**35**
26	39 818	99 986	39 832	60 168	34
27	40 320	99 986	40 334	59 666	33
28	40 816	99 986	40 830	59 170	32
29	41 307	99 985	41 321	58 679	31
30	41 792	99 985	41 807	58 193	**30**
31	42 272	99 985	42 287	57 713	29
32	42 746	99 984	42 762	57 238	28
33	43 216	99 984	43 232	56 768	27
34	43 680	99 984	43 696	56 304	26
35	44 139	99 983	44 156	55 844	**25**
36	44 594	99 983	44 611	55 389	24
37	45 044	99 983	45 061	54 939	23
38	45 489	99 982	45 507	54 493	22
39	45 930	99 982	45 948	54 052	21
40	46 366	99 982	46 385	53 615	**20**
41	46 799	99 981	46 817	53 183	19
42	47 226	99 981	47 245	52 755	18
43	47 650	99 981	47 669	52 331	17
44	48 069	99 980	48 089	51 911	16
45	48 485	99 980	48 505	51 495	**15**
46	48 896	99 979	48 917	51 083	14
47	49 304	99 979	49 325	50 675	13
48	49 708	99 979	49 729	50 271	12
49	50 108	99 978	50 130	49 870	11
50	50 504	99 978	50 527	49 473	**10**
51	50 897	99 977	50 920	49 080	9
52	51 287	99 977	51 310	48 690	8
53	51 673	99 977	51 696	48 304	7
54	52 055	99 976	52 079	47 921	6
55	52 434	99 976	52 459	47 541	**5**
56	52 810	99 975	52 835	47 165	4
57	53 183	99 975	53 208	46 792	3
58	53 552	99 974	53 578	46 422	2
59	53 919	99 974	53 945	46 055	1
60	54 282	99 974	54 308	45 692	**0**
	8	9	8	11	
′	log cos	log sin	log cot	log tan	′

88°

2°

′	log sin	log cos	log tan	log cot	′
	8	9	8	11	
0	54 282	99 974	54 308	45 692	**60**
1	54 642	99 973	54 669	45 331	59
2	54 999	99 973	55 027	44 973	58
3	55 354	99 972	55 382	44 618	57
4	55 705	99 972	55 734	44 266	56
5	56 054	99 971	56 083	43 917	**55**
6	56 400	99 971	56 429	43 571	54
7	56 743	99 970	56 773	43 227	53
8	57 084	99 970	57 114	42 886	52
9	57 421	99 969	57 452	42 548	51
10	57 757	99 969	57 788	42 212	**50**
11	58 089	99 968	58 121	41 879	49
12	58 419	99 968	58 451	41 549	48
13	58 747	99 967	58 779	41 221	47
14	59 072	99 967	59 105	40 895	46
15	59 395	99 967	59 428	40 572	**45**
16	59 715	99 966	59 749	40 251	44
17	60 033	99 966	60 068	39 932	43
18	60 349	99 965	60 384	39 616	42
19	60 662	99 964	60 698	39 302	41
20	60 973	99 964	61 009	38 991	**40**
21	61 282	99 963	61 319	38 681	39
22	61 589	99 963	61 626	38 374	38
23	61 894	99 962	61 931	38 069	37
24	62 196	99 962	62 234	37 766	36
25	62 497	99 961	62 535	37 465	**35**
26	62 795	99 961	62 834	37 166	34
27	63 091	99 960	63 131	36 869	33
28	63 385	99 960	63 426	36 574	32
29	63 678	99 959	63 718	36 282	31
30	63 968	99 959	64 009	35 991	**30**
31	64 256	99 958	64 298	35 702	29
32	64 543	99 958	64 585	35 415	28
33	64 827	99 957	64 870	35 130	27
34	65 110	99 956	65 154	34 846	26
35	65 391	99 956	65 435	34 565	**25**
36	65 670	99 955	65 715	34 285	24
37	65 947	99 955	65 993	34 007	23
38	66 223	99 954	66 269	33 731	22
39	66 497	99 954	66 543	33 457	21
40	66 769	99 953	66 816	33 184	**20**
41	67 039	99 952	67 087	32 913	19
42	67 308	99 952	67 356	32 644	18
43	67 575	99 951	67 624	32 376	17
44	67 841	99 951	67 890	32 110	16
45	68 104	99 950	68 154	31 846	**15**
46	68 367	99 949	68 417	31 583	14
47	68 627	99 949	68 678	31 322	13
48	68 886	99 948	68 938	31 062	12
49	69 144	99 948	69 196	30 804	11
50	69 400	99 947	69 453	30 547	**10**
51	69 654	99 946	69 708	30 292	9
52	69 907	99 946	69 962	30 038	8
53	70 159	99 945	70 214	29 786	7
54	70 409	99 944	70 465	29 535	6
55	70 658	99 944	70 714	29 286	**5**
56	70 905	99 943	70 962	29 038	4
57	71 151	99 942	71 208	28 792	3
58	71 395	99 942	71 453	28 547	2
59	71 638	99 941	71 697	28 303	1
60	71 880	99 940	71 940	28 060	**0**
	8	9	8	11	
′	log cos	log sin	log cot	log tan	′

87°

3°

′	log sin	log cos	log tan	log cot	′
	8	9	8	11	
0	71 880	99 940	71 940	28 060	**60**
1	72 120	940	72 181	27 819	59
2	359	939	420	580	58
3	597	938	659	341	57
4	72 834	938	72 896	27 104	56
5	73 069	99 937	73 132	26 868	**55**
6	303	936	366	634	54
7	535	936	600	400	53
8	767	935	73 832	26 168	52
9	73 997	934	74 063	25 937	51
10	74 226	99 934	74 292	25 708	**50**
11	454	933	521	479	49
12	680	932	748	252	48
13	74 906	932	74 974	25 026	47
14	75 130	931	75 199	24 801	46
15	75 353	99 930	75 423	24 577	**45**
16	575	929	645	355	44
17	75 795	929	75 867	24 133	43
18	76 015	928	76 087	23 913	42
19	234	927	306	694	41
20	76 451	99 926	76 525	23 475	**40**
21	667	926	742	258	39
22	76 883	925	76 958	23 042	38
23	77 097	924	77 173	22 827	37
24	310	923	387	613	36
25	77 522	99 923	77 600	22 400	**35**
26	733	922	77 811	22 189	34
27	77 943	921	78 022	21 978	33
28	78 152	920	232	768	32
29	360	920	441	559	31
30	78 568	99 919	78 649	21 351	**30**
31	774	918	78 855	21 145	29
32	78 979	917	79 061	20 939	28
33	79 183	917	266	734	27
34	386	916	470	530	26
35	79 588	99 915	79 673	20 327	**25**
36	789	914	79 875	20 125	24
37	79 990	913	80 076	19 924	23
38	80 189	913	277	723	22
39	388	912	476	524	21
40	80 585	99 911	80 674	19 326	**20**
41	782	910	80 872	19 128	19
42	80 978	909	81 068	18 932	18
43	81 173	909	264	736	17
44	367	908	459	541	16
45	81 560	99 907	81 653	18 347	**15**
46	752	906	81 846	18 154	14
47	81 944	905	82 038	17 962	13
48	82 134	904	230	770	12
49	324	904	420	580	11
50	82 513	99 903	82 610	17 390	**10**
51	701	902	799	201	9
52	82 888	901	82 987	17 013	8
53	83 075	900	83 175	16 825	7
54	261	899	361	639	6
55	83 446	99 898	83 547	16 453	**5**
56	630	898	732	268	4
57	813	897	83 916	16 084	3
58	83 996	896	84 100	15 900	2
59	84 177	895	282	718	1
60	84 358	99 894	84 464	15 536	**0**
	8	9	8	11	
′	log cos	log sin	log cot	log tan	′

86°

4°

′	log sin	log cos	log tan	log cot	′
	8	9	8	11	
0	84 358	99 894	84 464	15 536	**60**
1	539	893	646	354	59
2	718	892	84 826	15 174	58
3	84 897	891	85 006	14 994	57
4	85 075	891	185	815	56
5	85 252	99 890	85 363	14 637	**55**
6	429	889	540	460	54
7	605	888	717	283	53
8	780	887	85 893	14 107	52
9	85 955	886	86 069	13 931	51
10	86 128	99 885	86 243	13 757	**50**
11	301	884	417	583	49
12	474	883	591	409	48
13	645	882	763	237	47
14	816	881	86 935	13 065	46
15	86 987	99 880	87 106	12 894	**45**
16	87 156	879	277	723	44
17	325	879	447	553	43
18	494	878	616	384	42
19	661	877	785	215	41
20	87 829	99 876	87 953	12 047	**40**
21	87 995	875	88 120	11 880	39
22	88 161	874	287	713	38
23	326	873	453	547	37
24	490	872	618	382	36
25	88 654	99 871	88 783	11 217	**35**
26	817	870	88 948	11 052	34
27	88 980	869	89 111	10 889	33
28	89 142	868	274	726	32
29	304	867	437	563	31
30	89 464	99 866	89 598	10 402	**30**
31	625	865	760	240	29
32	784	864	89 920	10 080	28
33	89 943	863	90 080	09 920	27
34	90 102	862	240	760	26
35	90 260	99 861	90 399	09 601	**25**
36	417	860	557	443	24
37	574	859	715	285	23
38	730	858	90 872	09 128	22
39	90 885	857	91 029	08 971	21
40	91 040	99 856	91 185	08 815	**20**
41	195	855	340	660	19
42	349	854	495	505	18
43	502	853	650	350	17
44	655	852	803	197	16
45	91 807	99 851	91 957	08 043	**15**
46	91 959	850	92 110	07 890	14
47	92 110	848	262	738	13
48	261	847	414	586	12
49	411	846	565	435	11
50	92 561	99 845	92 716	07 284	**10**
51	710	844	92 866	07 134	9
52	92 859	843	93 016	06 984	8
53	93 007	842	165	835	7
54	154	841	313	687	6
55	93 301	99 840	93 462	06 538	**5**
56	448	839	609	391	4
57	594	838	756	244	3
58	740	837	93 903	06 097	2
59	93 885	836	94 049	05 951	1
60	94 030	99 834	94 195	05 805	**0**
	8	9	8	11	
′	log cos	log sin	log cot	log tan	′

85°

5°

'	log sin 8	log cos 9	log tan 8	log cot 11	'
0	94 030	99 834	94 195	05 805	**60**
1	174	833	340	660	59
2	317	832	485	515	58
3	461	831	630	370	57
4	603	830	773	227	56
5	94 746	99 829	94 917	05 083	**55**
6	94 887	828	95 060	04 940	54
7	95 029	827	202	798	53
8	170	825	344	656	52
9	310	824	486	514	51
10	95 450	99 823	95 627	04 373	**50**
11	589	822	767	233	49
12	728	821	95 908	04 092	48
13	95 867	820	96 047	03 953	47
14	96 005	819	187	813	46
15	96 143	99 817	96 325	03 675	**45**
16	280	816	464	536	44
17	417	815	602	398	43
18	553	814	739	261	42
19	689	813	96 877	03 123	41
20	96 825	99 812	97 013	02 987	**40**
21	96 960	810	150	850	39
22	97 095	809	285	715	38
23	229	808	421	579	37
24	363	807	556	444	36
25	97 496	99 806	97 691	02 309	**35**
26	629	804	825	175	34
27	762	803	97 959	02 041	33
28	97 894	802	98 092	01 908	32
29	98 026	801	225	775	31
30	98 157	99 800	98 358	01 642	**30**
31	288	798	490	510	29
32	419	797	622	378	28
33	549	796	753	247	27
34	679	795	98 884	01 116	26
35	98 808	99 793	99 015	00 985	**25**
36	98 937	792	145	855	24
37	99 066	791	275	725	23
38	194	790	405	595	22
39	322	788	534	466	21
40	99 450	99 787	99 662	00 338	**20**
41	577	786	791	209	19
42	704	785	99 919	00 081	18
43	830	783	00 046	99 954	17
44	99 956	782	174	826	16
45	00 082	99 781	00 301	99 699	**15**
46	207	780	427	573	14
47	332	778	553	447	13
48	456	777	679	321	12
49	581	776	805	195	11
50	00 704	99 775	00 930	99 070	**10**
51	828	773	01 055	98 945	9
52	00 951	772	179	821	8
53	01 074	771	303	697	7
54	196	769	427	573	6
55	01 318	99 768	01 550	98 450	**5**
56	440	767	673	327	4
57	561	765	796	204	3
58	682	764	01 918	98 082	2
59	803	763	02 040	97 960	1
60	01 923	99 761	02 162	97 838	**0**
'	9 log cos	9 log sin	9 log cot	10 log tan	'

84°

6°

'	log sin 9	log cos 9	log tan 9	log cot 10	'
0	01 923	99 761	02 162	97 838	**60**
1	02 043	760	283	717	59
2	163	759	404	596	58
3	283	757	525	475	57
4	402	756	645	355	56
5	02 520	99 755	02 766	97 234	**55**
6	639	753	02 885	97 115	54
7	757	752	03 005	96 995	53
8	874	751	124	876	52
9	02 992	749	242	758	51
10	03 109	99 748	03 361	96 639	**50**
11	226	747	479	521	49
12	342	745	597	403	48
13	458	744	714	286	47
14	574	742	832	168	46
15	03 690	99 741	03 948	96 052	**45**
16	805	740	04 065	95 935	44
17	03 920	738	181	819	43
18	04 034	737	297	703	42
19	149	736	413	587	41
20	04 262	99 734	04 528	95 472	**40**
21	376	733	643	357	39
22	490	731	758	242	38
23	603	730	873	127	37
24	715	728	04 987	95 013	36
25	04 828	99 727	05 101	94 899	**35**
26	04 940	726	214	786	34
27	05 052	724	328	672	33
28	164	723	441	559	32
29	275	721	553	447	31
30	05 386	99 720	05 666	94 334	**30**
31	497	718	778	222	29
32	607	717	05 890	94 110	28
33	717	716	06 002	93 998	27
34	827	714	113	887	26
35	05 937	99 713	06 224	93 776	**25**
36	06 046	711	335	665	24
37	155	710	445	555	23
38	264	708	556	444	22
39	372	707	666	334	21
40	06 481	99 705	06 775	93 225	**20**
41	589	704	885	115	19
42	696	702	06 994	93 006	18
43	804	701	07 103	92 897	17
44	06 911	699	211	789	16
45	07 018	99 698	07 320	92 680	**15**
46	124	696	428	572	14
47	231	695	536	464	13
48	337	693	643	357	12
49	442	692	751	249	11
50	07 548	99 690	07 858	92 142	**10**
51	653	689	07 964	92 036	9
52	758	687	08 071	91 929	8
53	863	686	177	823	7
54	07 968	684	283	717	6
55	08 072	99 683	08 389	91 611	**5**
56	176	681	495	505	4
57	280	680	600	400	3
58	383	678	705	295	2
59	486	677	810	190	1
60	08 589	99 675	08 914	91 086	**0**
'	9 log cos	9 log sin	9 log cot	10 log tan	'

83°

7°

′	log sin	log cos	log tan	log cot	′
	9	9	9	10	
0	08 589	99 675	08 914	91 086	**60**
1	692	674	09 019	90 981	59
2	795	672	123	877	58
3	897	670	227	773	57
4	08 999	669	330	670	56
5	09 101	99 667	09 434	90 566	**55**
6	202	666	537	463	54
7	304	664	640	360	53
8	405	663	742	258	52
9	506	661	845	155	51
10	09 606	99 659	09 947	90 053	**50**
11	707	658	10 049	89 951	49
12	807	656	150	850	48
13	09 907	655	252	748	47
14	10 006	653	353	647	46
15	10 106	99 651	10 454	89 546	**45**
16	205	650	555	445	44
17	304	648	656	344	43
18	402	647	756	244	42
19	501	645	856	144	41
20	10 599	99 643	10 956	89 044	**40**
21	697	642	11 056	88 944	39
22	795	640	155	845	38
23	893	638	254	746	37
24	10 990	637	353	647	36
25	11 087	99 635	11 452	88 548	**35**
26	184	633	551	449	34
27	281	632	649	351	33
28	377	630	747	253	32
29	474	629	845	155	31
30	11 570	99 627	11 943	88 057	**30**
31	666	625	12 040	87 960	29
32	761	624	138	862	28
33	857	622	235	765	27
34	11 952	620	332	668	26
35	12 047	99 618	12 428	87 572	**25**
36	142	617	525	475	24
37	236	615	621	379	23
38	331	613	717	283	22
39	425	612	813	187	21
40	12 519	99 610	12 909	87 091	**20**
41	612	608	13 004	86 996	19
42	706	607	099	901	18
43	799	605	194	806	17
44	892	603	289	711	16
45	12 985	99 601	13 384	86 616	**15**
46	13 078	600	478	522	14
47	171	598	573	427	13
48	263	596	667	333	12
49	355	595	761	239	11
50	13 447	99 593	13 854	86 146	**10**
51	539	591	13 948	86 052	9
52	630	589	14 041	85 959	8
53	722	588	134	866	7
54	813	586	227	773	6
55	13 904	99 584	14 320	85 680	**5**
56	13 994	582	412	588	4
57	14 085	581	504	496	3
58	175	579	597	403	2
59	266	577	688	312	1
60	14 356	99 575	14 780	85 220	**0**
	9	9	9	10	
′	log cos	log sin	log cot	log tan	′

82°

8°

′	log sin	log cos	log tan	log cot	′
	9	9	9	10	
0	14 356	99 575	14 780	85 220	**60**
1	445	574	872	128	59
2	535	572	14 963	85 037	58
3	624	570	15 054	84 946	57
4	714	568	145	855	56
5	14 803	99 566	15 236	84 764	**55**
6	891	565	327	673	54
7	14 980	563	417	583	53
8	15 069	561	508	492	52
9	157	559	598	402	51
10	15 245	99 557	15 688	84 312	**50**
11	333	556	777	223	49
12	421	554	867	133	48
13	508	552	15 956	84 044	47
14	596	550	16 046	83 954	46
15	15 683	99 548	16 135	83 865	**45**
16	770	546	224	776	44
17	857	545	312	688	43
18	15 944	543	401	599	42
19	16 030	541	489	511	41
20	16 116	99 539	16 577	83 423	**40**
21	203	537	665	335	39
22	289	535	753	247	38
23	374	533	841	159	37
24	460	532	16 928	83 072	36
25	16 545	99 530	17 016	82 984	**35**
26	631	528	103	897	34
27	716	526	190	810	33
28	801	524	277	723	32
29	886	522	363	637	31
30	16 970	99 520	17 450	82 550	**30**
31	17 055	518	536	464	29
32	139	517	622	378	28
33	223	515	708	292	27
34	307	513	794	206	26
35	17 391	99 511	17 880	82 120	**25**
36	474	509	17 965	82 035	24
37	558	507	18 051	81 949	23
38	641	505	136	864	22
39	724	503	221	779	21
40	17 807	99 501	18 306	81 694	**20**
41	890	499	391	609	19
42	17 973	497	475	525	18
43	18 055	495	560	440	17
44	137	494	644	356	16
45	18 220	99 492	18 728	81 272	**15**
46	302	490	812	188	14
47	383	488	896	104	13
48	465	486	18 979	81 021	12
49	547	484	19 063	80 937	11
50	18 628	99 482	19 146	80 854	**10**
51	709	480	229	771	9
52	790	478	312	688	8
53	871	476	395	605	7
54	18 952	474	478	522	6
55	19 033	99 472	19 561	80 439	**5**
56	113	470	643	357	4
57	193	468	725	275	3
58	273	466	807	193	2
59	353	464	889	111	1
60	19 433	99 462	19 971	80 029	**0**
	9	9	9	10	
′	log cos	log sin	log cot	log tan	′

81°

9°

′	log sin 9	log cos 9	log tan 9	log cot 10	′
0	19 433	99 462	19 971	80 029	**60**
1	513	460	20 053	79 947	59
2	592	458	134	866	58
3	672	456	216	784	57
4	751	454	297	703	56
5	19 830	99 452	20 378	79 622	**55**
6	909	450	459	541	54
7	19 988	448	540	460	53
8	20 067	446	621	379	52
9	145	444	701	299	51
10	20 223	99 442	20 782	79 218	**50**
11	302	440	862	138	49
12	380	438	20 942	79 058	48
13	458	436	21 022	78 978	47
14	535	434	102	898	46
15	20 613	99 432	21 182	78 818	**45**
16	691	429	261	739	44
17	768	427	341	659	43
18	845	425	420	580	42
19	922	423	499	501	41
20	20 999	99 421	21 578	78 422	**40**
21	21 076	419	657	343	39
22	153	417	736	264	38
23	229	415	814	186	37
24	306	413	893	107	36
25	21 382	99 411	21 971	78 029	**35**
26	458	409	22 049	77 951	34
27	534	407	127	873	33
28	610	404	205	795	32
29	685	402	283	717	31
30	21 761	99 400	22 361	77 639	**30**
31	836	398	438	562	29
32	912	396	516	484	28
33	21 987	394	593	407	27
34	22 062	392	670	330	26
35	22 137	99 390	22 747	77 253	**25**
36	211	388	824	176	24
37	286	385	901	099	23
38	361	383	22 977	77 023	22
39	435	381	23 054	76 946	21
40	22 509	99 379	23 130	76 870	**20**
41	583	377	206	794	19
42	657	375	283	717	18
43	731	372	359	641	17
44	805	370	435	565	16
45	22 878	99 368	23 510	76 490	**15**
46	22 952	366	586	414	14
47	23 025	364	661	339	13
48	098	362	737	263	12
49	171	359	812	188	11
50	23 244	99 357	23 887	76 113	**10**
51	317	355	23 962	76 038	9
52	390	353	24 037	75 963	8
53	462	351	112	888	7
54	535	348	186	814	6
55	23 607	99 346	24 261	75 739	**5**
56	679	344	335	665	4
57	752	342	410	590	3
58	823	340	484	516	2
59	895	337	558	442	1
60	23 967	99 335	24 632	75 368	**0**
′	9 log cos	9 log sin	9 log cot	10 log tan	′

80°

10°

′	log sin 9	log cos 9	log tan 9	log cot 10	′
0	23 967	99 335	24 632	75 368	**60**
1	24 039	333	706	294	59
2	110	331	779	221	58
3	181	328	853	147	57
4	253	326	24 926	074	56
5	24 324	99 324	25 000	75 000	**55**
6	395	322	073	74 927	54
7	466	319	146	854	53
8	536	317	219	781	52
9	607	315	292	708	51
10	24 677	99 313	25 365	74 635	**50**
11	748	310	437	563	49
12	818	308	510	490	48
13	888	306	582	418	47
14	24 958	304	655	345	46
15	25 028	99 301	25 727	74 273	**45**
16	098	299	799	201	44
17	168	297	871	129	43
18	237	294	25 943	74 057	42
19	307	292	26 015	73 985	41
20	25 376	99 290	26 086	73 914	**40**
21	445	288	158	842	39
22	514	285	229	771	38
23	583	283	301	699	37
24	652	281	372	628	36
25	25 721	99 278	26 443	73 557	**35**
26	790	276	514	486	34
27	858	274	585	415	33
28	927	271	655	345	32
29	25 995	269	726	274	31
30	26 063	99 267	26 797	73 203	**30**
31	131	264	867	133	29
32	199	262	26 937	73 063	28
33	267	260	27 008	72 992	27
34	335	257	078	922	26
35	26 403	99 255	27 148	72 852	**25**
36	470	252	218	782	24
37	538	250	288	712	23
38	605	248	357	643	22
39	672	245	427	573	21
40	26 739	99 243	27 496	72 504	**20**
41	806	241	566	434	19
42	873	238	635	365	18
43	26 940	236	704	296	17
44	27 007	233	773	227	16
45	27 073	99 231	27 842	72 158	**15**
46	140	229	911	089	14
47	206	226	27 980	72 020	13
48	273	224	28 049	71 951	12
49	339	221	117	883	11
50	27 405	99 219	28 186	71 814	**10**
51	471	217	254	746	9
52	537	214	323	677	8
53	602	212	391	609	7
54	668	209	459	541	6
55	27 734	99 207	28 527	71 473	**5**
56	799	204	595	405	4
57	864	202	662	338	3
58	930	200	730	270	2
59	27 995	197	798	202	1
60	28 060	99 195	28 865	71 135	**0**
′	9 log cos	9 log sin	9 log cot	10 log tan	′

79°

11°

′	log sin 9	log cos 9	log tan 9	log cot 10	′
0	28 060	99 195	28 865	71 135	60
1	125	192	28 933	067	59
2	190	190	29 000	71 000	58
3	254	187	067	70 933	57
4	319	185	134	866	56
5	28 384	99 182	29 201	70 799	55
6	448	180	268	732	54
7	512	177	335	665	53
8	577	175	402	598	52
9	641	172	468	532	51
10	28 705	99 170	29 535	70 465	50
11	769	167	601	399	49
12	833	165	668	332	48
13	896	162	734	266	47
14	28 960	160	800	200	46
15	29 024	99 157	29 866	70 134	45
16	087	155	932	068	44
17	150	152	29 998	70 002	43
18	214	150	30 064	69 936	42
19	277	147	130	870	41
20	29 340	99 145	30 195	69 805	40
21	403	142	261	739	39
22	466	140	326	674	38
23	529	137	391	609	37
24	591	135	457	543	36
25	29 654	99 132	30 522	69 478	35
26	716	130	587	413	34
27	779	127	652	348	33
28	841	124	717	283	32
29	903	122	782	218	31
30	29 966	99 119	30 846	69 154	30
31	30 028	117	911	089	29
32	090	114	30 975	69 025	28
33	151	112	31 040	68 960	27
34	213	109	104	896	26
35	30 275	99 106	31 168	68 832	25
36	336	104	233	767	24
37	398	101	297	703	23
38	459	099	361	639	22
39	521	096	425	575	21
40	30 582	99 093	31 489	68 511	20
41	643	091	552	448	19
42	704	088	616	384	18
43	765	086	679	321	17
44	826	083	743	257	16
45	30 887	99 080	31 806	68 194	15
46	30 947	078	870	130	14
47	31 008	075	933	067	13
48	068	072	31 996	68 004	12
49	129	070	32 059	67 941	11
50	31 189	99 067	32 122	67 878	10
51	250	064	185	815	9
52	310	062	248	752	8
53	370	059	311	689	7
54	430	056	373	627	6
55	31 490	99 054	32 436	67 564	5
56	549	051	498	502	4
57	609	048	561	439	3
58	669	046	623	377	2
59	728	043	685	315	1
60	31 788	99 040	32 747	67 253	0
′	9 log cos	9 log sin	9 log cot	10 log tan	′

78°

12°

′	log sin 9	log cos 9	log tan 9	log cot 10	′
0	31 788	99 040	32 747	67 253	60
1	847	038	810	190	59
2	907	035	872	128	58
3	31 966	032	933	067	57
4	32 025	030	32 995	67 005	56
5	32 084	99 027	33 057	66 943	55
6	143	024	119	881	54
7	202	022	180	820	53
8	261	019	242	758	52
9	319	016	303	697	51
10	32 378	99 013	33 365	66 635	50
11	437	011	426	574	49
12	495	008	487	513	48
13	553	005	548	452	47
14	612	002	609	391	46
15	32 670	99 000	33 670	66 330	45
16	728	98 997	731	269	44
17	786	994	792	208	43
18	844	991	853	147	42
19	902	989	913	087	41
20	32 960	98 986	33 974	66 026	40
21	33 018	983	34 034	65 966	39
22	075	980	095	905	38
23	133	978	155	845	37
24	190	975	215	785	36
25	33 248	98 972	34 276	65 724	35
26	305	969	336	664	34
27	362	967	396	604	33
28	420	964	456	544	32
29	477	961	516	484	31
30	33 534	98 958	34 576	65 424	30
31	591	955	635	365	29
32	647	953	695	305	28
33	704	950	755	245	27
34	761	947	814	186	26
35	33 818	98 944	34 874	65 126	25
36	874	941	933	067	24
37	931	938	34 992	65 008	23
38	33 987	936	35 051	64 949	22
39	34 043	933	111	889	21
40	34 100	98 930	35 170	64 830	20
41	156	927	229	771	19
42	212	924	288	712	18
43	268	921	347	653	17
44	324	919	405	595	16
45	34 380	98 916	35 464	64 536	15
46	436	913	523	477	14
47	491	910	581	419	13
48	547	907	640	360	12
49	602	904	698	302	11
50	34 658	98 901	35 757	64 243	10
51	713	898	815	185	9
52	769	896	873	127	8
53	824	893	931	069	7
54	879	890	35 989	64 011	6
55	34 934	98 887	36 047	63 953	5
56	34 989	884	105	895	4
57	35 044	881	163	837	3
58	099	878	221	779	2
59	154	875	279	721	1
60	35 209	98 872	36 336	63 664	0
′	9 log cos	9 log sin	9 log cot	10 log tan	′

77°

13°

′	log sin 9	log cos 9	log tan 9	log cot 10	′
0	35 209	98 872	36 336	63 664	60
1	263	869	394	606	59
2	318	867	452	548	58
3	373	864	509	491	57
4	427	861	566	434	56
5	35 481	98 858	36 624	63 376	55
6	536	855	681	319	54
7	590	852	738	262	53
8	644	849	795	205	52
9	698	846	852	148	51
10	35 752	98 843	36 909	63 091	50
11	806	840	36 966	63 034	49
12	860	837	37 023	62 977	48
13	914	834	080	920	47
14	35 968	831	137	863	46
15	36 022	98 828	37 193	62 807	45
16	075	825	250	750	44
17	129	822	306	694	43
18	182	819	363	637	42
19	236	816	419	581	41
20	36 289	98 813	37 476	62 524	40
21	342	810	532	468	39
22	395	807	588	412	38
23	449	804	644	356	37
24	502	801	700	300	36
25	36 555	98 798	37 756	62 244	35
26	608	795	812	188	34
27	660	792	868	132	33
28	713	789	924	076	32
29	766	786	37 980	62 020	31
30	36 819	98 783	38 035	61 965	30
31	871	780	091	909	29
32	924	777	147	853	28
33	36 976	774	202	798	27
34	37 028	771	257	743	26
35	37 081	98 768	38 313	61 687	25
36	133	765	368	632	24
37	185	762	423	577	23
38	237	759	479	521	22
39	289	756	534	466	21
40	37 341	98 753	38 589	61 411	20
41	393	750	644	356	19
42	445	746	699	301	18
43	497	743	754	246	17
44	549	740	808	192	16
45	37 600	98 737	38 863	61 137	15
46	652	734	918	082	14
47	703	731	38 972	61 028	13
48	755	728	39 027	60 973	12
49	806	725	082	918	11
50	37 858	98 722	39 136	60 864	10
51	909	719	190	810	9
52	37 960	715	245	755	8
53	38 011	712	299	701	7
54	062	709	353	647	6
55	38 113	98 706	39 407	60 593	5
56	164	703	461	539	4
57	215	700	515	485	3
58	266	697	569	431	2
59	317	694	623	377	1
60	38 368	98 690	39 677	60 323	0
′	log cos 9	log sin 9	log cot 9	log tan 10	′

76°

14°

′	log sin 9	log cos 9	log tan 9	log cot 10	′
0	38 368	98 690	39 677	60 323	60
1	418	687	731	269	59
2	469	684	785	215	58
3	519	681	838	162	57
4	570	678	892	108	56
5	38 620	98 675	39 945	60 055	55
6	670	671	39 999	60 001	54
7	721	668	40 052	59 948	53
8	771	665	106	894	52
9	821	662	159	841	51
10	38 871	98 659	40 212	59 788	50
11	921	656	266	734	49
12	38 971	652	319	681	48
13	39 021	649	372	628	47
14	071	646	425	575	46
15	39 121	98 643	40 478	59 522	45
16	170	640	531	469	44
17	220	636	584	416	43
18	270	633	636	364	42
19	319	630	689	311	41
20	39 369	98 627	40 742	59 258	40
21	418	623	795	205	39
22	467	620	847	153	38
23	517	617	900	100	37
24	566	614	40 952	59 048	36
25	39 615	98 610	41 005	58 995	35
26	664	607	057	943	34
27	713	604	109	891	33
28	762	601	161	839	32
29	811	597	214	786	31
30	39 860	98 594	41 266	58 734	30
31	909	591	318	682	29
32	39 958	588	370	630	28
33	40 006	584	422	578	27
34	055	581	474	526	26
35	40 103	98 578	41 526	58 474	25
36	152	574	578	422	24
37	200	571	629	371	23
38	249	568	681	319	22
39	297	565	733	267	21
40	40 346	98 561	41 784	58 216	20
41	394	558	836	164	19
42	442	555	887	113	18
43	490	551	939	061	17
44	538	548	41 990	58 010	16
45	40 586	98 545	42 041	57 959	15
46	634	541	093	907	14
47	682	538	144	856	13
48	730	535	195	805	12
49	778	531	246	754	11
50	40 825	98 528	42 297	57 703	10
51	873	525	348	652	9
52	921	521	399	601	8
53	40 968	518	450	550	7
54	41 016	515	501	499	6
55	41 063	98 511	42 552	57 448	5
56	111	508	603	397	4
57	158	505	653	347	3
58	205	501	704	296	2
59	252	498	755	245	1
60	41 300	98 494	42 805	57 195	0
′	log cos 9	log sin 9	log cot 9	log tan 10	′

75°

15°

′	log sin	log cos	log tan	log cot	′
	9	9	9	10	
0	41 300	98 494	42 805	57 195	60
1	347	491	856	144	59
2	394	488	906	094	58
3	441	484	42 957	57 043	57
4	488	481	43 007	56 993	56
5	41 535	98 477	43 057	56 943	55
6	582	474	108	892	54
7	628	471	158	842	53
8	675	467	208	792	52
9	722	464	258	742	51
10	41 768	98 460	43 308	56 692	50
11	815	457	358	642	49
12	861	453	408	592	48
13	908	450	458	542	47
14	41 954	447	508	492	46
15	42 001	98 443	43 558	56 442	45
16	047	440	607	393	44
17	093	436	657	343	43
18	140	433	707	293	42
19	186	429	756	244	41
20	42 232	98 426	43 806	56 194	40
21	278	422	855	145	39
22	324	419	905	095	38
23	370	415	43 954	56 046	37
24	416	412	44 004	55 996	36
25	42 461	98 409	44 053	55 947	35
26	507	405	102	898	34
27	553	402	151	849	33
28	599	398	201	799	32
29	644	395	250	750	31
30	42 690	98 391	44 299	55 701	30
31	735	388	348	652	29
32	781	384	397	603	28
33	826	381	446	554	27
34	872	377	495	505	26
35	42 917	98 373	44 544	55 456	25
36	42 962	370	592	408	24
37	43 008	366	641	359	23
38	053	363	690	310	22
39	098	359	738	262	21
40	43 143	98 356	44 787	55 213	20
41	188	352	836	164	19
42	233	349	884	116	18
43	278	345	933	067	17
44	323	342	44 981	55 019	16
45	43 367	98 338	45 029	54 971	15
46	412	334	078	922	14
47	457	331	126	874	13
48	502	327	174	826	12
49	546	324	222	778	11
50	43 591	98 320	45 271	54 729	10
51	635	317	319	681	9
52	680	313	367	633	8
53	724	309	415	585	7
54	769	306	463	537	6
55	43 813	98 302	45 511	54 489	5
56	857	299	559	441	4
57	901	295	606	394	3
58	946	291	654	346	2
59	43 990	288	702	298	1
60	44 034	98 284	45 750	54 250	0
	9	9	9	10	
′	log cos	log sin	log cot	log tan	′

74°

16°

′	log sin	log cos	log tan	log cot	′
	9	9	9	10	
0	44 034	98 284	45 750	54 250	60
1	078	281	797	203	59
2	122	277	845	155	58
3	166	273	892	108	57
4	210	270	940	060	56
5	44 253	98 266	45 987	54 013	55
6	297	262	46 035	53 965	54
7	341	259	082	918	53
8	385	255	130	870	52
9	428	251	177	823	51
10	44 472	98 248	46 224	53 776	50
11	516	244	271	729	49
12	559	240	319	681	48
13	602	237	366	634	47
14	646	233	413	587	46
15	44 689	98 229	46 460	53 540	45
16	733	226	507	493	44
17	776	222	554	446	43
18	819	218	601	399	42
19	862	215	648	352	41
20	44 905	98 211	46 694	53 306	40
21	948	207	741	259	39
22	44 992	204	788	212	38
23	45 035	200	835	165	37
24	077	196	881	119	36
25	45 120	98 192	46 928	53 072	35
26	163	189	46 975	53 025	34
27	206	185	47 021	52 979	33
28	249	181	068	932	32
29	292	177	114	886	31
30	45 334	98 174	47 160	52 840	30
31	377	170	207	793	29
32	419	166	253	747	28
33	462	162	299	701	27
34	504	159	346	654	26
35	45 547	98 155	47 392	52 608	25
36	589	151	438	562	24
37	632	147	484	516	23
38	674	144	530	470	22
39	716	140	576	424	21
40	45 758	98 136	47 622	52 378	20
41	801	132	668	332	19
42	843	129	714	286	18
43	885	125	760	240	17
44	927	121	806	194	16
45	45 969	98 117	47 852	52 148	15
46	46 011	113	897	103	14
47	053	110	943	057	13
48	095	106	47 989	52 011	12
49	136	102	48 035	51 965	11
50	46 178	98 098	48 080	51 920	10
51	220	094	126	874	9
52	262	090	171	829	8
53	303	087	217	783	7
54	345	083	262	738	6
55	46 386	98 079	48 307	51 693	5
56	428	075	353	647	4
57	469	071	398	602	3
58	511	067	443	557	2
59	552	063	489	511	1
60	46 594	98 060	48 534	51 466	0
	9	9	9	10	
′	log cos	log sin	log cot	log tan	′

73°

17°

′	log sin 9	log cos 9	log tan 9	log cot 10	′
0	46 594	98 060	48 534	51 466	**60**
1	635	056	579	421	59
2	676	052	624	376	58
3	717	048	669	331	57
4	758	044	714	286	56
5	46 800	98 040	48 759	51 241	**55**
6	841	036	804	196	54
7	882	032	849	151	53
8	923	029	894	106	52
9	46 964	025	939	061	51
10	47 005	98 021	48 984	51 016	**50**
11	045	017	49 029	50 971	49
12	086	013	073	927	48
13	127	009	118	882	47
14	168	005	163	837	46
15	47 209	98 001	49 207	50 793	**45**
16	249	97 997	252	748	44
17	290	993	296	704	43
18	330	989	341	659	42
19	371	986	385	615	41
20	47 411	97 982	49 430	50 570	**40**
21	452	978	474	526	39
22	492	974	519	481	38
23	533	970	563	437	37
24	573	966	607	393	36
25	47 613	97 962	49 652	50 348	**35**
26	654	958	696	304	34
27	694	954	740	260	33
28	734	950	784	216	32
29	774	946	828	172	31
30	47 814	97 942	49 872	50 128	**30**
31	854	938	916	084	29
32	894	934	49 960	50 040	28
33	934	930	50 004	49 996	27
34	47 974	926	048	952	26
35	48 014	97 922	50 092	49 908	**25**
36	054	918	136	864	24
37	094	914	180	820	23
38	133	910	223	777	22
39	173	906	267	733	21
40	48 213	97 902	50 311	49 689	**20**
41	252	898	355	645	19
42	292	894	398	602	18
43	332	890	442	558	17
44	371	886	485	515	16
45	48 411	97 882	50 529	49 471	**15**
46	450	878	572	428	14
47	490	874	616	384	13
48	529	870	659	341	12
49	568	866	703	297	11
50	48 607	97 861	50 746	49 254	**10**
51	647	857	789	211	9
52	686	853	833	167	8
53	725	849	876	124	7
54	764	845	919	081	6
55	48 803	97 841	50 962	49 038	**5**
56	842	837	51 005	48 995	4
57	881	833	048	952	3
58	920	829	092	908	2
59	959	825	135	865	1
60	48 998	97 821	51 178	48 822	**0**
′	9 log cos	9 log sin	9 log cot	10 log tan	′

72°

18°

′	log sin 9	log cos 9	log tan 9	log cot 10	′
0	48 998	97 821	51 178	48 822	**60**
1	49 037	817	221	779	59
2	076	812	264	736	58
3	115	808	306	694	57
4	153	804	349	651	56
5	49 192	97 800	51 392	48 608	**55**
6	231	796	435	565	54
7	269	792	478	522	53
8	308	788	520	480	52
9	347	784	563	437	51
10	49 385	97 779	51 606	48 394	**50**
11	424	775	648	352	49
12	462	771	691	309	48
13	500	767	734	266	47
14	539	763	776	224	46
15	49 577	97 759	51 819	48 181	**45**
16	615	754	861	139	44
17	654	750	903	097	43
18	692	746	946	054	42
19	730	742	51 988	48 012	41
20	49 768	97 738	52 031	47 969	**40**
21	806	734	073	927	39
22	844	729	115	885	38
23	882	725	157	843	37
24	920	721	200	800	36
25	49 958	97 717	52 242	47 758	**35**
26	49 996	713	284	716	34
27	50 034	708	326	674	33
28	072	704	368	632	32
29	110	700	410	590	31
30	50 148	97 696	52 452	47 548	**30**
31	185	691	494	506	29
32	223	687	536	464	28
33	261	683	578	422	27
34	298	679	620	380	26
35	50 336	97 674	52 661	47 339	**25**
36	374	670	703	297	24
37	411	666	745	255	23
38	449	662	787	213	22
39	486	657	829	171	21
40	50 523	97 653	52 870	47 130	**20**
41	561	649	912	088	19
42	598	645	953	047	18
43	635	640	52 995	47 005	17
44	673	636	53 037	46 963	16
45	50 710	97 632	53 078	46 922	**15**
46	747	628	120	880	14
47	784	623	161	839	13
48	821	619	202	798	12
49	858	615	244	756	11
50	50 896	97 610	53 285	46 715	**10**
51	933	606	327	673	9
52	50 970	602	368	632	8
53	51 007	597	409	591	7
54	043	593	450	550	6
55	51 080	97 589	53 492	46 508	**5**
56	117	584	533	467	4
57	154	580	574	426	3
58	191	576	615	385	2
59	227	571	656	344	1
60	51 264	97 567	53 697	46 303	**0**
′	9 log cos	9 log sin	9 log cot	10 log tan	′

71°

19°

′	log sin 9	log cos 9	log tan 9	log cot 10	′
0	51 264	97 567	53 697	46 303	**60**
1	301	563	738	262	59
2	338	558	779	221	58
3	374	554	820	180	57
4	411	550	861	139	56
5	51 447	97 545	53 902	46 098	**55**
6	484	541	943	057	54
7	520	536	53 984	46 016	53
8	557	532	54 025	45 975	52
9	593	528	065	935	51
10	51 629	97 523	54 106	45 894	**50**
11	666	519	147	853	49
12	702	515	187	813	48
13	738	510	228	772	47
14	774	506	269	731	46
15	51 811	97 501	54 309	45 691	**45**
16	847	497	350	650	44
17	883	492	390	610	43
18	919	488	431	569	42
19	955	484	471	529	41
20	51 991	97 479	54 512	45 488	**40**
21	52 027	475	552	448	39
22	063	470	593	407	38
23	099	466	633	367	37
24	135	461	673	327	36
25	52 171	97 457	54 714	45 286	**35**
26	207	453	754	246	34
27	242	448	794	206	33
28	278	444	835	165	32
29	314	439	875	125	31
30	52 350	97 435	54 915	45 085	**30**
31	385	430	955	045	29
32	421	426	54 995	45 005	28
33	456	421	55 035	44 965	27
34	492	417	075	925	26
35	52 527	97 412	55 115	44 885	**25**
36	563	408	155	845	24
37	598	403	195	805	23
38	634	399	235	765	22
39	669	394	275	725	21
40	52 705	97 390	55 315	44 685	**20**
41	740	385	355	645	19
42	775	381	395	605	18
43	811	376	434	566	17
44	846	372	474	526	16
45	52 881	97 367	55 514	44 486	**15**
46	916	363	554	446	14
47	951	358	593	407	13
48	52 986	353	633	367	12
49	53 021	349	673	327	11
50	53 056	97 344	55 712	44 288	**10**
51	092	340	752	248	9
52	126	335	791	209	8
53	161	331	831	169	7
54	196	326	870	130	6
55	53 231	97 322	55 910	44 090	**5**
56	266	317	949	051	4
57	301	312	55 989	44 011	3
58	336	308	56 028	43 972	2
59	370	303	067	933	1
60	53 405	97 299	56 107	43 893	**0**
′	9 log cos	9 log sin	9 log cot	10 log tan	′

70°

20°

′	log sin 9	log cos 9	log tan 9	log cot 10	′
0	53 405	97 299	56 107	43 893	**60**
1	440	294	146	854	59
2	475	289	185	815	58
3	509	285	224	776	57
4	544	280	264	736	56
5	53 578	97 276	56 303	43 697	**55**
6	613	271	342	658	54
7	647	266	381	619	53
8	682	262	420	580	52
9	716	257	459	541	51
10	53 751	97 252	56 498	43 502	**50**
11	785	248	537	463	49
12	819	243	576	424	48
13	854	238	615	385	47
14	888	234	654	346	46
15	53 922	97 229	56 693	43 307	**45**
16	957	224	732	268	44
17	53 991	220	771	229	43
18	54 025	215	810	190	42
19	059	210	849	151	41
20	54 093	97 206	56 887	43 113	**40**
21	127	201	926	074	39
22	161	196	56 965	43 035	38
23	195	192	57 004	42 996	37
24	229	187	042	958	36
25	54 263	97 182	57 081	42 919	**35**
26	297	178	120	880	34
27	331	173	158	842	33
28	365	168	197	803	32
29	399	163	235	765	31
30	54 433	97 159	57 274	42 726	**30**
31	466	154	312	688	29
32	500	149	351	649	28
33	534	145	389	611	27
34	567	140	428	572	26
35	54 601	97 135	57 466	42 534	**25**
36	635	130	504	496	24
37	668	126	543	457	23
38	702	121	581	419	22
39	735	116	619	381	21
40	54 769	97 111	57 658	42 342	**20**
41	802	107	696	304	19
42	836	102	734	266	18
43	869	097	772	228	17
44	903	092	810	190	16
45	54 936	97 087	57 849	42 151	**15**
46	54 969	083	887	113	14
47	55 003	078	925	075	13
48	036	073	57 963	42 037	12
49	069	068	58 001	41 999	11
50	55 102	97 063	58 039	41 961	**10**
51	136	059	077	923	9
52	169	054	115	885	8
53	202	049	153	847	7
54	235	044	191	809	6
55	55 268	97 039	58 229	41 771	**5**
56	301	035	267	733	4
57	334	030	304	696	3
58	367	025	342	658	2
59	400	020	380	620	1
60	55 433	97 015	58 418	41 582	**0**
′	9 log cos	9 log sin	9 log cot	10 log tan	′

69°

21°

′	log sin 9	log cos 9	log tan 9	log cot 10	′
0	55 433	97 015	58 418	41 582	**60**
1	466	010	455	545	59
2	499	005	493	507	58
3	532	97 001	531	469	57
4	564	96 996	569	431	56
5	55 597	96 991	58 606	41 394	**55**
6	630	986	644	356	54
7	663	981	681	319	53
8	695	976	719	281	52
9	728	971	757	243	51
10	55 761	96 966	58 794	41 206	**50**
11	793	962	832	168	49
12	826	957	869	131	48
13	858	952	907	093	47
14	891	947	944	056	46
15	55 923	96 942	58 981	41 019	**45**
16	956	937	59 019	40 981	44
17	55 988	932	056	944	43
18	56 021	927	094	906	42
19	053	922	131	869	41
20	56 085	96 917	59 168	40 832	**40**
21	118	912	205	795	39
22	150	907	243	757	38
23	182	903	280	720	37
24	215	898	317	683	36
25	56 247	96 893	59 354	40 646	**35**
26	279	888	391	609	34
27	311	883	429	571	33
28	343	878	466	534	32
29	375	873	503	497	31
30	56 408	96 868	59 540	40 460	**30**
31	440	863	577	423	29
32	472	858	614	386	28
33	504	853	651	349	27
34	536	848	688	312	26
35	56 568	96 843	59 725	40 275	**25**
36	599	838	762	238	24
37	631	833	799	201	23
38	663	828	835	165	22
39	695	823	872	128	21
40	56 727	96 818	59 909	40 091	**20**
41	759	813	946	054	19
42	790	808	59 983	40 017	18
43	822	803	60 019	39 981	17
44	854	798	056	944	16
45	56 886	96 793	60 093	39 907	**15**
46	917	788	130	870	14
47	949	783	166	834	13
48	56 980	778	203	797	12
49	57 012	772	240	760	11
50	57 044	96 767	60 276	39 724	**10**
51	075	762	313	687	9
52	107	757	349	651	8
53	138	752	386	614	7
54	169	747	422	578	6
55	57 201	96 742	60 459	39 541	**5**
56	232	737	495	505	4
57	264	732	532	468	3
58	295	727	568	432	2
59	326	722	605	395	1
60	57 358	96 717	60 641	39 359	**0**
′	9 log cos	9 log sin	9 log cot	10 log tan	′

68°

22°

′	log sin 9	log cos 9	log tan 9	log cot 10	′
0	57 358	96 717	60 641	39 359	**60**
1	389	711	677	323	59
2	420	706	714	286	58
3	451	701	750	250	57
4	482	696	786	214	56
5	57 514	96 691	60 823	39 177	**55**
6	545	686	859	141	54
7	576	681	895	105	53
8	607	676	931	069	52
9	638	670	60 967	39 033	51
10	57 669	96 665	61 004	38 996	**50**
11	700	660	040	960	49
12	731	655	076	924	48
13	762	650	112	888	47
14	793	645	148	852	46
15	57 824	96 640	61 184	38 816	**45**
16	855	634	220	780	44
17	885	629	256	744	43
18	916	624	292	708	42
19	947	619	328	672	41
20	57 978	96 614	61 364	38 636	**40**
21	58 008	608	400	600	39
22	039	603	436	564	38
23	070	598	472	528	37
24	101	593	508	492	36
25	58 131	96 588	61 544	38 456	**35**
26	162	582	579	421	34
27	192	577	615	385	33
28	223	572	651	349	32
29	253	567	687	313	31
30	58 284	96 562	61 722	38 278	**30**
31	314	556	758	242	29
32	345	551	794	206	28
33	375	546	830	170	27
34	406	541	865	135	26
35	58 436	96 535	61 901	38 099	**25**
36	467	530	936	064	24
37	497	525	61 972	38 028	23
38	527	520	62 008	37 992	22
39	557	514	043	957	21
40	58 588	96 509	62 079	37 921	**20**
41	618	504	114	886	19
42	648	498	150	850	18
43	678	493	185	815	17
44	709	488	221	779	16
45	58 739	96 483	62 256	37 744	**15**
46	769	477	292	708	14
47	799	472	327	673	13
48	829	467	362	638	12
49	859	461	398	602	11
50	58 889	96 456	62 433	37 567	**10**
51	919	451	468	532	9
52	949	445	504	496	8
53	58 979	440	539	461	7
54	59 009	435	574	426	6
55	59 039	96 429	62 609	37 391	**5**
56	069	424	645	355	4
57	098	419	680	320	3
58	128	413	715	285	2
59	158	408	750	250	1
60	59 188	96 403	62 785	37 215	**0**
′	9 log cos	9 log sin	9 log cot	10 log tan	′

67°

23°

′	log sin 9	log cos 9	log tan 9	log cot 10	′
0	59 188	96 403	62 785	37 215	**60**
1	218	397	820	180	59
2	247	392	855	145	58
3	277	387	890	110	57
4	307	381	926	074	56
5	59 336	96 376	62 961	37 039	**55**
6	366	370	62 996	37 004	54
7	396	365	63 031	36 969	53
8	425	360	066	934	52
9	455	354	101	899	51
10	59 484	96 349	63 135	36 865	**50**
11	514	343	170	830	49
12	543	338	205	795	48
13	573	333	240	760	47
14	602	327	275	725	46
15	59 632	96 322	63 310	36 690	**45**
16	661	316	345	655	44
17	690	311	379	621	43
18	720	305	414	586	42
19	749	300	449	551	41
20	59 778	96 294	63 484	36 516	**40**
21	808	289	519	481	39
22	837	284	553	447	38
23	866	278	588	412	37
24	895	273	623	377	36
25	59 924	96 267	63 657	36 343	**35**
26	954	262	692	308	34
27	59 983	256	726	274	33
28	60 012	251	761	239	32
29	041	245	796	204	31
30	60 070	96 240	63 830	36 170	**30**
31	099	234	865	135	29
32	128	229	899	101	28
33	157	223	934	066	27
34	186	218	63 968	36 032	26
35	60 215	96 212	64 003	35 997	**25**
36	244	207	037	963	24
37	273	201	072	928	23
38	302	196	106	894	22
39	331	190	140	860	21
40	60 359	96 185	64 175	35 825	**20**
41	388	179	209	791	19
42	417	174	243	757	18
43	446	168	278	722	17
44	474	162	312	688	16
45	60 503	96 157	64 346	35 654	**15**
46	532	151	381	619	14
47	561	146	415	585	13
48	589	140	449	551	12
49	618	135	483	517	11
50	60 646	96 129	64 517	35 483	**10**
51	675	123	552	448	9
52	704	118	586	414	8
53	732	112	620	380	7
54	761	107	654	346	6
55	60 789	96 101	64 688	35 312	**5**
56	818	095	722	278	4
57	846	090	756	244	3
58	875	084	790	210	2
59	903	079	824	176	1
60	60 931	96 073	64 858	35 142	**0**
′	9 log cos	9 log sin	9 log cot	10 log tan	′

66°

24°

′	log sin 9	log cos 9	log tan 9	log cot 10	′
0	60 931	96 073	64 858	35 142	**60**
1	960	067	892	108	59
2	60 988	062	926	074	58
3	61 016	056	960	040	57
4	045	050	64 994	35 006	56
5	61 073	96 045	65 028	34 972	**55**
6	101	039	062	938	54
7	129	034	096	904	53
8	158	028	130	870	52
9	186	022	164	836	51
10	61 214	96 017	65 197	34 803	**50**
11	242	011	231	769	49
12	270	005	265	735	48
13	298	96 000	299	701	47
14	326	95 994	333	667	46
15	61 354	95 988	65 366	34 634	**45**
16	382	982	400	600	44
17	411	977	434	566	43
18	438	971	467	533	42
19	466	965	501	499	41
20	61 494	95 960	65 535	34 465	**40**
21	522	954	568	432	39
22	550	948	602	398	38
23	578	942	636	364	37
24	606	937	669	331	36
25	61 634	95 931	65 703	34 297	**35**
26	662	925	736	264	34
27	689	920	770	230	33
28	717	914	803	197	32
29	745	908	837	163	31
30	61 773	95 902	65 870	34 130	**30**
31	800	897	904	096	29
32	828	891	937	063	28
33	856	885	65 971	34 029	27
34	883	879	66 004	33 996	26
35	61 911	95 873	66 038	33 962	**25**
36	939	868	071	929	24
37	966	862	104	896	23
38	61 994	856	138	862	22
39	62 021	850	171	829	21
40	62 049	95 844	66 204	33 796	**20**
41	076	839	238	762	19
42	104	833	271	729	18
43	131	827	304	696	17
44	159	821	337	663	16
45	62 186	95 815	66 371	33 629	**15**
46	214	810	404	596	14
47	241	804	437	563	13
48	268	798	470	530	12
49	296	792	503	497	11
50	62 323	95 786	66 537	33 463	**10**
51	350	780	570	430	9
52	377	775	603	397	8
53	405	769	636	364	7
54	432	763	669	331	6
55	62 459	95 757	66 702	33 298	**5**
56	486	751	735	265	4
57	513	745	768	232	3
58	541	739	801	199	2
59	568	733	834	166	1
60	62 595	95 728	66 867	33 133	**0**
′	9 log cos	9 log sin	9 log cot	10 log tan	′

65°

25°

′	log sin	log cos	log tan	log cot	′
	9	9	9	10	
0	62 595	95 728	66 867	33 133	**60**
1	622	722	900	100	59
2	649	716	933	067	58
3	676	710	966	034	57
4	703	704	66 999	33 001	56
5	62 730	95 698	67 032	32 968	**55**
6	757	692	065	935	54
7	784	686	098	902	53
8	811	680	131	869	52
9	838	674	163	837	51
10	62 865	95 668	67 196	32 804	**50**
11	892	663	229	771	49
12	918	657	262	738	48
13	945	651	295	705	47
14	972	645	327	673	46
15	62 999	95 639	67 360	32 640	**45**
16	63 026	633	393	607	44
17	052	627	426	574	43
18	079	621	458	542	42
19	106	615	491	509	41
20	63 133	95 609	67 524	32 476	**40**
21	159	603	556	444	39
22	186	597	589	411	38
23	213	591	622	378	37
24	239	585	654	346	36
25	63 266	95 579	67 687	32 313	**35**
26	292	573	719	281	34
27	319	567	752	248	33
28	345	561	785	215	32
29	372	555	817	183	31
30	63 398	95 549	67 850	32 150	**30**
31	425	543	882	118	29
32	451	537	915	085	28
33	478	531	947	053	27
34	504	525	67 980	32 020	26
35	63 531	95 519	68 012	31 988	**25**
36	557	513	044	956	24
37	583	507	077	923	23
38	610	500	109	891	22
39	636	494	142	858	21
40	63 662	95 488	68 174	31 826	**20**
41	689	482	206	794	19
42	715	476	239	761	18
43	741	470	271	729	17
44	767	464	303	697	16
45	63 794	95 458	68 336	31 664	**15**
46	820	452	368	632	14
47	846	446	400	600	13
48	872	440	432	568	12
49	898	434	465	535	11
50	63 924	95 427	68 497	31 503	**10**
51	950	421	529	471	9
52	63 976	415	561	439	8
53	64 002	409	593	407	7
54	028	403	626	374	6
55	64 054	95 397	68 658	31 342	**5**
56	080	391	690	310	4
57	106	384	722	278	3
58	132	378	754	246	2
59	158	372	786	214	1
60	64 184	95 366	68 818	31 182	**0**
	9	9	9	10	
′	log cos	log sin	log cot	log tan	′

64°

26°

′	log sin	log cos	log tan	log cot	′
	9	9	9	10	
0	64 184	95 366	68 818	31 182	**60**
1	210	360	850	150	59
2	236	354	882	118	58
3	262	348	914	086	57
4	288	341	946	054	56
5	64 313	95 335	68 978	31 022	**55**
6	339	329	69 010	30 990	54
7	365	323	042	958	53
8	391	317	074	926	52
9	417	310	106	894	51
10	64 442	95 304	69 138	30 862	**50**
11	468	298	170	830	49
12	494	292	202	798	48
13	519	286	234	766	47
14	545	279	266	734	46
15	64 571	95 273	69 298	30 702	**45**
16	596	267	329	671	44
17	622	261	361	639	43
18	647	254	393	607	42
19	673	248	425	575	41
20	64 698	95 242	69 457	30 543	**40**
21	724	236	488	512	39
22	749	229	520	480	38
23	775	223	552	448	37
24	800	217	584	416	36
25	64 826	95 211	69 615	30 385	**35**
26	851	204	647	353	34
27	877	198	679	321	33
28	902	192	710	290	32
29	927	185	742	258	31
30	64 953	95 179	69 774	30 226	**30**
31	64 978	173	805	195	29
32	65 003	167	837	163	28
33	029	160	868	132	27
34	054	154	900	100	26
35	65 079	95 148	69 932	30 068	**25**
36	104	141	963	037	24
37	130	135	69 995	30 005	23
38	155	129	70 026	29 974	22
39	180	122	058	942	21
40	65 205	95 116	70 089	29 911	**20**
41	230	110	121	879	19
42	255	103	152	848	18
43	281	097	184	816	17
44	306	090	215	785	16
45	65 331	95 084	70 247	29 753	**15**
46	356	078	278	722	14
47	381	071	309	691	13
48	406	065	341	659	12
49	431	059	372	628	11
50	65 456	95 052	70 404	29 596	**10**
51	481	046	435	565	9
52	506	039	466	534	8
53	531	033	498	502	7
54	556	027	529	471	6
55	65 580	95 020	70 560	29 440	**5**
56	605	014	592	408	4
57	630	007	623	377	3
58	655	95 001	654	346	2
59	680	94 995	685	315	1
60	65 705	94 988	70 717	29 283	**0**
	9	9	9	10	
′	log cos	log sin	log cot	log tan	′

63°

27°

′	log sin 9	log cos 9	log tan 9	log cot 10	′
0	65 705	94 988	70 717	29 283	60
1	729	982	748	252	59
2	754	975	779	221	58
3	779	969	810	190	57
4	804	962	841	159	56
5	65 828	94 956	70 873	29 127	55
6	853	949	904	096	54
7	878	943	935	065	53
8	902	936	966	034	52
9	927	930	70 997	29 003	51
10	65 952	94 923	71 028	28 972	50
11	65 976	917	059	941	49
12	66 001	911	090	910	48
13	025	904	121	879	47
14	050	898	153	847	46
15	66 075	94 891	71 184	28 816	45
16	099	885	215	785	44
17	124	878	246	754	43
18	148	871	277	723	42
19	173	865	308	692	41
20	66 197	94 858	71 339	28 661	40
21	221	852	370	630	39
22	246	845	401	599	38
23	270	839	431	569	37
24	295	832	462	538	36
25	66 319	94 826	71 493	28 507	35
26	343	819	524	476	34
27	368	813	555	445	33
28	392	806	586	414	32
29	416	799	617	383	31
30	66 441	94 793	71 648	28 352	30
31	465	786	679	321	29
32	489	780	709	291	28
33	513	773	740	260	27
34	537	767	771	229	26
35	66 562	94 760	71 802	28 198	25
36	586	753	833	167	24
37	610	747	863	137	23
38	634	740	894	106	22
39	658	734	925	075	21
40	66 682	94 727	71 955	28 045	20
41	706	720	71 986	28 014	19
42	731	714	72 017	27 983	18
43	755	707	048	952	17
44	779	700	078	922	16
45	66 803	94 694	72 109	27 891	15
46	827	687	140	860	14
47	851	680	170	830	13
48	875	674	201	799	12
49	899	667	231	769	11
50	66 922	94 660	72 262	27 738	10
51	946	654	293	707	9
52	970	647	323	677	8
53	66 994	640	354	646	7
54	67 018	634	384	616	6
55	67 042	94 627	72 415	27 585	5
56	066	620	445	555	4
57	090	614	476	524	3
58	113	607	506	494	2
59	137	600	537	463	1
60	67 161	94 593	72 567	27 433	0
′	9 log cos	9 log sin	9 log cot	10 log tan	′

62°

28°

′	log sin 9	log cos 9	log tan 9	log cot 10	′
0	67 161	94 593	72 567	27 433	60
1	185	587	598	402	59
2	208	580	628	372	58
3	232	573	659	341	57
4	256	567	689	311	56
5	67 280	94 560	72 720	27 280	55
6	303	553	750	250	54
7	327	546	780	220	53
8	350	540	811	189	52
9	374	533	841	159	51
10	67 398	94 526	72 872	27 128	50
11	421	519	902	098	49
12	445	513	932	068	48
13	468	506	963	037	47
14	492	499	72 993	27 007	46
15	67 515	94 492	73 023	26 977	45
16	539	485	054	946	44
17	562	479	084	916	43
18	586	472	114	886	42
19	609	465	144	856	41
20	67 633	94 458	73 175	26 825	40
21	656	451	205	795	39
22	680	445	235	765	38
23	703	438	265	735	37
24	726	431	295	705	36
25	67 750	94 424	73 326	26 674	35
26	773	417	356	644	34
27	796	410	386	614	33
28	820	404	416	584	32
29	843	397	446	554	31
30	67 866	94 390	73 476	26 524	30
31	890	383	507	493	29
32	913	376	537	463	28
33	936	369	567	433	27
34	959	362	597	403	26
35	67 982	94 355	73 627	26 373	25
36	68 006	349	657	343	24
37	029	342	687	313	23
38	052	335	717	283	22
39	075	328	747	253	21
40	68 098	94 321	73 777	26 223	20
41	121	314	807	193	19
42	144	307	837	163	18
43	167	300	867	133	17
44	190	293	897	103	16
45	68 213	94 286	73 927	26 073	15
46	237	279	957	043	14
47	260	273	73 987	26 013	13
48	283	266	74 017	25 983	12
49	305	259	047	953	11
50	68 328	94 252	74 077	25 923	10
51	351	245	107	893	9
52	374	238	137	863	8
53	397	231	166	834	7
54	420	224	196	804	6
55	68 443	94 217	74 226	25 774	5
56	466	210	256	744	4
57	489	203	286	714	3
58	512	196	316	684	2
59	534	189	345	655	1
60	68 557	94 182	74 375	25 625	0
′	9 log cos	9 log sin	9 log cot	10 log tan	′

61°

29°

′	log sin 9	log cos 9	log tan 9	log cot 10	′
0	68 557	94 182	74 375	25 625	**60**
1	580	175	405	595	59
2	603	168	435	565	58
3	625	161	465	535	57
4	648	154	494	506	56
5	68 671	94 147	74 524	25 476	**55**
6	694	140	554	446	54
7	716	133	583	417	53
8	739	126	613	387	52
9	762	119	643	357	51
10	68 784	94 112	74 673	25 327	**50**
11	807	105	702	298	49
12	829	098	732	268	48
13	852	090	762	238	47
14	875	083	791	209	46
15	68 897	94 076	74 821	25 179	**45**
16	920	069	851	149	44
17	942	062	880	120	43
18	965	055	910	090	42
19	68 987	048	939	061	41
20	69 010	94 041	74 969	25 031	**40**
21	032	034	74 998	25 002	39
22	055	027	75 028	24 972	38
23	077	020	058	942	37
24	100	012	087	913	36
25	69 122	94 005	75 117	24 883	**35**
26	144	93 998	146	854	34
27	167	991	176	824	33
28	189	984	205	795	32
29	212	977	235	765	31
30	69 234	93 970	75 264	24 736	**30**
31	256	963	294	706	29
32	279	955	323	677	28
33	301	948	353	647	27
34	323	941	382	618	26
35	69 345	93 934	75 411	24 589	**25**
36	368	927	441	559	24
37	390	920	470	530	23
38	412	912	500	500	22
39	434	905	529	471	21
40	69 456	93 898	75 558	24 442	**20**
41	479	891	588	412	19
42	501	884	617	383	18
43	523	876	647	353	17
44	545	869	676	324	16
45	69 567	93 862	75 705	24 295	**15**
46	589	855	735	265	14
47	611	847	764	236	13
48	633	840	793	207	12
49	655	833	822	178	11
50	69 677	93 826	75 852	24 148	**10**
51	699	819	881	119	9
52	721	811	910	090	8
53	743	804	939	061	7
54	765	797	969	031	6
55	69 787	93 789	75 998	24 002	**5**
56	809	782	76 027	23 973	4
57	831	775	056	944	3
58	853	768	086	914	2
59	875	760	115	885	1
60	69 897	93 753	76 144	23 856	**0**
′	9 log cos	9 log sin	9 log cot	10 log tan	′

60°

30°

′	log sin 9	log cos 9	log tan 9	log cot 10	′
0	69 897	93 753	76 144	23 856	**60**
1	919	746	173	827	59
2	941	738	202	798	58
3	963	731	231	769	57
4	69 984	724	261	739	56
5	70 006	93 717	76 290	23 710	**55**
6	028	709	319	681	54
7	050	702	348	652	53
8	072	695	377	623	52
9	093	687	406	594	51
10	70 115	93 680	76 435	23 565	**50**
11	137	673	464	536	49
12	159	665	493	507	48
13	180	658	522	478	47
14	202	650	551	449	46
15	70 224	93 643	76 580	23 420	**45**
16	245	636	609	391	44
17	267	628	639	361	43
18	288	621	668	332	42
19	310	614	697	303	41
20	70 332	93 606	76 725	23 275	**40**
21	353	599	754	246	39
22	375	591	783	217	38
23	396	584	812	188	37
24	418	577	841	159	36
25	70 439	93 569	76 870	23 130	**35**
26	461	562	899	101	34
27	482	554	928	072	33
28	504	547	957	043	32
29	525	539	76 986	23 014	31
30	70 547	93 532	77 015	22 985	**30**
31	568	525	044	956	29
32	590	517	073	927	28
33	611	510	101	899	27
34	633	502	130	870	26
35	70 654	93 495	77 159	22 841	**25**
36	675	487	188	812	24
37	697	480	217	783	23
38	718	472	246	754	22
39	739	465	274	726	21
40	70 761	93 457	77 303	22 697	**20**
41	782	450	332	668	19
42	803	442	361	639	18
43	824	435	390	610	17
44	846	427	418	582	16
45	70 867	93 420	77 447	22 553	**15**
46	888	412	476	524	14
47	909	405	505	495	13
48	931	397	533	467	12
49	952	390	562	438	11
50	70 973	93 382	77 591	22 409	**10**
51	70 994	375	619	381	9
52	71 015	367	648	352	8
53	036	360	677	323	7
54	058	352	706	294	6
55	71 079	93 344	77 734	22 266	**5**
56	100	337	763	237	4
57	121	329	791	209	3
58	142	322	820	180	2
59	163	314	849	151	1
60	71 184	93 307	77 877	22 123	**0**
′	9 log cos	9 log sin	9 log cot	10 log tan	′

59°

31°

'	log sin	log cos	log tan	log cot	'
	9	9	9	10	
0	71 184	93 307	77 877	22 123	**60**
1	205	299	906	094	59
2	226	291	935	065	58
3	247	284	963	037	57
4	268	276	77 992	22 008	56
5	71 289	93 269	78 020	21 980	**55**
6	310	261	049	951	54
7	331	253	077	923	53
8	352	246	106	894	52
9	373	238	135	865	51
10	71 393	93 230	78 163	21 837	**50**
11	414	223	192	808	49
12	435	215	220	780	48
13	456	207	249	751	47
14	477	200	277	723	46
15	71 498	93 192	78 306	21 694	**45**
16	519	184	334	666	44
17	539	177	363	637	43
18	560	169	391	609	42
19	581	161	419	581	41
20	71 602	93 154	78 448	21 552	**40**
21	622	146	476	524	39
22	643	138	505	495	38
23	664	131	533	467	37
24	685	123	562	438	36
25	71 705	93 115	78 590	21 410	**35**
26	726	108	618	382	34
27	747	100	647	353	33
28	767	092	675	325	32
29	788	084	704	296	31
30	71 809	93 077	78 732	21 268	**30**
31	829	069	760	240	29
32	850	061	789	211	28
33	870	053	817	183	27
34	891	046	845	155	26
35	71 911	93 038	78 874	21 126	**25**
36	932	030	902	098	24
37	952	022	930	070	23
38	973	014	959	041	22
39	71 994	93 007	78 987	21 013	21
40	72 014	92 999	79 015	20 985	**20**
41	034	991	043	957	19
42	055	983	072	928	18
43	075	976	100	900	17
44	096	968	128	872	16
45	72 116	92 960	79 156	20 844	**15**
46	137	952	185	815	14
47	157	944	213	787	13
48	177	936	241	759	12
49	198	929	269	731	11
50	72 218	92 921	79 297	20 703	**10**
51	238	913	326	674	9
52	259	905	354	646	8
53	279	897	382	618	7
54	299	889	410	590	6
55	72 320	92 881	79 438	20 562	**5**
56	340	874	466	534	4
57	360	866	495	505	3
58	381	858	523	477	2
59	401	850	551	449	1
60	72 421	92 842	79 579	20 421	**0**
	9	9	9	10	
'	log cos	log sin	log cot	log tan	'

58°

32°

'	log sin	log cos	log tan	log cot	'
	9	9	9	10	
0	72 421	92 842	79 579	20 421	**60**
1	441	834	607	393	59
2	461	826	635	365	58
3	482	818	663	337	57
4	502	810	691	309	56
5	72 522	92 803	79 719	20 281	**55**
6	542	795	747	253	54
7	562	787	776	224	53
8	582	779	804	196	52
9	602	771	832	168	51
10	72 622	92 763	79 860	20 140	**50**
11	643	755	888	112	49
12	663	747	916	084	48
13	683	739	944	056	47
14	703	731	79 972	20 028	46
15	72 723	92 723	80 000	20 000	**45**
16	743	715	028	19 972	44
17	763	707	056	944	43
18	783	699	084	916	42
19	803	691	112	888	41
20	72 823	92 683	80 140	19 860	**40**
21	843	675	168	832	39
22	863	667	195	805	38
23	883	659	223	777	37
24	902	651	251	749	36
25	72 922	92 643	80 279	19 721	**35**
26	942	635	307	693	34
27	962	627	335	665	33
28	72 982	619	363	637	32
29	73 002	611	391	609	31
30	73 022	92 603	80 419	19 581	**30**
31	041	595	447	553	29
32	061	587	474	526	28
33	081	579	502	498	27
34	101	571	530	470	26
35	73 121	92 563	80 558	19 442	**25**
36	140	555	586	414	24
37	160	546	614	386	23
38	180	538	642	358	22
39	200	530	669	331	21
40	73 219	92 522	80 697	19 303	**20**
41	239	514	725	275	19
42	259	506	753	247	18
43	278	498	781	219	17
44	298	490	808	192	16
45	73 318	92 482	80 836	19 164	**15**
46	337	473	864	136	14
47	357	465	892	108	13
48	377	457	919	081	12
49	396	449	947	053	11
50	73 416	92 441	80 975	19 025	**10**
51	435	433	81 003	18 997	9
52	455	425	030	970	8
53	474	416	058	942	7
54	494	408	086	914	6
55	73 513	92 400	81 113	18 887	**5**
56	533	392	141	859	4
57	552	384	169	831	3
58	572	376	196	804	2
59	591	367	224	776	1
60	73 611	92 359	81 252	18 748	**0**
	9	9	9	10	
'	log cos	log sin	log cot	log tan	'

57°

33°

′	log sin 9	log cos 9	log tan 9	log cot 10	′
0	73 611	92 359	81 252	18 748	**60**
1	630	351	279	721	59
2	650	343	307	693	58
3	669	335	335	665	57
4	689	326	362	638	56
5	73 708	92 318	81 390	18 610	**55**
6	727	310	418	582	54
7	747	302	445	555	53
8	766	293	473	527	52
9	785	285	500	500	51
10	73 805	92 277	81 528	18 472	**50**
11	824	269	556	444	49
12	843	260	583	417	48
13	863	252	611	389	47
14	882	244	638	362	46
15	73 901	92 235	81 666	18 334	**45**
16	921	227	693	307	44
17	940	219	721	279	43
18	959	211	748	252	42
19	978	202	776	224	41
20	73 997	92 194	81 803	18 197	**40**
21	74 017	186	831	169	39
22	036	177	858	142	38
23	055	169	886	114	37
24	074	161	913	087	36
25	74 093	92 152	81 941	18 059	**35**
26	113	144	968	032	34
27	132	136	81 996	18 004	33
28	151	127	82 023	17 977	32
29	170	119	051	949	31
30	74 189	92 111	82 078	17 922	**30**
31	208	102	106	894	29
32	227	094	133	867	28
33	246	086	161	839	27
34	265	077	188	812	26
35	74 284	92 069	82 215	17 785	**25**
36	303	060	243	757	24
37	322	052	270	730	23
38	341	044	298	702	22
39	360	035	325	675	21
40	74 379	92 027	82 352	17 648	**20**
41	398	018	380	620	19
42	417	010	407	593	18
43	436	92 002	435	565	17
44	455	91 993	462	538	16
45	74 474	91 985	82 489	17 511	**15**
46	493	976	517	483	14
47	512	968	544	456	13
48	531	959	571	429	12
49	549	951	599	401	11
50	74 568	91 942	82 626	17 374	**10**
51	587	934	653	347	9
52	606	925	681	319	8
53	625	917	708	292	7
54	644	908	735	265	6
55	74 662	91 900	82 762	17 238	**5**
56	681	891	790	210	4
57	700	883	817	183	3
58	719	874	844	156	2
59	737	866	871	129	1
60	74 756	91 857	82 899	17 101	**0**
′	9 log cos	9 log sin	9 log cot	10 log tan	′

56°

34°

′	log sin 9	log cos 9	log tan 9	log cot 10	′
0	74 756	91 857	82 899	17 101	**60**
1	775	849	926	074	59
2	794	840	953	047	58
3	812	832	82 980	17 020	57
4	831	823	83 008	16 992	56
5	74 850	91 815	83 035	16 965	**55**
6	868	806	062	938	54
7	887	798	089	911	53
8	906	789	117	883	52
9	924	781	144	856	51
10	74 943	91 772	83 171	16 829	**50**
11	961	763	198	802	49
12	980	755	225	775	48
13	74 999	746	252	748	47
14	75 017	738	280	720	46
15	75 036	91 729	83 307	16 693	**45**
16	054	720	334	666	44
17	073	712	361	639	43
18	091	703	388	612	42
19	110	695	415	585	41
20	75 128	91 686	83 442	16 558	**40**
21	147	677	470	530	39
22	165	669	497	503	38
23	184	660	524	476	37
24	202	651	551	449	36
25	75 221	91 643	83 578	16 422	**35**
26	239	634	605	395	34
27	258	625	632	368	33
28	276	617	659	341	32
29	294	608	686	314	31
30	75 313	91 599	83 713	16 287	**30**
31	331	591	740	260	29
32	350	582	768	232	28
33	368	573	795	205	27
34	386	565	822	178	26
35	75 405	91 556	83 849	16 151	**25**
36	423	547	876	124	24
37	441	538	903	097	23
38	459	530	930	070	22
39	478	521	957	043	21
40	75 496	91 512	83 984	16 016	**20**
41	514	504	84 011	15 989	19
42	533	495	038	962	18
43	551	486	065	935	17
44	569	477	092	908	16
45	75 587	91 469	84 119	15 881	**15**
46	605	460	146	854	14
47	624	451	173	827	13
48	642	442	200	800	12
49	660	433	227	773	11
50	75 678	91 425	84 254	15 746	**10**
51	696	416	280	720	9
52	714	407	307	693	8
53	733	398	334	666	7
54	751	389	361	639	6
55	75 769	91 381	84 388	15 612	**5**
56	787	372	415	585	4
57	805	363	442	558	3
58	823	354	469	531	2
59	841	345	496	504	1
60	75 859	91 336	84 523	15 477	**0**
′	9 log cos	9 log sin	9 log cot	10 log tan	′

55°

35°

′	log sin	log cos	log tan	log cot	′
	9	9	9	10	
0	75 859	91 336	84 523	15 477	**60**
1	877	328	550	450	59
2	895	319	576	424	58
3	913	310	603	397	57
4	931	301	630	370	56
5	75 949	91 292	84 657	15 343	**55**
6	967	283	684	316	54
7	75 985	274	711	289	53
8	76 003	266	738	262	52
9	021	257	764	236	51
10	76 039	91 248	84 791	15 209	**50**
11	057	239	818	182	49
12	075	230	845	155	48
13	093	221	872	128	47
14	111	212	899	101	46
15	76 129	91 203	84 925	15 075	**45**
16	146	194	952	048	44
17	164	185	84 979	15 021	43
18	182	176	85 006	14 994	42
19	200	167	033	967	41
20	76 218	91 158	85 059	14 941	**40**
21	236	149	086	914	39
22	253	141	113	887	38
23	271	132	140	860	37
24	289	123	166	834	36
25	76 307	91 114	85 193	14 807	**35**
26	324	105	220	780	34
27	342	096	247	753	33
28	360	087	273	727	32
29	378	078	300	700	31
30	76 395	91 069	85 327	14 673	**30**
31	413	060	354	646	29
32	431	051	380	620	28
33	448	042	407	593	27
34	466	033	434	566	26
35	76 484	91 023	85 460	14 540	**25**
36	501	014	487	513	24
37	519	91 005	514	486	23
38	537	90 996	540	460	22
39	554	987	567	433	21
40	76 572	90 978	85 594	14 406	**20**
41	590	969	620	380	19
42	607	960	647	353	18
43	625	951	674	326	17
44	642	942	700	300	16
45	76 660	90 933	85 727	14 273	**15**
46	677	924	754	246	14
47	695	915	780	220	13
48	712	906	807	193	12
49	730	896	834	166	11
50	76 747	90 887	85 860	14 140	**10**
51	765	878	887	113	9
52	782	869	913	087	8
53	800	860	940	060	7
54	817	851	967	033	6
55	76 835	90 842	85 993	14 007	**5**
56	852	832	86 020	13 980	4
57	870	823	046	954	3
58	887	814	073	927	2
59	904	805	100	900	1
60	76 922	90 796	86 126	13 874	**0**
	9	9	9	10	
′	log cos	log sin	log cot	log tan	′

54°

36°

′	log sin	log cos	log tan	log cot	′
	9	9	9	10	
0	76 922	90 796	86 126	13 874	**60**
1	939	787	153	847	59
2	957	777	179	821	58
3	974	768	206	794	57
4	76 991	759	232	768	56
5	77 009	90 750	86 259	13 741	**55**
6	026	741	285	715	54
7	043	731	312	688	53
8	061	722	338	662	52
9	078	713	365	635	51
10	77 095	90 704	86 392	13 608	**50**
11	112	694	418	582	49
12	130	685	445	555	48
13	147	676	471	529	47
14	164	667	498	502	46
15	77 181	90 657	86 524	13 476	**45**
16	199	648	551	449	44
17	216	639	577	423	43
18	233	630	603	397	42
19	250	620	630	370	41
20	77 268	90 611	86 656	13 344	**40**
21	285	602	683	317	39
22	302	592	709	291	38
23	319	583	736	264	37
24	336	574	762	238	36
25	77 353	90 565	86 789	13 211	**35**
26	370	555	815	185	34
27	387	546	842	158	33
28	405	537	868	132	32
29	422	527	894	106	31
30	77 439	90 518	86 921	13 079	**30**
31	456	509	947	053	29
32	473	499	86 974	026	28
33	490	490	87 000	13 000	27
34	507	480	027	12 973	26
35	77 524	90 471	87 053	12 947	**25**
36	541	462	079	921	24
37	558	452	106	894	23
38	575	443	132	868	22
39	592	434	158	842	21
40	77 609	90 424	87 185	12 815	**20**
41	626	415	211	789	19
42	643	405	238	762	18
43	660	396	264	736	17
44	677	386	290	710	16
45	77 694	90 377	87 317	12 683	**15**
46	711	368	343	657	14
47	728	358	369	631	13
48	744	349	396	604	12
49	761	339	422	578	11
50	77 778	90 330	87 448	12 552	**10**
51	795	320	475	525	9
52	812	311	501	499	8
53	829	301	527	473	7
54	846	292	554	446	6
55	77 862	90 282	87 580	12 420	**5**
56	879	273	606	394	4
57	896	263	633	367	3
58	913	254	659	341	2
59	930	244	685	315	1
60	77 946	90 235	87 711	12 289	**0**
	9	9	9	10	
′	log cos	log sin	log cot	log tan	′

53°

37°

′	log sin	log cos	log tan	log cot	′
	9	9	9	10	
0	77 946	90 235	87 711	12 289	**60**
1	963	225	738	262	59
2	980	216	764	236	58
3	77 997	206	790	210	57
4	78 013	197	817	183	56
5	78 030	90 187	87 843	12 157	**55**
6	047	178	869	131	54
7	063	168	895	105	53
8	080	159	922	078	52
9	097	149	948	052	51
10	78 113	90 139	87 974	12 026	**50**
11	130	130	88 000	12 000	49
12	147	120	027	11 973	48
13	163	111	053	947	47
14	180	101	079	921	46
15	78 197	90 091	88 105	11 895	**45**
16	213	082	131	869	44
17	230	072	158	842	43
18	246	063	184	816	42
19	263	053	210	790	41
20	78 280	90 043	88 236	11 764	**40**
21	296	034	262	738	39
22	313	024	289	711	38
23	329	014	315	685	37
24	346	90 005	341	659	36
25	78 362	89 995	88 367	11 633	**35**
26	379	985	393	607	34
27	395	976	420	580	33
28	412	966	446	554	32
29	428	956	472	528	31
30	78 445	89 947	88 498	11 502	**30**
31	461	937	524	476	29
32	478	927	550	450	28
33	494	918	577	423	27
34	510	908	603	397	26
35	78 527	89 898	88 629	11 371	**25**
36	543	888	655	345	24
37	560	879	681	319	23
38	576	869	707	293	22
39	592	859	733	267	21
40	78 609	89 849	88 759	11 241	**20**
41	625	840	786	214	19
42	642	830	812	188	18
43	658	820	838	162	17
44	674	810	864	136	16
45	78 691	89 801	88 890	11 110	**15**
46	707	791	916	084	14
47	723	781	942	058	13
48	739	771	968	032	12
49	756	761	88 994	11 006	11
50	78 772	89 752	89 020	10 980	**10**
51	788	742	046	954	9
52	805	732	073	927	8
53	821	722	099	901	7
54	837	712	125	875	6
55	78 853	89 702	89 151	10 849	**5**
56	869	693	177	823	4
57	886	683	203	797	3
58	902	673	229	771	2
59	918	663	255	745	1
60	78 934	89 653	89 281	10 719	**0**
	9	9	9	10	
′	log cos	log sin	log cot	log tan	′

52°

38°

′	log sin	log cos	log tan	log cot	′
	9	9	9	10	
0	78 934	89 653	89 281	10 719	**60**
1	950	643	307	693	59
2	967	633	333	667	58
3	983	624	359	641	57
4	78 999	614	385	615	56
5	79 015	89 604	89 411	10 589	**55**
6	031	594	437	563	54
7	047	584	463	537	53
8	063	574	489	511	52
9	079	564	515	485	51
10	79 095	89 554	89 541	10 459	**50**
11	111	544	567	433	49
12	128	534	593	407	48
13	144	524	619	381	47
14	160	514	645	355	46
15	79 176	89 504	89 671	10 329	**45**
16	192	495	697	303	44
17	208	485	723	277	43
18	224	475	749	251	42
19	240	465	775	225	41
20	79 256	89 455	89 801	10 199	**40**
21	272	445	827	173	39
22	288	435	853	147	38
23	304	425	879	121	37
24	319	415	905	095	36
25	79 335	89 405	89 931	10 069	**35**
26	351	395	957	043	34
27	367	385	89 983	10 017	33
28	383	375	90 009	09 991	32
29	399	364	035	965	31
30	79 415	89 354	90 061	09 939	**30**
31	431	344	086	914	29
32	447	334	112	888	28
33	463	324	138	862	27
34	478	314	164	836	26
35	79 494	89 304	90 190	09 810	**25**
36	510	294	216	784	24
37	526	284	242	758	23
38	542	274	268	732	22
39	558	264	294	706	21
40	79 573	89 254	90 320	09 680	**20**
41	589	244	346	654	19
42	605	233	371	629	18
43	621	223	397	603	17
44	636	213	423	577	16
45	79 652	89 203	90 449	09 551	**15**
46	668	193	475	525	14
47	684	183	501	499	13
48	699	173	527	473	12
49	715	162	553	447	11
50	79 731	89 152	90 578	09 422	**10**
51	746	142	604	396	9
52	762	132	630	370	8
53	778	122	656	344	7
54	793	112	682	318	6
55	79 809	89 101	90 708	09 292	**5**
56	825	091	734	266	4
57	840	081	759	241	3
58	856	071	785	215	2
59	872	060	811	189	1
60	79 887	89 050	90 837	09 163	**0**
	9	9	9	10	
′	log cos	log sin	log cot	log tan	′

51°

39°

'	log sin	log cos	log tan	log cot	'
	9	9	9	10	
0	79 887	89 050	90 837	09 163	**60**
1	903	040	863	137	59
2	918	030	889	111	58
3	934	020	914	086	57
4	950	89 009	940	060	56
5	79 965	88 999	90 966	09 034	**55**
6	981	989	90 992	09 008	54
7	79 996	978	91 018	08 982	53
8	80 012	968	043	957	52
9	027	958	069	931	51
10	80 043	88 948	91 095	08 905	**50**
11	058	937	121	879	49
12	074	927	147	853	48
13	089	917	172	828	47
14	105	906	198	802	46
15	80 120	88 896	91 224	08 776	**45**
16	136	886	250	750	44
17	151	875	276	724	43
18	166	865	301	699	42
19	182	855	327	673	41
20	80 197	88 844	91 353	08 647	**40**
21	213	834	379	621	39
22	228	824	404	596	38
23	244	813	430	570	37
24	259	803	456	544	36
25	80 274	88 793	91 482	08 518	**35**
26	290	782	507	493	34
27	305	772	533	467	33
28	320	761	559	441	32
29	336	751	585	415	31
30	80 351	88 741	91 610	08 390	**30**
31	366	730	636	364	29
32	382	720	662	338	28
33	397	709	688	312	27
34	412	699	713	287	26
35	80 428	88 688	91 739	08 261	**25**
36	443	678	765	235	24
37	458	668	791	209	23
38	473	657	816	184	22
39	489	647	842	158	21
40	80 504	88 636	91 868	08 132	**20**
41	519	626	893	107	19
42	534	615	919	081	18
43	550	605	945	055	17
44	565	594	971	029	16
45	80 580	88 584	91 996	08 004	**15**
46	595	573	92 022	07 978	14
47	610	563	048	952	13
48	625	552	073	927	12
49	641	542	099	901	11
50	80 656	88 531	92 125	07 875	**10**
51	671	521	150	850	9
52	686	510	176	824	8
53	701	499	202	798	7
54	716	489	227	773	6
55	80 731	88 478	92 253	07 747	**5**
56	746	468	279	721	4
57	762	457	304	696	3
58	777	447	330	670	2
59	792	436	356	644	1
60	80 807	88 425	92 381	07 619	**0**
	9	9	9	10	
'	log cos	log sin	log cot	log tan	'

50°

40°

'	log sin	log cos	log tan	log cot	'
	9	9	9	10	
0	80 807	88 425	92 381	07 619	**60**
1	822	415	407	593	59
2	837	404	433	567	58
3	852	394	458	542	57
4	867	383	484	516	56
5	80 882	88 372	92 510	07 490	**55**
6	897	362	535	465	54
7	912	351	561	439	53
8	927	340	587	413	52
9	942	330	612	388	51
10	80 957	88 319	92 638	07 362	**50**
11	972	308	663	337	49
12	80 987	298	689	311	48
13	81 002	287	715	285	47
14	017	276	740	260	46
15	81 032	88 266	92 766	07 234	**45**
16	047	255	792	208	44
17	061	244	817	183	43
18	076	234	843	157	42
19	091	223	868	132	41
20	81 106	88 212	92 894	07 106	**40**
21	121	201	920	080	39
22	136	191	945	055	38
23	151	180	971	029	37
24	166	169	92 996	07 004	36
25	81 180	88 158	93 022	06 978	**35**
26	195	148	048	952	34
27	210	137	073	927	33
28	225	126	099	901	32
29	240	115	124	876	31
30	81 254	88 105	93 150	06 850	**30**
31	269	094	175	825	29
32	284	083	201	799	28
33	299	072	227	773	27
34	314	061	252	748	26
35	81 328	88 051	93 278	06 722	**25**
36	343	040	303	697	24
37	358	029	329	671	23
38	372	018	354	646	22
39	387	88 007	380	620	21
40	81 402	87 996	93 406	06 594	**20**
41	417	985	431	569	19
42	431	975	457	543	18
43	446	964	482	518	17
44	461	953	508	492	16
45	81 475	87 942	93 533	06 467	**15**
46	490	931	559	441	14
47	505	920	584	416	13
48	519	909	610	390	12
49	534	898	636	364	11
50	81 549	87 887	93 661	06 339	**10**
51	563	877	687	313	9
52	578	866	712	288	8
53	592	855	738	262	7
54	607	844	763	237	6
55	81 622	87 833	93 789	06 211	**5**
56	636	822	814	186	4
57	651	811	840	160	3
58	665	800	865	135	2
59	680	789	891	109	1
60	81 694	87 778	93 916	06 084	**0**
	9	9	9	10	
'	log cos	log sin	log cot	log tan	'

49°

41°

′	log sin 9	log cos 9	log tan 9	log cot 10	′
0	81 694	87 778	93 916	06 084	**60**
1	709	767	942	058	59
2	723	756	967	033	58
3	738	745	93 993	06 007	57
4	752	734	94 018	05 982	56
5	81 767	87 723	94 044	05 956	**55**
6	781	712	069	931	54
7	796	701	095	905	53
8	810	690	120	880	52
9	825	679	146	854	51
10	81 839	87 668	94 171	05 829	**50**
11	854	657	197	803	49
12	868	646	222	778	48
13	882	635	248	752	47
14	897	624	273	727	46
15	81 911	87 613	94 299	05 701	**45**
16	926	601	324	676	44
17	940	590	350	650	43
18	955	579	375	625	42
19	969	568	401	599	41
20	81 983	87 557	94 426	05 574	**40**
21	81 998	546	452	548	39
22	82 012	535	477	523	38
23	026	524	503	497	37
24	041	513	528	472	36
25	82 055	87 501	94 554	05 446	**35**
26	069	490	579	421	34
27	084	479	604	396	33
28	098	468	630	370	32
29	112	457	655	345	31
30	82 126	87 446	94 681	05 319	**30**
31	141	434	706	294	29
32	155	423	732	268	28
33	169	412	757	243	27
34	184	401	783	217	26
35	82 198	87 390	94 808	05 192	**25**
36	212	378	834	166	24
37	226	367	859	141	23
38	240	356	884	116	22
39	255	345	910	090	21
40	82 269	87 334	94 935	05 065	**20**
41	283	322	961	039	19
42	297	311	94 986	05 014	18
43	311	300	95 012	04 988	17
44	326	288	037	963	16
45	82 340	87 277	95 062	04 938	**15**
46	354	266	088	912	14
47	368	255	113	887	13
48	382	243	139	861	12
49	396	232	164	836	11
50	82 410	87 221	95 190	04 810	**10**
51	424	209	215	785	9
52	439	198	240	760	8
53	453	187	266	734	7
54	467	175	291	709	6
55	82 481	87 164	95 317	04 683	**5**
56	495	153	342	658	4
57	509	141	368	632	3
58	523	130	393	607	2
59	537	119	418	582	1
60	82 551	87 107	95 444	04 556	**0**
′	9 log cos	9 log sin	9 log cot	10 log tan	′

48°

42°

′	log sin 9	log cos 9	log tan 9	log cot 10	′
0	82 551	87 107	95 444	04 556	**60**
1	565	096	469	531	59
2	579	085	495	505	58
3	593	073	520	480	57
4	607	062	545	455	56
5	82 621	87 050	95 571	04 429	**55**
6	635	039	596	404	54
7	649	028	622	378	53
8	663	016	647	353	52
9	677	87 005	672	328	51
10	82 691	86 993	95 698	04 302	**50**
11	705	982	723	277	49
12	719	970	748	252	48
13	733	959	774	226	47
14	747	947	799	201	46
15	82 761	86 936	95 825	04 175	**45**
16	775	924	850	150	44
17	788	913	875	125	43
18	802	902	901	099	42
19	816	890	926	074	41
20	82 830	86 879	95 952	04 048	**40**
21	844	867	95 977	04 023	39
22	858	855	96 002	03 998	38
23	872	844	028	972	37
24	885	832	053	947	36
25	82 899	86 821	96 078	03 922	**35**
26	913	809	104	896	34
27	927	798	129	871	33
28	941	786	155	845	32
29	955	775	180	820	31
30	82 968	86 763	96 205	03 795	**30**
31	982	752	231	769	29
32	82 996	740	256	744	28
33	83 010	728	281	719	27
34	023	717	307	693	26
35	83 037	86 705	96 332	03 668	**25**
36	051	694	357	643	24
37	065	682	383	617	23
38	078	670	408	592	22
39	092	659	433	567	21
40	83 106	86 647	96 459	03 541	**20**
41	120	635	484	516	19
42	133	624	510	490	18
43	147	612	535	465	17
44	161	600	560	440	16
45	83 174	86 589	96 586	03 414	**15**
46	188	577	611	389	14
47	202	565	636	364	13
48	215	554	662	338	12
49	229	542	687	313	11
50	83 242	86 530	96 712	03 288	**10**
51	256	518	738	262	9
52	270	507	763	237	8
53	283	495	788	212	7
54	297	483	814	186	6
55	83 310	86 472	96 839	03 161	**5**
56	324	460	864	136	4
57	338	448	890	110	3
58	351	436	915	085	2
59	365	425	940	060	1
60	83 378	86 413	96 966	03 034	**0**
′	9 log cos	9 log sin	9 log cot	10 log tan	′

47°

43°

′	log sin 9	log cos 9	log tan 9	log cot 10	′
0	83 378	86 413	96 966	03 034	**60**
1	392	401	96 991	03 009	59
2	405	389	97 016	02 984	58
3	419	377	042	958	57
4	432	366	067	933	56
5	83 446	86 354	97 092	02 908	**55**
6	459	342	118	882	54
7	473	330	143	857	53
8	486	318	168	832	52
9	500	306	193	807	51
10	83 513	86 295	97 219	02 781	**50**
11	527	283	244	756	49
12	540	271	269	731	48
13	554	259	295	705	47
14	567	247	320	680	46
15	83 581	86 235	97 345	02 655	**45**
16	594	223	371	629	44
17	608	211	396	604	43
18	621	200	421	579	42
19	634	188	447	553	41
20	83 648	86 176	97 472	02 528	**40**
21	661	164	497	503	39
22	674	152	523	477	38
23	688	140	548	452	37
24	701	128	573	427	36
25	83 715	86 116	97 598	02 402	**35**
26	728	104	624	376	34
27	741	092	649	351	33
28	755	080	674	326	32
29	768	068	700	300	31
30	83 781	86 056	97 725	02 275	**30**
31	795	044	750	250	29
32	808	032	776	224	28
33	821	020	801	199	27
34	834	86 008	826	174	26
35	83 848	85 996	97 851	02 149	**25**
36	861	984	877	123	24
37	874	972	902	098	23
38	887	960	927	073	22
39	901	948	953	047	21
40	83 914	85 936	97 978	02 022	**20**
41	927	924	98 003	01 997	19
42	940	912	029	971	18
43	954	900	054	946	17
44	967	888	079	921	16
45	83 980	85 876	98 104	01 896	**15**
46	83 993	864	130	870	14
47	84 006	851	155	845	13
48	020	839	180	820	12
49	033	827	206	794	11
50	84 046	85 815	98 231	01 769	**10**
51	059	803	256	744	9
52	072	791	281	719	8
53	085	779	307	693	7
54	098	766	332	668	6
55	84 112	85 754	98 357	01 643	**5**
56	125	742	383	617	4
57	138	730	408	592	3
58	151	718	433	567	2
59	164	706	458	542	1
60	84 177	85 693	98 484	01 516	**0**
′	log cos 9	log sin 9	log cot 9	log tan 10	′

46°

44°

′	log sin 9	log cos 9	log tan 9	log cot 10	′
0	84 177	85 693	98 484	01 516	**60**
1	190	681	509	491	59
2	203	669	534	466	58
3	216	657	560	440	57
4	229	645	585	415	56
5	84 242	85 632	98 610	01 390	**55**
6	255	620	635	365	54
7	269	608	661	339	53
8	282	596	686	314	52
9	295	583	711	289	51
10	84 308	85 571	98 737	01 263	**50**
11	321	559	762	238	49
12	334	547	787	213	48
13	347	534	812	188	47
14	360	522	838	162	46
15	84 373	85 510	98 863	01 137	**45**
16	385	497	888	112	44
17	398	485	913	087	43
18	411	473	939	061	42
19	424	460	964	036	41
20	84 437	85 448	98 989	01 011	**40**
21	450	436	99 015	00 985	39
22	463	423	040	960	38
23	476	411	065	935	37
24	489	399	090	910	36
25	84 502	85 386	99 116	00 884	**35**
26	515	374	141	859	34
27	528	361	166	834	33
28	540	349	191	809	32
29	553	337	217	783	31
30	84 566	85 324	99 242	00 758	**30**
31	579	312	267	733	29
32	592	299	293	707	28
33	605	287	318	682	27
34	618	274	343	657	26
35	84 630	85 262	99 368	00 632	**25**
36	643	250	394	606	24
37	656	237	419	581	23
38	669	225	444	556	22
39	682	212	469	531	21
40	84 694	85 200	99 495	00 505	**20**
41	707	187	520	480	19
42	720	175	545	455	18
43	733	162	570	430	17
44	745	150	596	404	16
45	84 758	85 137	99 621	00 379	**15**
46	771	125	646	354	14
47	784	112	672	328	13
48	796	100	697	303	12
49	809	087	722	278	11
50	84 822	85 074	99 747	00 253	**10**
51	835	062	773	227	9
52	847	049	798	202	8
53	860	037	823	177	7
54	873	024	848	152	6
55	84 885	85 012	99 874	00 126	**5**
56	898	84 999	899	101	4
57	911	986	924	076	3
58	923	974	949	051	2
59	936	961	975	025	1
60	84 949	84 949	00 000	00 000	**0**
′	log cos 9	log sin 9	log cot 10	log tan 10	′

45°

TABLE VII

FOR DETERMINING THE FOLLOWING WITH GREATER ACCURACY THAN CAN BE DONE BY MEANS OF TABLE VI

1. *log sin, log tan,* and *log cot,* when the angle is between 0° and 2°;
2. *log cos, log tan,* and *log cot,* when the angle is between 88° and 90°;
3. The value of the angle when the logarithm of the function does not lie between the limits 8.54 684 and 11. 45 316.

FORMULAS FOR THE USE OF THE NUMBERS S AND T

I. When the angle α is between 0° and 2°:

$$\log \sin \alpha = \log \alpha'' + S. \qquad \log \alpha'' = \log \sin \alpha - S$$
$$\log \tan \alpha = \log \alpha'' + T. \qquad = \log \tan \alpha - T$$
$$\log \cot \alpha = \operatorname{colog} \tan \alpha. \qquad = \operatorname{colog} \cot \alpha - T.$$

II. When the angle α is between 88° and 90°:

$$\log \cos \alpha = \log (90° - \alpha)'' + S. \qquad \log (90° - \alpha)'' = \log \cos \alpha - S$$
$$\log \cot \alpha = \log (90° - \alpha)'' + T. \qquad = \log \cot \alpha - T$$
$$\log \tan \alpha = \operatorname{colog} \cot \alpha. \qquad = \operatorname{colog} \tan \alpha - T;$$
$$\alpha = 90° - (90° - \alpha).$$

Values of S and T

α''	S	log sin α	α''	T	log tan α	α	T	log tan α
0		—	0		—	5 146		8. 39 713
	4. 68 557			4. 68 557			4. 68 567	
2 409		8. 06 740	200		6. 98 660	5 424		8. 41 999
	4. 68 556			4. 68 558			4. 68 568	
3 417		8. 21 920	1 726		7. 92 263	5 689		8. 44 072
	4. 68 555			4. 68 559			4. 68 569	
3 823		8. 26 795	2 432		8. 07 156	5 941		8. 45 955
	4. 68 55$\underline{5}$			4. 68 560			4. 68 570	
4 190		8. 30 776	2 976		8. 15 924	6 184		8. 47 697
	4. 68 554			4. 68 561			4. 68 571	
4 840		8. 37 038	3 434		8. 22 142	6 417		8. 49 305
	4. 68 553			4. 68 562			4. 68 572	
5 414		8. 41 904	3 838		8. 26 973	6 642		8. 50 802
	4. 68 552			4. 68 563			4. 68 573	
5 932		8. 45 872	4 204		8. 30 930	6 859		8. 52 200
	4. 68 551			4. 68 564			4. 68 574	
6 408		8. 49 223	4 540		8. 34 270	7 070		8. 53 516
	4. 68 550			4. 68 56$\underline{5}$			4. 68 57$\underline{5}$	
6 633		8. 50 721	4 699		8. 35 766	7 173		8. 54 145
	4. 68 5$\underline{5}$0			4. 68 565			4. 68 575	
6 851		8. 52 125	4 853		8. 37 167	7 274		8. 54 753
	4. 68 549			4. 68 566				
7 267		8. 54 684	5 146		8. 39 713			
α''	S	log sin α	α''	T	log tan α	α	T	log tan α

TABLE VIII

NATURAL FUNCTIONS

Owing to the rapid change in the functions, interpolation is not accurate for the cotangents from 0° to 3°, nor for the tangents from 87° to 90°. For the same functions interpolation is not accurate, in general, in the last figure from 3° to 6° and from 84° to 87°, respectively.

0°

′	sin	cos	tan	cot	′
0	0.0000	1.0000	0.0000	Infinite	60
1	03	00	03	3437.75	59
2	06	00	06	1718.87	58
3	09	00	09	1145.92	57
4	12	00	12	859.436	56
5	0.0015	1.0000	0.0015	687.549	55
6	17	00	17	572.957	54
7	20	00	20	491.106	53
8	23	00	23	429.718	52
9	26	00	26	381.971	51
10	0.0029	1.0000	0.0029	343.774	50
11	32	00	32	312.521	49
12	35	00	35	286.478	48
13	38	00	38	264.441	47
14	41	00	41	245.552	46
15	0.0044	1.0000	0.0044	229.182	45
16	47	00	47	214.858	44
17	49	00	49	202.219	43
18	52	00	52	190.984	42
19	55	00	55	180.932	41
20	0.0058	1.0000	0.0058	171.885	40
21	61	00	61	163.700	39
22	64	00	64	156.259	38
23	67	00	67	149.465	37
24	70	00	70	143.237	36
25	0.0073	1.0000	0.0073	137.507	35
26	76	00	76	132.219	34
27	79	00	79	127.321	33
28	81	00	81	122.774	32
29	84	00	84	118.540	31
30	0.0087	1.0000	0.0087	114.589	30
′	cos	sin	cot	tan	′

89°

0°

′	sin	cos	tan	cot	′
30	0.0087	1.0000	0.0087	114.589	30
31	90	00	90	110.892	29
32	93	00	93	107.426	28
33	96	00	96	104.171	27
34	99	1.0000	99	101.107	26
35	0.0102	0.9999	0.0102	98.2179	25
36	05	99	05	95.4895	24
37	08	99	08	92.9085	23
38	11	99	11	90.4633	22
39	13	99	13	88.1436	21
40	0.0116	0.9999	0.0116	85.9398	20
41	19	99	19	83.8435	19
42	22	99	22	81.8470	18
43	25	99	25	79.9434	17
44	28	99	28	78.1263	16
45	0.0131	0.9999	0.0131	76.3900	15
46	34	99	34	74.7292	14
47	37	99	37	73.1390	13
48	40	99	40	71.6151	12
49	43	99	43	70.1533	11
50	0.0145	0.9999	0.0145	68.7501	10
51	48	99	48	67.4019	9
52	51	99	51	66.1055	8
53	54	99	54	64.8580	7
54	57	99	57	63.6567	6
55	0.0160	0.9999	0.0160	62.4992	5
56	63	99	63	61.3829	4
57	66	99	66	60.3058	3
58	69	99	69	59.2659	2
59	72	99	72	58.2612	1
60	0.0175	0.9998	0.0175	57.2900	0
′	cos	sin	cot	tan	′

89°

1°

′	sin	cos	tan	cot	′
0	0.0175	0.9998	0.0175	57.2900	**60**
1	77	98	77	56.3506	59
2	80	98	80	55.4415	58
3	83	98	83	54.5613	57
4	86	98	86	53.7086	56
5	0.0189	0.9998	0.0189	52.8821	**55**
6	92	98	92	52.0807	54
7	95	98	95	51.3032	53
8	0198	98	0198	50.5485	52
9	0201	98	0201	49.8157	51
10	0.0204	0.9998	0.0204	49.1039	**50**
11	07	98	07	48.4121	49
12	09	98	09	47.7395	48
13	12	98	12	47.0853	47
14	15	98	15	46.4489	46
15	0.0218	0.9998	0.0218	45.8294	**45**
16	21	98	21	45.2261	44
17	24	97	24	44.6386	43
18	27	97	27	44.0661	42
19	30	97	30	43.5081	41
20	0.0233	0.9997	0.0233	42.9641	**40**
21	36	97	36	42.4335	39
22	39	97	39	41.9158	38
23	41	97	41	41.4106	37
24	44	97	44	40.9174	36
25	0.0247	0.9997	0.0247	40.4358	**35**
26	50	97	50	39.9655	34
27	53	97	53	39.5059	33
28	56	97	56	39.0568	32
29	59	97	59	38.6177	31
30	0.0262	0.9997	0.0262	38.1885	**30**
31	65	96	65	37.7686	29
32	68	96	68	37.3579	28
33	70	96	71	36.9560	27
34	73	96	74	36.5627	26
35	0.0276	0.9996	0.0276	36.1776	**25**
36	79	96	79	35.8006	24
37	82	96	82	35.4313	23
38	85	96	85	35.0695	22
39	88	96	88	34.7151	21
40	0.0291	0.9996	0.0291	34.3678	**20**
41	94	96	94	34.0273	19
42	0297	96	0297	33.6935	18
43	0300	96	0300	33.3662	17
44	02	95	03	33.0452	16
45	0.0305	0.9995	0.0306	32.7303	**15**
46	08	95	08	32.4213	14
47	11	95	11	32.1181	13
48	14	95	14	31.8205	12
49	17	95	17	31.5284	11
50	0.0320	0.9995	0.0320	31.2416	**10**
51	23	95	23	30.9599	9
52	26	95	26	30.6833	8
53	29	95	29	30.4116	7
54	32	95	32	30.1446	6
55	0.0334	0.9994	0.0335	29.8823	**5**
56	37	94	38	29.6245	4
57	40	94	40	29.3711	3
58	43	94	43	29.1220	2
59	46	94	46	28.8771	1
60	0.0349	0.9994	0.0349	28.6363	**0**
′	cos	sin	cot	tan	′

88°

2°

′	sin	cos	tan	cot	′
0	0.0349	0.9994	0.0349	28.6363	**60**
1	52	94	52	28.3994	59
2	55	94	55	28.1664	58
3	58	94	58	27.9372	57
4	61	93	61	27.7117	56
5	0.0364	0.9993	0.0364	27.4899	**55**
6	66	93	67	27.2715	54
7	69	93	70	27.0566	53
8	72	93	73	26.8450	52
9	75	93	75	26.6367	51
10	0.0378	0.9993	0.0378	26.4316	**50**
11	81	93	81	26.2296	49
12	84	93	84	26.0307	48
13	87	93	87	25.8348	47
14	90	92	90	25.6418	46
15	0.0393	0.9992	0.0393	25.4517	**45**
16	96	92	96	25.2644	44
17	0398	92	0399	25.0798	43
18	0401	92	0402	24.8978	42
19	04	92	05	24.7185	41
20	0.0407	0.9992	0.0407	24.5418	**40**
21	10	92	10	24.3675	39
22	13	91	13	24.1957	38
23	16	91	16	24.0263	37
24	19	91	19	23.8593	36
25	0.0422	0.9991	0.0422	23.6945	**35**
26	25	91	25	23.5321	34
27	27	91	28	23.3718	33
28	30	91	31	23.2137	32
29	33	91	34	23.0577	31
30	0.0436	0.9990	0.0437	22.9038	**30**
31	39	90	40	22.7519	29
32	42	90	42	22.6020	28
33	45	90	45	22.4541	27
34	48	90	48	22.3081	26
35	0.0451	0.9990	0.0451	22.1640	**25**
36	54	90	54	22.0217	24
37	57	90	57	21.8813	23
38	59	89	60	21.7426	22
39	62	89	63	21.6056	21
40	0.0465	0.9989	0.0466	21.4704	**20**
41	68	89	69	21.3369	19
42	71	89	72	21.2049	18
43	74	89	75	21.0747	17
44	77	89	77	20.9460	16
45	0.0480	0.9988	0.0480	20.8188	**15**
46	83	88	83	20.6932	14
47	86	88	86	20.5691	13
48	88	88	89	20.4465	12
49	91	88	92	20.3253	11
50	0.0494	0.9988	0.0495	20.2056	**10**
51	0497	88	0498	20.0872	9
52	0500	87	0501	19.9702	8
53	03	87	04	19.8546	7
54	06	87	07	19.7403	6
55	0.0509	0.9987	0.0509	19.6273	**5**
56	12	87	12	19.5156	4
57	15	87	15	19.4051	3
58	18	87	18	19.2959	2
59	20	86	21	19.1879	1
60	0.0523	0.9986	0.0524	19.0811	**0**
′	cos	sin	cot	tan	′

87°

3°

′	sin	cos	tan	cot	′
0	0.0523	0.9986	0.0524	19.0811	**60**
1	26	86	27	18.9755	59
2	29	86	30	18.8711	58
3	32	86	33	18.7678	57
4	35	86	36	18.6656	56
5	0.0538	0.9986	0.0539	18.5645	**55**
6	41	85	42	18.4645	54
7	44	85	44	18.3655	53
8	47	85	47	18.2677	52
9	50	85	50	18.1708	51
10	0.0552	0.9985	0.0553	18.0750	**50**
11	55	85	56	17.9802	49
12	58	84	59	17.8863	48
13	61	84	62	17.7934	47
14	64	84	65	17.7015	46
15	0.0567	0.9984	0.0568	17.6106	**45**
16	70	84	71	17.5205	44
17	73	84	74	17.4314	43
18	76	83	77	17.3432	42
19	79	83	80	17.2558	41
20	0.0581	0.9983	0.0582	17.1693	**40**
21	84	83	85	17.0837	39
22	87	83	88	16.9990	38
23	90	83	91	16.9150	37
24	93	82	94	16.8319	36
25	0.0596	0.9982	0.0597	16.7496	**35**
26	0599	82	0600	16.6681	34
27	0602	82	03	16.5874	33
28	05	82	06	16.5075	32
29	08	82	09	16.4283	31
30	0.0610	0.9981	0.0612	16.3499	**30**
31	13	81	15	16.2722	29
32	16	81	17	16.1952	28
33	19	81	20	16.1190	27
34	22	81	23	16.0435	26
35	0.0625	0.9980	0.0626	15.9687	**25**
36	28	80	29	15.8945	24
37	31	80	32	15.8211	23
38	34	80	35	15.7483	22
39	37	80	38	15.6762	21
40	0.0640	0.9980	0.0641	15.6048	**20**
41	42	79	44	15.5340	19
42	45	79	47	15.4638	18
43	48	79	50	15.3943	17
44	51	79	53	15.3254	16
45	0.0654	0.9979	0.0655	15.2571	**15**
46	57	78	58	15.1893	14
47	60	78	61	15.1222	13
48	63	78	64	15.0557	12
49	66	78	67	14.9898	11
50	0.0669	0.9978	0.0670	14.9244	**10**
51	71	77	73	14.8596	9
52	74	77	76	14.7954	8
53	77	77	79	14.7317	7
54	80	77	82	14.6685	6
55	0.0683	0.9977	0.0685	14.6059	**5**
56	86	76	88	14.5438	4
57	89	76	90	14.4823	3
58	92	76	93	14.4212	2
59	95	76	96	14.3607	1
60	0.0698	0.9976	0.0699	14.3007	**0**
′	cos	sin	cot	tan	′

86°

4°

′	sin	cos	tan	cot	′
0	0.0698	0.9976	0.0699	14.3007	**60**
1	0700	75	0702	2411	59
2	03	75	05	1821	58
3	06	75	08	1235	57
4	09	75	11	0655	56
5	0.0712	0.9975	0.0714	14.0079	**55**
6	15	74	17	13.9507	54
7	18	74	20	8940	53
8	21	74	23	8378	52
9	24	74	26	7821	51
10	0.0727	0.9974	0.0729	13.7267	**50**
11	29	73	31	6719	49
12	32	73	34	6174	48
13	35	73	37	5634	47
14	38	73	40	5098	46
15	0.0741	0.9973	0.0743	13.4566	**45**
16	44	72	46	4039	44
17	47	72	49	3515	43
18	50	72	52	2996	42
19	53	72	55	2480	41
20	0.0756	0.9971	0.0758	13.1969	**40**
21	58	71	61	1461	39
22	61	71	64	0958	38
23	64	71	67	13.0458	37
24	67	71	69	12.9962	36
25	0.0770	0.9970	0.0772	12.9469	**35**
26	73	70	75	8981	34
27	76	70	78	8496	33
28	79	70	81	8014	32
29	82	69	84	7536	31
30	0.0785	0.9969	0.0787	12.7062	**30**
31	87	69	90	6591	29
32	90	69	93	6124	28
33	93	68	96	5660	27
34	96	68	0799	5199	26
35	0.0799	0.9968	0.0802	12.4742	**25**
36	0802	68	05	4288	24
37	05	68	08	3838	23
38	08	67	10	3390	22
39	11	67	13	2946	21
40	0.0814	0.9967	0.0816	12.2505	**20**
41	16	67	19	2067	19
42	19	66	22	1632	18
43	22	66	25	1201	17
44	25	66	28	0772	16
45	0.0828	0.9966	0.0831	12.0346	**15**
46	31	65	34	11.9923	14
47	34	65	37	9504	13
48	37	65	40	9087	12
49	40	65	43	8673	11
50	0.0843	0.9964	0.0846	11.8262	**10**
51	45	64	49	7853	9
52	48	64	51	7448	8
53	51	64	54	7045	7
54	54	63	57	6645	6
55	0.0857	0.9963	0.0860	11.6248	**5**
56	60	63	63	5853	4
57	63	63	66	5461	3
58	66	62	69	5072	2
59	69	62	72	4685	1
60	0.0872	0.9962	0.0875	11.4301	**0**
′	cos	sin	cot	tan	′

85°

5°

′	sin	cos	tan	cot	′
0	0.0872	0.9962	0.0875	11.4301	**60**
1	74	62	78	3919	59
2	77	61	81	3540	58
3	80	61	84	3163	57
4	83	61	87	2789	56
5	0.0886	0.9961	0.0890	11.2417	**55**
6	89	60	92	2048	54
7	92	60	95	1681	53
8	95	60	0898	1316	52
9	0898	60	0901	0954	51
10	0.0901	0.9959	0.0904	11.0594	**50**
11	03	59	07	11.0237	49
12	06	59	10	10.9882	48
13	09	59	13	9529	47
14	12	58	16	9178	46
15	0.0915	0.9958	0.0919	10.8829	**45**
16	18	58	22	8483	44
17	21	58	25	8139	43
18	24	57	28	7797	42
19	27	57	31	7457	41
20	0.0929	0.9957	0.0934	10.7119	**40**
21	32	56	36	6783	39
22	35	56	39	6450	38
23	38	56	42	6118	37
24	41	56	45	5789	36
25	0.0944	0.9955	0.0948	10.5462	**35**
26	47	55	51	5136	34
27	50	55	54	4813	33
28	53	55	57	4491	32
29	56	54	60	4172	31
30	0.0958	0.9954	0.0963	10.3854	**30**
31	61	54	66	3538	29
32	64	53	69	3224	28
33	67	53	72	2913	27
34	70	53	75	2602	26
35	0.0973	0.9953	0.0978	10.2294	**25**
36	76	52	81	1988	24
37	79	52	83	1683	23
38	82	52	86	1381	22
39	85	51	89	1080	21
40	0.0987	0.9951	0.0992	10.0780	**20**
41	90	51	95	0483	19
42	93	51	0998	10.0187	18
43	96	50	1001	9.9893	17
44	0999	50	04	9601	16
45	0.1002	0.9950	0.1007	9.9310	**15**
46	05	49	10	9021	14
47	08	49	13	8734	13
48	11	49	16	8448	12
49	13	49	19	8164	11
50	0.1016	0.9948	0.1022	9.7882	**10**
51	19	48	25	7601	9
52	22	48	28	7322	8
53	25	47	30	7044	7
54	28	47	33	6768	6
55	0.1031	0.9947	0.1036	9.6493	**5**
56	34	46	39	6220	4
57	37	46	42	5949	3
58	39	46	45	5679	2
59	42	46	48	5411	1
60	0.1045	0.9945	0.1051	9.5144	**0**
′	cos	sin	cot	tan	′

84°

6°

′	sin	cos	tan	cot	′
0	0.1045	0.9945	0.1051	9.5144	**60**
1	48	45	54	4878	59
2	51	45	57	4614	58
3	54	44	60	4352	57
4	57	44	63	4090	56
5	0.1060	0.9944	0.1066	9.3831	**55**
6	63	43	69	3572	54
7	66	43	72	3315	53
8	68	43	75	3060	52
9	71	42	78	2806	51
10	0.1074	0.9942	0.1080	9.2553	**50**
11	77	42	83	2302	49
12	80	42	86	2052	48
13	83	41	89	1803	47
14	86	41	92	1555	46
15	0.1089	0.9941	0.1095	9.1309	**45**
16	92	40	1098	1065	44
17	94	40	1101	0821	43
18	1097	40	04	0579	42
19	1100	39	07	0338	41
20	0.1103	0.9939	0.1110	9.0098	**40**
21	06	39	13	8.9860	39
22	09	38	16	9623	38
23	12	38	19	9387	37
24	15	38	22	9152	36
25	0.1118	0.9937	0.1125	8.8919	**35**
26	20	37	28	8686	34
27	23	37	31	8455	33
28	26	36	33	8225	32
29	29	36	36	7996	31
30	0.1132	0.9936	0.1139	8.7769	**30**
31	35	35	42	7542	29
32	38	35	45	7317	28
33	41	35	48	7093	27
34	44	34	51	6870	26
35	0.1146	0.9934	0.1154	8.6648	**25**
36	49	34	57	6427	24
37	52	33	60	6208	23
38	55	33	63	5989	22
39	58	33	66	5772	21
40	0.1161	0.9932	0.1169	8.5555	**20**
41	64	32	72	5340	19
42	67	32	75	5126	18
43	70	31	78	4913	17
44	72	31	81	4701	16
45	0.1175	0.9931	0.1184	8.4490	**15**
46	78	30	87	4280	14
47	81	30	89	4071	13
48	84	30	92	3863	12
49	87	29	95	3656	11
50	0.1190	0.9929	0.1198	8.3450	**10**
51	93	29	1201	3245	9
52	96	28	04	3041	8
53	1198	28	07	2838	7
54	1201	28	10	2636	6
55	0.1204	0.9927	0.1213	8.2434	**5**
56	07	27	16	2234	4
57	10	27	19	2035	3
58	13	26	22	1837	2
59	16	26	25	1640	1
60	0.1219	0.9925	0.1228	8.1443	**0**
′	cos	sin	cot	tan	′

83°

7°

′	sin	cos	tan	cot	′
0	0.1219	0.9925	0.1228	8.1443	**60**
1	22	25	31	1248	59
2	24	25	34	1054	58
3	27	24	37	0860	57
4	30	24	40	0667	56
5	0.1233	0.9924	0.1243	8.0476	**55**
6	36	23	46	0285	54
7	39	23	49	8.0095	53
8	42	23	51	7.9906	52
9	45	22	54	9718	51
10	0.1248	0.9922	0.1257	7.9530	**50**
11	50	22	60	9344	49
12	53	21	63	9158	48
13	56	21	66	8973	47
14	59	20	69	8789	46
15	0.1262	0.9920	0.1272	7.8606	**45**
16	65	20	75	8424	44
17	68	19	78	8243	43
18	71	19	81	8062	42
19	74	19	84	7883	41
20	0.1276	0.9918	0.1287	7.7704	**40**
21	79	18	90	7525	39
22	82	17	93	7348	38
23	85	17	96	7171	37
24	88	17	99	6996	36
25	0.1291	0.9916	0.1302	7.6821	**35**
26	94	16	05	6647	34
27	97	16	08	6473	33
28	1299	15	11	6301	32
29	1302	15	14	6129	31
30	0.1305	0.9914	0.1317	7.5958	**30**
31	08	14	19	5787	29
32	11	14	22	5618	28
33	14	13	25	5449	27
34	17	13	28	5281	26
35	0.1320	0.9913	0.1331	7.5113	**25**
36	23	12	34	4947	24
37	25	12	37	4781	23
38	28	11	40	4615	22
39	31	11	43	4451	21
40	0.1334	0.9911	0.1346	7.4287	**20**
41	37	10	49	4124	19
42	40	10	52	3962	18
43	43	09	55	3800	17
44	46	09	58	3639	16
45	0.1349	0.9909	0.1361	7.3479	**15**
46	51	08	64	3319	14
47	54	08	67	3160	13
48	57	07	70	3002	12
49	60	07	73	2844	11
50	0.1363	0.9907	0.1376	7.2687	**10**
51	66	06	79	2531	9
52	69	06	82	2375	8
53	72	05	85	2220	7
54	74	05	88	2066	6
55	0.1377	0.9905	0.1391	7.1912	**5**
56	80	04	94	1759	4
57	83	04	97	1607	3
58	86	03	1399	1455	2
59	89	03	1402	1304	1
60	0.1392	0.9903	0.1405	7.1154	**0**
′	cos	sin	cot	tan	′

82°

8°

′	sin	cos	tan	cot	′
0	0.1392	0.9903	0.1405	7.1154	**60**
1	95	02	08	1004	59
2	1397	02	11	0855	58
3	1400	01	14	0706	57
4	03	01	17	0558	56
5	0.1406	0.9901	0.1420	7.0410	**55**
6	09	00	23	0264	54
7	12	9900	26	7.0117	53
8	15	9899	29	6.9972	52
9	18	99	32	9827	51
10	0.1421	0.9899	0.1435	6.9682	**50**
11	23	98	38	9538	49
12	26	98	41	9395	48
13	29	97	44	9252	47
14	32	97	47	9110	46
15	0.1435	0.9897	0.1450	6.8969	**45**
16	38	96	53	8828	44
17	41	96	56	8687	43
18	44	95	59	8548	42
19	46	95	62	8408	41
20	0.1449	0.9894	0.1465	6.8269	**40**
21	52	94	68	8131	39
22	55	94	71	7994	38
23	58	93	74	7856	37
24	61	93	77	7720	36
25	0.1464	0.9892	0.1480	6.7584	**35**
26	67	92	83	7448	34
27	69	91	86	7313	33
28	72	91	89	7179	32
29	75	91	92	7045	31
30	0.1478	0.9890	0.1495	6.6912	**30**
31	81	90	1497	6779	29
32	84	89	1500	6646	28
33	87	89	03	6514	27
34	90	88	06	6383	26
35	0.1492	0.9888	0.1509	6.6252	**25**
36	95	88	12	6122	24
37	1498	87	15	5992	23
38	1501	87	18	5863	22
39	04	86	21	5734	21
40	0.1507	0.9886	0.1524	6.5606	**20**
41	10	85	27	5478	19
42	13	85	30	5350	18
43	15	84	33	5223	17
44	18	84	36	5097	16
45	0.1521	0.9884	0.1539	6.4971	**15**
46	24	83	42	4846	14
47	27	83	45	4721	13
48	30	82	48	4596	12
49	33	82	51	4472	11
50	0.1536	0.9881	0.1554	6.4348	**10**
51	38	81	57	4225	9
52	41	80	60	4103	8
53	44	80	63	3980	7
54	47	80	66	3859	6
55	0.1550	0.9879	0.1569	6.3737	**5**
56	53	79	72	3617	4
57	56	78	75	3496	3
58	59	78	78	3376	2
59	61	77	81	3257	1
60	0.1564	0.9877	0.1584	6.3138	**0**
′	cos	sin	cot	tan	′

81°

9°

'	sin	cos	tan	cot	'
0	0.1564	0.9877	0.1584	6.3138	**60**
1	67	76	87	6.3019	59
2	70	76	90	6.2901	58
3	73	76	93	783	57
4	76	75	96	666	56
5	0.1579	0.9875	0.1599	6.2549	**55**
6	82	74	1602	432	54
7	84	74	05	316	53
8	87	73	08	200	52
9	90	73	11	6.2085	51
10	0.1593	0.9872	0.1614	6.1970	**50**
11	96	72	17	856	49
12	1599	71	20	742	48
13	1602	71	23	628	47
14	05	70	26	515	46
15	0.1607	0.9870	0.1629	6.1402	**45**
16	10	69	32	290	44
17	13	69	35	178	43
18	16	69	38	6.1066	42
19	19	68	41	6.0955	41
20	0.1622	0.9868	0.1644	6.0844	**40**
21	25	67	47	734	39
22	28	67	50	624	38
23	30	66	53	514	37
24	33	66	55	405	36
25	0.1636	0.9865	0.1658	6.0296	**35**
26	39	65	61	188	34
27	42	64	64	6.0080	33
28	45	64	67	5.9972	32
29	48	63	70	865	31
30	0.1650	0.9863	0.1673	5.9758	**30**
31	53	62	76	651	29
32	56	62	79	545	28
33	59	61	82	439	27
34	62	61	85	333	26
35	0.1665	0.9860	0.1688	5.9228	**25**
36	68	60	91	124	24
37	71	59	94	5.9019	23
38	73	59	1697	5.8915	22
39	76	59	1700	811	21
40	0.1679	0.9858	0.1703	5.8708	**20**
41	82	58	06	605	19
42	85	57	09	502	18
43	88	57	12	400	17
44	91	56	15	298	16
45	0.1693	0.9856	0.1718	5.8197	**15**
46	96	55	21	5.8095	14
47	1699	55	24	5.7994	13
48	1702	54	27	894	12
49	05	54	30	794	11
50	0.1708	0.9853	0.1733	5.7694	**10**
51	11	53	36	594	9
52	14	52	39	495	8
53	16	52	42	396	7
54	19	51	45	297	6
55	0.1722	0.9851	0.1748	5.7199	**5**
56	25	50	51	101	4
57	28	50	54	5.7004	3
58	31	49	57	5.6906	2
59	34	49	60	809	1
60	0.1736	0.9848	0.1763	5.6713	**0**
'	cos	sin	cot	tan	'

80°

10°

'	sin	cos	tan	cot	'
0	0.1736	0.9848	0.1763	5.6713	**60**
1	39	48	66	617	59
2	42	47	69	521	58
3	45	47	72	425	57
4	48	46	75	330	56
5	0.1751	0.9846	0.1778	5.6234	**55**
6	54	45	81	140	54
7	57	45	84	5.6045	53
8	59	44	87	5.5951	52
9	62	43	90	857	51
10	0.1765	0.9843	0.1793	5.5764	**50**
11	68	42	96	671	49
12	71	42	1799	578	48
13	74	41	1802	485	47
14	77	41	05	393	46
15	0.1779	0.9840	0.1808	5.5301	**45**
16	82	40	11	209	44
17	85	39	14	118	43
18	88	39	17	5.5026	42
19	91	38	20	5.4936	41
20	0.1794	0.9838	0.1823	5.4845	**40**
21	97	37	26	755	39
22	1799	37	29	665	38
23	1802	36	32	575	37
24	05	36	35	486	36
25	0.1808	0.9835	0.1838	5.4397	**35**
26	11	35	41	308	34
27	14	34	44	219	33
28	17	34	47	131	32
29	19	33	50	5.4043	31
30	0.1822	0.9833	0.1853	5.3955	**30**
31	25	32	56	868	29
32	28	31	59	781	28
33	31	31	62	694	27
34	34	30	65	607	26
35	0.1837	0.9830	0.1868	5.3521	**25**
36	40	29	71	435	24
37	42	29	74	349	23
38	45	28	77	263	22
39	48	28	80	178	21
40	0.1851	0.9827	0.1883	5.3093	**20**
41	54	27	87	5.3008	19
42	57	26	90	5.2924	18
43	60	26	93	839	17
44	62	25	96	755	16
45	0.1865	0.9825	0.1899	5.2672	**15**
46	68	24	1902	588	14
47	71	23	05	505	13
48	74	23	08	422	12
49	77	22	11	339	11
50	0.1880	0.9822	0.1914	5.2257	**10**
51	82	21	17	174	9
52	85	21	20	092	8
53	88	20	23	5.2011	7
54	91	20	26	5.1929	6
55	0.1894	0.9819	0.1929	5.1848	**5**
56	1897	18	32	767	4
57	1900	18	35	686	3
58	02	17	38	606	2
59	05	17	41	526	1
60	0.1908	0.9816	0.1944	5.1446	**0**
'	cos	sin	cot	tan	'

79°

11°

′	sin	cos	tan	cot	′
0	0.1908	0.9816	0.1944	5.1446	**60**
1	11	16	47	366	59
2	14	15	50	286	58
3	17	15	53	207	57
4	20	14	56	128	56
5	0.1922	0.9813	0.1959	5.1049	**55**
6	25	13	62	5.0970	54
7	28	12	65	892	53
8	31	12	68	814	52
9	34	11	71	736	51
10	0.1937	0.9811	0.1974	5.0658	**50**
11	39	10	77	581	49
12	42	10	80	504	48
13	45	09	83	427	47
14	48	08	86	350	46
15	0.1951	0.9808	0.1989	5.0273	**45**
16	54	07	92	197	44
17	57	07	95	121	43
18	59	06	1998	5.0045	42
19	62	06	2001	4.9969	41
20	0.1965	0.9805	0.2004	4.9894	**40**
21	68	04	07	819	39
22	71	04	10	744	38
23	74	03	13	669	37
24	77	03	16	594	36
25	0.1979	0.9802	0.2019	4.9520	**35**
26	82	02	22	446	34
27	85	01	25	372	33
28	88	00	28	298	32
29	91	9800	31	225	31
30	0.1994	0.9799	0.2035	4.9152	**30**
31	97	99	38	078	29
32	1999	98	41	4.9006	28
33	2002	98	44	4.8933	27
34	05	97	47	860	26
35	0.2008	0.9796	0.2050	4.8788	**25**
36	11	96	53	716	24
37	14	95	56	644	23
38	16	95	59	573	22
39	19	94	62	501	21
40	0.2022	0.9793	0.2065	4.8430	**20**
41	25	93	68	359	19
42	28	92	71	288	18
43	31	92	74	218	17
44	34	91	77	147	16
45	0.2036	0.9790	0.2080	4.8077	**15**
46	39	90	83	4.8007	14
47	42	89	86	4.7937	13
48	45	89	89	867	12
49	48	88	92	798	11
50	0.2051	0.9787	0.2095	4.7729	**10**
51	54	87	2098	659	9
52	56	86	2101	591	8
53	59	86	04	522	7
54	62	85	07	453	6
55	0.2065	0.9784	0.2110	4.7385	**5**
56	68	84	13	317	4
57	71	83	16	249	3
58	73	83	19	181	2
59	76	82	23	114	1
60	0.2079	0.9781	0.2126	4.7046	**0**
′	cos	sin	cot	tan	′

78°

12°

′	sin	cos	tan	cot	′
0	0.2079	0.9781	0.2126	4.7046	**60**
1	82	81	29	4.6979	59
2	85	80	32	912	58
3	88	80	35	845	57
4	90	79	38	779	56
5	0.2093	0.9778	0.2141	4.6712	**55**
6	96	78	44	646	54
7	2099	77	47	580	53
8	2102	77	50	514	52
9	05	76	53	448	51
10	0.2108	0.9775	0.2156	4.6382	**50**
11	10	75	59	317	49
12	13	74	62	252	48
13	16	74	65	187	47
14	19	73	68	122	46
15	0.2122	0.9772	0.2171	4.6057	**45**
16	25	72	74	4.5993	44
17	27	71	77	928	43
18	30	70	80	864	42
19	33	70	83	800	41
20	0.2136	0.9769	0.2186	4.5736	**40**
21	39	69	89	673	39
22	42	68	93	609	38
23	45	67	96	546	37
24	47	67	2199	483	36
25	0.2150	0.9766	0.2202	4.5420	**35**
26	53	65	05	357	34
27	56	65	08	294	33
28	59	64	11	232	32
29	62	64	14	169	31
30	0.2164	0.9763	0.2217	4.5107	**30**
31	67	62	20	4.5045	29
32	70	62	23	4.4983	28
33	73	61	26	922	27
34	76	60	29	860	26
35	0.2179	0.9760	0.2232	4.4799	**25**
36	81	59	35	737	24
37	84	59	38	676	23
38	87	58	41	615	22
39	90	57	44	555	21
40	0.2193	0.9757	0.2247	4.4494	**20**
41	96	56	51	434	19
42	2198	55	54	374	18
43	2201	55	57	313	17
44	04	54	60	253	16
45	0.2207	0.9753	0.2263	4.4194	**15**
46	10	53	66	134	14
47	13	52	69	075	13
48	15	51	72	4.4015	12
49	18	51	75	4.3956	11
50	0.2221	0.9750	0.2278	4.3897	**10**
51	24	50	81	838	9
52	27	49	84	779	8
53	30	48	87	721	7
54	33	48	90	662	6
55	0.2235	0.9747	0.2293	4.3604	**5**
56	38	46	96	546	4
57	41	46	2299	488	3
58	44	45	2303	430	2
59	47	44	06	372	1
60	0.2250	0.9744	0.2309	4.3315	**0**
′	cos	sin	cot	tan	′

77°

13°

′	sin	cos	tan	cot	′
0	0.2250	0.9744	0.2309	4.3315	**60**
1	52	43	12	257	59
2	55	42	15	200	58
3	58	42	18	143	57
4	61	41	21	086	56
5	0.2264	0.9740	0.2324	4.3029	**55**
6	67	40	27	4.2972	54
7	69	39	30	916	53
8	72	38	33	859	52
9	75	38	36	803	51
10	0.2278	0.9737	0.2339	4.2747	**50**
11	81	36	42	691	49
12	84	36	45	635	48
13	86	35	49	580	47
14	89	34	52	524	46
15	0.2292	0.9734	0.2355	4.2468	**45**
16	95	33	58	413	44
17	2298	32	61	358	43
18	2300	32	64	303	42
19	03	31	67	248	41
20	0.2306	0.9730	0.2370	4.2193	**40**
21	09	30	73	139	39
22	12	29	76	084	38
23	15	28	79	4.2030	37
24	17	28	82	4.1976	36
25	0.2320	0.9727	0.2385	4.1922	**35**
26	23	26	88	868	34
27	26	26	92	814	33
28	29	25	95	760	32
29	32	24	2398	706	31
30	0.2334	0.9724	0.2401	4.1653	**30**
31	37	23	04	600	29
32	40	22	07	547	28
33	43	22	10	493	27
34	46	21	13	441	26
35	0.2349	0.9720	0.2416	4.1388	**25**
36	51	20	19	335	24
37	54	19	22	282	23
38	57	18	25	230	22
39	60	18	28	178	21
40	0.2363	0.9717	0.2432	4.1126	**20**
41	66	16	35	074	19
42	68	15	38	4.1022	18
43	71	15	41	4.0970	17
44	74	14	44	918	16
45	0.2377	0.9713	0.2447	4.0867	**15**
46	80	13	50	815	14
47	83	12	53	764	13
48	85	11	56	713	12
49	88	11	59	662	11
50	0.2391	0.9710	0.2462	4.0611	**10**
51	94	09	65	560	9
52	97	09	69	509	8
53	2399	08	72	459	7
54	2402	07	75	408	6
55	0.2405	0.9706	0.2478	4.0358	**5**
56	08	06	81	308	4
57	11	05	84	257	3
58	14	04	87	207	2
59	16	04	90	158	1
60	0.2419	0.9703	0.2493	4.0108	**0**
′	cos	sin	cot	tan	′

76°

14°

′	sin	cos	tan	cot	′
0	0.2419	0.9703	0.2493	4.0108	**60**
1	22	02	96	058	59
2	25	02	2499	4.0009	58
3	28	01	2503	3.9959	57
4	31	9700	06	910	56
5	0.2433	0.9699	0.2509	3.9861	**55**
6	36	99	12	812	54
7	39	98	15	763	53
8	42	97	18	714	52
9	45	97	21	665	51
10	0.2447	0.9696	0.2524	3.9617	**50**
11	50	95	27	568	49
12	53	94	30	520	48
13	56	94	33	471	47
14	59	93	37	423	46
15	0.2462	0.9692	0.2540	3.9375	**45**
16	64	92	43	327	44
17	67	91	46	279	43
18	70	90	49	232	42
19	73	89	52	184	41
20	0.2476	0.9689	0.2555	3.9136	**40**
21	78	88	58	089	39
22	81	87	61	3.9042	38
23	84	87	64	3.8995	37
24	87	86	68	947	36
25	0.2490	0.9685	0.2571	3.8900	**35**
26	93	84	74	854	34
27	95	84	77	807	33
28	2498	83	80	760	32
29	2501	82	83	714	31
30	0.2504	0.9681	0.2586	3.8667	**30**
31	07	81	89	621	29
32	09	80	92	575	28
33	12	79	95	528	27
34	15	79	2599	482	26
35	0.2518	0.9678	0.2602	3.8436	**25**
36	21	77	05	391	24
37	24	76	08	345	23
38	26	76	11	299	22
39	29	75	14	254	21
40	0.2532	0.9674	0.2617	3.8208	**20**
41	35	73	20	163	19
42	38	73	23	118	18
43	40	72	27	073	17
44	43	71	30	3.8028	16
45	0.2546	0.9670	0.2633	3.7983	**15**
46	49	70	36	938	14
47	52	69	39	893	13
48	54	68	42	848	12
49	57	67	45	804	11
50	0.2560	0.9667	0.2648	3.7760	**10**
51	63	66	51	715	9
52	66	65	55	671	8
53	69	65	58	627	7
54	71	64	61	583	6
55	0.2574	0.9663	0.2664	3.7539	**5**
56	77	62	67	495	4
57	80	62	70	451	3
58	83	61	73	408	2
59	85	60	76	364	1
60	0.2588	0.9659	0.2679	3.7321	**0**
′	cos	sin	cot	tan	′

75°

15°

′	sin	cos	tan	cot	′
0	0.2588	0.9659	0.2679	3.7321	**60**
1	91	59	83	277	59
2	94	58	86	234	58
3	97	57	89	191	57
4	2599	56	92	148	56
5	0.2602	0.9655	0.2695	3.7105	**55**
6	05	55	2698	062	54
7	08	54	2701	3.7019	53
8	11	53	04	3.6976	52
9	13	52	08	933	51
10	0.2616	0.9652	0.2711	3.6891	**50**
11	19	51	14	848	49
12	22	50	17	806	48
13	25	49	20	764	47
14	28	49	23	722	46
15	0.2630	0.9648	0.2726	3.6680	**45**
16	33	47	29	638	44
17	36	46	33	596	43
18	39	46	36	554	42
19	42	45	39	512	41
20	0.2644	0.9644	0.2742	3.6470	**40**
21	47	43	45	429	39
22	50	42	48	387	38
23	53	42	51	346	37
24	56	41	54	305	36
25	0.2658	0.9640	0.2758	3.6264	**35**
26	61	39	61	222	34
27	64	39	64	181	33
28	67	38	67	140	32
29	70	37	70	100	31
30	0.2672	0.9636	0.2773	3.6059	**30**
31	75	36	76	3.6018	29
32	78	35	80	3.5978	28
33	81	34	83	937	27
34	84	33	86	897	26
35	0.2686	0.9632	0.2789	3.5856	**25**
36	89	32	92	816	24
37	92	31	95	776	23
38	95	30	2798	736	22
39	2698	29	2801	696	21
40	0.2700	0.9628	0.2805	3.5656	**20**
41	03	28	08	616	19
42	06	27	11	576	18
43	09	26	14	536	17
44	12	25	17	497	16
45	0.2714	0.9625	0.2820	3.5457	**15**
46	17	24	23	418	14
47	20	23	27	379	13
48	23	22	30	339	12
49	26	21	33	300	11
50	0.2728	0.9621	0.2836	3.5261	**10**
51	31	20	39	222	9
52	34	19	42	183	8
53	37	18	45	144	7
54	40	17	49	105	6
55	0.2742	0.9617	0.2852	3.5067	**5**
56	45	16	55	3.5028	4
57	48	15	58	3.4989	3
58	51	14	61	951	2
59	54	13	64	912	1
60	0.2756	0.9613	0.2867	3.4874	**0**
′	cos	sin	cot	tan	′

74°

16°

′	sin	cos	tan	cot	′
0	0.2756	0.9613	0.2867	3.4874	**60**
1	59	12	71	836	59
2	62	11	74	798	58
3	65	10	77	760	57
4	68	09	80	722	56
5	0.2770	0.9609	0.2883	3.4684	**55**
6	73	08	86	646	54
7	76	07	90	608	53
8	79	06	93	570	52
9	82	05	96	533	51
10	0.2784	0.9605	0.2899	3.4495	**50**
11	87	04	2902	458	49
12	90	03	05	420	48
13	93	02	08	383	47
14	95	01	12	346	46
15	0.2798	0.9600	0.2915	3.4308	**45**
16	2801	9600	18	271	44
17	04	9599	21	234	43
18	07	98	24	197	42
19	09	97	27	160	41
20	0.2812	0.9596	0.2931	3.4124	**40**
21	15	96	34	087	39
22	18	95	37	050	38
23	21	94	40	3.4014	37
24	23	93	43	3.3977	36
25	0.2826	0.9592	0.2946	3.3941	**35**
26	29	91	49	904	34
27	32	91	53	868	33
28	35	90	56	832	32
29	37	89	59	796	31
30	0.2840	0.9588	0.2962	3.3759	**30**
31	43	87	65	723	29
32	46	87	68	687	28
33	49	86	72	652	27
34	51	85	75	616	26
35	0.2854	0.9584	0.2978	3.3580	**25**
36	57	83	81	544	24
37	60	82	84	509	23
38	62	82	87	473	22
39	65	81	91	438	21
40	0.2868	0.9580	0.2994	3.3402	**20**
41	71	79	2997	367	19
42	74	78	3000	332	18
43	76	77	03	297	17
44	79	77	06	261	16
45	0.2882	0.9576	0.3010	3.3226	**15**
46	85	75	13	191	14
47	88	74	16	156	13
48	90	73	19	122	12
49	93	72	22	087	11
50	0.2896	0.9572	0.3026	3.3052	**10**
51	2899	71	29	3.3017	9
52	2901	70	32	3.2983	8
53	04	69	35	948	7
54	07	68	38	914	6
55	0.2910	0.9567	0.3041	3.2880	**5**
56	13	66	45	845	4
57	15	66	48	811	3
58	18	65	51	777	2
59	21	64	54	743	1
60	0.2924	0.9563	0.3057	3.2709	**0**
′	cos	sin	cot	tan	′

73°

17°

′	sin	cos	tan	cot	′
0	0.2924	0.9563	0.3057	3.2709	**60**
1	26	62	60	675	59
2	29	61	64	641	58
3	32	60	67	607	57
4	35	60	70	573	56
5	0.2938	0.9559	0.3073	3.2539	**55**
6	40	58	76	506	54
7	43	57	80	472	53
8	46	56	83	438	52
9	49	55	86	405	51
10	0.2952	0.9555	0.3089	3.2371	**50**
11	54	54	92	338	49
12	57	53	96	305	48
13	60	52	3099	272	47
14	63	51	3102	238	46
15	0.2965	0.9550	0.3105	3.2205	**45**
16	68	49	08	172	44
17	71	48	11	139	43
18	74	48	15	106	42
19	77	47	18	073	41
20	0.2979	0.9546	0.3121	3.2041	**40**
21	82	45	24	3.2008	39
22	85	44	27	3.1975	38
23	88	43	31	943	37
24	90	42	34	910	36
25	0.2993	0.9542	0.3137	3.1878	**35**
26	96	41	40	845	34
27	2999	40	43	813	33
28	3002	39	47	780	32
29	04	38	50	748	31
30	0.3007	0.9537	0.3153	3.1716	**30**
31	10	36	56	684	29
32	13	35	59	652	28
33	15	35	63	620	27
34	18	34	66	588	26
35	0.3021	0.9533	0.3169	3.1556	**25**
36	24	32	72	524	24
37	26	31	75	492	23
38	29	30	79	460	22
39	32	29	82	429	21
40	0.3035	0.9528	0.3185	3.1397	**20**
41	38	27	88	366	19
42	40	27	91	334	18
43	43	26	95	303	17
44	46	25	3198	271	16
45	0.3049	0.9524	0.3201	3.1240	**15**
46	51	23	04	209	14
47	54	22	07	178	13
48	57	21	11	146	12
49	60	20	14	115	11
50	0.3062	0.9520	0.3217	3.1084	**10**
51	65	19	20	053	9
52	68	18	23	3.1022	8
53	71	17	27	3.0991	7
54	74	16	30	961	6
55	0.3076	0.9515	0.3233	3.0930	**5**
56	79	14	36	899	4
57	82	13	40	868	3
58	85	12	43	838	2
59	87	11	46	807	1
60	0.3090	0.9511	0.3249	3.0777	**0**
′	cos	sin	cot	tan	′

72°

18°

′	sin	cos	tan	cot	′
0	0.3090	0.9511	0.3249	3.0777	**60**
1	93	10	52	746	59
2	96	09	56	716	58
3	3098	08	59	686	57
4	3101	07	62	655	56
5	0.3104	0.9506	0.3265	3.0625	**55**
6	07	05	69	595	54
7	10	04	72	565	53
8	12	03	75	535	52
9	15	02	78	505	51
10	0.3118	0.9502	0.3281	3.0475	**50**
11	21	01	85	445	49
12	23	9500	88	415	48
13	26	9499	91	385	47
14	29	98	94	356	46
15	0.3132	0.9497	0.3298	3.0326	**45**
16	34	96	3301	296	44
17	37	95	04	267	43
18	40	94	07	237	42
19	43	93	10	208	41
20	0.3145	0.9492	0.3314	3.0178	**40**
21	48	92	17	149	39
22	51	91	20	120	38
23	54	90	23	090	37
24	56	89	27	061	36
25	0.3159	0.9488	0.3330	3.0032	**35**
26	62	87	33	3.0003	34
27	65	86	36	2.9974	33
28	68	85	39	945	32
29	70	84	43	916	31
30	0.3173	0.9483	0.3346	2.9887	**30**
31	76	82	49	858	29
32	79	81	52	829	28
33	81	80	56	800	27
34	84	80	59	772	26
35	0.3187	0.9479	0.3362	2.9743	**25**
36	90	78	65	714	24
37	92	77	69	686	23
38	95	76	72	657	22
39	3198	75	75	629	21
40	0.3201	0.9474	0.3378	2.9600	**20**
41	03	73	82	572	19
42	06	72	85	544	18
43	09	71	88	515	17
44	12	70	91	487	16
45	0.3214	0.9469	0.3395	2.9459	**15**
46	17	68	3398	431	14
47	20	67	3401	403	13
48	23	66	04	375	12
49	25	66	08	347	11
50	0.3228	0.9465	0.3411	2.9319	**10**
51	31	64	14	291	9
52	34	63	17	263	8
53	36	62	21	235	7
54	39	61	24	208	6
55	0.3242	0.9460	0.3427	2.9180	**5**
56	45	59	30	152	4
57	47	58	34	125	3
58	50	57	37	097	2
59	53	56	40	070	1
60	0.3256	0.9455	0.3443	2.9042	**0**
′	cos	sin	cot	tan	′

71°

19°

′	sin	cos	tan	cot	′
0	0.3256	0.9455	0.3443	2.9042	**60**
1	58	54	47	2.9015	59
2	61	53	50	2.8987	58
3	64	52	53	960	57
4	67	51	56	933	56
5	0.3269	0.9450	0.3460	2.8905	**55**
6	72	49	63	878	54
7	75	49	66	851	53
8	78	48	69	824	52
9	80	47	73	797	51
10	0.3283	0.9446	0.3476	2.8770	**50**
11	86	45	79	743	49
12	89	44	82	716	48
13	91	43	86	689	47
14	94	42	89	662	46
15	0.3297	0.9441	0.3492	2.8636	**45**
16	3300	40	95	609	44
17	02	39	3499	582	43
18	05	38	3502	556	42
19	08	37	05	529	41
20	0.3311	0.9436	0.3508	2.8502	**40**
21	13	35	12	476	39
22	16	34	15	449	38
23	19	33	18	423	37
24	22	32	22	397	36
25	0.3324	0.9431	0.3525	2.8370	**35**
26	27	30	28	344	34
27	30	29	31	318	33
28	33	28	35	291	32
29	35	27	38	265	31
30	0.3338	0.9426	0.3541	2.8239	**30**
31	41	25	44	213	29
32	44	24	48	187	28
33	46	23	51	161	27
34	49	23	54	135	26
35	0.3352	0.9422	0.3558	2.8109	**25**
36	55	21	61	083	24
37	57	20	64	057	23
38	60	19	67	032	22
39	63	18	71	2.8006	21
40	0.3365	0.9417	0.3574	2.7980	**20**
41	68	16	77	955	19
42	71	15	81	929	18
43	74	14	84	903	17
44	76	13	87	878	16
45	0.3379	0.9412	0.3590	2.7852	**15**
46	82	11	94	827	14
47	85	10	3597	801	13
48	87	09	3600	776	12
49	90	08	04	751	11
50	0.3393	0.9407	0.3607	2.7725	**10**
51	96	06	10	700	9
52	3398	05	13	675	8
53	3401	04	17	650	7
54	04	03	20	625	6
55	0.3407	0.9402	0.3623	2.7600	**5**
56	09	01	27	575	4
57	12	9400	30	550	3
58	15	9399	33	525	2
59	17	98	36	500	1
60	0.3420	0.9397	0.3640	2.7475	**0**
′	cos	sin	cot	tan	′

70°

20°

′	sin	cos	tan	cot	′
0	0.3420	0.9397	0.3640	2.7475	**60**
1	23	96	43	450	59
2	26	95	46	425	58
3	28	94	50	400	57
4	31	93	53	376	56
5	0.3434	0.9392	0.3656	2.7351	**55**
6	37	91	59	326	54
7	39	90	63	302	53
8	42	89	66	277	52
9	45	88	69	253	51
10	0.3448	0.9387	0.3673	2.7228	**50**
11	50	86	76	204	49
12	53	85	79	179	48
13	56	84	83	155	47
14	58	83	86	130	46
15	0.3461	0.9382	0.3689	2.7106	**45**
16	64	81	93	082	44
17	67	80	96	058	43
18	69	79	3699	034	42
19	72	78	3702	2.7009	41
20	0.3475	0.9377	0.3706	2.6985	**40**
21	78	76	09	961	39
22	80	75	12	937	38
23	83	74	16	913	37
24	86	73	19	889	36
25	0.3488	0.9372	0.3722	2.6865	**35**
26	91	71	26	841	34
27	94	70	29	818	33
28	97	69	32	794	32
29	3499	68	36	770	31
30	0.3502	0.9367	0.3739	2.6746	**30**
31	05	66	42	723	29
32	08	65	45	699	28
33	10	64	49	675	27
34	13	63	52	652	26
35	0.3516	0.9362	0.3755	2.6628	**25**
36	18	61	59	605	24
37	21	60	62	581	23
38	24	59	65	558	22
39	27	58	69	534	21
40	0.3529	0.9356	0.3772	2.6511	**20**
41	32	55	75	488	19
42	35	54	79	464	18
43	37	53	82	441	17
44	40	52	85	418	16
45	0.3543	0.9351	0.3789	2.6395	**15**
46	46	50	92	371	14
47	48	49	95	348	13
48	51	48	3799	325	12
49	54	47	3802	302	11
50	0.3557	0.9346	0.3805	2.6279	**10**
51	59	45	09	256	9
52	62	44	12	233	8
53	65	43	15	210	7
54	67	42	19	187	6
55	0.3570	0.9341	0.3822	2.6165	**5**
56	73	40	25	142	4
57	76	39	29	119	3
58	78	38	32	096	2
59	81	37	35	074	1
60	0.3584	0.9336	0.3839	2.6051	**0**
′	cos	sin	cot	tan	′

69°

21°

′	sin	cos	tan	cot	′
0	0.3584	0.9336	0.3839	2.6051	**60**
1	86	35	42	028	59
2	89	34	45	2.6006	58
3	92	33	49	2.5983	57
4	95	32	52	961	56
5	0.3597	0.9331	0.3855	2.5938	**55**
6	3600	30	59	916	54
7	03	28	62	893	53
8	05	27	65	871	52
9	08	26	69	848	51
10	0.3611	0.9325	0.3872	2.5826	**50**
11	14	24	75	804	49
12	16	23	79	782	48
13	19	22	82	759	47
14	22	21	85	737	46
15	0.3624	0.9320	0.3889	2.5715	**45**
16	27	19	92	693	44
17	30	18	95	671	43
18	33	17	3899	649	42
19	35	16	3902	627	41
20	0.3638	0.9315	0.3906	2.5605	**40**
21	41	14	09	583	39
22	43	13	12	561	38
23	46	12	16	539	37
24	49	11	19	517	36
25	0.3651	0.9309	0.3922	2.5495	**35**
26	54	08	26	473	34
27	57	07	29	452	33
28	60	06	32	430	32
29	62	05	36	408	31
30	0.3665	0.9304	0.3939	2.5386	**30**
31	68	03	42	365	29
32	70	02	46	343	28
33	73	01	49	322	27
34	76	9300	53	300	26
35	0.3679	0.9299	0.3956	2.5279	**25**
36	81	98	59	257	24
37	84	97	63	236	23
38	87	96	66	214	22
39	89	95	69	193	21
40	0.3692	0.9293	0.3973	2.5172	**20**
41	95	92	76	150	19
42	3697	91	79	129	18
43	3700	90	83	108	17
44	03	89	86	086	16
45	0.3706	0.9288	0.3990	2.5065	**15**
46	08	87	93	044	14
47	11	86	3996	023	13
48	14	85	4000	2.5002	12
49	16	84	03	2.4981	11
50	0.3719	0.9283	0.4006	2.4960	**10**
51	22	82	10	939	9
52	24	81	13	918	8
53	27	79	17	897	7
54	30	78	20	876	6
55	0.3733	0.9277	0.4023	2.4855	**5**
56	35	76	27	834	4
57	38	75	30	813	3
58	41	74	33	792	2
59	43	73	37	772	1
60	0.3746	0.9272	0.4040	2.4751	**0**
′	cos	sin	cot	tan	′

68°

22°

′	sin	cos	tan	cot	′
0	0.3746	0.9272	0.4040	2.4751	**60**
1	49	71	44	730	59
2	51	70	47	709	58
3	54	69	50	689	57
4	57	67	54	668	56
5	0.3760	0.9266	0.4057	2.4648	**55**
6	62	65	61	627	54
7	65	64	64	606	53
8	68	63	67	586	52
9	70	62	71	566	51
10	0.3773	0.9261	0.4074	2.4545	**50**
11	76	60	78	525	49
12	78	59	81	504	48
13	81	58	84	484	47
14	84	57	88	464	46
15	0.3786	0.9255	0.4091	2.4443	**45**
16	89	54	95	423	44
17	92	53	4098	403	43
18	95	52	4101	383	42
19	3797	51	05	362	41
20	0.3800	0.9250	0.4108	2.4342	**40**
21	03	49	11	322	39
22	05	48	15	302	38
23	08	47	18	282	37
24	11	45	22	262	36
25	0.3813	0.9244	0.4125	2.4242	**35**
26	16	43	29	222	34
27	19	42	32	202	33
28	21	41	35	182	32
29	24	40	39	162	31
30	0.3827	0.9239	0.4142	2.4142	**30**
31	30	38	46	122	29
32	32	37	49	102	28
33	35	35	52	083	27
34	38	34	56	063	26
35	0.3840	0.9233	0.4159	2.4043	**25**
36	43	32	63	023	24
37	46	31	66	2.4004	23
38	48	30	69	2.3984	22
39	51	29	73	964	21
40	0.3854	0.9228	0.4176	2.3945	**20**
41	56	27	80	925	19
42	59	25	83	906	18
43	62	24	87	886	17
44	64	23	90	867	16
45	0.3867	0.9222	0.4193	2.3847	**15**
46	70	21	4197	828	14
47	72	20	4200	808	13
48	75	19	04	789	12
49	78	18	07	770	11
50	0.3881	0.9216	0.4210	2.3750	**10**
51	83	15	14	731	9
52	86	14	17	712	8
53	89	13	21	693	7
54	91	12	24	673	6
55	0.3894	0.9211	0.4228	2.3654	**5**
56	97	10	31	635	4
57	3899	08	34	616	3
58	3902	07	38	597	2
59	05	06	41	578	1
60	0.3907	0.9205	0.4245	2.3559	**0**
′	cos	sin	cot	tan	′

67°

23°

′	sin	cos	tan	cot	′
0	0.3907	0.9205	0.4245	2.3559	**60**
1	10	04	48	539	59
2	13	03	52	520	58
3	15	02	55	501	57
4	18	9200	58	483	56
5	0.3921	0.9199	0.4262	2.3464	**55**
6	23	98	65	445	54
7	26	97	69	426	53
8	29	96	72	407	52
9	31	95	76	388	51
10	0.3934	0.9194	0.4279	2.3369	**50**
11	37	92	83	351	49
12	39	91	86	332	48
13	42	90	89	313	47
14	45	89	93	294	46
15	0.3947	0.9188	0.4296	2.3276	**45**
16	50	87	4300	257	44
17	53	86	03	238	43
18	55	84	07	220	42
19	58	83	10	201	41
20	0.3961	0.9182	0.4314	2.3183	**40**
21	63	81	17	164	39
22	66	80	20	146	38
23	69	79	24	127	37
24	71	78	27	109	36
25	0.3974	0.9176	0.4331	2.3090	**35**
26	77	75	34	072	34
27	79	74	38	053	33
28	82	73	41	035	32
29	85	72	45	2.3017	31
30	0.3987	0.9171	0.4348	2.2998	**30**
31	90	69	52	980	29
32	93	68	55	962	28
33	95	67	59	944	27
34	3998	66	62	925	26
35	0.4001	0.9165	0.4365	2.2907	**25**
36	03	64	69	889	24
37	06	62	72	871	23
38	09	61	76	853	22
39	11	60	79	835	21
40	0.4014	0.9159	0.4383	2.2817	**20**
41	17	58	86	799	19
42	19	57	90	781	18
43	22	55	93	763	17
44	25	54	4397	745	16
45	0.4027	0.9153	0.4400	2.2727	**15**
46	30	52	04	709	14
47	33	51	07	691	13
48	35	50	11	673	12
49	38	48	14	655	11
50	0.4041	0.9147	0.4417	2.2637	**10**
51	43	46	21	620	9
52	46	45	24	602	8
53	49	44	28	584	7
54	51	43	31	566	6
55	0.4054	0.9141	0.4435	2.2549	**5**
56	57	40	38	531	4
57	59	39	42	513	3
58	62	38	45	496	2
59	65	37	49	478	1
60	0.4067	0.9135	0.4452	2.2460	**0**
′	cos	sin	cot	tan	′

66°

24°

′	sin	cos	tan	cot	′
0	0.4067	0.9135	0.4452	2.2460	**60**
1	70	34	56	443	59
2	73	33	59	425	58
3	75	32	63	408	57
4	78	31	66	390	56
5	0.4081	0.9130	0.4470	2.2373	**55**
6	83	28	73	355	54
7	86	27	77	338	53
8	89	26	80	320	52
9	91	25	84	303	51
10	0.4094	0.9124	0.4487	2.2286	**50**
11	97	22	91	268	49
12	4099	21	94	251	48
13	4102	20	4498	234	47
14	05	19	4501	216	46
15	0.4107	0.9118	0.4505	2.2199	**45**
16	10	16	08	182	44
17	12	15	12	165	43
18	15	14	15	148	42
19	18	13	19	130	41
20	0.4120	0.9112	0.4522	2.2113	**40**
21	23	10	26	096	39
22	26	09	29	079	38
23	28	08	33	062	37
24	31	07	36	045	36
25	0.4134	0.9106	0.4540	2.2028	**35**
26	36	04	43	2.2011	34
27	39	03	47	2.1994	33
28	42	02	50	977	32
29	44	01	54	960	31
30	0.4147	0.9100	0.4557	2.1943	**30**
31	50	9098	61	926	29
32	52	97	64	909	28
33	55	96	68	892	27
34	58	95	71	876	26
35	0.4160	0.9094	0.4575	2.1859	**25**
36	63	92	78	842	24
37	65	91	82	825	23
38	68	90	85	808	22
39	71	89	89	792	21
40	0.4173	0.9088	0.4592	2.1775	**20**
41	76	86	96	758	19
42	79	85	4599	742	18
43	81	84	4603	725	17
44	84	83	07	708	16
45	0.4187	0.9081	0.4610	2.1692	**15**
46	89	80	14	675	14
47	92	79	17	659	13
48	95	78	21	642	12
49	4197	77	24	625	11
50	0.4200	0.9075	0.4628	2.1609	**10**
51	02	74	31	592	9
52	05	73	35	576	8
53	08	72	38	560	7
54	10	70	42	543	6
55	0.4213	0.9069	0.4645	2.1527	**5**
56	16	68	49	510	4
57	18	67	52	494	3
58	21	66	56	478	2
59	24	64	60	461	1
60	0.4226	0.9063	0.4663	2.1445	**0**
′	cos	sin	cot	tan	′

65°

25°

′	sin	cos	tan	cot	′
0	0.4226	0.9063	0.4663	2.1445	**60**
1	29	62	67	429	59
2	31	61	70	413	58
3	34	59	74	396	57
4	37	58	77	380	56
5	0.4239	0.9057	0.4681	2.1364	**55**
6	42	56	84	348	54
7	45	54	88	332	53
8	47	53	91	315	52
9	50	52	95	299	51
10	0.4253	0.9051	0.4699	2.1283	**50**
11	55	50	4702	267	49
12	58	48	06	251	48
13	60	47	09	235	47
14	63	46	13	219	46
15	0.4266	0.9045	0.4716	2.1203	**45**
16	68	43	20	187	44
17	71	42	23	171	43
18	74	41	27	155	42
19	76	40	31	139	41
20	0.4279	0.9038	0.4734	2.1123	**40**
21	81	37	38	107	39
22	84	36	41	092	38
23	87	35	45	076	37
24	89	33	48	060	36
25	0.4292	0.9032	0.4752	2.1044	**35**
26	95	31	55	028	34
27	4297	30	59	2.1013	33
28	4300	28	63	2.0997	32
29	02	27	66	981	31
30	0.4305	0.9026	0.4770	2.0965	**30**
31	08	25	73	950	29
32	10	23	77	934	28
33	13	22	80	918	27
34	16	21	84	903	26
35	0.4318	0.9020	0.4788	2.0887	**25**
36	21	18	91	872	24
37	23	17	95	856	23
38	26	16	4798	840	22
39	29	15	4802	825	21
40	0.4331	0.9013	0.4806	2.0809	**20**
41	34	12	09	794	19
42	37	11	13	778	18
43	39	10	16	763	17
44	42	08	20	748	16
45	0.4344	0.9007	0.4823	2.0732	**15**
46	47	06	27	717	14
47	50	04	31	701	13
48	52	03	34	686	12
49	55	02	38	671	11
50	0.4358	0.9001	0.4841	2.0655	**10**
51	60	8999	45	640	9
52	63	98	49	625	8
53	65	97	52	609	7
54	68	96	56	594	6
55	0.4371	0.8994	0.4859	2.0579	**5**
56	73	93	63	564	4
57	76	92	67	549	3
58	78	90	70	533	2
59	81	89	74	518	1
60	0.4384	0.8988	0.4877	2.0503	**0**
′	cos	sin	cot	tan	′

64°

26°

′	sin	cos	tan	cot	′
0	0.4384	0.8988	0.4877	2.0503	**60**
1	86	87	81	488	59
2	89	85	85	473	58
3	92	84	88	458	57
4	94	83	92	443	56
5	0.4397	0.8982	0.4895	2.0428	**55**
6	4399	80	4899	413	54
7	4402	79	4903	398	53
8	05	78	06	383	52
9	07	76	10	368	51
10	0.4410	0.8975	0.4913	2.0353	**50**
11	12	74	17	338	49
12	15	73	21	323	48
13	18	71	24	308	47
14	20	70	28	293	46
15	0.4423	0.8969	0.4931	2.0278	**45**
16	25	67	35	263	44
17	28	66	39	248	43
18	31	65	42	233	42
19	33	64	46	219	41
20	0.4436	0.8962	0.4950	2.0204	**40**
21	39	61	53	189	39
22	41	60	57	174	38
23	44	58	60	160	37
24	46	57	64	145	36
25	0.4449	0.8956	0.4968	2.0130	**35**
26	52	55	71	115	34
27	54	53	75	101	33
28	57	52	79	086	32
29	59	51	82	072	31
30	0.4462	0.8949	0.4986	2.0057	**30**
31	65	48	89	042	29
32	67	47	93	028	28
33	70	45	4997	2.0013	27
34	72	44	5000	1.9999	26
35	0.4475	0.8943	0.5004	1.9984	**25**
36	78	42	08	970	24
37	80	40	11	955	23
38	83	39	15	941	22
39	85	38	19	926	21
40	0.4488	0.8936	0.5022	1.9912	**20**
41	91	35	26	897	19
42	93	34	29	883	18
43	96	32	33	868	17
44	4498	31	37	854	16
45	0.4501	0.8930	0.5040	1.9840	**15**
46	04	28	44	825	14
47	06	27	48	811	13
48	09	26	51	797	12
49	11	25	55	782	11
50	0.4514	0.8923	0.5059	1.9768	**10**
51	17	22	62	754	9
52	19	21	66	740	8
53	22	19	70	725	7
54	24	18	73	711	6
55	0.4527	0.8917	0.5077	1.9697	**5**
56	30	15	81	683	4
57	32	14	84	669	3
58	35	13	88	654	2
59	37	11	92	640	1
60	0.4540	0.8910	0.5095	1.9626	**0**
′	cos	sin	cot	tan	′

63°

27°

′	sin	cos	tan	cot	′
0	0.4540	0.8910	0.5095	1.9626	**60**
1	42	09	5099	612	59
2	45	07	5103	598	58
3	48	06	06	584	57
4	50	05	10	570	56
5	0.4553	0.8903	0.5114	1.9556	**55**
6	55	02	17	542	54
7	58	8901	21	528	53
8	61	8899	25	514	52
9	63	98	28	500	51
10	0.4566	0.8897	0.5132	1.9486	**50**
11	68	95	36	472	49
12	71	94	39	458	48
13	74	93	43	444	47
14	76	92	47	430	46
15	0.4579	0.8890	0.5150	1.9416	**45**
16	81	89	54	402	44
17	84	88	58	388	43
18	86	86	61	375	42
19	89	85	65	361	41
20	0.4592	0.8884	0.5169	1.9347	**40**
21	94	82	72	333	39
22	97	81	76	319	38
23	4599	79	80	306	37
24	4602	78	84	292	36
25	0.4605	0.8877	0.5187	1.9278	**35**
26	07	75	91	265	34
27	10	74	95	251	33
28	12	73	5198	237	32
29	15	71	5202	223	31
30	0.4617	0.8870	0.5206	1.9210	**30**
31	20	69	09	196	29
32	23	67	13	183	28
33	25	66	17	169	27
34	28	65	20	155	26
35	0.4630	0.8863	0.5224	1.9142	**25**
36	33	62	28	128	24
37	36	61	32	115	23
38	38	59	35	101	22
39	41	58	39	088	21
40	0.4643	0.8857	0.5243	1.9074	**20**
41	46	55	46	061	19
42	48	54	50	047	18
43	51	53	54	034	17
44	54	51	58	020	16
45	0.4656	0.8850	0.5261	1.9007	**15**
46	59	49	65	1.8993	14
47	61	47	69	980	13
48	64	46	72	967	12
49	66	44	76	953	11
50	0.4669	0.8843	0.5280	1.8940	**10**
51	72	42	84	927	9
52	74	40	87	913	8
53	77	39	91	900	7
54	79	38	95	887	6
55	0.4682	0.8836	0.5298	1.8873	**5**
56	84	35	5302	860	4
57	87	34	06	847	3
58	90	32	10	834	2
59	92	31	13	820	1
60	0.4695	0.8829	0.5317	1.8807	**0**
′	cos	sin	cot	tan	′

62°

28°

′	sin	cos	tan	cot	′
0	0.4695	0.8829	0.5317	1.8807	**60**
1	4697	28	21	794	59
2	4700	27	25	781	58
3	02	25	28	768	57
4	05	24	32	755	56
5	0.4708	0.8823	0.5336	1.8741	**55**
6	10	21	40	728	54
7	13	20	43	715	53
8	15	19	47	702	52
9	18	17	51	689	51
10	0.4720	0.8816	0.5354	1.8676	**50**
11	23	14	58	663	49
12	26	13	62	650	48
13	28	12	66	637	47
14	31	10	69	624	46
15	0.4733	0.8809	0.5373	1.8611	**45**
16	36	08	77	598	44
17	38	06	81	585	43
18	41	05	84	572	42
19	43	03	88	559	41
20	0.4746	0.8802	0.5392	1.8546	**40**
21	49	8801	96	533	39
22	51	8799	5399	520	38
23	54	98	5403	507	37
24	56	96	07	495	36
25	0.4759	0.8795	0.5411	1.8482	**35**
26	61	94	15	469	34
27	64	92	18	456	33
28	66	91	22	443	32
29	69	90	26	430	31
30	0.4772	0.8788	0.5430	1.8418	**30**
31	74	87	33	405	29
32	77	85	37	392	28
33	79	84	41	379	27
34	82	83	45	367	26
35	0.4784	0.8781	0.5448	1.8354	**25**
36	87	80	52	341	24
37	89	78	56	329	23
38	92	77	60	316	22
39	95	76	64	303	21
40	0.4797	0.8774	0.5467	1.8291	**20**
41	4800	73	71	278	19
42	02	71	75	265	18
43	05	70	79	253	17
44	07	69	82	240	16
45	0.4810	0.8767	0.5486	1.8228	**15**
46	12	66	90	215	14
47	15	64	94	202	13
48	18	63	5498	190	12
49	20	62	5501	177	11
50	0.4823	0.8760	0.5505	1.8165	**10**
51	25	59	09	152	9
52	28	57	13	140	8
53	30	56	17	127	7
54	33	55	20	115	6
55	0.4835	0.8753	0.5524	1.8103	**5**
56	38	52	28	090	4
57	40	50	32	078	3
58	43	49	35	065	2
59	46	48	39	053	1
60	0.4848	0.8746	0.5543	1.8040	**0**
′	cos	sin	cot	tan	′

61°

29°

′	sin	cos	tan	cot	′
0	0.4848	0.8746	0.5543	1.8040	**60**
1	51	45	47	028	59
2	53	43	51	016	58
3	56	42	55	1.8003	57
4	58	41	58	1.7991	56
5	0.4861	0.8739	0.5562	1.7979	**55**
6	63	38	66	966	54
7	66	36	70	954	53
8	68	35	74	942	52
9	71	33	77	930	51
10	0.4874	0.8732	0.5581	1.7917	**50**
11	76	31	85	905	49
12	79	29	89	893	48
13	81	28	93	881	47
14	84	26	5596	868	46
15	0.4886	0.8725	0.5600	1.7856	**45**
16	89	24	04	844	44
17	91	22	08	832	43
18	94	21	12	820	42
19	96	19	16	808	41
20	0.4899	0.8718	0.5619	1.7796	**40**
21	4901	16	23	783	39
22	04	15	27	771	38
23	07	14	31	759	37
24	09	12	35	747	36
25	0.4912	0.8711	0.5639	1.7735	**35**
26	14	09	42	723	34
27	17	08	46	711	33
28	19	06	50	699	32
29	22	05	54	687	31
30	0.4924	0.8704	0.5658	1.7675	**30**
31	27	02	62	663	29
32	29	8701	65	651	28
33	32	8699	69	639	27
34	34	98	73	627	26
35	0.4937	0.8696	0.5677	1.7615	**25**
36	39	95	81	603	24
37	42	94	85	591	23
38	44	92	88	579	22
39	47	91	92	567	21
40	0.4950	0.8689	0.5696	1.7556	**20**
41	52	88	5700	544	19
42	55	86	04	532	18
43	57	85	08	520	17
44	60	83	12	508	16
45	0.4962	0.8682	0.5715	1.7496	**15**
46	65	81	19	485	14
47	67	79	23	473	13
48	70	78	27	461	12
49	72	76	31	449	11
50	0.4975	0.8675	0.5735	1.7437	**10**
51	77	73	39	426	9
52	80	72	43	414	8
53	82	70	46	402	7
54	85	69	50	391	6
55	0.4987	0.8668	0.5754	1.7379	**5**
56	90	66	58	367	4
57	92	65	62	355	3
58	95	63	66	344	2
59	4997	62	70	332	1
60	0.5000	0.8660	0.5774	1.7321	**0**
′	cos	sin	cot	tan	′

60°

30°

′	sin	cos	tan	cot	′
0	0.5000	0.8660	0.5774	1.7321	**60**
1	03	59	77	309	59
2	05	57	81	297	58
3	08	56	85	286	57
4	10	54	89	274	56
5	0.5013	0.8653	0.5793	1.7262	**55**
6	15	52	5797	251	54
7	18	50	5801	239	53
8	20	49	05	228	52
9	23	47	08	216	51
10	0.5025	0.8646	0.5812	1.7205	**50**
11	28	44	16	193	49
12	30	43	20	182	48
13	33	41	24	170	47
14	35	40	28	159	46
15	0.5038	0.8638	0.5832	1.7147	**45**
16	40	37	36	136	44
17	43	35	40	124	43
18	45	34	44	113	42
19	48	32	47	102	41
20	0.5050	0.8631	0.5851	1.7090	**40**
21	53	30	55	079	39
22	55	28	59	067	38
23	58	27	63	056	37
24	60	25	67	045	36
25	0.5063	0.8624	0.5871	1.7033	**35**
26	65	22	75	022	34
27	68	21	79	1.7011	33
28	70	19	83	1.6999	32
29	73	18	87	988	31
30	0.5075	0.8616	0.5890	1.6977	**30**
31	78	15	94	965	29
32	80	13	5898	954	28
33	83	12	5902	943	27
34	85	10	06	932	26
35	0.5088	0.8609	0.5910	1.6920	**25**
36	90	07	14	909	24
37	93	06	18	898	23
38	95	04	22	887	22
39	5098	03	26	875	21
40	0.5100	0.8601	0.5930	1.6864	**20**
41	03	8600	34	853	19
42	05	8599	38	842	18
43	08	97	42	831	17
44	10	96	45	820	16
45	0.5113	0.8594	0.5949	1.6808	**15**
46	15	93	53	797	14
47	18	91	57	786	13
48	20	90	61	775	12
49	23	88	65	764	11
50	0.5125	0.8587	0.5969	1.6753	**10**
51	28	85	73	742	9
52	30	84	77	731	8
53	33	82	81	720	7
54	35	81	85	709	6
55	0.5138	0.8579	0.5989	1.6698	**5**
56	40	78	93	687	4
57	43	76	5997	676	3
58	45	75	6001	665	2
59	48	73	05	654	1
60	0.5150	0.8572	0.6009	1.6643	**0**
′	cos	sin	cot	tan	′

59°

31°

′	sin	cos	tan	cot	′
0	0.5150	0.8572	0.6009	1.6643	**60**
1	53	70	13	632	59
2	55	69	17	621	58
3	58	67	20	610	57
4	60	66	24	599	56
5	0.5163	0.8564	0.6028	1.6588	**55**
6	65	63	32	577	54
7	68	61	36	566	53
8	70	60	40	555	52
9	73	58	44	545	51
10	0.5175	0.8557	0.6048	1.6534	**50**
11	78	55	52	523	49
12	80	54	56	512	48
13	83	52	60	501	47
14	85	51	64	490	46
15	0.5188	0.8549	0.6068	1.6479	**45**
16	90	48	72	469	44
17	93	46	76	458	43
18	95	45	80	447	42
19	5198	43	84	436	41
20	0.5200	0.8542	0.6088	1.6426	**40**
21	03	40	92	415	39
22	05	39	6096	404	38
23	08	37	6100	393	37
24	10	36	04	383	36
25	0.5213	0.8534	0.6108	1.6372	**35**
26	15	32	12	361	34
27	18	31	16	351	33
28	20	29	20	340	32
29	23	28	24	329	31
30	0.5225	0.8526	0.6128	1.6319	**30**
31	27	25	32	308	29
32	30	23	36	297	28
33	32	22	40	287	27
34	35	20	44	276	26
35	0.5237	0.8519	0.6148	1.6265	**25**
36	40	17	52	255	24
37	42	16	56	244	23
38	45	14	60	234	22
39	47	13	64	223	21
40	0.5250	0.8511	0.6168	1.6212	**20**
41	52	10	72	202	19
42	55	08	76	191	18
43	57	07	80	181	17
44	60	05	84	170	16
45	0.5262	0.8504	0.6188	1.6160	**15**
46	65	02	92	149	14
47	67	8500	6196	139	13
48	70	8499	6200	128	12
49	72	97	04	118	11
50	0.5275	0.8496	0.6208	1.6107	**10**
51	77	94	12	097	9
52	79	93	16	087	8
53	82	91	20	076	7
54	84	90	24	066	6
55	0.5287	0.8488	0.6228	1.6055	**5**
56	89	87	33	045	4
57	92	85	37	034	3
58	94	84	41	024	2
59	97	82	45	014	1
60	0.5299	0.8480	0.6249	1.6003	**0**
′	cos	sin	cot	tan	′

58°

32°

′	sin	cos	tan	cot	′
0	0.5299	0.8480	0.6249	1.6003	**60**
1	5302	79	53	1.5993	59
2	04	77	57	983	58
3	07	76	61	972	57
4	09	74	65	962	56
5	0.5312	0.8473	0.6269	1.5952	**55**
6	14	71	73	941	54
7	16	70	77	931	53
8	19	68	81	921	52
9	21	67	85	911	51
10	0.5324	0.8465	0.6289	1.5900	**50**
11	26	63	93	890	49
12	29	62	6297	880	48
13	31	60	6301	869	47
14	34	59	05	859	46
15	0.5336	0.8457	0.6310	1.5849	**45**
16	39	56	14	839	44
17	41	54	18	829	43
18	44	53	22	818	42
19	46	51	26	808	41
20	0.5348	0.8450	0.6330	1.5798	**40**
21	51	48	34	788	39
22	53	46	38	778	38
23	56	45	42	768	37
24	58	43	46	757	36
25	0.5361	0.8442	0.6350	1.5747	**35**
26	63	40	54	737	34
27	66	39	58	727	33
28	68	37	63	717	32
29	71	35	67	707	31
30	0.5373	0.8434	0.6371	1.5697	**30**
31	75	32	75	687	29
32	78	31	79	677	28
33	80	29	83	667	27
34	83	28	87	657	26
35	0.5385	0.8426	0.6391	1.5647	**25**
36	88	25	95	637	24
37	90	23	6399	627	23
38	93	21	6403	617	22
39	95	20	08	607	21
40	0.5398	0.8418	0.6412	1.5597	**20**
41	5400	17	16	587	19
42	02	15	20	577	18
43	05	14	24	567	17
44	07	12	28	557	16
45	0.5410	0.8410	0.6432	1.5547	**15**
46	12	09	36	537	14
47	15	07	40	527	13
48	17	06	45	517	12
49	20	04	49	507	11
50	0.5422	0.8403	0.6453	1.5497	**10**
51	24	8401	57	487	9
52	27	8399	61	477	8
53	29	98	65	468	7
54	32	96	69	458	6
55	0.5434	0.8395	0.6473	1.5448	**5**
56	37	93	78	438	4
57	39	91	82	428	3
58	42	90	86	418	2
59	44	88	90	408	1
60	0.5446	0.8387	0.6494	1.5399	**0**
′	cos	sin	cot	tan	′

57°

33°

′	sin	cos	tan	cot	′
0	0.5446	0.8387	0.6494	1.5399	**60**
1	49	85	6498	389	59
2	51	84	6502	379	58
3	54	82	06	369	57
4	56	80	11	359	56
5	0.5459	0.8379	0.6515	1.5350	**55**
6	61	77	19	340	54
7	63	76	23	330	53
8	66	74	27	320	52
9	68	72	31	311	51
10	0.5471	0.8371	0.6536	1.5301	**50**
11	73	69	40	291	49
12	76	68	44	282	48
13	78	66	48	272	47
14	80	64	52	262	46
15	0.5483	0.8363	0.6556	1.5253	**45**
16	85	61	60	243	44
17	88	60	65	233	43
18	90	58	69	224	42
19	93	56	73	214	41
20	0.5495	0.8355	0.6577	1.5204	**40**
21	5498	53	81	195	39
22	5500	52	85	185	38
23	02	50	90	175	37
24	05	48	94	166	36
25	0.5507	0.8347	0.6598	1.5156	**35**
26	10	45	6602	147	34
27	12	44	06	137	33
28	15	42	10	127	32
29	17	40	15	118	31
30	0.5519	0.8339	0.6619	1.5108	**30**
31	22	37	23	099	29
32	24	36	27	089	28
33	27	34	31	080	27
34	29	32	36	070	26
35	0.5531	0.8331	0.6640	1.5061	**25**
36	34	29	44	051	24
37	36	28	48	042	23
38	39	26	52	032	22
39	41	24	57	023	21
40	0.5544	0.8323	0.6661	1.5013	**20**
41	46	21	65	1.5004	19
42	48	20	69	1.4994	18
43	51	18	73	985	17
44	53	16	78	975	16
45	0.5556	0.8315	0.6682	1.4966	**15**
46	58	13	86	957	14
47	61	11	90	947	13
48	63	10	94	938	12
49	65	08	6699	928	11
50	0.5568	0.8307	0.6703	1.4919	**10**
51	70	05	07	910	9
52	73	03	11	900	8
53	75	02	16	891	7
54	77	8300	20	882	6
55	0.5580	0.8299	0.6724	1.4872	**5**
56	82	97	28	863	4
57	85	95	32	854	3
58	87	94	37	844	2
59	90	92	41	835	1
60	0.5592	0.8290	0.6745	1.4826	**0**
′	cos	sin	cot	tan	′

56°

34°

′	sin	cos	tan	cot	′
0	0.5592	0.8290	0.6745	1.4826	**60**
1	94	89	49	816	59
2	97	87	54	807	58
3	5599	85	58	798	57
4	5602	84	62	788	56
5	0.5604	0.8282	0.6766	1.4779	**55**
6	06	81	71	770	54
7	09	79	75	761	53
8	11	77	79	751	52
9	14	76	83	742	51
10	0.5616	0.8274	0.6787	1.4733	**50**
11	18	72	92	724	49
12	21	71	6796	715	48
13	23	69	6800	705	47
14	26	68	05	696	46
15	0.5628	0.8266	0.6809	1.4687	**45**
16	30	64	13	678	44
17	33	63	17	669	43
18	35	61	22	659	42
19	38	59	26	650	41
20	0.5640	0.8258	0.6830	1.4641	**40**
21	42	56	34	632	39
22	45	54	39	623	38
23	47	53	43	614	37
24	50	51	47	605	36
25	0.5652	0.8249	0.6851	1.4596	**35**
26	54	48	56	586	34
27	57	46	60	577	33
28	59	45	64	568	32
29	62	43	69	559	31
30	0.5664	0.8241	0.6873	1.4550	**30**
31	66	40	77	541	29
32	69	38	81	532	28
33	71	36	86	523	27
34	74	35	90	514	26
35	0.5676	0.8233	0.6894	1.4505	**25**
36	78	31	6899	496	24
37	81	30	6903	487	23
38	83	28	07	478	22
39	86	26	11	469	21
40	0.5688	0.8225	0.6916	1.4460	**20**
41	90	23	20	451	19
42	93	21	24	442	18
43	95	20	29	433	17
44	5698	18	33	424	16
45	0.5700	0.8216	0.6937	1.4415	**15**
46	02	15	42	406	14
47	05	13	46	397	13
48	07	11	50	388	12
49	10	10	54	379	11
50	0.5712	0.8208	0.6959	1.4370	**10**
51	14	07	63	361	9
52	17	05	67	352	8
53	19	03	72	344	7
54	21	02	76	335	6
55	0.5724	0.8200	0.6980	1.4326	**5**
56	26	8198	85	317	4
57	29	97	89	308	3
58	31	95	93	299	2
59	33	93	6998	290	1
60	0.5736	0.8192	0.7002	1.4281	**0**
′	cos	sin	cot	tan	′

55°

35°

′	sin	cos	tan	cot	′
0	0.5736	0.8192	0.7002	1.4281	**60**
1	38	90	06	273	59
2	41	88	11	264	58
3	43	87	15	255	57
4	45	85	19	246	56
5	0.5748	0.8183	0.7024	1.4237	**55**
6	50	81	28	229	54
7	52	80	32	220	53
8	55	78	37	211	52
9	57	76	41	202	51
10	0.5760	0.8175	0.7046	1.4193	**50**
11	62	73	50	185	49
12	64	71	54	176	48
13	67	70	59	167	47
14	69	68	63	158	46
15	0.5771	0.8166	0.7067	1.4150	**45**
16	74	65	72	141	44
17	76	63	76	132	43
18	79	61	80	124	42
19	81	60	85	115	41
20	0.5783	0.8158	0.7089	1.4106	**40**
21	86	56	94	097	39
22	88	55	7098	089	38
23	90	53	7102	080	37
24	93	51	07	071	36
25	0.5795	0.8150	0.7111	1.4063	**35**
26	5798	48	15	054	34
27	5800	46	20	045	33
28	02	45	24	037	32
29	05	43	29	028	31
30	0.5807	0.8141	0.7133	1.4019	**30**
31	09	39	37	011	29
32	12	38	42	1.4002	28
33	14	36	46	1.3994	27
34	16	34	51	985	26
35	0.5819	0.8133	0.7155	1.3976	**25**
36	21	31	59	968	24
37	24	29	64	959	23
38	26	28	68	951	22
39	28	26	73	942	21
40	0.5831	0.8124	0.7177	1.3934	**20**
41	33	23	81	925	19
42	35	21	86	916	18
43	38	19	90	908	17
44	40	17	95	899	16
45	0.5842	0.8116	0.7199	1.3891	**15**
46	45	14	7203	882	14
47	47	12	08	874	13
48	50	11	12	865	12
49	52	09	17	857	11
50	0.5854	0.8107	0.7221	1.3848	**10**
51	57	06	26	840	9
52	59	04	30	831	8
53	61	02	34	823	7
54	64	8100	39	814	6
55	0.5866	0.8099	0.7243	1.3806	**5**
56	68	97	48	798	4
57	71	95	52	789	3
58	73	94	57	781	2
59	75	92	61	772	1
60	0.5878	0.8090	0.7265	1.3764	**0**
′	cos	sin	cot	tan	′

54°

36°

′	sin	cos	tan	cot	′
0	0.5878	0.8090	0.7265	1.3764	**60**
1	80	88	70	755	59
2	83	87	74	747	58
3	85	85	79	739	57
4	87	83	83	730	56
5	0.5890	0.8082	0.7288	1.3722	**55**
6	92	80	92	713	54
7	94	78	7297	705	53
8	97	76	7301	697	52
9	5899	75	06	688	51
10	0.5901	0.8073	0.7310	1.3680	**50**
11	04	71	14	672	49
12	06	70	19	663	48
13	08	68	23	655	47
14	11	66	28	647	46
15	0.5913	0.8064	0.7332	1.3638	**45**
16	15	63	37	630	44
17	18	61	41	622	43
18	20	59	46	613	42
19	22	58	50	605	41
20	0.5925	0.8056	0.7355	1.3597	**40**
21	27	54	59	588	39
22	30	52	64	580	38
23	32	51	68	572	37
24	34	49	73	564	36
25	0.5937	0.8047	0.7377	1.3555	**35**
26	39	45	82	547	34
27	41	44	86	539	33
28	44	42	91	531	32
29	46	40	7395	522	31
30	0.5948	0.8039	0.7400	1.3514	**30**
31	51	37	04	506	29
32	53	35	09	498	28
33	55	33	13	490	27
34	58	32	18	481	26
35	0.5960	0.8030	0.7422	1.3473	**25**
36	62	28	27	465	24
37	65	26	31	457	23
38	67	25	36	449	22
39	69	23	40	440	21
40	0.5972	0.8021	0.7445	1.3432	**20**
41	74	19	49	424	19
42	76	18	54	416	18
43	79	16	58	408	17
44	81	14	63	400	16
45	0.5983	0.8013	0.7467	1.3392	**15**
46	86	11	72	384	14
47	88	09	76	375	13
48	90	07	81	367	12
49	93	06	85	359	11
50	0.5995	0.8004	0.7490	1.3351	**10**
51	5997	02	95	343	9
52	6000	8000	7499	335	8
53	02	7999	7504	327	7
54	04	97	08	319	6
55	0.6007	0.7995	0.7513	1.3311	**5**
56	09	93	17	303	4
57	11	92	22	295	3
58	14	90	26	287	2
59	16	88	31	278	1
60	0.6018	0.7986	0.7536	1.3270	**0**
′	cos	sin	cot	tan	′

53°

37°

′	sin	cos	tan	cot	′
0	0.6018	0.7986	0.7536	1.3270	**60**
1	20	85	40	262	59
2	23	83	45	254	58
3	25	81	49	246	57
4	27	79	54	238	56
5	0.6030	0.7978	0.7558	1.3230	**55**
6	32	76	63	222	54
7	34	74	68	214	53
8	37	72	72	206	52
9	39	71	77	198	51
10	0.6041	0.7969	0.7581	1.3190	**50**
11	44	67	86	182	49
12	46	65	90	175	48
13	48	64	7595	167	47
14	51	62	7600	159	46
15	0.6053	0.7960	0.7604	1.3151	**45**
16	55	58	09	143	44
17	58	56	13	135	43
18	60	55	18	127	42
19	62	53	23	119	41
20	0.6065	0.7951	0.7627	1.3111	**40**
21	67	50	32	103	39
22	69	48	36	095	38
23	71	46	41	087	37
24	74	44	46	079	36
25	0.6076	0.7942	0.7650	1.3072	**35**
26	78	41	55	064	34
27	81	39	59	056	33
28	83	37	64	048	32
29	85	35	69	040	31
30	0.6088	0.7934	0.7673	1.3032	**30**
31	90	32	78	024	29
32	92	30	83	017	28
33	95	28	87	009	27
34	97	26	92	1.3001	26
35	0.6099	0.7925	0.7696	1.2993	**25**
36	6101	23	7701	985	24
37	04	21	06	977	23
38	06	19	10	970	22
39	08	18	15	962	21
40	0.6111	0.7916	0.7720	1.2954	**20**
41	13	14	24	946	19
42	15	12	29	938	18
43	18	10	34	931	17
44	20	09	38	923	16
45	0.6122	0.7907	0.7743	1.2915	**15**
46	24	05	47	907	14
47	27	03	52	900	13
48	29	02	57	892	12
49	31	7900	61	884	11
50	0.6134	0.7898	0.7766	1.2876	**10**
51	36	96	71	869	9
52	38	94	75	861	8
53	41	93	80	853	7
54	43	91	85	846	6
55	0.6145	0.7889	0.7789	1.2838	**5**
56	47	87	94	830	4
57	50	85	7799	822	3
58	52	84	7803	815	2
59	54	82	08	807	1
60	0.6157	0.7880	0.7813	1.2799	**0**
′	cos	sin	cot	tan	′

52°

38°

′	sin	cos	tan	cot	′
0	0.6157	0.7880	0.7813	1.2799	**60**
1	59	78	18	792	59
2	61	77	22	784	58
3	63	75	27	776	57
4	66	73	32	769	56
5	0.6168	0.7871	0.7836	1.2761	**55**
6	70	69	41	753	54
7	73	68	46	746	53
8	75	66	50	738	52
9	77	64	55	731	51
10	0.6180	0.7862	0.7860	1.2723	**50**
11	82	60	65	715	49
12	84	59	69	708	48
13	86	57	74	700	47
14	89	55	79	693	46
15	0.6191	0.7853	0.7883	1.2685	**45**
16	93	51	88	677	44
17	96	50	93	670	43
18	6198	48	7898	662	42
19	6200	46	7902	655	41
20	0.6202	0.7844	0.7907	1.2647	**40**
21	05	42	12	640	39
22	07	41	16	632	38
23	09	39	21	624	37
24	11	37	26	617	36
25	0.6214	0.7835	0.7931	1.2609	**35**
26	16	33	35	602	34
27	18	32	40	594	33
28	21	30	45	587	32
29	23	28	50	579	31
30	0.6225	0.7826	0.7954	1.2572	**30**
31	27	24	59	564	29
32	30	22	64	557	28
33	32	21	69	549	27
34	34	19	73	542	26
35	0.6237	0.7817	0.7978	1.2534	**25**
36	39	15	83	527	24
37	41	13	88	519	23
38	43	12	92	512	22
39	46	10	7997	504	21
40	0.6248	0.7808	0.8002	1.2497	**20**
41	50	06	07	489	19
42	52	04	12	482	18
43	55	02	16	475	17
44	57	7801	21	467	16
45	0.6259	0.7799	0.8026	1.2460	**15**
46	62	97	31	452	14
47	64	95	35	445	13
48	66	93	40	437	12
49	68	92	45	430	11
50	0.6271	0.7790	0.8050	1.2423	**10**
51	73	88	55	415	9
52	75	86	59	408	8
53	77	84	64	401	7
54	80	82	69	393	6
55	0.6282	0.7781	0.8074	1.2386	**5**
56	84	79	79	378	4
57	86	77	83	371	3
58	89	75	88	364	2
59	91	73	93	356	1
60	0.6293	0.7771	0.8098	1.2349	**0**
′	cos	sin	cot	tan	′

51°

39°

′	sin	cos	tan	cot	′
0	0.6293	0.7771	0.8098	1.2349	**60**
1	95	70	8103	342	59
2	6298	68	07	334	58
3	6300	66	12	327	57
4	02	64	17	320	56
5	0.6305	0.7762	0.8122	1.2312	**55**
6	07	60	27	305	54
7	09	59	32	298	53
8	11	57	36	290	52
9	14	55	41	283	51
10	0.6316	0.7753	0.8146	1.2276	**50**
11	18	51	51	268	49
12	20	49	56	261	48
13	23	48	61	254	47
14	25	46	65	247	46
15	0.6327	0.7744	0.8170	1.2239	**45**
16	29	42	75	232	44
17	32	40	80	225	43
18	34	38	85	218	42
19	36	37	90	210	41
20	0.6338	0.7735	0.8195	1.2203	**40**
21	41	33	8199	196	39
22	43	31	8204	189	38
23	45	29	09	181	37
24	47	27	14	174	36
25	0.6350	0.7725	0.8219	1.2167	**35**
26	52	24	24	160	34
27	54	22	29	153	33
28	56	20	34	145	32
29	59	18	38	138	31
30	0.6361	0.7716	0.8243	1.2131	**30**
31	63	14	48	124	29
32	65	13	53	117	28
33	68	11	58	109	27
34	70	09	63	102	26
35	0.6372	0.7707	0.8268	1.2095	**25**
36	74	05	73	088	24
37	76	03	78	081	23
38	79	01	83	074	22
39	81	7700	87	066	21
40	0.6383	0.7698	0.8292	1.2059	**20**
41	85	96	8297	052	19
42	88	94	8302	045	18
43	90	92	07	038	17
44	92	90	12	031	16
45	0.6394	0.7688	0.8317	1.2024	**15**
46	97	87	22	017	14
47	6399	85	27	009	13
48	6401	83	32	1.2002	12
49	03	81	37	1.1995	11
50	0.6406	0.7679	0.8342	1.1988	**10**
51	08	77	46	981	9
52	10	75	51	974	8
53	12	74	56	967	7
54	14	72	61	960	6
55	0.6417	0.7670	0.8366	1.1953	**5**
56	19	68	71	946	4
57	21	66	76	939	3
58	23	64	81	932	2
59	26	62	86	925	1
60	0.6428	0.7660	0.8391	1.1918	**0**
′	cos	sin	cot	tan	′

50°

40°

′	sin	cos	tan	cot	′
0	0.6428	0.7660	0.8391	1.1918	**60**
1	30	59	8396	910	59
2	32	57	8401	903	58
3	35	55	06	896	57
4	37	53	11	889	56
5	0.6439	0.7651	0.8416	1.1882	**55**
6	41	49	21	875	54
7	43	47	26	868	53
8	46	45	31	861	52
9	48	44	36	854	51
10	0.6450	0.7642	0.8441	1.1847	**50**
11	52	40	46	840	49
12	55	38	51	833	48
13	57	36	56	826	47
14	59	34	61	819	46
15	0.6461	0.7632	0.8466	1.1812	**45**
16	63	30	71	806	44
17	66	29	76	799	43
18	68	27	81	792	42
19	70	25	86	785	41
20	0.6472	0.7623	0.8491	1.1778	**40**
21	75	21	8496	771	39
22	77	19	8501	764	38
23	79	17	06	757	37
24	81	15	11	750	36
25	0.6483	0.7613	0.8516	1.1743	**35**
26	86	12	21	736	34
27	88	10	26	729	33
28	90	08	31	722	32
29	92	06	36	715	31
30	0.6494	0.7604	0.8541	1.1708	**30**
31	97	02	46	702	29
32	6499	7600	51	695	28
33	6501	7598	56	688	27
34	03	96	61	681	26
35	0.6506	0.7595	0.8566	1.1674	**25**
36	08	93	71	667	24
37	10	91	76	660	23
38	12	89	81	653	22
39	14	87	86	647	21
40	0.6517	0.7585	0.8591	1.1640	**20**
41	19	83	8596	633	19
42	21	81	8601	626	18
43	23	79	06	619	17
44	25	78	11	612	16
45	0.6528	0.7576	0.8617	1.1606	**15**
46	30	74	22	599	14
47	32	72	27	592	13
48	34	70	32	585	12
49	36	68	37	578	11
50	0.6539	0.7566	0.8642	1.1571	**10**
51	41	64	47	565	9
52	43	62	52	558	8
53	45	60	57	551	7
54	47	59	62	544	6
55	0.6550	0.7557	0.8667	1.1538	**5**
56	52	55	72	531	4
57	54	53	78	524	3
58	56	51	83	517	2
59	58	49	88	510	1
60	0.6561	0.7547	0.8693	1.1504	**0**
′	cos	sin	cot	tan	′

49°

41°

′	sin	cos	tan	cot	′
0	0.6561	0.7547	0.8693	1.1504	**60**
1	63	45	8698	497	59
2	65	43	8703	490	58
3	67	41	08	483	57
4	69	39	13	477	56
5	0.6572	0.7538	0.8718	1.1470	**55**
6	74	36	24	463	54
7	76	34	29	456	53
8	78	32	34	450	52
9	80	30	39	443	51
10	0.6583	0.7528	0.8744	1.1436	**50**
11	85	26	49	430	49
12	87	24	54	423	48
13	89	22	59	416	47
14	91	20	65	410	46
15	0.6593	0.7518	0.8770	1.1403	**45**
16	96	16	75	396	44
17	6598	15	80	389	43
18	6600	13	85	383	42
19	02	11	90	376	41
20	0.6604	0.7509	0.8796	1.1369	**40**
21	07	07	8801	363	39
22	09	05	06	356	38
23	11	03	11	349	37
24	13	7501	16	343	36
25	0.6615	0.7499	0.8821	1.1336	**35**
26	17	97	27	329	34
27	20	95	32	323	33
28	22	93	37	316	32
29	24	91	42	310	31
30	0.6626	0.7490	0.8847	1.1303	**30**
31	28	88	52	296	29
32	31	86	58	290	28
33	33	84	63	283	27
34	35	82	68	276	26
35	0.6637	0.7480	0.8873	1.1270	**25**
36	39	78	78	263	24
37	41	76	84	257	23
38	44	74	89	250	22
39	46	72	94	243	21
40	0.6648	0.7470	0.8899	1.1237	**20**
41	50	68	8904	230	19
42	52	66	10	224	18
43	54	64	15	217	17
44	57	63	20	211	16
45	0.6659	0.7461	0.8925	1.1204	**15**
46	61	59	31	197	14
47	63	57	36	191	13
48	65	55	41	184	12
49	67	53	46	178	11
50	0.6670	0.7451	0.8952	1.1171	**10**
51	72	49	57	165	9
52	74	47	62	158	8
53	76	45	67	152	7
54	78	43	72	145	6
55	0.6680	0.7441	0.8978	1.1139	**5**
56	83	39	83	132	4
57	85	37	88	126	3
58	87	35	94	119	2
59	89	33	8999	113	1
60	0.6691	0.7431	0.9004	1.1106	**0**
′	cos	sin	cot	tan	′

48°

42°

′	sin	cos	tan	cot	′
0	0.6691	0.7431	0.9004	1.1106	**60**
1	93	30	09	100	59
2	96	28	15	093	58
3	6698	26	20	087	57
4	6700	24	25	080	56
5	0.6702	0.7422	0.9030	1.1074	**55**
6	04	20	36	067	54
7	06	18	41	061	53
8	09	16	46	054	52
9	11	14	52	048	51
10	0.6713	0.7412	0.9057	1.1041	**50**
11	15	10	62	035	49
12	17	08	67	028	48
13	19	06	73	022	47
14	22	04	78	016	46
15	0.6724	0.7402	0.9083	1.1009	**45**
16	26	7400	89	1.1003	44
17	28	7398	94	1.0996	43
18	30	96	9099	990	42
19	32	94	9105	983	41
20	0.6734	0.7392	0.9110	1.0977	**40**
21	37	90	15	971	39
22	39	88	21	964	38
23	41	87	26	958	37
24	43	85	31	951	36
25	0.6745	0.7383	0.9137	1.0945	**35**
26	47	81	42	939	34
27	49	79	47	932	33
28	52	77	53	926	32
29	54	75	58	919	31
30	0.6756	0.7373	0.9163	1.0913	**30**
31	58	71	69	907	29
32	60	69	74	900	28
33	62	67	79	894	27
34	64	65	85	888	26
35	0.6767	0.7363	0.9190	1.0881	**25**
36	69	61	9195	875	24
37	71	59	9201	869	23
38	73	57	06	862	22
39	75	55	12	856	21
40	0.6777	0.7353	0.9217	1.0850	**20**
41	79	51	22	843	19
42	82	49	28	837	18
43	84	47	33	831	17
44	86	45	39	824	16
45	0.6788	0.7343	0.9244	1.0818	**15**
46	90	41	49	812	14
47	92	39	55	805	13
48	94	37	60	799	12
49	97	35	66	793	11
50	0.6799	0.7333	0.9271	1.0786	**10**
51	6801	31	76	780	9
52	03	29	82	774	8
53	05	27	87	768	7
54	07	25	93	761	6
55	0.6809	0.7323	0.9298	1.0755	**5**
56	11	21	9303	749	4
57	14	19	09	742	3
58	16	18	14	736	2
59	18	16	20	730	1
60	0.6820	0.7314	0.9325	1.0724	**0**
′	cos	sin	cot	tan	′

47°

43°

′	sin	cos	tan	cot	′
0	0.6820	0.7314	0.9325	1.0724	**60**
1	22	12	31	717	59
2	24	10	36	711	58
3	26	08	41	705	57
4	28	06	47	699	56
5	0.6831	0.7304	0.9352	1.0692	**55**
6	33	02	58	686	54
7	35	7300	63	680	53
8	37	7298	69	674	52
9	39	96	74	668	51
10	0.6841	0.7294	0.9380	1.0661	**50**
11	43	92	85	655	49
12	45	90	91	649	48
13	48	88	9396	643	47
14	50	86	9402	637	46
15	0.6852	0.7284	0.9407	1.0630	**45**
16	54	82	13	624	44
17	56	80	18	618	43
18	58	78	24	612	42
19	60	76	29	606	41
20	0.6862	0.7274	0.9435	1.0599	**40**
21	65	72	40	593	39
22	67	70	46	587	38
23	69	68	51	581	37
24	71	66	57	575	36
25	0.6873	0.7264	0.9462	1.0569	**35**
26	75	62	68	562	34
27	77	60	73	556	33
28	79	58	79	550	32
29	81	56	84	544	31
30	0.6884	0.7254	0.9490	1.0538	**30**
31	86	52	9495	532	29
32	88	50	9501	526	28
33	90	48	06	519	27
34	92	46	12	513	26
35	0.6894	0.7244	0.9517	1.0507	**25**
36	96	42	23	501	24
37	6898	40	28	495	23
38	6900	38	34	489	22
39	03	36	40	483	21
40	0.6905	0.7234	0.9545	1.0477	**20**
41	07	32	51	470	19
42	09	30	56	464	18
43	11	28	62	458	17
44	13	26	67	452	16
45	0.6915	0.7224	0.9573	1.0446	**15**
46	17	22	78	440	14
47	19	20	84	434	13
48	21	18	90	428	12
49	24	16	9595	422	11
50	0.6926	0.7214	0.9601	1.0416	**10**
51	28	12	06	410	9
52	30	10	12	404	8
53	32	08	18	398	7
54	34	06	23	392	6
55	0.6936	0.7203	0.9629	1.0385	**5**
56	38	7201	34	379	4
57	40	7199	40	373	3
58	42	97	46	367	2
59	44	95	51	361	1
60	0.6947	0.7193	0.9657	1.0355	**0**
′	cos	sin	cot	tan	′

46°

44°

′	sin	cos	tan	cot	′
0	0.6947	0.7193	0.9657	1.0355	**60**
1	49	91	63	349	59
2	51	89	68	343	58
3	53	87	74	337	57
4	55	85	79	331	56
5	0.6957	0.7183	0.9685	1.0325	**55**
6	59	81	91	319	54
7	61	79	9696	313	53
8	63	77	9702	307	52
9	65	75	08	301	51
10	0.6967	0.7173	0.9713	1.0295	**50**
11	70	71	19	289	49
12	72	69	25	283	48
13	74	67	30	277	47
14	76	65	36	271	46
15	0.6978	0.7163	0.9742	1.0265	**45**
16	80	61	47	259	44
17	82	59	53	253	43
18	84	57	59	247	42
19	86	55	64	241	41
20	0.6988	0.7153	0.9770	1.0235	**40**
21	90	51	76	230	39
22	92	49	81	224	38
23	95	47	87	218	37
24	97	45	93	212	36
25	0.6999	0.7143	0.9798	1.0206	**35**
26	7001	41	9804	200	34
27	03	39	10	194	33
28	05	37	16	188	32
29	07	35	21	182	31
30	0.7009	0.7133	0.9827	1.0176	**30**
31	11	30	33	170	29
32	13	28	38	164	28
33	15	26	44	158	27
34	17	24	50	152	26
35	0.7019	0.7122	0.9856	1.0147	**25**
36	22	20	61	141	24
37	24	18	67	135	23
38	26	16	73	129	22
39	28	14	79	123	21
40	0.7030	0.7112	0.9884	1.0117	**20**
41	32	10	90	111	19
42	34	08	9896	105	18
43	36	06	9902	099	17
44	38	04	07	094	16
45	0.7040	0.7102	0.9913	1.0088	**15**
46	42	7100	19	082	14
47	44	7098	25	076	13
48	46	96	30	070	12
49	48	94	36	064	11
50	0.7050	0.7092	0.9942	1.0058	**10**
51	53	90	48	052	9
52	55	88	54	047	8
53	57	85	59	041	7
54	59	83	65	035	6
55	0.7061	0.7081	0.9971	1.0029	**5**
56	63	79	77	023	4
57	65	77	83	017	3
58	67	75	88	012	2
59	69	73	94	006	1
60	0.7071	0.7071	1.0000	1.0000	**0**
′	cos	sin	cot	tan	′

45°

TABLE IX

CONVERSION TABLE—DEGREES TO RADIANS

$1° = \frac{\pi}{180}$ radians 1 radian $= \frac{180}{\pi}$ degrees

0°—45°

°	0′	10′	20′	30′	40′	50′
0	0.0000	0.0029	0.0058	0.0087	0.0116	0.0145
1	0175	0204	0233	0262	0291	0320
2	0349	0378	0407	0436	0465	0495
3	0524	0553	0582	0611	0640	0669
4	0698	0727	0756	0785	0814	0844
5	0.0873	0.0902	0.0931	0.0960	0.0989	0.1018
6	1047	1076	1105	1134	1164	1193
7	1222	1251	1280	1309	1338	1367
8	1396	1425	1454	1484	1513	1542
9	1571	1600	1629	1658	1687	1716
10	0.1745	0.1774	0.1804	0.1833	0.1862	0.1891
11	1920	1949	1978	2007	2036	2065
12	2094	2123	2153	2182	2211	2240
13	2269	2298	2327	2356	2385	2414
14	2443	2473	2502	2531	2560	2589
15	0.2618	0.2647	0.2676	0.2705	0.2734	0.2763
16	2793	2822	2851	2880	2909	2938
17	2967	2996	3025	3054	3083	3113
18	3142	3171	3200	3229	3258	3287
19	3316	3345	3374	3403	3432	3462
20	0.3491	0.3520	0.3549	0.3578	0.3607	0.3636
21	3665	3694	3723	3752	3782	3811
22	3840	3869	3898	3927	3956	3985
23	4014	4043	4072	4102	4131	4160
24	4189	4218	4247	4276	4305	4334
25	0.4363	0.4392	0.4422	0.4451	0.4480	0.4508
26	4538	4567	4596	4625	4654	4683
27	4712	4741	4771	4800	4829	4858
28	4887	4916	4945	4974	5003	5032
29	5061	5091	5120	5149	5178	5207
30	0.5236	0.5265	0.5294	0.5323	0.5352	0.5381
31	5411	5440	5469	5498	5527	5556
32	5585	5614	5643	5672	5701	5730
33	5760	5789	5818	5847	5876	5905
34	5934	5963	5992	6021	6050	6080
35	0.6109	0.6138	0.6167	0.6196	0.6225	0.6254
36	6283	6312	6341	6370	6400	6429
37	6458	6487	6516	6545	6574	6603
38	6632	6661	6690	6720	6749	6778
39	6807	6836	6865	6894	6923	6952
40	0.6981	0.7010	0.7039	0.7069	0.7098	0.7127
41	7156	7185	7214	7243	7272	7301
42	7330	7359	7389	7418	7447	7476
43	7505	7534	7563	7592	7621	7650
44	7679	7709	7738	7767	7796	7825
45	0.7854	0.7883	0.7912	0.7941	0.7970	0.7999
°	0′	10′	20′	30′	40′	50′

In using this table, interpolations may be made as with other tables. Thus to find the number of radians corresponding to $49^\circ\ 15'$, we have:

$$\begin{aligned} 49^\circ\ 10' &= 0.8581 \text{ radians} \\ \text{Tabular diff.} &= 0.0029 \\ \tfrac{5}{10} \text{ of } 0.0029 &= \underline{0.0015} \\ \text{Adding, } 49^\circ\ 15' &= 0.8596 \text{ radians} \end{aligned}$$

45°—90°

°	0′	10′	20′	30′	40′	50′
45	0.7854	0.7883	0.7912	0.7941	0.7970	0.7999
46	8029	8058	8087	8116	8145	8174
47	8203	8232	8261	8290	8319	8348
48	8378	8407	8436	8465	8494	8523
49	8552	8581	8610	8639	8668	8698
50	0.8727	0.8756	0.8785	0.8814	0.8843	0.8872
51	8901	8930	8959	8988	9018	9047
52	9076	9105	9134	9163	9192	9221
53	9250	9279	9308	9338	9367	9396
54	9425	9454	9483	9512	9541	9570
55	0.9599	0.9628	0.9657	0.9687	0.9716	0.9745
56	9774	9803	9832	9861	9890	9919
57	9948	9977	1.0007	1.0036	1.0065	1.0094
58	1.0123	1.0152	0181	0210	0239	0268
59	0297	0326	0356	0385	0414	0443
60	1.0472	1.0501	1.0530	1.0559	1.0588	1.0617
61	0647	0676	0705	0734	0763	0792
62	0821	0850	0879	0908	0937	0966
63	0996	1025	1054	1083	1112	1141
64	1170	1199	1228	1257	1286	1316
65	1.1345	1.1374	1.1403	1.1432	1.1461	1.1490
66	1519	1548	1577	1606	1636	1665
67	1694	1723	1752	1781	1810	1839
68	1868	1897	1926	1956	1985	2014
69	2043	2072	2101	2130	2159	2188
70	1.2217	1.2246	1.2275	1.2305	1.2334	1.2363
71	2392	2421	2450	2479	2508	2537
72	2566	2595	2625	2654	2683	2712
73	2741	2770	2799	2828	2857	2886
74	2915	2945	2974	3003	3032	3061
75	1.3090	1.3119	1.3148	1.3177	1.3206	1.3235
76	3265	3294	3323	3352	3381	3410
77	3439	3468	3497	3526	3555	3584
78	3614	3643	3672	3701	3730	3759
79	3788	3817	3846	3875	3904	3934
80	1.3963	1.3992	1.4021	1.4050	1.4079	1.4108
81	4137	4166	4195	4224	4254	4283
82	4312	4341	4370	4399	4428	4457
83	4486	4515	4544	4573	4603	4632
84	4661	4690	4719	4748	4777	4806
85	1.4835	1.4864	1.4893	1.4923	1.4952	1.4981
86	5010	5039	5068	5097	5126	5155
87	5184	5213	5243	5272	5301	5330
88	5359	5388	5417	5446	5475	5504
89	5533	5563	5592	5621	5650	5679
90	1.5708	1.5737	1.5766	1.5795	1.5824	1.5853
°	0′	10′	20′	30′	40′	50′

TABLE X. CONVERSION OF MINUTES AND SECONDS TO DECIMALS OF A DEGREE, AND OF DECIMALS OF A DEGREE TO MINUTES AND SECONDS

′	°	″	°	°	′ and ″	°	′ and ″
0	0.0000	**0**	0.00000	**0.000**	0′ 0″	**0.50**	30′ 0″
1	0167	1	028	001	0′ 4″	51	30′ 36″
2	0333	2	056	002	0′ 7″	52	31′ 12″
3	0500	3	083	003	0′ 11″	53	31′ 48″
4	0667	4	111	004	0′ 14″	54	32′ 24″
5	0.0833	**5**	0.00139	**0.005**	0′ 18″	**0.55**	33′ 0″
6	1000	6	167	006	0′ 22″	56	33′ 36″
7	1167	7	194	007	0′ 25″	57	34′ 12″
8	1333	8	222	008	0′ 29″	58	34′ 48″
9	1500	9	250	009	0′ 32″	59	35′ 24″
10	0.1667	**10**	0.00278	**0.00**	0′ 0″	**0.60**	36′ 0″
11	1833	11	306	01	0′ 36″	61	36′ 36″
12	2000	12	333	02	1′ 12″	62	37′ 12″
13	2167	13	361	03	1′ 48″	63	37′ 48″
14	2333	14	389	04	2′ 24″	64	38′ 24″
15	0.2500	**15**	0.00417	**0.05**	3′ 0″	**0.65**	39′ 0″
16	2667	16	444	06	3′ 36″	66	39′ 36″
17	2833	17	472	07	4′ 12″	67	40′ 12″
18	3000	18	500	08	4′ 48″	68	40′ 48″
19	3167	19	528	09	5′ 24″	69	41′ 24″
20	0.3333	**20**	0.00556	**0.10**	6′ 0″	**0.70**	42′ 0″
21	3500	21	583	11	6′ 36″	71	42′ 36″
22	3667	22	611	12	7′ 12″	72	43′ 12″
23	3833	23	639	13	7′ 48″	73	43′ 48″
24	4000	24	667	14	8′ 24″	74	44′ 24″
25	0.4167	**25**	0.00694	**0.15**	9′ 0″	**0.75**	45′ 0″
26	4333	26	722	16	9′ 36″	76	45′ 36″
27	4500	27	750	17	10′ 12″	77	46′ 12″
28	4667	28	778	18	10′ 48″	78	46′ 48″
29	4833	29	806	19	11′ 24″	79	47′ 24″
30	0.5000	**30**	0.00833	**0.20**	12′ 0″	**0.80**	48′ 0″
31	5167	31	861	21	12′ 36″	81	48′ 36″
32	5333	32	889	22	13′ 12″	82	49′ 12″
33	5500	33	917	23	13′ 48″	83	49′ 48″
34	5667	34	944	24	14′ 24″	84	50′ 24″
35	0.5833	**35**	0.00972	**0.25**	15′ 0″	**0.85**	51′ 0″
36	6000	36	01000	26	15′ 36″	86	51′ 36″
37	6167	37	028	27	16′ 12″	87	52′ 12″
38	6333	38	056	28	16′ 48″	88	52′ 48″
39	6500	39	083	29	17′ 24″	89	53′ 24″
40	0.6667	**40**	0.01111	**0.30**	18′ 0″	**0.90**	54′ 0″
41	6833	41	139	31	18′ 36″	91	54′ 36″
42	7000	42	167	32	19′ 12″	92	55′ 12″
43	7167	43	194	33	19′ 48″	93	55′ 48″
44	7333	44	222	34	20′ 24″	94	56′ 24″
45	0.7500	**45**	0.01250	**0.35**	21′ 0″	**0.95**	57′ 0″
46	7667	46	278	36	21′ 36″	96	57′ 36″
47	7833	47	306	37	22′ 12″	97	58′ 12″
48	8000	48	333	38	22′ 48″	98	58′ 48″
49	8167	49	361	39	23′ 24″	99	59′ 24″
50	0.8333	**50**	0.01389	**0.40**	24′ 0″	**1.00**	60′ 0″
51	8500	51	417	41	24′ 36″	10	66′ 0″
52	8667	52	444	42	25′ 12″	20	72′ 0″
53	8833	53	472	43	25′ 48″	30	78′ 0″
54	9000	54	500	44	26′ 24″	40	84′ 0″
55	0.9167	**55**	0.01528	**0.45**	27′ 0″	**1.50**	90′ 0″
56	9333	56	556	46	27′ 36″	60	96′ 0″
57	9500	57	583	47	28′ 12″	70	102′ 0″
58	9667	58	611	48	28′ 48″	80	108′ 0″
59	9833	59	639	49	29′ 24″	90	114′ 0″
60	1.0000	**60**	0.01667	**0.50**	30′ 0″	**2.00**	120′ 0″
′	°	″	°	°	′ and ″	°	′ and ″

$\sin A = \frac{1}{\csc A}$

$\csc A = \frac{1}{\sin A}$

$\cos A = \frac{1}{\sec A}$

$\sec A = \frac{1}{\cos A}$

$\tan A = \frac{1}{\cot A}$

$\cot A = \frac{1}{\tan A}$

$\frac{a^2}{c^2} + \frac{b^2}{c^2} = \frac{c^2}{c^2}$

$\sin^2 A + \cos^2 A = 1$

$\sin^2 A = 1 - \cos^2 A$

$\sin A = \sqrt{1 - \cos^2 A}$

$\cos^2 A = 1 - \sin^2 A$

$\cos A = \pm\sqrt{1 - \sin^2 A}$

$\frac{a^2}{b^2} + \frac{b^2}{b^2} = \frac{c^2}{b^2}$

$\tan^2 A + 1 = \sec^2 A$

$\sec A = \pm\sqrt{1 + \tan^2 A}$

$\tan^2 A = \sec^2 A - 1$

$\tan A = \pm\sqrt{\sec^2 A - 1}$

$\frac{a^2}{a^2} + \frac{b^2}{a^2} = \frac{c^2}{a^2}$

$1 + \cot^2 A = \csc^2 A$

$\csc A = \pm\sqrt{1 + \cot^2 A}$

$\cot^2 A = \csc^2 A - 1$

$\cot A = \pm\sqrt{\csc^2 A - 1}$

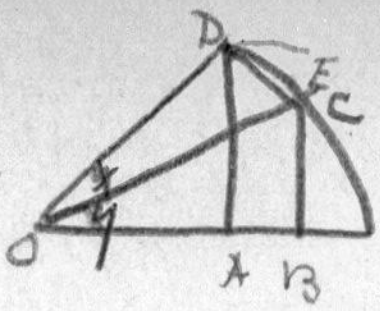

D E C O A B x y

$\sin(x-y) = \frac{BC}{OC} = AD \div C$

$\sin x = \frac{AD}{OD}$ $AD = \sin x$

$\sin y \cos$

$\cos x = \frac{CE}{DC}$ $CE = \cos x\, DC$

$\cos x \sin y$

$\sin(x+y) = \sin x \cos y - \cos x \sin y$

$\cos(x-y) = \frac{OB}{OC}$

$OA + DE$

$\cos x = \frac{OA}{OD}$ $OA = \cos x\, OD$

$\cos x \cos y$

$DE \sin x \frac{DE}{DC}$

$\sin x = DE = \sin x\, DC$

$\cos(x+y) = \cos x \cdot \cos y + \sin x + \sin y$

$\tan(x-y) = \frac{\sin(x-y)}{\cos(x-y)} = \frac{\sin x \cos y - \cos x \sin y}{\cos x \cos y + \sin x + \sin y}$

$\frac{\sin x \cos y}{\cos x \cos y} - \frac{\cos x \sin y}{\cos x \cos y}$

$\frac{\cos x \cos y}{\cos x \cos y} \quad \frac{\sin x \sin y}{\cos x \cos y}$

$\frac{\tan x - \tan y}{1 + \tan x \tan y}$

① $\sin^2 A + \cos^2 A = 1$

$\sin^2 A = 1 - \cos^2 A$

② $\sin A = \pm\sqrt{1 - \cos^2 A}$

$\cos^2 A = 1 - \sin^2 A$

③ $\cos A = \pm\sqrt{1 - \sin^2 A}$

④ $\tan^2 A + 1 = \sec^2 A$

⑤ $\tan^2 A = \sec^2 A - 1$

⑥ $1 + \cot^2 A = \csc^2 A$

⑦ $\cot^2 A = \csc^2 A - 1$

$\tan A = \frac{\sin A}{\cos A}$

$\cot A = \frac{\cos A}{\sin A}$

1. $\sin^2 A + \cos^2 A = 1$
2. $\sin^2 A = 1 - \cos^2 A$
3. $\cos^2 A = 1 - \sin^2 A$
4. $\tan^2 A + 1 = \sec^2 A$
5. $\tan^2 A = \sin^2 A$

7. $\cot^2 A = \csc^2 A -$

6 $1 + \cot^2 A = \csc^2$

3 on 67

$a = 3$

$b = 5.196$

$A = 30°$

$c = 6$

$B = 60°$

Area $K = 7.794$

$\tan A = \frac{a}{b}$

$b \tan A = a$

$\log a = \log b + \log \tan A$

$\log 3 = 0.47712$

$\log \tan 30° \quad .23856$

$.71568$

$b = 5.196$

$K = \frac{ab}{2}$

$\log K = \log a + \log b +$ ~~colog~~ 2

$\log 3 = .47712$

$.71568$

$9.69897 - 10$

10.89177

$K = 7.794$

$\sin A = \frac{a}{c}$

$c \sin A = a$

$c = \frac{a}{\sin A}$

$\log c = \log a + \text{colog} \sin A$

$\log c = 6$

$\log a = .47712$

$\text{colog} \sin 30° = .30103$

$.77815$

$c = 6$